Student Solutions Manual

Intermediate Algebra

An Applied Approach

STUDENT SOLUTIONS MANUAL

Intermediate Algebra:
An Applied Approach, Fifth Edition
Aufmann/Barker/Lockwood

Senior Sponsoring Editor: Maureen O'Connor
Senior Associate Editor: Dawn Nuttall
Marketing Manager: Rosalyn Kane
Editorial Assistant: John Brister
Senior Manufacturing Coordinator: Marie Barnes

Printed in the U.S.A.

ISBN: 0-395-93455-9

123456789-BB-02 01 00 99 98

Table of Contents

TABLE OF CONTENTS

Chapter 1: Review of Real Numbers

SECTION 1.1

Objective A Exercises

1. Integers: 0, –3

Rational numbers: $-\frac{15}{2}, 0, -3, -2.\overline{33}$

Irrational numbers: π, 4.232232223..., $\frac{\sqrt{5}}{4}$, $\sqrt{7}$

Real numbers: all

3. –27

5. $-\frac{3}{4}$

7. 0

9. $\sqrt{33}$

11. 91

13. Replace x with each element in the set and determine whether the inequality is true.

$x < 5$

$-3 < 5$ True

$0 < 5$ True

$7 < 5$ False

15. Replace y with each element in the set and determine whether the inequality is true.

$y > -4$

$-6 > -4$ False

$-4 > -4$ False

$7 > -4$ True

17. Replace w with each element in the set and determine whether the inequality is true.

$w \le -1$

$-2 \le -1$ True

$-1 \le -1$ True

$0 \le -1$ False

$1 \le -1$ False

19. Replace b with each element in the set and evaluate the expression.

$-b$

$-(-9) = 9$

$-(0) = 0$

$-(9) = -9$

21. Replace c with each element in the set and evaluate the expression.

$|c|$

$|-4| = 4$

$|0| = 0$

$|4| = 4$

23. Replace m with each element in the set and evaluate the expression.

$-|m|$

$-|-6| = -6$

$-|-2| = -2$

$-|0| = 0$

$-|1| = -1$

$-|4| = -4$

Objective B Exercises

25. $\{-2, -1, 1, 2, 3, 4\}$

27. $\{2, 4, 6, 8, 10, 12\}$

29. $\{3, 6, 9, 12, 15, 18, 21, 24, 27, 30\}$

31. $\{-35, -30, -25, -20, -15, -10, -5\}$

33. $\{x | x > 4,\ x \in \text{integers}\}$

35. $\{x | x \ge -2, x \in \text{ real numbers}\}$

37. $\{x | 0 < x < 1,\ x \in \text{real numbers}\}$

39. $\{x | 1 \le x < 4,\ x \in \text{real numbers}\}$

Objective C Exercises

41. $A \cup B = \{1, 2, 4, 6, 9\}$

43. $A \cup B = \{2, 3, 5, 8, 9, 10\}$

45. $A \cup B = \{-4, -2, 0, 2, 4, 8\}$

47. $A \cup B = \{1, 2, 3, 4, 5\}$

49. $A \cap B = \{6\}$

51. $A \cap B = \{5, 10, 20\}$

53. $A \cap B = \varnothing$

55. $A \cap B = \{4, 6\}$

57. $\{x | x < 2\}$

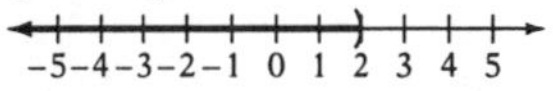

59. $\{x|x \geq 1\}$

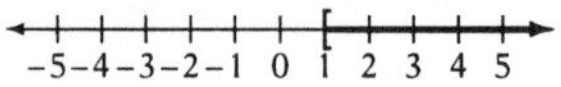

61. $\{x|-1 < x < 5\}$

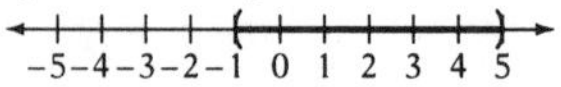

63. $\{x|0 \leq x \leq 3\}$

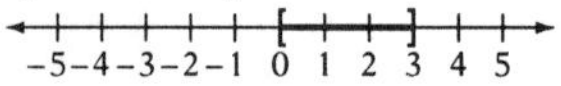

65. $\{x|x > 1\} \cup \{x|x < -1\}$

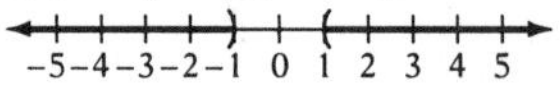

67. $\{x|x \leq 2\} \cap \{x|x \geq 0\}$

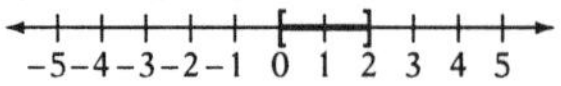

69. $\{x|x > 1\} \cap \{x|x \geq -2\}$

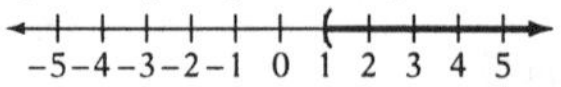

71. $\{x|x > 2\} \cup \{x|x > 1\}$

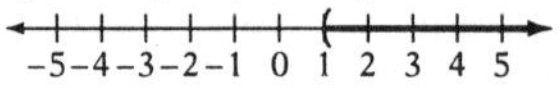

73. $\{x|0 < x < 8\}$

75. $\{x|-5 \leq x \leq 7\}$

77. $\{x|-3 \leq x < 6\}$

79. $\{x|x \leq 4\}$

81. $\{x|x > 5\}$

83. $(-2, 4)$

85. $[-1, 5]$

87. $(-\infty, 1)$

89. $[-2, \infty)$

91. $(-2, 5)$

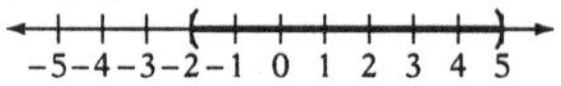

93. $[-1, 2]$

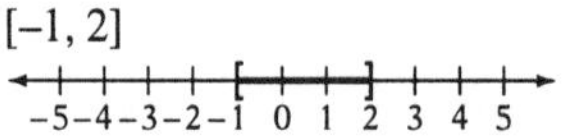

95. $(-\infty, 3]$

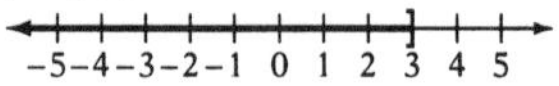

97. $[3, \infty)$

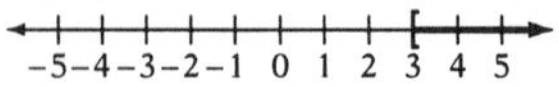

Applying the Concepts

99. $A \cup B = \{x|-1 \leq x \leq 1\} \cup \{x|0 \leq x \leq 1\}$
$= \{x|-1 \leq x \leq 1\}$
$= A$

101. $B \cap B$ is set B.

103. $A \cap R$ is $\{x|-1 \leq x \leq 1\}$, which is set A.

105. $B \cup R$ is the set of real numbers, R.

107. $R \cup R$ is the set of real numbers, R.

109. $B \cap C$ is $\{x|0 \leq x \leq 1\} \cap \{x|-1 \leq x \leq 0\}$, which contains only the number 0.

SECTION 1.2

Objective A Exercises

1. $-18 + (-12) = -30$

3. $5 - 22 = 5 + (-22) = -17$

5. $3 \cdot 4 \cdot (-8) = 12 \cdot (-8) = -96$

7. $18 \div (-3) = -6$

9. $-60 \div (-12) = 5$

11. $-20(35)(-16) = -700(-16) = 11{,}200$

13. $(-271)(-365) = 98{,}915$

15. $|12(-8)| = |-96| = 96$

17. $|15 - (-8)| = |15 + 8| = |23| = 23$

19. $|-56 \div 8| = |-7| = 7$

21. $|-153 \div (-9)| = |17| = 17$

23. $-|-8| + |-4| = -8 + 4 = -4$

25. $-30 + (-16) - 14 - 2 = -30 + (-16) + (-14) + (-2)$
$= -46 + (-14) + (-2)$
$= -60 + (-2)$
$= -62$

27. $-2 + (-19) - 16 + 12 = -2 + (-19) + (-16) + 12$
$= -21 + (-16) + 12$
$= -37 + 12$
$= -25$

29. $13 - |6 - 12| = 13 - |6 + (-12)|$
$= 13 - |-6|$
$= 13 - 6$
$= 13 + (-6) = 7$

31. $738-46+(-105)-219$
$=738+(-46)+(-105)+(-219)$
$=692+(-105)+(-219)$
$=587+(-219)$
$=368$

33. $-442\div(-17)=26$

35. $-4897\div 59=-83$

Objective B Exercises

37. $\frac{7}{12}+\frac{5}{16}=\frac{28}{48}+\frac{15}{48}=\frac{28+15}{48}=\frac{43}{48}$

39. $-\frac{5}{9}-\frac{14}{15}=-\frac{25}{45}-\frac{42}{45}$
$=\frac{-25-42}{45}$
$=-\frac{67}{45}$

41. $-\frac{1}{3}+\frac{5}{9}-\frac{7}{12}=-\frac{12}{36}+\frac{20}{36}-\frac{21}{36}$
$=\frac{-12+20-21}{36}$
$=-\frac{13}{36}$

43. $\frac{2}{3}-\frac{5}{12}+\frac{5}{24}=\frac{16}{24}-\frac{10}{24}+\frac{5}{24}$
$=\frac{16-10+5}{24}$
$=\frac{11}{24}$

45. $\frac{5}{8}-\frac{7}{12}+\frac{1}{2}=\frac{15}{24}-\frac{14}{24}+\frac{12}{24}$
$=\frac{15-14+12}{24}$
$=\frac{13}{24}$

47. $\left(\frac{6}{35}\right)\left(-\frac{5}{16}\right)=-\frac{6\cdot 5}{35\cdot 16}$
$=-\frac{\overset{1}{\cancel{2}}\cdot 3\cdot\overset{1}{\cancel{5}}}{\underset{1}{\cancel{5}}\cdot 7\cdot\underset{1}{\cancel{2}}\cdot 2\cdot 2\cdot 2}=-\frac{3}{56}$

49. $-\frac{8}{15}\div\frac{4}{5}=-\frac{8}{15}\cdot\frac{5}{4}$
$=-\frac{8\cdot 5}{15\cdot 4}$
$=-\frac{\overset{1}{\cancel{2}}\cdot\overset{1}{\cancel{2}}\cdot 2\cdot\overset{1}{\cancel{5}}}{3\cdot\underset{1}{\cancel{5}}\cdot\underset{1}{\cancel{2}}\cdot\underset{1}{\cancel{2}}}=-\frac{2}{3}$

51. $-\frac{11}{24}\div\frac{7}{12}=-\frac{11}{24}\cdot\frac{12}{7}$
$=-\frac{11\cdot 12}{24\cdot 7}$
$=-\frac{11\cdot\overset{1}{\cancel{2}}\cdot\overset{1}{\cancel{2}}\cdot\overset{1}{\cancel{3}}}{\underset{1}{\cancel{2}}\cdot\underset{1}{\cancel{2}}\cdot 2\cdot\underset{1}{\cancel{3}}\cdot 7}=-\frac{11}{14}$

53. $\left(-\frac{5}{12}\right)\left(\frac{4}{35}\right)\left(\frac{7}{8}\right)=-\frac{5\cdot 4\cdot 7}{12\cdot 35\cdot 8}$
$=-\frac{\overset{1}{\cancel{5}}\cdot\overset{1}{\cancel{2}}\cdot\overset{1}{\cancel{2}}\cdot\overset{1}{\cancel{7}}}{\underset{1}{\cancel{2}}\cdot\underset{1}{\cancel{2}}\cdot 3\cdot\underset{1}{\cancel{5}}\cdot\underset{1}{\cancel{7}}\cdot 2\cdot 2\cdot 2}$
$=-\frac{1}{24}$

55.
$$\begin{array}{r}-14.270\\ \underline{+\ 1.296}\\ 12.974\end{array}$$

57.
$$\begin{array}{r}-7.840\\ \underline{+1.832}\\ -6.008\end{array}$$

59. $(0.03)(10.5)(6.1)=(0.315)(6.1)=1.9215$

61.
$$\begin{array}{r}6.02\\ 0.9\overline{)5.418}\\ \underline{-54}\\ 001\\ \underline{-0}\\ 18\\ \underline{-18}\\ 0\end{array}$$

$5.418\div(-0.9)=-6..02$

63.
$$\begin{array}{r}6.7\\ 0.065\overline{)0.4355}\\ \underline{-390}\\ 455\\ \underline{-455}\\ 0\end{array}$$

$-0.4355\div 0.065=-6.7$

65. $38.241\div[-(-6.027)]-7.453$
$=38.241\div 6.027+(-7.453)$
$=-1.11$

67. $-287.3069\div 0.1415=-2030.44$

Objective C Exercises

69. $5^3=5\cdot 5\cdot 5=125$

71. $-2^3=-(2\cdot 2\cdot 2)=-8$

73. $(-5)^3=(-5)(-5)(-5)=-125$

75. $2^2 \cdot 3^4 = (2)(2)\cdot(3)(3)(3)(3)$
$= 4 \cdot 81$
$= 324$

77. $-2^2 \cdot 3^2 = -(2)(2)\cdot(3)(3)$
$= -4 \cdot 9$
$= -36$

79. $(-2)^3 \cdot (-3)^2 = (-2)(-2)(-2)\cdot(-3)(-3)$
$= -8 \cdot 9$
$= -72$

81. $4 \cdot 2^3 \cdot 3^3 = 4\cdot(2)(2)(2)\cdot(3)(3)(3)$
$= 4 \cdot 8 \cdot 27$
$= 32 \cdot 27$
$= 864$

83. $2^2 \cdot (-10)(-2)^2 = 2\cdot 2\cdot(-10)(-2)(-2)$
$= 4\cdot(-10)(4)$
$= -40(4)$
$= -160$

85. $(-3)^3 \cdot 15 \cdot (-2)^4 = (-27)\cdot 15\cdot(16)$
$= -405\cdot(16)$
$= -6480$

87. $2^5 \cdot (-3)^4 \cdot 4^5 = 32\cdot(81)\cdot 1024$
$= 2592 \cdot 1024$
$= 2,654,208$

Objective D Exercises

89. $5 - 3(8 \div 4)^2 = 5 - 3(2)^2$
$= 5 - 3(4)$
$= 5 - 12 = -7$

91. $16 - \dfrac{2^2 - 5}{3^2 + 2} = 16 - \dfrac{4-5}{9+2}$
$= 16 - \dfrac{-1}{11}$
$= 16 + \dfrac{1}{11} = \dfrac{177}{11}$

93. $\dfrac{3 + \frac{2}{3}}{\frac{11}{16}} = \dfrac{\frac{11}{3}}{\frac{11}{16}} = \dfrac{11}{3}\cdot\dfrac{16}{11} = \dfrac{16}{3}$

95. $5[(2-4)\cdot 3 - 2] = 5[(-2)\cdot 3 - 2]$
$= 5[-6-2]$
$= 5[-8] = -40$

97. $16 - 4\left(\dfrac{8-2}{3-6}\right) \div \dfrac{1}{2} = 16 - 4\left(\dfrac{6}{-3}\right) \div \dfrac{1}{2}$
$= 16 - 4(-2) \div \dfrac{1}{2}$
$= 16 - (-8) \div \dfrac{1}{2}$
$= 16 - (-8)\cdot 2$
$= 16 - (-16) = 16 + 16 = 32$

99. $6[3 - (-4+2) \div 2] = 6[3 - (-2) \div 2]$
$= 6[3 - (-1)]$
$= 6[3+1] = 6[4] = 24$

101. $\dfrac{1}{2} - \left(\dfrac{2}{3} \div \dfrac{5}{9}\right) + \dfrac{5}{6} = \dfrac{1}{2} - \left(\dfrac{2}{3}\cdot\dfrac{9}{5}\right) + \dfrac{5}{6}$
$= \dfrac{1}{2} - \dfrac{6}{5} + \dfrac{5}{6}$
$= \dfrac{15}{30} - \dfrac{36}{30} + \dfrac{25}{30}$
$= \dfrac{15 - 36 + 25}{30}$
$= \dfrac{4}{30} = \dfrac{2}{15}$

103. $\dfrac{1}{2} - \dfrac{\frac{17}{25}}{4 - \frac{3}{5}} \div \dfrac{1}{5} = \dfrac{1}{2} - \dfrac{\frac{17}{25}}{\frac{17}{5}} \div \dfrac{1}{5}$
$= \dfrac{1}{2} - \left(\dfrac{17}{25}\cdot\dfrac{5}{17}\right) \div \dfrac{1}{5}$
$= \dfrac{1}{2} - \dfrac{1}{5} \div \dfrac{1}{5}$
$= \dfrac{1}{2} - \dfrac{1}{5}\cdot\dfrac{5}{1}$
$= \dfrac{1}{2} - 1 = -\dfrac{1}{2}$

105. $\dfrac{2}{3} - \left[\dfrac{3}{8} + \dfrac{5}{6}\right] \div \dfrac{3}{5} = \dfrac{2}{3} - \left[\dfrac{9}{24} + \dfrac{20}{24}\right] \div \dfrac{3}{5}$
$= \dfrac{2}{3} - \dfrac{29}{24} \div \dfrac{3}{5}$
$= \dfrac{2}{3} - \dfrac{29}{24}\cdot\dfrac{5}{3}$
$= \dfrac{2}{3} - \dfrac{145}{72}$
$= \dfrac{48}{72} - \dfrac{145}{72} = -\dfrac{97}{72}$

107. $0.4(1.2 - 2.3)^2 + 5.8 = 0.4(-1.1)^2 + 5.8$
$= 0.4(1.21) + 5.8$
$= 0.484 + 5.8$
$= 6.284$

109. $1.75 \div 0.25 - (1.25)^2 = 1.75 \div 0.25 - 1.5625$
$= 7 - 1.5625$
$= 5.4375$

111. $25.76 \div (6.96 - 3.27)^2 = 25.76 \div (3.69)^2$
$= 25.76 \div 13.6161$
$= 1.891878$

Applying the Concepts

113. 0

115. No, the number zero has a multiplicative inverse that is undefined.

117. $7^{18} = 1,628,413,597,910,449$
The ones digit is 9.

119. 5^{234} has over 150 digits. The last three are 625.

121. The order of operations is $a^{(b^c)}$; first find b^c, then find a^{b^c}.

SECTION 1.3

Objective A Exercises

1. $3 \cdot 4 = 4 \cdot 3$

3. $(3 + 4) + 5 = 3 + (4 + 5)$

5. $\frac{5}{0}$ is undefined.

7. $3(x + 2) = 3x + 6$

9. $\frac{0}{-6} = 0$

11. $\frac{1}{mn}(mn) = 1$

13. $2(3x) = (2 \cdot 3) \cdot x$

15. The Division Property of Zero

17. The Inverse Property of Multiplication

19. The Addition Property of Zero

21. The Division Property of Zero

23. The Distributive Property

25. The Associative Property of Multiplication

Objective B Exercises

27.
$$\begin{aligned} ab + dc &= (2)(3) + (-4)(-1) \\ &= 6 + 4 \\ &= 10 \end{aligned}$$

29.
$$\begin{aligned} 4cd \div a^2 &= 4(-1)(-4) \div (2)^2 \\ &= 4(-1)(-4) \div 4 \\ &= (-4)(-4) \div 4 \\ &= 16 \div 4 = 4 \end{aligned}$$

31.
$$\begin{aligned} (b - 2a)^2 + c &= [3 - 2(2)]^2 + (-1) \\ &= [3 - 4]^2 + (-1) \\ &= [-1]^2 + (-1) \\ &= 1 + (-1) = 0 \end{aligned}$$

33.
$$\begin{aligned} (bc + a)^2 \div (d - b) &= [(3)(-1) + 2]^2 \div (-4 - 3) \\ &= [-3 + 2]^2 \div (-7) \\ &= [-1]^2 \div (-7) \\ &= 1 \div (-7) = -\frac{1}{7} \end{aligned}$$

35.
$$\begin{aligned} \frac{1}{4}a^4 - \frac{1}{6}bc &= \frac{1}{4}(2)^4 - \frac{1}{6}(3)(-1) \\ &= \frac{1}{4}(16) - \frac{1}{6}(3)(-1) \\ &= 4 - \frac{1}{6}(3)(-1) \\ &= 4 - \frac{1}{2}(-1) \\ &= 4 - \left(-\frac{1}{2}\right) \\ &= 4 + \frac{1}{2} = \frac{9}{2} \end{aligned}$$

37.
$$\begin{aligned} \frac{3ac}{-4} - c^2 &= \frac{3(2)(-1)}{-4} - (-1)^2 \\ &= \frac{6(-1)}{-4} - (-1)^2 \\ &= \frac{-6}{-4} - (-1)^2 \\ &= \frac{3}{2} - (-1)^2 \\ &= \frac{3}{2} - 1 = \frac{1}{2} \end{aligned}$$

39.
$$\begin{aligned} \frac{3b - 5c}{3a - c} &= \frac{3(3) - 5(-1)}{3(2) - (-1)} \\ &= \frac{9 - (-5)}{6 - (-1)} \\ &= \frac{9 + 5}{6 + 1} \\ &= \frac{14}{7} = 2 \end{aligned}$$

41.
$$\begin{aligned} \frac{a - d}{b + c} &= \frac{2 - (-4)}{3 + (-1)} \\ &= \frac{2 + 4}{3 + (-1)} \\ &= \frac{6}{2} = 3 \end{aligned}$$

43.
$$\begin{aligned} -a|a + 2d| &= -2|2 + 2(-4)| \\ &= -2|2 + (-8)| \\ &= -2|-6| \\ &= -2(6) = -12 \end{aligned}$$

45.
$$\begin{aligned} \frac{2a - 4d}{3b - c} &= \frac{2(2) - 4(-4)}{3(3) - (-1)} \\ &= \frac{4 - (-16)}{9 - (-1)} \\ &= \frac{4 + 16}{9 + 1} = \frac{20}{10} = 2 \end{aligned}$$

47. $-3d \div \left|\dfrac{ab-4c}{2b+c}\right| = -3(-4) \div \left|\dfrac{2(3)-4(-1)}{2(3)+(-1)}\right|$
$= -3(-4) \div \left|\dfrac{6-(-4)}{6+(-1)}\right|$
$= -3(-4) \div \left|\dfrac{6+4}{6+(-1)}\right|$
$= -3(-4) \div \left|\dfrac{10}{5}\right|$
$= -3(-4) \div |2|$
$= -3(-4) \div 2$
$= 12 \div 2 = 6$

49. $2(d-b) \div (3a-c) = 2(-4-3) \div [3(2)-(-1)]$
$= 2(-7) \div [6-(-1)]$
$= 2(-7) \div [6+1]$
$= 2(-7) \div 7$
$= -14 \div 7 = -2$

51. $-d^2 - c^3a = -(-4)^2 - (-1)^3 2$
$= -16 - (-1)2$
$= -16 + 2 = -14$

53. $-d^3 + 4ac = -(-4)^3 + 4(2)(-1)$
$= -(-64) + 8(-1)$
$= 64 - 8 = 56$

55. $4^{(a^2)} = 4^{(2^2)} = 4^4 = 256$

Objective C Exercises

57. $5x + 7x = 12x$

59. $-8ab - 5ab = -13ab$

61. $3x - 5x + 9x = -2x + 9x = 7x$

63. $5b - 8a - 12b = -8a - 7b$

65. $\dfrac{1}{3}(3y) = y$

67. $-5(x-9) = -5x + 45$

69. $-(x+y) = -x - y$

71. $3(a-5) = 3a - 15$

73. $4x - 3(2y-5) = 4x - 6y + 15$

75. $3x - 2(5x-7) = 3x - 10x + 14$
$= -7x + 14$

77. $3[a - 5(5-3a)] = 3[a - 25 + 15a]$
$= 3[16a - 25]$
$= 48a - 75$

79. $3[x - 2(x+2y)] = 3[x - 2x - 4y]$
$= 3[-x - 4y]$
$= -3x - 12y$

81. $-2(x-3y) + 2(3y-5x) = -2x + 6y + 6y - 10x$
$= -12x + 12y$

83. $5(3a-2b) - 3(-6a+5b) = 15a - 10b + 18a - 15b$
$= 33a - 25b$

85. $3x - 2[y - 2(x + 3[2x + 3y])]$
$= 3x - 2[y - 2(x + 6x + 9y)]$
$= 3x - 2[y - 2(7x + 9y)]$
$= 3x - 2[y - 14x - 18y]$
$= 3x - 2[-17y - 14x]$
$= 3x + 34y + 28x$
$= 31x + 34y$

87. $4 - 2(7x - 2y) - 3(-2x + 3y)$
$= 4 - 14x + 4y + 6x - 9y$
$= 4 - 8x - 5y$

89. $\dfrac{1}{3}[8x - 2(x-12) + 3] = \dfrac{1}{3}[8x - 2x + 24 + 3]$
$= \dfrac{1}{3}[6x + 27]$
$= 2x + 9$

Applying the Concepts

91. $4(3y+1) = 12y + 4$
The statement is correct; it uses the Distributive Property.

93. $2 + 3x + (2+3)x = 5$
The statement is not correct; it mistakenly uses the Distributive Property. It is an irreducible state. That is, the answer is $2 + 3x$.

95. $2(3y) = (2 \cdot 3)(2y) = 12y$
The statement is not correct; it mistakenly uses the Associative Property of Multiplication. The correct answer is $(2 \cdot 3)y = 6y$.

97. $-x^2 + y^2 = y^2 - x^2$
The statement is correct. it uses the Commutative Property of Addition.

SECTION 1.4

Objective A Exercises

1. The unknown number: n
The sum of the number and two: $n + 2$
$n - (n+2) = n - n - 2$
$= -2$

3. The unknown number: n
The product of eight and the number: $8n$
$5(8n) = 40n$

5. The unknown number: n
The product of seventeen and the number: $17n$
twice the number: $2n$
$17n - 2n = 15n$

7. The unknown number: n
The square of the number: n^2
The total of twelve and the square of the number:
$12+n^2$
$n^2-(12+n^2)=n^2-12-n^2=-12$

9. The unknown number: n
The sum of five times the number and 12: $5n+12$
The product of the number and fifteen: $15n$
$$\begin{aligned}(5n+12)+15n&=5n+12+15n\\&=20n+12\end{aligned}$$

11. Let the smaller number be x.
The larger number is $15-x$.
The sum of twice the smaller number and two more than the larger number.
$$\begin{aligned}2x+(15-x+2)&=2x+(17-x)\\&=x+17\end{aligned}$$

13. Let the larger number be x.
The smaller number is $34-x$.
The quotient of five times the smaller number and the difference between the larger number and three.
$$\frac{5(34-x)}{x-3}=\frac{170-5x}{x-3}$$

Objective B Application Problems

15. The distance from Earth to the moon: d
The distance from Earth to the sun is 390 times d: $390d$

17. The amount of caramel in the mixture: c
The mixture contains 3 lb more of chocolate than of caramel: $c+3$

19. The length of an ultraviolet ray: L
The length of an infrared ray is twice the length of an ultraviolet ray: $2L$

21. The amount in the first account: x
The total amount is 10,000.
The amount in the second account: $10{,}000-x$

23. The measure of angle B: x
The measure of angle A is twice that of angle B: $2x$
The measure of angle C is twice the measure of angle A: $2(2x)=4x$

Applying the Concepts

25. The sum of twice x and 3.

27. Twice the sum of x and 3.

29. a. One-half the acceleration due to gravity: $\frac{1}{2}g$
Time squared: t^2
The product: $\frac{1}{2}gt^2$

b. The product of m and a: ma

c. The product of A and v^2: Av^2

d. The quotient of k and m: $\frac{k}{m}$
The square root of the quotient: $\sqrt{\frac{k}{m}}$

CHAPTER REVIEW

1. $\{-2, -1, 0, 1, 2, 3\}$

2. $A\cap B=\{2, 3\}$

3. $(-2, 4]$

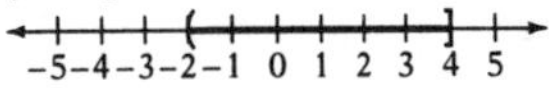

4. The Associative Property of Multiplication

5. $-4.07+2.3-1.07=-1.77-1.07=-2.84$

6. $$\begin{aligned}(a-2b^2)\div ab&=(4-2(-3)^2)\div(4)(-3)\\&=(4-2(9))\div(4)(-3)\\&=(4-18)\div(4)(-3)\\&=-14\div[(4)(-3)]\\&=-14\div-12=\frac{-14}{-12}=\frac{7}{6}\end{aligned}$$

7. $$\begin{aligned}-2\cdot(4^2)\cdot(-3)^2&=-2\cdot16\cdot9\\&=-32\cdot9\\&=-288\end{aligned}$$

8. $$\begin{aligned}&4y-3[x-2(3-2x)-4y]\\&=4y-3[x-6+4x-4y]\\&=4y-3[5x-6-4y]\\&=4y-15x+18+12y\\&=16y-15x+18\end{aligned}$$

9. $\frac{3}{4}$; $-\frac{3}{4}+\frac{3}{4}=0$

10. $\{x|x<-3,\ x\in \text{real numbers}\}$

11. $\{x|x<1\}$

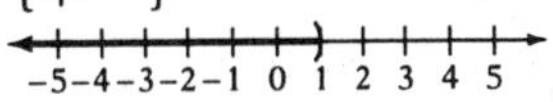

12. $$\begin{aligned}-10-(-3)-8&=-10+3+(-8)\\&=-7+(-8)\\&=-15\end{aligned}$$

13. $-\frac{2}{3}+\frac{3}{5}-\frac{1}{6}=-\frac{20}{30}+\frac{18}{30}-\frac{5}{30}$
$=\frac{-20+18-5}{30}$
$=\frac{-7}{30}=-\frac{7}{30}$

14. 4

15. $-\frac{3}{8}\div\frac{3}{5}=-\frac{3}{8}\cdot\frac{5}{3}$
$=-\frac{\overset{1}{\cancel{3}}\cdot 5}{8\cdot\underset{1}{\cancel{3}}}$
$=-\frac{5}{8}$

16. Replace x with the elements in the set and determine whether the inequality is true.
$x>-1$
$-4>-1$ False
$-2>-1$ False
$0>-1$ True
$2>-1$ True

17. $2a^2-\frac{3b}{a}=2(-3)^2-\frac{3(2)}{-3}$
$=2(-3)^2-\frac{6}{-3}$
$=2(-3)^2-(-2)$
$=2(9)-(-2)$
$=18+2=20$

18. $18-|-12+8|=18-|-4|$
$=18-4$
$=14$

19. $20\div\frac{3^2-2^2}{3^2+2^2}=20\div\frac{9-4}{9+4}$
$=20\div\frac{5}{13}$
$=20\cdot\frac{13}{5}=52$

20. $[-3,\infty)$

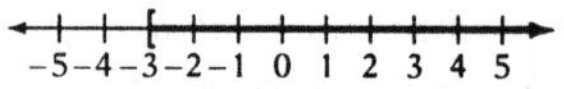

21. $A\cup B=\{1, 2, 3, 4, 5, 6, 7, 8\}$

22. $-204\div(-17)=12$

23. $\{x|-2\le x\le 3\}$

24. $\frac{3}{5}\left(-\frac{10}{21}\right)\left(-\frac{7}{15}\right)=\frac{3\cdot 10\cdot 7}{5\cdot 21\cdot 15}$
$=\frac{\overset{1}{\cancel{3}}\cdot 2\cdot\overset{1}{\cancel{5}}\cdot\overset{1}{\cancel{7}}}{\underset{1}{\cancel{5}}\cdot\underset{1}{\cancel{3}}\cdot\underset{1}{\cancel{7}}\cdot 3\cdot 5}$
$=\frac{2}{15}$

25. 3

26. $\{x|x\le -3\}\cup\{x|x>0\}$

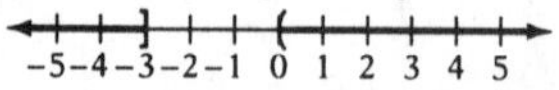

27. $-2(x-3)+4(2-x)=-2x+6+8-4x$
$=-6x+14$

28. $p\in\{-4, 0, 7\}$
$-|p|$
$-|-4|=-4$
$-|0|=0$
$-|7|=-7$

29. The Inverse Property of Addition

30. $-3.286\div(-1.06)=3.1$

31. The unknown number: x
Three more than a number: $x+3$
The quotient of three more than a number and the number: $\frac{x+3}{x}$
$12-\frac{x+3}{x}=\frac{12x}{x}-\frac{x+3}{x}$
$=\frac{12x-x-3}{x}$
$=\frac{11x-3}{x}$

32. Let x be the smaller of the numbers. Then the larger number is $40-x$.
$2x+(40-x+5)=x+45$

33. The width of the rectangle: w
The length is 3 feet less than 3 w.
The length is $3w-3$

34. The number of vehicles sold by Ford: x
The number of vehicles sold by Chrysler: $x-341{,}062$

CHAPTER TEST

1. $(-2)(-3)(-5)=(6)(-5)=-30$

2. $A\cap B=\{5, 7\}$

3. $(-2)^3(-3)^2=(-8)(9)=-72$

4. $(-\infty, 1]$

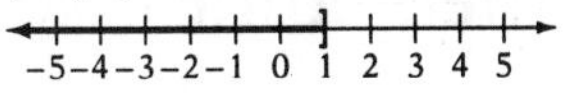

5. $A \cap B = \{-1, 0, 1\}$

6. $$\begin{aligned}(a-b)^2 \div (2b+1) &= (2-(-3))^2 \div (2(-3)+1)\\ &= (5)^2 \div (-6+1)\\ &= (5)^2 \div (-5)\\ &= 25 \div (-5) = -5\end{aligned}$$

7. $$\begin{aligned}|-3-(-5)| &= |-3+5|\\ &= |2|\\ &= 2\end{aligned}$$

8. $$\begin{aligned}2x-4[2-3(x+4y)-2] &= 2x-4[2-3x-12y-2]\\ &= 2x-4[-3x-12y]\\ &= 2x+12x+48y\\ &= 14x+48y\end{aligned}$$

9. 12

10. $-5^2 \cdot 4 = -25 \cdot 4 = -100$

11. $\{x|x<3\} \cap \{x|x>-2\}$

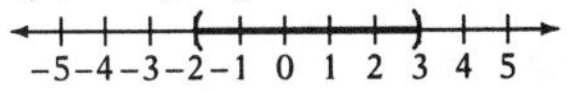

12. $$\begin{aligned}2-(-12)+3-5 &= 2+12+3+(-5)\\ &= 14+3+(-5)\\ &= 17+(-5)\\ &= 12\end{aligned}$$

13. $$\begin{aligned}\frac{2}{3}-\frac{5}{12}+\frac{4}{9} &= \frac{24}{36}-\frac{15}{36}+\frac{16}{36}\\ &= \frac{24-15+16}{36}\\ &= \frac{25}{36}\end{aligned}$$

14. 4

15. $$\left(-\frac{2}{3}\right)\left(\frac{9}{15}\right)\left(\frac{10}{27}\right) = -\frac{2\cdot\overset{1}{\cancel{3}}\cdot\overset{1}{\cancel{3}}\cdot 2\cdot\overset{1}{\cancel{5}}}{\underset{1}{\cancel{3}}\cdot\underset{1}{\cancel{3}}\cdot\underset{1}{\cancel{5}}\cdot 3\cdot 3\cdot 3} = -\frac{4}{27}$$

16. Replace x with each element in the set and determine whether the inequality is true.

$x < -1$

$-5 < -1$ True

$3 < -1$ False

$7 < -1$ False

17. $$\begin{aligned}\frac{b^2-c^2}{a-2c} &= \frac{(3)^2-(-1)^2}{2-2(-1)}\\ &= \frac{9-1}{2-(-2)}\\ &= \frac{8}{4} = 2\end{aligned}$$

18. $-180 \div 12 = -15$

19. $$\begin{aligned}12-4\left(\frac{5^2-1}{3}\right)\div 16 &= 12-4\left(\frac{25-1}{3}\right)\div 16\\ &= 12-4\left(\frac{24}{3}\right)\div 16\\ &= 12-4(8)\div 16\\ &= 12-32\div 16\\ &= 12-2 = 10\end{aligned}$$

20. $(3, \infty)$

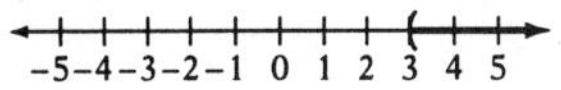

21. $A \cup B = \{1, 2, 3, 4, 5, 7\}$

22. $$\begin{aligned}3x-2(x-y)-3(y-4x) &= 3x-2x+2y-3y+12x\\ &= 13x-y\end{aligned}$$

23. $$\begin{aligned}8-4(2-3)^2 \div 2 &= 8-4(-1)^2 \div 2\\ &= 8-4(1)\div 2\\ &= 8-4\div 2\\ &= 8-2 = 6\end{aligned}$$

24. $$\frac{3}{5}\left(-\frac{10}{21}\right)\left(-\frac{7}{15}\right) = \frac{\overset{1}{\cancel{3}}\cdot 2\cdot\overset{1}{\cancel{5}}\cdot\overset{1}{\cancel{7}}}{5\cdot\underset{1}{\cancel{3}}\cdot\underset{1}{\cancel{7}}\cdot 3\cdot\underset{1}{\cancel{5}}} = \frac{2}{15}$$

25. The Distributive Property

26. $\{x|x\le 3\} \cup \{x|x<-2\}$

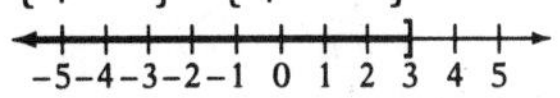

27. $4.27 - 6.98 + 1.3 = -2.71 + 1.3 = -1.41$

28. $A \cup B = \{-2, -1, 0, 1, 2, 3\}$

29. The unknown number: n

Three less than the number: $n - 3$

The product of three less than the number and nine: $(n - 3)(9)$

$$\begin{aligned}13-(n-3)(9) &= 13-9n+27\\ &= 40-9n\end{aligned}$$

30. The larger number: x

The smaller number: $9 - x$

The difference between one more than the larger number and twice the smaller number.

$$\begin{aligned}(x+1)-2(9-x) &= x+1-18+2x\\ &= 3x-17\end{aligned}$$

Chapter 2: First-Degree Equations and Inequalities

SECTION 2.1

Objective A Exercises

1.
$$x-2=7$$
$$x-2+2=7+2$$
$$x=9$$
The solution is 9.

3.
$$a+3=-7$$
$$a+3+(-3)=-7+(-3)$$
$$a=-10$$
The solution is –10.

5.
$$b-3=-5$$
$$b-3+3=-5+3$$
$$b=-2$$
The solution is –2.

7.
$$-7=x+8$$
$$-7+(-8)=x+8+(-8)$$
$$-15=x$$
The solution is –15.

9.
$$3x=12$$
$$\frac{1}{3}(3x)=\frac{1}{3}(12)$$
$$x=4$$

11.
$$-3x=2$$
$$-\frac{1}{3}(-3x)=-\frac{1}{3}(2)$$
$$x=-\frac{2}{3}$$
The solution is $-\frac{2}{3}$.

13.
$$-\frac{3}{2}+x=\frac{4}{3}$$
$$-\frac{3}{2}+\frac{3}{2}+x=\frac{4}{3}+\frac{3}{2}$$
$$x=\frac{8}{6}+\frac{9}{6}$$
$$x=\frac{17}{6}$$
The solution is $\frac{17}{6}$.

15.
$$x+\frac{2}{3}=\frac{5}{6}$$
$$x+\frac{2}{3}+\left(-\frac{2}{3}\right)=\frac{5}{6}+\left(-\frac{2}{3}\right)$$
$$x=\frac{5}{6}+\left(-\frac{4}{6}\right)$$
$$x=\frac{1}{6}$$
The solution is $\frac{1}{6}$.

17.
$$\frac{2}{3}y=5$$
$$\frac{3}{2}\left(\frac{2}{3}\right)y=\frac{3}{2}(5)$$
$$y=\frac{15}{2}$$
The solution is $\frac{15}{2}$.

19.
$$-\frac{5}{8}x=\frac{4}{5}$$
$$-\frac{8}{5}\left(-\frac{5}{8}x\right)=-\frac{8}{5}\left(\frac{4}{5}\right)$$
$$x=-\frac{32}{25}$$
The solution is $-\frac{32}{25}$.

21.
$$-\frac{3b}{5}=-\frac{3}{5}$$
$$-\frac{5}{3}\left(-\frac{3}{5}b\right)=-\frac{5}{3}\left(-\frac{3}{5}\right)$$
$$b=1$$
The solution is 1.

23.
$$-\frac{2}{3}x=-\frac{5}{8}$$
$$-\frac{3}{2}\left(-\frac{2}{3}x\right)=-\frac{3}{2}\left(-\frac{5}{8}\right)$$
$$x=\frac{15}{16}$$
The solution is $\frac{15}{16}$.

25.
$$-\frac{5}{8}x=40$$
$$-\frac{8}{5}\left(-\frac{5}{8}x\right)=-\frac{8}{5}(40)$$
$$x=-64$$
The solution is –64.

27.
$$-\frac{5}{6}y = -\frac{25}{36}$$
$$-\frac{6}{5}\left(-\frac{5}{6}y\right) = -\frac{6}{5}\left(-\frac{25}{36}\right)$$
$$y = \frac{5}{6}$$
The solution is $\frac{5}{6}$.

Objective B Exercises

29.
$$3x + 5x = 12$$
$$8x = 12$$
$$\frac{1}{8}(8x) = \frac{1}{8}(12)$$
$$x = \frac{3}{2}$$
The solution is $\frac{3}{2}$.

31.
$$2x - 4 = 12$$
$$2x - 4 + 4 = 12 + 4$$
$$2x = 16$$
$$\frac{1}{2}(2x) = \frac{1}{2}(16)$$
$$x = 8$$
The solution is 8.

33.
$$3y - 5y = 0$$
$$-2y = 0$$
$$-\frac{1}{2}(-2y) = -\frac{1}{2}(0)$$
$$y = 0$$
The solution is 0.

35.
$$4x - 6 = 3x$$
$$4x + (-4x) - 6 = 3x + (-4x)$$
$$-6 = -x$$
$$(-1)(-6) = (-1)(-x)$$
$$6 = x$$
The solution is 6.

37.
$$7x + 12 = 9x$$
$$7x + (-7x) + 12 = 9x + (-7x)$$
$$12 = 2x$$
$$\frac{1}{2}(12) = \frac{1}{2}(2x)$$
$$6 = x$$
The solution is 6.

39.
$$4x + 2 = 4x$$
$$4x + (-4x) + 2 = 4x + (-4x)$$
$$2 = 0$$
The equation has no solution.

41.
$$2x + 2 = 3x + 5$$
$$2x + (-3x) + 2 = 3x + (-3x) + 5$$
$$-x + 2 = 5$$
$$-x + 2 + (-2) = 5 + (-2)$$
$$-x = 3$$
$$(-1)(-x) = (-1)(3)$$
$$x = -3$$
The solution is –3.

43.
$$2 - 3t = 3t - 4$$
$$2 - 3t + (-3t) = 3t + (-3t) - 4$$
$$2 - 6t = -4$$
$$2 + (-2) - 6t = -4 + (-2)$$
$$-6t = -6$$
$$-\frac{1}{6}(-6t) = -\frac{1}{6}(-6)$$
$$t = 1$$
The solution is 1.

45.
$$3b - 2b = 4 - 2b$$
$$b = 4 - 2b$$
$$b + 2b = 4 - 2b + 2b$$
$$3b = 4$$
$$\frac{1}{3}(3b) = \frac{1}{3}(4)$$
$$b = \frac{4}{3}$$
The solution is $\frac{4}{3}$.

47.
$$3x + 7 = 3 + 7x$$
$$3x + (-7x) + 7 = 3 + 7x + (-7x)$$
$$-4x + 7 = 3$$
$$-4x + 7 + (-7) = 3 + (-7)$$
$$-4x = -4$$
$$-\frac{1}{4}(-4x) = -\frac{1}{4}(-4)$$
$$x = 1$$
The solution is 1.

49.
$$\frac{1}{3} - 2b = 3$$
$$\frac{1}{3} + \left(-\frac{1}{3}\right) - 2b = 3 + \left(-\frac{1}{3}\right)$$
$$-2b = \frac{8}{3}$$
$$-\frac{1}{2}(-2b) = -\frac{1}{2}\left(\frac{8}{3}\right)$$
$$b = -\frac{4}{3}$$
The solution is $-\frac{4}{3}$.

Objective C Exercises

51.
$$\begin{aligned} 2x+3(x-5) &= 15 \\ 2x+3x-15 &= 15 \\ 5x-15 &= 15 \\ 5x &= 30 \\ \frac{1}{5}(5x) &= \frac{1}{5}(30) \\ x &= 6 \end{aligned}$$

The solution is 6.

53.
$$\begin{aligned} 5(2-b) &= -3(b-3) \\ 10-5b &= -3b+9 \\ 10-2b &= 9 \\ -2b &= -1 \\ -\frac{1}{2}(-2b) &= -\frac{1}{2}(-1) \\ b &= \frac{1}{2} \end{aligned}$$

The solution is $\frac{1}{2}$.

55.
$$\begin{aligned} 3(y-5)-5y &= 2y+9 \\ 3y-15-5y &= 2y+9 \\ -2y-15 &= 2y+9 \\ -4y-15 &= 9 \\ -4y &= 24 \\ -\frac{1}{4}(-4y) &= -\frac{1}{4}(24) \\ y &= -6 \end{aligned}$$

The solution is –6.

57.
$$\begin{aligned} 4-3x &= 7x-2(3-x) \\ 4-3x &= 7x-6+2x \\ 4-3x &= 9x-6 \\ 4-12x &= -6 \\ -12x &= -10 \\ -\frac{1}{12}(-12x) &= -\frac{1}{12}(-10) \\ x &= \frac{5}{6} \end{aligned}$$

The solution is $\frac{5}{6}$.

59.
$$\begin{aligned} -3x-2(4+5x) &= 14-3(2x-3) \\ -3x-8-10x &= 14-6x+9 \\ -13x-8 &= 23-6x \\ -13x+6x-8 &= 23-6x+6x \\ -7x-8 &= 23 \\ -7x-8+8 &= 23+8 \\ -7x &= 31 \\ -\frac{1}{7}(-7x) &= -\frac{1}{7}(31) \\ x &= -\frac{31}{7} \end{aligned}$$

The solution is $-\frac{31}{7}$.

61.
$$\begin{aligned} 3y &= 2[5-3(2-y)] \\ 3y &= 2[5-6+3y] \\ 3y &= 2[-1+3y] \\ 3y &= -2+6y \\ -3y &= -2 \\ -\frac{1}{3}(-3y) &= -\frac{1}{3}(-2) \\ y &= \frac{2}{3} \end{aligned}$$

The solution is $\frac{2}{3}$.

63.
$$\begin{aligned} 2[4+2(5-x)-2x] &= 4x-7 \\ 2[4+10-2x-2x] &= 4x-7 \\ 2[14-4x] &= 4x-7 \\ 28-8x &= 4x-7 \\ 28-12x &= -7 \\ -12x &= -35 \\ -\frac{1}{12}(-12x) &= -\frac{1}{12}(-35) \\ x &= \frac{35}{12} \end{aligned}$$

The solution is $\frac{35}{12}$.

65.
$$\begin{aligned} 2[3-2(z+4)] &= 3(4-z) \\ 2[3-2z-8] &= 12-3z \\ 2[-5-2z] &= 12-3z \\ -10-4z &= 12-3z \\ -10-z &= 12 \\ -z &= 22 \\ (-1)(-z) &= (-1)(22) \\ z &= -22 \end{aligned}$$

The solution is –22.

67.
$$\begin{aligned} 3[x-(2-x)-2x] &= 3(4-x) \\ 3[x-2+x-2x] &= 12-3x \\ 3[-2] &= 12-3x \\ -6 &= 12-3x \\ -18 &= -3x \\ -\frac{1}{3}(-18) &= -\frac{1}{3}(-3x) \\ 6 &= x \end{aligned}$$

The solution is 6.

69.
$$\begin{aligned} \frac{3}{4}t-\frac{7}{12}t &= 1 \\ 12\left(\frac{3}{4}t-\frac{7}{12}t\right) &= 12\cdot 1 \\ \frac{12\cdot 3t}{4}-\frac{12\cdot 7t}{12} &= 12 \\ 9t-7t &= 12 \\ 2t &= 12 \\ \frac{1}{2}(2t) &= \frac{1}{2}(12) \\ t &= 6 \end{aligned}$$

The solution is 6.

71.
$$\begin{aligned}\frac{1}{2}x-\frac{3}{4}x+\frac{5}{8}&=\frac{3}{2}x-\frac{5}{2}\\ 8\left(\frac{1}{2}x-\frac{3}{4}x+\frac{5}{8}\right)&=8\left(\frac{3}{2}x-\frac{5}{2}\right)\\ \frac{8\cdot x}{2}-\frac{8\cdot 3x}{4}+\frac{8\cdot 5}{8}&=\frac{8\cdot 3x}{2}-\frac{8\cdot 5}{2}\\ 4x-6x+5&=12x-20\\ -2x+5&=12x-20\\ -14x+5&=-20\\ -14x&=-25\\ -\frac{1}{14}(-14x)&=-\frac{1}{14}(-25)\\ x&=\frac{25}{14}\end{aligned}$$

The solution is $\frac{25}{14}$.

73.
$$\begin{aligned}\frac{2x-5}{12}-\frac{3-x}{6}&=\frac{11}{12}\\ 12\left(\frac{2x-5}{12}-\frac{3-x}{6}\right)&=12\cdot\frac{11}{12}\\ \frac{12(2x-5)}{12}-\frac{12(3-x)}{6}&=11\\ 2x-5-2(3-x)&=11\\ 2x-5-6+2x&=11\\ 4x-11&=11\\ 4x&=22\\ \frac{1}{4}(4x)&=\frac{1}{4}(22)\\ x&=\frac{11}{2}\end{aligned}$$

The solution is $\frac{11}{2}$.

75.
$$\begin{aligned}\frac{2x-1}{4}+\frac{3x+4}{8}&=\frac{1-4x}{12}\\ 24\left(\frac{2x-1}{4}+\frac{3x+4}{8}\right)&=24\left(\frac{1-4x}{12}\right)\\ \frac{24(2x-1)}{4}+\frac{24(3x+4)}{8}&=\frac{24(1-4x)}{12}\\ 6(2x-1)+3(3x+4)&=2(1-4x)\\ 12x-6+9x+12&=2-8x\\ 21x+6&=2-8x\\ 29x+6&=2\\ 29x&=-4\\ \frac{1}{29}(29x)&=\frac{1}{29}(-4)\\ x&=-\frac{4}{29}\end{aligned}$$

The solution is $-\frac{4}{29}$.

77.
$$\begin{aligned}3x-5&=9x+4\\ -6x-5&=4\\ -6x&=9\\ -\frac{1}{6}(-6x)&=-\frac{1}{6}(9)\\ x&=-\frac{3}{2}\\ 6x-3&=6\left(-\frac{3}{2}\right)-3\\ &=-9-3\\ &=-12\end{aligned}$$

The solution is –12.

79.
$$\begin{aligned}3(2x+1)&=5-2(x-2)\\ 6x+3&=5-2x+4\\ 6x+3&=9-2x\\ 8x+3&=9\\ 8x&=6\\ \frac{1}{8}(8x)&=\frac{1}{8}(6)\\ x&=\frac{3}{4}\\ 2x^2+1&=2\left(\frac{3}{4}\right)^2+1\\ &=2\left(\frac{9}{16}\right)+1\\ &=\frac{18}{16}+1\\ &=\frac{9}{8}+\frac{8}{8}\\ &=\frac{17}{8}\end{aligned}$$

The solution is $\frac{17}{8}$.

81.
$$\begin{aligned}5-2(4x-1)&=3x+7\\ 5-8x+2&=3x+7\\ 7-8x&=3x+7\\ 7-11x&=7\\ -11x&=0\\ -\frac{1}{11}(-11x)&=-\frac{1}{11}(0)\\ x&=0\\ x^4-x^2&=0^4-0^2\\ &=0-0\\ &=0\end{aligned}$$

The solution is 0.

Objective D Exercises

83.
$$\begin{aligned}C&=2\pi r\\ \frac{C}{2\pi}&=\frac{2\pi r}{2\pi}\\ \frac{C}{2\pi}&=r\end{aligned}$$

85.
$$A = \frac{1}{2}bh$$
$$2 \cdot A = 2 \cdot \frac{1}{2}bh$$
$$2A = bh$$
$$\frac{2A}{b} = \frac{bh}{b}$$
$$\frac{2A}{b} = h$$

87.
$$I = \frac{100M}{C}$$
$$\frac{C}{100} \cdot I = \frac{C}{100} \cdot \frac{100}{C}M$$
$$\frac{IC}{100} = M$$

89.
$$A = P + Prt$$
$$A - P = Prt$$
$$\frac{A-P}{Pt} = \frac{Prt}{Pt}$$
$$\frac{A-P}{Pt} = r$$

91.
$$s = \frac{1}{2}(a+b+c)$$
$$2 \cdot s = \frac{2}{1} \cdot \frac{1}{2}(a+b+c)$$
$$2s = a+b+c$$
$$2s - a - b = c$$

93.
$$S = 2\pi r^2 + 2\pi rh$$
$$S - 2\pi r^2 = 2\pi rh$$
$$\frac{S - 2\pi r^2}{2\pi r} = \frac{2\pi rh}{2\pi r}$$
$$\frac{S - 2\pi r^2}{2\pi r} = h$$

95.
$$P = \frac{R-C}{n}$$
$$P \cdot n = \frac{R-C}{n} \cdot n$$
$$Pn = R - C$$
$$Pn + C = R$$

97.
$$S = 2WH + 2WL + 2LH$$
$$S - 2WL = 2WH + 2LH$$
$$S - 2WL = H(2W + 2L)$$
$$\frac{S - 2WL}{2W + 2L} = \frac{H(2W+2L)}{2W+2L}$$
$$\frac{S - 2WL}{2W + 2L} = H$$

Applying the Concepts

99. The statement is not correct. You cannot divide each side of an equation by x, unless x is not equal to 0. The correct answer is:
$$5x = 8x$$
$$0 = 3x$$
$$0 = x \text{ or } x = 0$$
Since x is equal to 0, dividing by x on the next to last step is incorrect.

101. If a, b, and c are algebraic expressions and $c \neq 0$, then the solution to $a = b$ is the same as the solution to $ac = bc$.

SECTION 2.2

Objective A Application Problems

1. Strategy: The number added to the numerator x

The fraction $\frac{3+x}{10}$ must equal $\frac{4}{5}$.

Solution:
$$\frac{3+x}{10} = \frac{4}{5}$$
$$5(3+x) = 10(4)$$
$$15 + 5x = 40$$
$$5x = 25$$
$$x = 5$$
The number is 5.

3. Strategy
- The smaller integer: n
  The larger integer: $10 - n$
- Three times the larger integer is three less than eight times the smaller integer.

Solution:
$$3(10-n) = 8n - 3$$
$$30 - 3n = 8n - 3$$
$$-11n = -33$$
$$n = 3$$
$$10 - n = 10 - 3 = 7$$
The integers are 3 and 7.

5. Strategy
- The larger integer: n
  The smaller integer: $n - 8$
- The sum of the two integers is fifty.

Solution:
$$n + (n-8) = 50$$
$$2n - 8 = 50$$
$$2n = 58$$
$$n = 29$$
$$n - 8 = 29 - 8 = 21$$
The integers are 21 and 29.

7. Strategy
- The first number: n
  The second number: $2n+2$
  The third number: $3n-5$
- The sum of the three numbers is 123.

Solution
$$n+(2n+2)+(3n-5)=123$$
$$6n-3=123$$
$$6n=126$$
$$n=21$$
$$2n+2=2(21)+2=42+2=44$$
$$3n-5=3(21)-5=63-5=58$$
The numbers are 21, 44, and 58.

9. Strategy
- The first integer: n
  The second consecutive integer: $n+1$
  The third consecutive integer: $n+2$
- The sum of the integers is –57.

Solution
$$n+(n+1)+(n+2)=-57$$
$$3n+3=-57$$
$$3n=-60$$
$$n=-20$$
$$n+1=-20+1=-19$$
$$n+2=-20+2=-18$$
The integers are –20, –19, and –18.

11. Strategy
- The first odd integer: n
  The second consecutive odd integer: $n+2$
  The third consecutive odd integer: $n+4$
- Five times the smallest of the three integers is ten more than twice the largest.

Solution
$$5n=2(n+4)+10$$
$$5n=2n+8+10$$
$$5n=2n+18$$
$$3n=18$$
$$n=6$$
Since 6 is not an odd integer, there is no solution.

13. Strategy
- The first odd integer: n
  The second consecutive odd integer: $n+2$
  The third consecutive odd integer: $n+4$
- Three times the middle is seven more than the sum of the first and third integers.

Solution
$$3(n+2)=[n+(n+4)]+7$$
$$3n+6=2n+11$$
$$n=5$$
$$n+2=5+2=7 \qquad n+4=5+4=9$$
The integers are 5, 7, and 9.

Objective B Application Problems

15. Strategy
- Number of nickels: x
  Number of dimes: $53-x$

Coin	Number	Value	Total Value
Nickel	x	5	$5x$
Dime	$53-x$	10	$10(53-x)$

- The sum of the total values of each denomination of coin equals the total value of all the coins (370 cents).

Solution
$$5x+10(53-x)=370$$
$$5x+530-10x=370$$
$$-5x+530=370$$
$$-5x=-160$$
$$x=-32$$
$$53-x=53-32=21$$
There are 21 dimes in the collection.

17. Strategy
- Number of quarters: x
  Number of dimes: $4x$
  Number of nickels: $22-5x$

Coin	Number	Value	Total Value
Quarter	x	25	$25x$
Dime	$4x$	10	$10(4x)$
Nickel	$22-5x$	5	$5(22-5x)$

- The sum of the total values of each denomination of coin equals the total value of all the coins (230 cents).

Solution
$$25x+10(4x)+5(22-5x)=230$$
$$25x+40x+110-25x=230$$
$$40x+110=230$$
$$40x=120$$
$$x=3$$
$$4x=4\cdot 3=12$$
There are 12 dimes in the bank.

19. Strategy
- Number of 20¢ stamps: x
  Number of 15¢ stamps: $3x - 8$

Stamp	Number	Value	Total Value
20¢	x	20	$20x$
15¢	$3x - 8$	15	$15(3x - 8)$

- The sum of the total values of each denomination of stamp equals the total value of all the stamps (400 cents).

Solution
$$\begin{aligned} 20x + 15(3x - 8) &= 400 \\ 20x + 45x - 120 &= 400 \\ 65x - 120 &= 400 \\ 65x &= 520 \\ x &= 8 \end{aligned}$$
$3x - 8 = 3(8) - 8 = 24 - 8 = 16$

There are eight 20¢ stamps and sixteen 15¢ stamps.

21. Strategy
- Number of 3¢ stamps: x
  Number of 8¢ stamps: $2x - 3$
  Number of 13¢ stamps: $2(2x - 3)$

Stamp	Number	Value	Total Value
3¢	x	3	$3x$
8¢	$2x - 3$	8	$8(2x - 3)$
13¢	$2(2x - 3)$	13	$13(2)(2x - 3)$

- The sum of the total values of each denomination of stamp equals the total value of all the stamps (253 cents).

Solution
$$\begin{aligned} 3x + 8(2x - 3) + 26(2x - 3) &= 253 \\ 3x + 16x - 24 + 52x - 78 &= 253 \\ 71x - 102 &= 253 \\ 71x &= 355 \\ x &= 5 \end{aligned}$$
There are five 3¢ stamps in the collection.

23. Strategy
- Number of 18¢ stamps: x
  Number of 8¢ stamps: $2x$
  Number of 13¢ stamps: $x + 3$

Stamp	Number	Value	Total Value
18¢	x	18	$18x$
8¢	$2x$	8	$8(2x)$
13¢	$x + 3$	13	$13(x + 3)$

- The sum of the total values of each denomination of stamp equals the total value of all the stamps (368 cents).

Solution
$$\begin{aligned} 18x + 8(2x) + 13(x + 3) &= 368 \\ 18x + 16x + 13x + 39 &= 368 \\ 47x + 39 &= 368 \\ 47x &= 329 \\ x &= 7 \end{aligned}$$
There are seven 18¢ stamps in the collection.

Applying the Concepts

25. Strategy
- The first odd integer: n
  The second consecutive odd integer: $n + 2$
  The third consecutive odd integer: $n + 4$
- The product of the second and third minus the product of the first and second is 42.

Solution
$$\begin{aligned} (n + 2)(n + 4) - n(n + 2) &= 42 \\ n^2 + 6n + 8 - n^2 - 2n &= 42 \\ 4n + 8 &= 42 \\ 4n &= 34 \\ n &= \frac{17}{2} \end{aligned}$$
There is no solution, because n is not an integer.

SECTION 2.3

Objective A Application Problems

1. Strategy • Selling price of the mixture: x

	Amount	Cost	Value
Cashews	40	5.60	40(5.60)
Peanuts	100	1.89	100(1.89)
Mixture	140	x	$140x$

• The sum of the values before mixing equals the value after mixing.

Solution
$$40(5.60) + 100(1.89) = 140x$$
$$224 + 189 = 140x$$
$$413 = 140x$$
$$2.95 = x$$
$$x = 2.95$$
The selling price of the mixture is \$2.95 per pound.

3. Strategy • Number of adult tickets: x
Number of children's tickets: $460 - x$

	Amount	Cost	Value
Adult	x	5.00	$5.00(x)$
Child	$460 - x$	2.00	$2.00(460 - x)$

• The total value of the tickets sold is \$1880.

Solution
$$5.00x + 2.00(460 - x) = 1880$$
$$5x + 920 - 2x = 1880$$
$$3x + 920 = 1880$$
$$3x = 960$$
$$x = 320$$
320 adult tickets were sold.

5. Strategy • Liters of imitation maple syrup: x

	Amount	Cost	Value
Imitation	x	4.00	$4x$
Maple	5	9.50	9.50(5)
Mixture	$5 + x$	5.00	$5(5 + x)$

• The sum of the values before mixing equals the value after mixing.

Solution
$$4x + 9.50(5) = 5(5 + x)$$
$$4x + 47.5 = 25 + 5x$$
$$-x + 47.5 = 25$$
$$-x = -22.5$$
$$x = 22.5$$
The mixture must contain 22.5 L of imitation maple syrup.

7. Strategy • Ounces of pure gold: x
Ounces of gold alloy: $50 - x$

	Amount	Cost	Value
Pure gold	x	400	$400x$
Gold alloy	$50 - x$	150	$150(50 - x)$
Mixture	50	250	250(50)

• The sum of the values before mixing equals the value after mixing.

Solution
$$400x + 150(50 - x) = 250(50)$$
$$400x + 7500 - 150x = 12{,}500$$
$$250x = 5000$$
$$x = 20$$
$$50 - x = 50 - 20 = 30$$
20 oz of pure gold and 30 oz of the alloy were used.

9. Strategy • Selling price per pound of the mixture: x

	Amount	Cost	Value
\$5.40 tea	40	5.40	5.40(40)
\$3.25 tea	60	3.25	3.25(60)
Mixture	100	x	$100x$

• The sum of the values before mixing equals the value after mixing.

Solution
$$5.40(40) + 3.25(60) = 100x$$
$$216 + 195 = 100x$$
$$411 = 100x$$
$$4.11 = x$$
The selling price of the mixture is \$4.11 per pound.

11. Strategy • Gallons of cranberry juice: x

	Amount	Cost	Value
Cranberry	x	4.60	$4.60x$
Apple	50	2.24	50(2.24)
Mixture	$50+x$	3.00	$3(50+x)$

• The sum of the values before mixing equals the value after mixing.

Solution
$$4.60x+50(2.24)=3(50+x)$$
$$4.60x+112=150+3x$$
$$1.60x+112=150$$
$$1.60x=38$$
$$x=23.75$$
The mixture must contain 23.8 gal of cranberry juice.

Objective B Application Problems

13. Strategy • Pounds of 15% aluminum alloy: x

	Amount	Percent	Quantity
15%	x	0.15	$0.15x$
22%	500	0.22	0.22(500)
20%	$500+x$	0.20	$0.20(500+x)$

• The sum of the quantities before mixing is equal to the quantity after mixing.

Solution
$$0.15x+0.22(500)=0.20(500+x)$$
$$0.15x+110=100+0.20x$$
$$-0.05x+110=100$$
$$-0.05x=-10$$
$$x=200$$
200 lb of the 15% aluminum alloy must be used.

15. Strategy • Ounces of pure water: x
Ounces of 70% alcohol: $3.5-x$

	Amount	Percent	Quantity
water	x	0	$0(x)$
70% alcohol	$3.5-x$	0.70	$0.70(3.5-x)$
45% mixture	3.5	0.45	0.45(3.5)

• The sum of the quantities before mixing is equal to the quantity after mixing.

Solution
$$0(x)+0.70(3.5-x)=0.45(3.5)$$
$$2.45-0.70x=1.575$$
$$-0.70x=-0.875$$
$$x=1.25$$
$3.5-x=3.5-1.25-2.25$
The solution should contain 2.25 oz of rubbing alcohol and 1.25 oz of water.

17. Strategy • Ounces of pure water: x

	Amount	Percent	Quantity
Pure water	x	0	0
8%	75	0.08	0.08(75)
5%	$75+x$	0.05	$0.05(75+x)$

• The sum of the quantities before mixing is equal to the quantity after mixing.

Solution
$$0+0.08(75)=0.05(75+x)$$
$$0+0.08(75)=0.05(75+x)$$
$$6=3.75+0.05x$$
$$2.25=0.05x$$
$$45=x$$
45 oz of pure water must be used.

19. Strategy • Milliliters of alcohol: x

	Amount	Percent	Quantity
Alcohol	x	0	0
25% iodine	200	0.25	0.25(200)
10% iodine	$200+x$	0.10	$0.10(200+x)$

• The sum of the quantities before mixing is equal to the quantity after mixing.

Solution
$$0+0.25(200)=0.10(200+x)$$
$$50=20+0.10x$$
$$30=0.10x$$
$$300=x$$
300 ml of alcohol must be added.

21. Strategy • Percent concentration of the resulting drink: x

	Amount	Percent	Quantity
5% fruit juice	12	0.05	0.05(12)
water	2	0	0(2)
Mixture	10	x	$10x$

• The sum of the quantities before mixing is equal to the quantity after mixing.

Solution
$$0.05(12) + 0(2) = 10(x)$$
$$0.6 = 10x$$
$$0.06 = x$$
The resulting drink is 6% fruit juice.

23. Strategy • Quarts of 40% antifreeze replaced: x
Quarts of pure antifreeze added: x

	Amount	Percent	Quantity
40% antifreeze	12	0.40	0.40(12)
40% antifreeze	x	0.40	$0.40x$
replaced by pure antifreeze	x	1.00	x
added 60% antifreeze	12	0.60	0.60(12)

• The quantity in the radiator minus the quantity replaced plus the quantity added equals the quantity in the resulting solution.

Solution
$$0.40(12) - 0.40x + x = 0.60(12)$$
$$4.8 + 0.60x = 7.2$$
$$0.60x = 2.4$$
$$x = 4$$
4 qt will have to be replaced with pure antifreeze.

Objective C Application Problems

25. Strategy • Time for the car: t
Time for the helicopter: $t - \frac{1}{2}$

	Rate	Time	Distance
Car	80	t	$80t$
Helicopter	130	$t - \frac{1}{2}$	$130\left(t - \frac{1}{2}\right)$

• The car and the helicopter travel the same distance.

Solution
$$80t = 130\left(t - \frac{1}{2}\right)$$
$$80t = 130t - 65$$
$$-50t = -65$$
$$t = 1.3$$
$$d = rt = 80(1.3) = 104$$
The helicopter will overtake the car 104 mi from the starting point.

27. Strategy • Rate of the first car: r
Rate of the second car: $r + 8$

	Rate	Time	Distance
1st car	r	2.5	$2.5r$
2nd car	$r+8$	2.5	$2.5(r+8)$

• The total distance traveled by the two cars is 310 mi.

Solution
$$2.5r + 2.5(r+8) = 310$$
$$2.5r + 2.5r + 20 = 310$$
$$5r + 20 = 310$$
$$5r = 290$$
$$r = 58$$
$$r + 8 = 58 + 8 = 66$$
The speed of the first car is 58 mph.
The speed of the second car is 66 mph.

29. Strategy

- Time flying to a city: t
  Time returning to the international airport: $4 - t$

	Rate	Time	Distance
Going	250	t	$250t$
Returning	150	$4-t$	$150(4-t)$

- The distance to the city is the same as the distance returning to the international airport.

Solution

$$250t = 150(4-t)$$
$$250t = 600 - 150t$$
$$400t = 600$$
$$t = 1.5$$
$$d = rt = 250(1.5) = 375$$

The distance between the two airports is 375 mi.

31. Strategy

- Rate of freight train: r
  Rate of the passenger train: $r + 18$

	Rate	Time	Distance
Freight train	r	4	$4r$
Passenger train	$r+18$	2.5	$2.5(r+18)$

- The distance the freight train travels is equal to the distance the passenger train travels.

Solution

$$4r = 2.5(r+18)$$
$$4r = 2.5r + 45$$
$$1.5r = 45$$
$$r = 30$$
$$r + 18 = 30 + 18 = 48$$

The rate of the freight train is 30 mph. The rate of the passenger train is 48 mph.

33. Strategy

- Rate of the jogger: x
  Rate of the cyclist: $4x$

	Rate	Time	Distance
Jogger	x	2	$2x$
Cyclist	$4x$	2	$2(4x)$

- In 2 hours the cyclist is 33 mi ahead of the jogger.

Solution

$$2(4x) - 2x = 33$$
$$8x - 2x = 33$$
$$6x = 33$$
$$x = 5.5$$
$$4x = 4(5.5) = 22$$

The rate of the cyclist is 22 mph.

$$d = rt = 22(2) = 44$$

The cyclist traveled 44 mi.

Applying the Concepts

35. Strategy

- Amount of 12 karat gold: x

	Amount	Percent	Quantity
12 karat gold	x	$\frac{12}{24}$	$\frac{12}{24}x$
24 karat gold	3	$\frac{24}{24}$	$\frac{24}{24}(3)$
14 karat gold	$x+3$	$\frac{14}{24}$	$\frac{14}{24}(x+3)$

- The sum of the quantities before mixing is equal to the quantity after mixing.

Solution

$$\frac{12}{24}x + \frac{24}{24}(3) = \frac{14}{24}(x+3)$$
$$12x + 24(3) = 14(x+3)$$
$$12x + 72 = 14x + 42$$
$$-2x = -30$$
$$x = 15$$

15 oz of the 12 karat gold was used.

37. The distance between them 2 minutes before impact is equal to the sum of the distances each one can travel during 2 minutes.

$$2 \text{ minutes} \frac{1 \text{ hour}}{60 \text{ minutes}} = 0.03\overline{3} \text{ hour}$$

Distance between cars = rate of first car $\cdot\ 0.03\overline{3}$
+ rate of second car $\cdot\ 0.03\overline{3}$

Distance between cars

$$= 40 \cdot 0.03\overline{3} + 60 \cdot 0.03\overline{3} = 3.3\overline{3}$$

The cars are $3.3\overline{3}$ (or $3\frac{1}{3}$ miles) apart 2 minutes before impact.

39. Strategy • Distance from 40-ft tower to grass seed: x
Distance from top of 40-ft tower to seed (using Pythagorean theorem): $\sqrt{40^2+x^2}$
Distance from top of 30-ft tower to seed: $\sqrt{30^2+(50-x)^2}$

Solution Let the rate of both birds be r, because they are flying at the same rate.

	Rate	Distance	Time
Bird 1	r	$\sqrt{40^2+x^2}$	$\frac{\sqrt{40^2+x^2}}{r}$
Bird 2	r	$\sqrt{30^2+(50-x)^2}$	$\frac{\sqrt{30^2+(50-x)^2}}{r}$

They arrive at the seed at the same time.

$$\frac{\sqrt{40^2+x^2}}{r}=\frac{\sqrt{30^2+(50-x)^2}}{r}$$

Thus

$$\begin{aligned}\sqrt{40^2+x^2}&=\sqrt{30^2+(50-x)^2}\\40^2+x^2&=30^2+(50-x)^2\\1600+x^2&=900+2500-100x+x^2\\-1800&=-100x\\x&=18\end{aligned}$$

The grass seed is 18 feet from the 40-foot tower.

SECTION 2.4

Objective A Exercises

1. $x-3<2$
$x<5$
$\{x|x<5\}$

3. $4x\le 8$
$\frac{1}{4}(4x)\le\frac{1}{4}(8)$
$x\le 2$
$\{x|x\le 2\}$

5. $-2x>8$
$-\frac{1}{2}(-2x)<-\frac{1}{2}(8)$
$x<-4$
$\{x|x<-4\}$

7. $3x-1>2x+2$
$x-1>2$
$x>3$
$\{x|x>3\}$

9. $2x-1>7$
$2x>8$
$\frac{1}{2}(2x)>\frac{1}{2}(8)$
$x>4$
$\{x|x>4\}$

11. $5x-2\le 8$
$5x\le 10$
$\frac{1}{5}(5x)\le\frac{1}{5}(10)$
$x\le 2$
$\{x|x\le 2\}$

13. $6x+3>4x-1$
$2x+3>-1$
$2x>-4$
$\frac{1}{2}(2x)>\frac{1}{2}(-4)$
$x>-2$
$\{x|x>-2\}$

15. $8x+1\ge 2x+13$
$6x+1\ge 13$
$6x\ge 12$
$\frac{1}{6}(6x)\ge\frac{1}{6}(12)$
$x\ge 2$
$\{x|x\ge 2\}$

17. $4-3x<10$
$-3x<6$
$-\frac{1}{3}(-3x)>-\frac{1}{3}(6)$
$x>-2$
$\{x|x>-2\}$

19. $7-2x\ge 1$
$-2x\ge -6$
$-\frac{1}{2}(-2x)\le-\frac{1}{2}(-6)$
$x\le 3$
$\{x|x\le 3\}$

21. $-3-4x>-11$
$-4x>-8$
$-\frac{1}{4}(-4x)<-\frac{1}{4}(-8)$
$x<2$
$\{x|x<2\}$

23. $4x-2<x-11$
$3x-2<-11$
$3x<-9$
$\frac{1}{3}(3x)<\frac{1}{3}(-9)$
$x<-3$
$\{x|x<-3\}$

25.
$$x+7 \ge 4x-8$$
$$-3x+7 \ge -8$$
$$-3x \ge -15$$
$$-\frac{1}{3}(-3x) \le -\frac{1}{3}(-15)$$
$$x \le 5$$
$$\{x \mid x \le 5\}$$

27.
$$3x+2 \le 7x+4$$
$$-4x+2 \le 4$$
$$-4x \le 2$$
$$-\frac{1}{4}(-4x) \ge -\frac{1}{4}(2)$$
$$x \ge -\frac{1}{2}$$
$$\left\{x \middle| x \ge -\frac{1}{2}\right\}$$

29.
$$\frac{3}{5}x-2 < \frac{3}{10}-x$$
$$10\left(\frac{3}{5}x-2\right) < 10\left(\frac{3}{10}-x\right)$$
$$6x-20 < 3-10x$$
$$16x-20 < 3$$
$$16x < 23$$
$$\frac{1}{16}(16x) < \frac{1}{16}(23)$$
$$x < \frac{23}{16}$$
$$\left\{x \middle| x < \frac{23}{16}\right\}$$

31.
$$\frac{2}{3}x-\frac{3}{2} < \frac{7}{6}-\frac{1}{3}x$$
$$6\left(\frac{2}{3}x-\frac{3}{2}\right) < 6\left(\frac{7}{6}-\frac{1}{3}x\right)$$
$$4x-9 < 7-2x$$
$$6x-9 < 7$$
$$6x < 16$$
$$\frac{1}{6}(6x) < \frac{1}{6}(16)$$
$$x < \frac{8}{3}$$
$$\left\{x \middle| x < \frac{8}{3}\right\}$$

33.
$$\frac{1}{2}x-\frac{3}{4} < \frac{7}{4}x-2$$
$$4\left(\frac{1}{2}x-\frac{3}{4}\right) < 4\left(\frac{7}{4}x-2\right)$$
$$2x-3 < 7x-8$$
$$-5x-3 < -8$$
$$-5x < -5$$
$$-\frac{1}{5}(-5x) > -\frac{1}{5}(-5)$$
$$x > 1$$
$$\{x \mid x > 1\}$$

35.
$$4(2x-1) > 3x-2(3x-5)$$
$$8x-4 > 3x-6x+10$$
$$8x-4 > -3x+10$$
$$11x-4 > 10$$
$$11x > 14$$
$$\frac{1}{11}(11x) > \frac{1}{11}(14)$$
$$x > \frac{14}{11}$$
$$\left\{x \middle| x > \frac{14}{11}\right\}$$

37.
$$2-5(x+1) \ge 3(x-1)-8$$
$$2-5x-5 \ge 3x-3-8$$
$$-5x-3 \ge 3x-11$$
$$-8x-3 \ge -11$$
$$-8x \ge -8$$
$$-\frac{1}{8}(-8x) \le -\frac{1}{8}(-8)$$
$$x \le 1$$
$$\{x \mid x \le 1\}$$

39.
$$3(4x+3) \le 7-4(x-2)$$
$$12x+9 \le 7-4x+8$$
$$12x+9 \le 15-4x$$
$$16x+9 \le 15$$
$$16x \le 6$$
$$\frac{1}{16}(16x) \le \frac{1}{16}(6)$$
$$x \le \frac{3}{8}$$
$$\left\{x \middle| x \le \frac{3}{8}\right\}$$

41.
$$3+2(x+5)\ge x+5(x+1)+1$$
$$3+2x+10\ge x+5x+5+1$$
$$2x+13\ge 6x+6$$
$$-4x+13\ge 6$$
$$-4x\ge -7$$
$$-\frac{1}{4}(-4x)\le -\frac{1}{4}(-7)$$
$$x\le \frac{7}{4}$$
$$\left\{x\middle|x\le \frac{7}{4}\right\}$$

43.
$$3-4(x+2)\le 6+4(2x+1)$$
$$3-4x-8\le 6+8x+4$$
$$-4x-5\le 10+8x$$
$$-12x-5\le 10$$
$$-12x\le 15$$
$$-\frac{1}{12}(-12x)\ge -\frac{1}{12}(15)$$
$$x\ge -\frac{5}{4}$$
$$\left\{x\middle|x\ge -\frac{5}{4}\right\}$$

45.
$$12-2(3x-2)\ge 5x-2(5-x)$$
$$12-6x+4\ge 5x-10+2x$$
$$16-6x\ge 7x-10$$
$$16-13x\ge -10$$
$$-13x\ge -26$$
$$-\frac{1}{13}(-13x)\le -\frac{1}{13}(-26)$$
$$x\le 2$$
$$\{x|x\le 2\}$$

Objective B Exercises

47. $x-3\le 1$ and $2x\ge -4$

$x\le 4$ $\qquad$ $x\ge -2$

$\{x|x<4\}$ $\qquad$ $\{x|x\ge -2\}$

$\{x|x\le 4\}\cap\{x|x\ge -2\}=\{x|-2\le x\le 4\}$

49. $2x<6$ or $x-4>1$

$x<3$ $\qquad$ $x>5$

$\{x|x<3\}$ $\qquad$ $\{x|x>5\}$

$\{x|x<3\}\cup\{x|x>5\}=\{x|x<3 \text{ or } x>5\}$

51. $\frac{1}{2}x>-2$ and $5x<10$

$x>-4$ $\qquad$ $x<2$

$\{x|x>-4\}$ $\qquad$ $\{x|x<2\}$

$\{x|x>-4\}\cap\{x|x<2\}=\{x|-4<x<2\}$

53. $\frac{2}{3}x>4$ or $2x<-8$

$x>6$ $\qquad$ $x<-4$

$\{x|x>6\}$ $\qquad$ $\{x|x<-4\}$

$\{x|x>6\}\cup\{x|x<-4\}=\{x|x>6 \text{ or } x<-4\}$

55. $3x<-9$ and $x-2<2$

$x<-3$ $\qquad$ $x<4$

$\{x|x<-3\}$ $\qquad$ $\{x|x<4\}$

$\{x|x<-3\}\cap\{x|x<4\}=\{x|x<-3\}$

57. $7x<14$ and $1-x<4$

$x<2$ $\qquad$ $-x<3$

$x>-3$

$\{x|x<2\}$ $\qquad$ $\{x|x>-3\}$

$\{x|x<2\}\cap\{x|x>-3\}=\{x|-3<x<2\}$

59. $4x+1<5$ and $4x+7>-1$

$4x<4$ $\qquad$ $4x>-8$

$x<1$ $\qquad$ $x>-2$

$\{x|x<1\}$ $\qquad$ $\{x|x>-2\}$

$\{x|x<1\}\cap\{x|x>-2\}=\{x|-2<x<1\}$

61. $6x-2<-14$ or $5x+1>11$

$6x<-12$ $\qquad$ $5x>10$

$x<-2$ $\qquad$ $x>2$

$\{x|x<-2\}$ $\qquad$ $\{x|x>2\}$

$\{x|x<-2\}\cup\{x|x>2\}=\{x|x<-2 \text{ or } x>2\}$

63.
$$5<4x-3<21$$
$$5+3<4x-3+3<21+3$$
$$8<4x<24$$
$$\frac{1}{4}(8)<\frac{1}{4}(4x)<\frac{1}{4}(24)$$
$$2<x<6$$
$$\{x|2<x<6\}$$

65.
$$-2<3x+7<1$$
$$-2+(-7)<3+7+(-7)<1+(-7)$$
$$-9<3x<-6$$
$$\frac{1}{3}(-9)<\frac{1}{3}(3x)<\frac{1}{3}(-6)$$
$$-3<x<-2$$
$$\{x|-3<x<-2\}$$

67. $3x-5>10$ or $3x-5<-10$

$3x>15$ $\qquad$ $3x<-5$

$x>5$ $\qquad$ $x<-\frac{5}{3}$

$\{x|x>5\}$ $\qquad$ $\left\{x\middle|x<-\frac{5}{3}\right\}$

$\{x|x>5\}\cup\left\{x\middle|x<-\frac{5}{3}\right\}=\left\{x\middle|x>5 \text{ or } x<-\frac{5}{3}\right\}$

69. $6x-2<5$ or $7x-5<16$

$6x<7$ $\quad 7x<21$

$x<\frac{7}{6}$ $\quad x<3$

$\left\{x \middle| x<\frac{7}{6}\right\}$ $\quad \{x|x<3\}$

$\left\{x \middle| x<\frac{7}{6}\right\} \cup \{x|x<3\} = \{x|x<3\}$

71. $8x+2\le -14$ and $4x-2>10$

$8x\le -16$ $\quad 4x>12$

$x\le -2$ $\quad x>3$

$\{x|x\le -2\}$ $\quad \{x|x>3\}$

$\{x|x\le -2\} \cap \{x|x>3\} = \varnothing$

73. $5x+12\ge 2$ or $7x-1\le 13$

$5x\ge -10$ $\quad 7x\le 14$

$x\ge -2$ $\quad x\le 2$

$\{x|x\ge -2\}$ $\quad \{x|x\le 2\}$

$\{x|x\ge 2\} \cup \{x|x\le 2\} = \{\text{real numbers}\}$

75.

$$3\le 7x-14\le 31$$
$$3+14\le 7x-14+14\le 31+14$$
$$17\le 7x\le 45$$
$$\frac{1}{7}(17)\le \frac{1}{7}(7x)\le \frac{1}{7}(45)$$
$$\frac{17}{7}\le x\le \frac{45}{7}$$
$$\left\{x \middle| \frac{17}{7}\le x<\frac{45}{7}\right\}$$

77. $1-3x<16$ and $1-3x>-16$

$-3x<15$ $\quad -3x>-17$

$x>-5$ $\quad x<\frac{17}{3}$

$\{x|x>-5\}$ $\quad \left\{x \middle| x<\frac{17}{3}\right\}$

$\{x|x>-5\} \cap \left\{x \middle| x<\frac{17}{3}\right\} = \left\{x \middle| -5<x<\frac{17}{3}\right\}$

79. $6x+5<-1$ or $1-2x<7$

$6x<-6$ $\quad -2x<6$

$x<-1$ $\quad x>-3$

$\{x|x<-1\}$ $\quad \{x|x>-3\}$

$\{x|x<-1\} \cup \{x|x>-3\} = \{\text{real numbers}\}$

81. $9-x\ge 7$ and $9-2x<3$

$-x\ge -2$ $\quad -2x<-6$

$x\le 2$ $\quad x>3$

$\{x|x\le 2\}$ $\quad \{x|x>3\}$

$\{x|x\le 2\} \cap \{x|x>3\} = \varnothing$

Objective C Application Problems

83. Strategy The unknown number: x

Two times the difference between the number and eight: $2(x-8)$

Five times the sum of the number and four: $5(x+4)$

Solution

two times the difference between the number and eight > five times the sum of the number and four

$$2(x-8)\le 5(x+4)$$
$$2x-16\le 5x+20$$
$$-3x-16\le 20$$
$$-3x\le 36$$
$$x\ge -12$$

The smallest number is −12.

85. Strategy The width of the rectangle: x
The length of the rectangle: $2x - 5$
To find the maximum width, substitute the given values in the inequality $2L + 2W < 60$ and solve.

Solution

$$2L + 2W < 60$$
$$2(2x - 5) + 2x < 60$$
$$4x - 10 + 2x < 60$$
$$6x - 10 < 60$$
$$6x < 70$$
$$x < \frac{70}{6}$$
$$x < 11\frac{2}{3}$$

The maximum width of the rectangle is 11 cm.

87. Strategy To find the number of pages, write and solve an inequality using P to represent the number of pages. Then $P - 400$ is the number of pages for which you are charged an extra fee per page.

Solution Cost of Top Page < Cost of competitor

$$6.95 + 0.10(P - 400) < 3.95 + 0.15(P - 400)$$
$$6.95 + 0.10P - 40 < 3.95 + 0.15P - 60$$
$$0.10P - 33.05 < 0.15P - 56.05$$
$$-0.05P < -23$$
$$P > 460$$

The TopPage plan is less expensive when service is for more than 460 pages.

89. Strategy To find the number of minutes, write and solve an inequality using x to represent the number of minutes.

Solution Cost of paying with coins < Cost of paying with calling card

$$0.70 + 0.15(x - 3) < 0.35 + 0.196(1) + 0.126(x - 1)$$
$$0.70 + 0.15x - 0.45 < 0.35 + 0.196 + 0.126x - 0.126$$
$$0.15x + 0.25 < 0.42 + 0.126x$$
$$0.024x < 0.17$$
$$x < 7.08$$

Paying with cash is less expensive when the call is 7 min or less.

91. Strategy To find the temperature range in Fahrenheit degrees, write and solve a compound inequality using F to represent Fahrenheit degrees.

Solution

$$0 < \frac{5(F - 32)}{9} < 30$$
$$\frac{9}{5}(0) < \frac{9}{5}\left(\frac{5(F - 32)}{9}\right) < \frac{9}{5}(30)$$
$$0 < F - 32 < 54$$
$$0 + 32 < F - 32 + 32 < 54 + 32$$
$$32° < F < 86°$$

93. Strategy To find the minimum amount of sales, write and solve an inequality using N to represent the amount of sales.

Solution

$$1000 + 0.05N \geq 3200$$
$$0.05N \geq 2200$$
$$N \geq 44{,}000$$

George's amount of sales must be \$44,000 or more.

95. Strategy To find the number of checks, write and solve an inequality using N to represent the number of checks.

Solution Cost of the first account < Cost of the second account

$$8 + 0.12(N - 100) < 5 + 0.15(N - 100)$$
$$8 + 0.12N - 12 < 5 + 0.15N - 15$$
$$0.12N - 4 < 0.15N - 10$$
$$-0.03N < -6$$
$$N > 200$$

The first account is less expensive if more than 200 checks are written.

97. Strategy To find the range of scores, write and solve an inequality using N to represent the score on the last test.

Solution

$$70 \leq \frac{56 + 91 + 83 + 62 + N}{5} \leq 79$$
$$70 \leq \frac{292 + N}{5} \leq 79$$
$$5 \cdot 70 \leq 5\left(\frac{292 + N}{5}\right) \leq 5 \cdot 79$$
$$350 \leq 292 + N \leq 395$$
$$350 - 292 \leq 292 + N - 292 \leq 395 - 292$$
$$58 \leq N \leq 103$$

Since 100 is a maximum score, the range of scores to receive a C grade is $58 \leq N \leq 100$.

99. Strategy: To find the three consecutive even integers, write and solve a compound inequality using x to represent the first even integer.

Solution: Lower limit of the sum < sum < Upper limit of the sum

$$30 < x + (x+2) + (x+4) < 51$$
$$30 < 3x + 6 < 51$$
$$30 - 6 < 3x + 6 - 6 < 51 - 6$$
$$24 < 3x < 45$$
$$\frac{1}{3}(24) < \frac{1}{3}(3x) < \frac{1}{3}(45)$$
$$8 < x < 15$$

The three even integers are 10, 12, and 14; or 12, 14, and 16; or 14, 16, and 18.

Applying the Concepts

101. The solution is all real numbers, so the statement is correct.

SECTION 2.5

Objective A Exercises

1. $|x| = 7$

$x = 7$ or $x = -7$

The solutions are 7 and –7.

3. $|b| = 4$

$b = 4$ or $b = -4$

The solutions are 4 and –4.

5. $|-y| = 6$

$-y = 6$ or $-y = -6$

$y = -6$ $\quad$ $y = 6$

The solutions are –6 and 6.

7. $|-a| = 7$

$-a = 7$ or $-a = -7$

$a = -7$ $\quad$ $a = 7$

The solutions are –7 and 7.

9. $|x| = -4$

There is no solution to this equation because the absolute value of a number must be non-negative.

11. $|-t| = -3$

There is no solution to this equation because the absolute value of a number must be non-negative.

13. $|x+2| = 3$

$x + 2 = 3$ or $x + 2 = -3$

$x = 1$ $\quad$ $x = -5$

The solutions are 1 and –5.

15. $|y-5| = 3$

$y - 5 = 3$ or $y - 5 = -3$

$y = 8$ $\quad$ $y = 2$

The solutions are 8 and 2.

17. $|a-2| = 0$

$a - 2 = 0$

$a = 2$

The solution is 2.

19. $|x-2| = -4$

There is no solution to this equation because the absolute value of a number must be non-negative.

21. $|3-4x| = 9$

$3 - 4x = 9$ or $3 - 4x = -9$

$-4x = 6$ $\quad$ $-4x = -12$

$x = -\frac{3}{2}$ $\quad$ $x = 3$

The solutions are $-\frac{3}{2}$ and 3.

23. $|2x-3| = 0$

$2x - 3 = 0$

$2x = 3$

$x = \frac{3}{2}$

The solution is $\frac{3}{2}$.

25. $|3x-2| = -4$

There is no solution to this equation because the absolute value of a number must be non-negative.

27. $|x-2| - 2 = 3$

$|x-2| = 5$

$x - 2 = 5$ or $x - 2 = -5$

$x = 7$ $\quad$ $x = -3$

The solutions are 7 and –3.

29. $|3a+2| - 4 = 4$

$|3a+2| = 8$

$3a + 2 = 8$ $\quad$ $3a + 2 = -8$

$3a = 6$ $\quad$ $3a = -10$

$a = 2$ $\quad$ $a = -\frac{10}{3}$

The solutions are 2 and $-\frac{10}{3}$.

31. $|2-y| + 3 = 4$

$|2-y| = 1$

$2 - y = 1$ or $2 - y = -1$

$-y = -1$ $\quad$ $-y = -3$

$y = 1$ $\quad$ $y = 3$

The solutions are 1 and 3.

33. $|2x-3|+3=3$
$|2x-3|=0$
$2x-3=0$
$2x=3$
$x=\frac{3}{2}$
The solution is $\frac{3}{2}$.

35. $|2x-3|+4=-4$
$|2x-3|=-8$
There is no solution to this equation because the absolute value of a number must be non-negative.

37. $|6x-5|-2=4$
$|6x-5|=6$
$6x-5=6$ $\quad$ $6x-5=-6$
$6x=11$ $\quad$ $6x=-1$
$x=\frac{11}{6}$ $\quad$ $x=-\frac{1}{6}$
The solutions are $\frac{11}{6}$ and $-\frac{1}{6}$.

39. $|3t+2|+3=4$
$|3t+2|=1$
$3t+2=1$ $\quad$ $3t+2=-1$
$3t=-1$ $\quad$ $3t=-3$
$t=-\frac{1}{3}$ $\quad$ $t=-1$
The solutions are $-\frac{1}{3}$ and -1.

41. $3-|x-4|=5$
$-|x-4|=2$
$|x-4|=-2$
There is no solution to this equation because the absolute value of a number must be non-negative.

43. $8-|2x-3|=5$
$-|2x-3|=-3$
$|2x-3|=3$
$2x-3=3$ $\quad$ $2x-3=-3$
$2x=6$ $\quad$ $2x=0$
$x=3$ $\quad$ $x=0$
The solutions are 3 and 0.

45. $|2-3x|+7=2$
$|2-3x|=-5$
There is no solution to this equation because the absolute value of a number must be non-negative.

47. $|8-3x|-3=2$
$|8-3x|=5$
$8-3x=5$ $\quad$ $8-3x=-5$
$-3x=-3$ $\quad$ $-3x=-13$
$x=1$ $\quad$ $x=\frac{13}{3}$
The solutions are 1 and $\frac{13}{3}$.

49. $|2x-8|+12=2$
$|2x-8|=10$
There is no solution to this equation because the absolute value of a number must be non-negative.

51. $2+|3x-4|=5$
$|3x-4|=3$
$3x-4=3$ $\quad$ $3x-4=-3$
$3x=7$ $\quad$ $3x=1$
$x=\frac{7}{3}$ $\quad$ $x=\frac{1}{3}$
The solutions are $\frac{7}{3}$ and $\frac{1}{3}$.

53. $5-|2x+1|=5$
$-|2x+1|=0$
$|2x+1|=0$
$2x+1=0$
$2x=-1$
$x=-\frac{1}{2}$
The solution is $-\frac{1}{2}$.

55. $6-|2x+4|=3$
$-|2x+4|=-3$
$|2x+4|=3$
$2x+4=3$ $\quad$ $2x+4=-3$
$2x=-1$ $\quad$ $2x=-7$
$x=-\frac{1}{2}$ $\quad$ $x=-\frac{7}{2}$
The solutions are $-\frac{1}{2}$ and $-\frac{7}{2}$.

57. $8-|1-3x|=-1$
$-|1-3x|=-9$
$|1-3x|=9$
$1-3x=9$ $\quad$ $1-3x=-9$
$-3x=8$ $\quad$ $-3x=-10$
$x=-\frac{8}{3}$ $\quad$ $x=\frac{10}{3}$
The solutions are $-\frac{8}{3}$ and $\frac{10}{3}$.

59. $5+|2-x|=3$
$|2-x|=-2$
There is no solution to this equation because the absolute value of a number must be non-negative.

61. $|x| > 3$

$x > 3$ or $x < -3$

$\{x|x > 3\}$ $\{x|x < -3\}$

$\{x|x > 3\} \cup \{x|x < -3\} = \{x|x > 3 \text{ or } x < -3\}$

63. $|x+1| > 2$

$x+1 > 2$ or $x+1 < -2$

$x > 1$ $x < -3$

$\{x|x > 1\}$ $\{x|x < -3\}$

$\{x|x > 1\} \cup \{x|x < -3\} = \{x|x > 1 \text{ or } x < -3\}$

65. $|x-5| \le 1$

$-1 \le x-5 \le 1$

$-1+5 \le x-5+5 \le 1+5$

$4 \le x \le 6$

$\{x|4 \le x \le 6\}$

67. $|2-x| \ge 3$

$2-x \le -3$ or $2-x \ge 3$

$-x \le -5$ $-x \ge 1$

$x \ge 5$ $x \le -1$

$\{x|x \ge 5\}$ $\{x|x \le -1\}$

$\{x|x \ge 5\} \cup \{x|x \le -1\} = \{x|x \ge 5 \text{ or } x \le -1\}$

69. $|2x+1| < 5$

$-5 < 2x+1 < 5$

$-5+(-1) < 2x+1+(-1) < 5+(-1)$

$-6 < 2x < 4$

$\frac{1}{2}(-6) < \frac{1}{2}(2x) < \frac{1}{2}(4)$

$-3 < x < 2$

$\{x|-3 < x < 2\}$

Objective B Exercises

71. $|5x+2| > 12$

$5x+2 > 12$ or $5x+2 < -12$

$5x > 10$ $5x < -14$

$x > 2$ $x < -\frac{14}{5}$

$\{x|x > 2\}$ $\left\{x\middle|x < -\frac{14}{5}\right\}$

$\{x|x > 2\} \cup \left\{x\middle|x < -\frac{14}{5}\right\} = \left\{x\middle|x > 2 \text{ or } x < -\frac{14}{5}\right\}$

73. $|4x-3| \le -2$

The absolute value of a number must be non-negative. The solution set is the empty set.

75. $|2x+7| > -5$

$2x+7 > -5$ or $2x+7 < 5$

$2x > -12$ $2x < -2$

$x > -6$ $x < -1$

$\{x|x > -6\}$ $\{x|x < -1\}$

$\{x|x > -6\} \cup \{x|x < -1\} = \{\text{real numbers}\}$

77. $|4-3x| \ge 5$

$4-3x \ge 5$ or $4-3x \le -5$

$-3x \ge 1$ $-3x \le -9$

$x \le -\frac{1}{3}$ $x \ge 3$

$\left\{x\middle|x \le -\frac{1}{3}\right\}$ $\{x|x \ge 3\}$

$\left\{x\middle|x \le -\frac{1}{3}\right\} \cup \{x|x \ge 3\} = \left\{x\middle|x \le -\frac{1}{3} \text{ or } x \ge 3\right\}$

79. $|5-4x| \le 13$

$-13 \le 5-4x \le 13$

$-13+(-5) \le 5+(-5)-4x \le 13+(-5)$

$-18 \le -4x \le 8$

$-\frac{1}{4}(-18) \ge -\frac{1}{4}(-4x) \ge -\frac{1}{4}(8)$

$\frac{9}{2} \ge x \ge -2$

$\left\{x\middle|-2 \le x \le \frac{9}{2}\right\}$

81. $|6-3x| \le 0$ or $6-3x \ge 0$

$6-3x \le 0$ $-3x \ge -6$

$-3x \le -6$ $x \le 2$

$x \ge 2$

$\{x|x \ge 2\}$ $\{x|x \le 2\}$

$\{x|x \ge 2\} \cup \{x|x \le 2\} = \{x|x = 2\}$

83. $|2-9x| > 20$

$2-9x > 20$ or $2-9x < -20$

$-9x > 18$ $-9x < -22$

$x < -2$ $x > \frac{22}{9}$

$\{x|x < -2\}$ $\left\{x\middle|x > \frac{22}{9}\right\}$

$\{x|x < -2\} \cup \left\{x\middle|x > \frac{22}{9}\right\} = \left\{x\middle|x < -2 \text{ or } x > \frac{22}{9}\right\}$

85. $|2x-3|+2<8$

$|2x-3|<6$

$-6<2x-3<6$

$-6+3<2x-3+3<6+3$

$-3<2x<9$

$\frac{1}{2}(-3)<\frac{1}{2}(2x)<\frac{1}{2}(9)$

$-\frac{3}{2}<x<\frac{9}{2}$

$\left\{x \middle| -\frac{3}{2}<x<\frac{9}{2}\right\}$

87. $|2-5x|-4>-2$

$|2-5x|>2$

$2-5x>2$ or $2-5x<-2$

$-5x>0$ $\quad -5x<-4$

$x<0$ $\quad x>\frac{4}{5}$

$\{x|x<0\}$ $\quad \left\{x \middle| x>\frac{4}{5}\right\}$

$\{x|x<0\}\cup\left\{x \middle| x>\frac{4}{5}\right\}=\left\{x \middle| x<0 \text{ or } x>\frac{4}{5}\right\}$

89. $8-|2x-5|<3$

$-|2x-5|<-5$

$|2x-5|>5$

$2x-5>5$ or $2x-5<-5$

$2x>10$ $\quad 2x<0$

$x>5$ $\quad x<0$

$\{x|x>5\}$ $\quad \{x|x<0\}$

$\{x|x>5\}\cup\{x|x<0\}=\{x|x>5 \text{ or } x<0\}$

Objective C Exercises

91. Strategy Let d represent the diameter of the bushing, T the tolerance, and x the lower and upper limits of the diameter. Solve the absolute value inequality $|x-d|\le T$ for x.

Solution

$|x-d|\le T$

$|x-1.75|\le 0.008$

$-0.008\le x-1.75\le 0.008$

$-0.008+1.75\le x-1.75\le 0.008+1.75$

$1.742\le x\le 1.758$

The lower and upper limits of the diameter of the bushing are 1.742 in. and 1.758 in.

93. Strategy Let V represent the amount of voltage, T the tolerance, and A the given amount of voltage. Solve the absolute value inequality $|V-A|\le T$ for V.

Solution

$|V-A|\le T$

$|V-220|\le 25$

$-25\le V-220\le 25$

$-25+220\le V-220+220\le 25+220$

$195\le V\le 245$

The lower and upper limits of the voltage of the electric motor are 195 volts and 245 volts.

95. Strategy Let r represent the length of the piston rod, T the tolerance, and L the lower and upper limits of the length. Solve the absolute value inequality $|L-r|\le T$ for L.

Solution

$|L-r|\le T$

$\left|L-9\frac{5}{8}\right|\le\frac{1}{32}$

$-\frac{1}{32}\le L-9\frac{5}{8}\le\frac{1}{32}$

$-\frac{1}{32}+9\frac{5}{8}\le L-9\frac{5}{8}+9\frac{5}{8}\le\frac{1}{32}+9\frac{5}{8}$

$9\frac{19}{32}\le L\le 9\frac{21}{32}$

The lower and upper limits of the length of the piston rod are $9\frac{19}{32}$ in. and $9\frac{21}{32}$ in.

97. Strategy Let M represent the amount of ohms, T the tolerance, and r the given amount of the resistor. Find the tolerance and solve $|M-r| \le T$ for M.

Solution
$$T = (.02)(29{,}000) = 580 \text{ ohms}$$
$$|M-r| \le T$$
$$|M-29{,}000| \le 580$$
$$-580 \le M-29{,}000 \le 580$$
$$-580+29{,}000 \le M-29{,}000+29{,}000 \le 580+29{,}000$$
$$28{,}420 \le M \le 29{,}580$$
The lower and upper limits of the resistor are 28,420 ohms and 29,580 ohms.

99. Strategy Let M represent the amount of ohms, T the tolerance, and r the given amount of the resistor. Find the tolerance and solve $|M-r| \le T$ for M.

Solution
$$T = (.05)(25{,}000) = 1250 \text{ ohms}$$
$$|M-r| \le T$$
$$|M-25{,}000| \le 1250$$
$$-1250 \le M-25{,}000 \le 1250$$
$$-1250+25{,}000 \le M-25{,}000+25{,}000 \le 1250+25{,}000$$
$$23{,}750 \le M \le 26{,}250$$
The lower and upper limits of the resistor are 23,750 ohms and 26,250 ohms.

Applying the Concepts

101. a. $|x+3| = x+3$

Any value of x that makes $x + 3$ negative will result in a false equation because the left side of the equation will be positive and the right side of the equation will be negative. Therefore, the equation is true if $x + 3$ is greater than or equal to zero.

$x+3 \ge 0$

$x \ge -3$

$\{x \mid x \ge -3\}$

b. $|a-4| = 4-a$

Any value of a that makes $4 - a$ negative will result in a false equation because the left side of the equation will be positive and the right side of the equation will be negative. Therefore, the equation is true if $4 - a$ is greater than or equal to zero.

$4-a \ge 0$

$a \le 4$

$\{a \mid a \le 4\}$

103. a. $|x+y| \le |x|+|y|$

b. $|x-y| \ge |x|-|y|$

c. $\big||x|-|y|\big| \ge |x|-|y|$

d. $\left|\dfrac{x}{y}\right| = \dfrac{|x|}{|y|},\ y \ne 0$

e. $|xy| = |x||y|$

CHAPTER REVIEW

1.
$$3t-3+2t = 7t-15$$
$$5t-3 = 7t-15$$
$$5t-3-7t = 7t-15-7t$$
$$-2t-3 = -15$$
$$-2t-3+3 = -15+3$$
$$-2t = -15+3$$
$$-2t = -12$$
$$-\frac{1}{2}(-2t) = -\frac{1}{2}(-12)$$
$$t = 6$$

2.
$$3x-7 > -2$$
$$3x > 5$$
$$\frac{3x}{3} > \frac{5}{3}$$
$$x > \frac{5}{3}$$
$$\left\{x \,\middle|\, x > \frac{5}{3}\right\}$$

3.
$$P = 2L+2W$$
$$-2L = -P+2W$$
$$2L = P-2W$$
$$L = \frac{P-2W}{2}$$

4.
$$x+4 = -5$$
$$x+4-4 = -5-4$$
$$x = -9$$

5. $3x < 4$ and $x + 2 > -1$

$x < \frac{4}{3}$ $\quad$ $x > -3$

$\left\{x \middle| x < \frac{4}{3}\right\}$ $\quad$ $\{x | x > -3\}$

$$\left\{x \middle| x < \frac{4}{3}\right\} \cap \{x | x > -3\} = \left\{x \middle| -3 < x < \frac{4}{3}\right\}$$

6.
$$\begin{aligned}
\frac{3}{5}x - 3 &= 2x + 5 \\
5\left(\frac{3}{5}x - 3\right) &= 5(2x + 5) \\
3x - 15 &= 10x + 25 \\
3x - 15 - 10x &= 10x + 25 - 10x \\
-7x - 15 &= 25 \\
-7x - 15 + 15 &= 25 + 15 \\
-7x &= 40 \\
-\frac{1}{7}(-7x) &= -\frac{1}{7}(40) \\
x &= -\frac{40}{7}
\end{aligned}$$

7.
$$\begin{aligned}
-\frac{2}{3}x &= \frac{4}{9} \\
-\frac{3}{2}\left(-\frac{2}{3}x\right) &= -\frac{3}{2}\left(\frac{4}{9}\right) \\
x &= -\frac{2}{3}
\end{aligned}$$

8. $|x - 4| - 8 = -3$

$|x - 4| = 5$

$x - 4 = 5$ or $x - 4 = -5$

$x = 9$ $\quad$ $x = -1$

The solutions are 9 and –1.

9.
$$\begin{aligned}
&|2x - 5| < 3 \\
&-3 < 2x - 5 < 3 \\
&-3 + 5 < 2x - 5 + 5 < 3 + 5 \\
&2 < 2x < 8 \\
&\frac{1}{2}(2) < \frac{1}{2}(2x) < \frac{1}{2}(8) \\
&1 < x < 4 \\
&\{x | 1 < x < 4\}
\end{aligned}$$

10.
$$\begin{aligned}
\frac{2x - 3}{3} + 2 &= \frac{2 - 3x}{5} \\
15\left(\frac{2x - 3}{3} + 2\right) &= 15\left(\frac{2 - 3x}{5}\right) \\
\frac{15(2x - 3)}{3} + 15(2) &= \frac{15(2 - 3x)}{5} \\
5(2x - 3) + 30 &= 3(2 - 3x) \\
10x - 15 + 30 &= 6 - 9x \\
10x + 15 &= 6 - 9x \\
10x + 15 + 9x &= 6 - 9x + 9x \\
19x + 15 &= 6 \\
19x + 15 - 15 &= 6 - 15 \\
19x &= -9 \\
\frac{1}{19}(19x) &= \frac{1}{19}(-9) \\
x &= -\frac{9}{19}
\end{aligned}$$

11.
$$\begin{aligned}
2(a - 3) &= 5(4 - 3a) \\
2a - 6 &= 20 - 15a \\
2a - 6 + 15a &= 20 - 15a + 15a \\
17a - 6 &= 20 \\
17a - 6 + 6 &= 20 + 6 \\
17a &= 26 \\
\frac{1}{17}(17a) &= \frac{1}{17}(26) \\
a &= \frac{26}{17}
\end{aligned}$$

12. $5x - 2 > 8$ or $3x + 2 < -4$

$5x > 10$ $\quad$ $3x < -6$

$x > 2$ $\quad$ $x < -2$

$\{x | x > 2\}$ $\quad$ $\{x | x < -2\}$

$$\{x | x > 2\} \cup \{x | x < -2\} = \{x | x > 2 \text{ or } x < -2\}$$

13. $|4x - 5| \ge 3$

$4x - 5 \ge 3$ or $4x - 5 \le -3$

$4x \ge 8$ $\quad$ $4x \le 2$

$x \ge 2$ $\quad$ $x \le \frac{1}{2}$

$\{x | x \ge 2\}$ $\quad$ $\left\{x \middle| x \le \frac{1}{2}\right\}$

$$\{x | x \ge 2\} \cup \left\{x \middle| x \le \frac{1}{2}\right\} = \left\{x \middle| x \ge 2 \text{ or } x \le \frac{1}{2}\right\}$$

14.
$$\begin{aligned}
P &= \frac{R - C}{n} \\
n \cdot P &= \frac{R - C}{n} \cdot n \\
Pn &= R - C \\
C &= R - Pn
\end{aligned}$$

15.

$$\frac{1}{2}x-\frac{5}{8}=\frac{3}{4}x+\frac{3}{2}$$
$$8\left(\frac{1}{2}x-\frac{5}{8}\right)=8\left(\frac{3}{4}x+\frac{3}{2}\right)$$
$$8\left(\frac{1}{2}x\right)-8\left(\frac{5}{8}\right)=8\left(\frac{3}{4}x\right)+8\left(\frac{3}{2}\right)$$
$$4x-5=6x+12$$
$$4x-5-6x=6x+12-6x$$
$$-2x-5=12$$
$$-2x-5+5=12+5$$
$$-2x=17$$
$$-\frac{1}{2}(-2x)=-\frac{1}{2}(17)$$
$$x=-\frac{17}{2}$$

16. $6+|3x-3|=2$

$|3x-3|=-4$

There is no solution to this equation because the absolute value of a number must be non-negative.

17.

$3x-2>x-4$	or	$7x-5<3x+3$
$2x-2>-4$		$4x-5<3$
$2x>-2$		$4x<8$
$\frac{2x}{2}>\frac{-2}{2}$		$\frac{4x}{4}<\frac{8}{4}$
$x>-1$		$x<2$
$\{x\mid x>-1\}$		$\{x\mid x<2\}$

$\{x\mid x>-1\}\cup\{x\mid x<2\}=\{x\mid x \text{ is any real number}\}$

The solution set is the set of real numbers.

18.

$$2x-(3-2x)=4-3(4-2x)$$
$$2x-3+2x=4-12+6x$$
$$4x-3=-8+6x$$
$$4x-3-6x=-8+6x-6x$$
$$-2x-3=-8$$
$$-2x-3+3=-8+3$$
$$-2x=-5$$
$$-\frac{1}{2}(-2x)=-\frac{1}{2}(-5)$$
$$x=\frac{5}{2}$$

19. Strategy

- Gallons of apple juice: x

	Amount	Cost	Value
Apple	x	3.20	$3.20x$
Cranberry	40	5.50	40(5.50
Mixture	$40 + x$	4.20	$4.20(40 + x)$

- The sum of the values before mixing equals the value after mixing.

Solution

$$3.20x+40(5.50)=4.20(40+x)$$
$$3.20x+220=168+4.20x$$
$$-x=-52$$
$$x=52$$

The mixture must contain 52 gallons of apple juice.

20. Strategy

To find the minimum amount of sales, write and solve an inequality using N to represent the amount of sales.

Solution

$$800+0.04N\ge 3000$$
$$0.04N\ge 2200$$
$$N\ge 55{,}000$$

The executive's amount of sales must be $55,000 or more.

21. Strategy

- Number of nickels: x
  Number of dimes: $x+3$
  Number of quarters:
  $30-(2x+3)=27-2x$

Coin	Number	Value	Total Value
Nickel	x	5	$5x$
Dime	$x+3$	10	$10(x+3)$
Quarter	$27-2x$	25	$25(27-2x)$

- The sum of the total values of each denomination of coin equals the total value of all the coins (355 cents).

Solution

$$5x+10(x+3)+25(27-2x)=355$$
$$5x+10x+30+675-50x=355$$
$$-35x+705=355$$
$$-35x=-350$$
$$x=10$$

$27-2x=27-2(10)=27-20=7$

There are 7 quarters in the collection.

22. Strategy Let b represent the diameter of the bushing, T the tolerance, and d the lower and upper limits of the diameter. Solve, the absolute value inequality $|d-b| \le T$ for d.

Solution

$$|d-b| \le T$$
$$|d-2.75| \le 0.003$$
$$-0.003 \le d-2.75 \le 0.003$$
$$-0.003+2.75 \le d-2.75+2.75 \le 0.003+2.75$$
$$2.747 \le d \le 2.753$$

The lower and upper limits of the diameter of the bushing are 2.747 in. and 2.753 in.

23. Strategy
- The smaller integer: n
  The larger integer: $20-n$
- Five times the smaller integer is two more than twice the larger integer.

Solution

$$5n = 2+2(20-n)$$
$$5n = 2+40-2n$$
$$5n = 42-2n$$
$$7n = 42$$
$$n = 6$$
$$20-n = 20-6 = 14$$

The integers are 6 and 14.

24. Strategy To find the range of scores, write and solve an inequality using N to represent the score on the last test.

Solution

$$80 \le \frac{92+66+72+88+N}{5} \le 90$$
$$80 \le \frac{318+N}{5} \le 90$$
$$5\cdot 80 \le 5\cdot\frac{318+N}{5} \le 5\cdot 90$$
$$400 \le 318+N \le 450$$
$$400-318 \le 318+N-318 \le 450-318$$
$$82 \le N \le 132$$

Since 100 is the maximum score, the range of scores to receive a C grade is $82 \le x \le 100$.

25. Strategy
- Rate of the first plane: r
  Rate of the second plane: $r+80$

	Rate	Time	Distance
1st plane	r	1.75	$1.75r$
2nd plane	$r+80$	1.75	$1.75(r+80)$

- The total distance traveled by the two planes is 1680 mi.

Solution

$$1.75r+1.75(r+80) = 1680$$
$$1.75r+1.75r+140 = 1680$$
$$3.5r+140 = 1680$$
$$3.5r = 1540$$
$$r = 440$$
$$r+80 = 440+80 = 520$$

The speed of the first plane is 440 mph. The speed of the second plane is 520 mph.

26. Strategy
- Pounds of 30% tin: x
  Pounds of 70% tin: $500-x$

	Amount	Percent	Quantity
30%	x	0.30	$0.30x$
70%	$500-x$	0.70	$0.70(500-x)$
40%	500	0.40	$0.40(500)$

- The sum of the quantities before mixing is equal to the quantity after mixing.

Solution

$$0.30x+0.70(500-x) = 0.40(500)$$
$$0.30x+350-0.70x = 200$$
$$-0.40x+350 = 200$$
$$-0.40x = -150$$
$$x = 375$$
$$500-x = 500-375 = 125$$

375 lb of the 30% tin alloy and 125 lb of the 70% tin alloy were used.

27. Strategy: Let r represent the length of the piston rod, T the tolerance, and L the lower and upper limits of the length. Solve the absolute value inequality $|L-r| \le T$ for L.

Solution

$$|L-r| \le T$$
$$\left|L-10\frac{3}{8}\right| \le \frac{1}{32}$$
$$-\frac{1}{32} \le L-10\frac{3}{8} \le \frac{1}{32}$$
$$-\frac{1}{32}+10\frac{3}{8} \le L-10\frac{3}{8}+10\frac{3}{8} \le \frac{1}{32}+10\frac{3}{8}$$
$$10\frac{11}{32} \le L \le 10\frac{13}{32}$$

The lower and upper limits of the length of the piston are $10\frac{11}{32}$ in. and $10\frac{13}{32}$ in.

CHAPTER TEST

1.
$$x-2=-4$$
$$x-2+2=-4+2$$
$$x=-2$$

2.
$$b+\frac{3}{4}=\frac{5}{8}$$
$$b+\frac{3}{4}-\frac{3}{4}=\frac{5}{8}-\frac{3}{4}$$
$$b=\frac{5}{8}-\frac{6}{8}$$
$$b=-\frac{1}{8}$$

3.
$$-\frac{3}{4}y=-\frac{5}{8}$$
$$-\frac{4}{3}\left(-\frac{3}{4}y\right)=-\frac{4}{3}\left(-\frac{5}{8}\right)$$
$$y=\frac{5}{6}$$

4.
$$3x-5=7$$
$$3x-5+5=7+5$$
$$3x=12$$
$$\frac{3x}{3}=\frac{12}{3}$$
$$x=4$$

5.
$$\frac{3}{4}y-2=6$$
$$\frac{3}{4}y-2+2=6+2$$
$$\frac{3}{4}y=8$$
$$\frac{4}{3}\left(\frac{3}{4}y\right)=\frac{4}{3}(8)$$
$$y=\frac{32}{3}$$

6.
$$2x-3-5x=8+2x-10$$
$$-3x-3=-2+2x$$
$$-3x-3+3x=-2+2x+3x$$
$$-3=-2+5x$$
$$-3+2=-2+5x+2$$
$$-1=5x$$
$$\frac{1}{5}(-1)=\frac{1}{5}(5x)$$
$$-\frac{1}{5}=x$$
$$x=-\frac{1}{5}$$

7.
$$2[a-(2-3a)-4]=a-5$$
$$2[a-2+3a-4]=a-5$$
$$2[4a-6]=a-5$$
$$8a-12=a-5$$
$$8a-a-12=a-a-5$$
$$7a-12=-5$$
$$7a-12+12=-5+12$$
$$7a=7$$
$$\frac{7a}{7}=\frac{7}{7}$$
$$a=1$$

8.
$$E=IR+Ir$$
$$-IR=-E+Ir$$
$$IR=E-Ir$$
$$R=\frac{E-Ir}{I}$$

9.
$$\frac{2x+1}{3}-\frac{3x+4}{6}=\frac{5x-9}{9}$$
$$18\left(\frac{2x+1}{3}-\frac{3x+4}{6}\right)=18\left(\frac{5x-9}{9}\right)$$
$$18\left(\frac{2x+1}{3}\right)-18\left(\frac{3x+4}{6}\right)=18\left(\frac{5x-9}{9}\right)$$
$$6(2x+1)-3(3x+4)=2(5x-9)$$
$$12x+6-9x-12=10x-18$$
$$3x-6=10x-18$$
$$3x-6-10x=10x-18-10x$$
$$-7x-6=-18$$
$$-7x-6+6=-18+6$$
$$-7x=-12$$
$$\frac{-7x}{-7}=\frac{-12}{-7}$$
$$x=\frac{12}{7}$$

10. $3x - 2 \geq 6x + 7$

$-3x \geq 9$

$\frac{-3x}{-3} \leq \frac{9}{-3}$

$x \leq -3$

$\{x | x \leq -3\}$

11. $4 - 3(x+2) < 2(2x+3) - 1$

$4 - 3x - 6 < 4x + 6 - 1$

$-2 - 3x < 4x + 5$

$-7x < 7$

$\frac{-7x}{-7} > \frac{7}{-7}$

$x > -1$

$\{x | x > -1\}$

12. $4x - 1 > 5$ or $2 - 3x < 8$

$4x > 6$ $\quad -3x < 6$

$\frac{4x}{4} > \frac{6}{4}$ $\quad \frac{-3x}{-3} > \frac{6}{-3}$

$x > \frac{3}{2}$ $\quad x > -2$

$\left\{x \middle| x > \frac{3}{2}\right\}$ $\quad \{x | x > -2\}$

$\left\{x \middle| x > \frac{3}{2}\right\} \cup \{x | x > -2\} = \{x | x > -2\}$

13. $4 - 3x \geq 7$ and $2x + 3 \geq 7$

$-3x \geq 3$ $\quad 2x \geq 4$

$\frac{-3x}{-3} \leq \frac{3}{-3}$ $\quad \frac{2x}{2} \geq \frac{4}{2}$

$x \leq -1$ $\quad x \geq 2$

$\{x | x \leq -1\}$ $\quad \{x | x \geq 2\}$

$\{x | x \leq -1\} \cap \{x | x \geq 2\} = \varnothing$

14. $|3 - 5x| = 12$

$3 - 5x = 12$ $\quad 3 - 5x = -12$

$-5x = 9$ $\quad -5x = -15$

$x = -\frac{9}{5}$ $\quad x = 3$

The solutions are $-\frac{9}{5}$ and 3.

15. $2 - |2x - 5| = -7$

$-|2x - 5| = -9$

$|2x - 5| = 9$

$2x - 5 = 9$ $\quad 2x - 5 = -9$

$2x = 14$ $\quad 2x = -4$

$x = 7$ $\quad x = -2$

The solutions are 7 and –2.

16. $|3x - 5| \leq 4$

$-4 \leq 3x - 5 \leq 4$

$-4 + 5 \leq 3x - 5 + 5 \leq 4 + 5$

$1 \leq 3x \leq 9$

$\frac{1}{3} \leq \frac{3x}{3} \leq \frac{9}{3}$

$\frac{1}{3} \leq x \leq 3$

$\left\{x \middle| \frac{1}{3} \leq x \leq 3\right\}$

17. $|4x - 3| > 5$

$4x - 3 < -5$ or $4x - 3 > 5$

$4x < -2$ $\quad 4x > 8$

$x < -\frac{2}{4}$ $\quad x > 2$

$x < -\frac{1}{2}$

$\left\{x \middle| x < -\frac{1}{2}\right\}$ $\quad \{x | x > 2\}$

$\left\{x \middle| x < -\frac{1}{2}\right\} \cup \{x | x > 2\} = \left\{x \middle| x < -\frac{1}{2} \text{ or } x > 2\right\}$

18. Strategy To find the number of miles, write and solve an inequality using N to represent the number of miles.

Solution Cost of Gambelli car
< Cost of McDougal car

$12 + 0.10N < 24$

$0.10N < 12$

$N < 120$

It costs less to rent from Gambelli agency if the car is driven less than 120 mi.

19. Strategy Let b represent the diameter of the bushing, T the tolerance, and d the lower and upper limits of the diameter. Solve the absolute value inequality $|d - b| \leq T$ for d.

Solution

$|d - b| \leq T$

$|d - 2.65| \leq 0.002$

$-0.002 \leq d - 2.65 \leq 0.002$

$-0.002 + 2.65 \leq d - 2.65 + 2.65 \leq 0.002 + 2.65$

$2.648 \leq d \leq 2.652$

The lower and upper limits of the diameter of the bushing are 2.648 in. and 2.652 in.

20. Strategy
- The smaller integer: n
  The larger integer: $15 - n$
- Eight times the smaller integer is one less than three times the larger integer.

Solution
$$8n = 3(15 - n) - 1$$
$$8n = 45 - 3n - 1$$
$$8n = 44 - 3n$$
$$8n + 3n = 44 - 3n + 3n$$
$$11n = 44$$
$$n = 4$$
$$15 - n = 15 - 4 = 11$$
The integers are 4 and 11.

21. Strategy
- Number of 15¢ stamps: x
  Number of 11¢ stamps: $2x$
  Number of 24¢ stamps: $30 - 3x$

Stamp	Number	Value	Total Value
15¢	x	15	$15x$
11¢	$2x$	11	$11(2x)$
24¢	$30 - 3x$	24	$24(30 - 3x)$

- The sum of the total values of each denomination of stamp equals the total value of all the stamps (440 cents).

Solution
$$15x + 11(2x) + 24(30 - 3x) = 440$$
$$15x + 22x + 720 - 72x = 440$$
$$-35x + 720 = 440$$
$$-35x = -280$$
$$x = 8$$
$$30 - 3x = 30 - 3(8) = 30 - 24 = 6$$
There are six 24¢ stamps.

22. Strategy
- Price of hamburger mixture: x

	Amount	Cost	Value
\$1.60 hamburger	100	1.60	1.60(100)
\$3.20 hamburger	60	3.20	3.20(60)
Mixture	160	x	$160x$

- The sum of the values before mixing equals the value after mixing.

Solution
$$1.60(100) + 3.20(60) = 160x$$
$$160 + 192 = 160x$$
$$352 = 160x$$
$$2.20 = x$$
The price of the hamburger mixture is \$2.20.

23. Strategy
- Time jogger runs a distance: t
  Time jogger returns same distance: $1\frac{45}{60} - t$

	Rate	Time	Distance
Jogger runs a distance	8	t	$8t$
Jogger returns same distance	6	$\frac{7}{4} - t$	$6\left(\frac{7}{4} - t\right)$

- The jogger runs a distance and returns the same distance.

Solution
$$8t = 6\left(\frac{7}{4} - t\right)$$
$$8t = \frac{21}{2} - 6t$$
$$14t = \frac{21}{2}$$
$$\frac{1}{14}(14t) = \frac{1}{14}\left(\frac{21}{2}\right)$$
$$t = \frac{3}{4}$$

The jogger ran for $\frac{3}{4}$ hr.
$$8t = 8 \cdot \frac{3}{4} = 6$$
The jogger ran a distance of 6 mi one way. The jogger ran a total distance of 12 miles.

24. Strategy
- Rate of the slower train: r
  Rate of the faster train: $r + 5$

	Rate	Time	Distance
Slower train	r	2	$2r$
Faster train	$r + 5$	2	$2(r + 5)$

- The total distance traveled by the two trains is 250 mi.

Solution
$$2r + 2(r + 5) = 250$$
$$2r + 2r + 10 = 250$$
$$4r + 10 = 250$$
$$4r = 240$$
$$r = 60$$
$$r + 5 = 60 + 5 = 65$$
The rate of the slower train is 60 mph.
The rate of the faster train is 65 mph.

25. Strategy • Ounces of pure water: x

	Amount	Percent	Quantity
Pure water	x	0	0
8% salt	60	0.08	0.08(60)
3% salt	60 + x	0.03	0.03(60 + x)

• The sum of the quantities before mixing is equal to the quantity after mixing.

Solution
$$\begin{aligned} 0+0.08(60) &= 0.03(60+x) \\ 4.8 = 1.8 &= 0.03x \\ 3 &= 0.03x \\ 100 &= x \end{aligned}$$
There are 100 oz of pure water.

CUMULATIVE REVIEW

1. $$\begin{aligned} -4-(-3)-8+(-2) &= -4+3+(-8)+(-2) \\ &= -1+(-8)+(-2) \\ &= -9+(-2) \\ &= -11 \end{aligned}$$

2. $$\begin{aligned} -2^2\cdot 3^3 &= -(2\cdot 2)(3\cdot 3\cdot 3) \\ &= -(4)(27) \\ &= -108 \end{aligned}$$

3. $$\begin{aligned} 4-(2-5)^2\div 3+2 &= 4-(-3)^2\div 3+2 \\ &= 4-9\div 3+2 \\ &= 4-3+2 \\ &= 1+2 \\ &= 3 \end{aligned}$$

4. $$\begin{aligned} 4\div\frac{\frac{3}{8}-1}{5}\cdot 2 &= 4\div\frac{-\frac{5}{8}}{5}\cdot 2 \\ &= 4\div\left(-\frac{5}{8}\cdot\frac{1}{5}\right)\cdot 2 \\ &= 4\div\left(-\frac{1}{8}\right)\cdot 2 \\ &= 4\cdot(-8)\cdot 2 \\ &= -32\cdot 2 \\ &= -64 \end{aligned}$$

5. $$\begin{aligned} 2a^2-(b-c)^2 &= 2(2)^2-(3-(-1))^2 \\ &= 2\cdot 4-(3+1)^2 \\ &= 2\cdot 4-4^2 \\ &= 2\cdot 4-16 \\ &= 8-16 \\ &= -8 \end{aligned}$$

6. $$\begin{aligned} \frac{a-b^2}{b-c} &= \frac{2-(-3)^2}{-3-4} \\ &= \frac{2-9}{-3-4} \\ &= \frac{-7}{-7} \\ &= 1 \end{aligned}$$

7. The Commutative Property of Addition

8. the unknown number: n
three times the number: $3n$
the sum of three times the number and six: $3n+6$
$(3n+6)+3n=6n+6$

9. $$\begin{aligned} F &= \frac{evB}{c} \\ Fc &= \frac{evB}{c}\cdot c \\ Fc &= evB \\ \frac{Fc}{ev} &= \frac{evB}{ev} \\ \frac{Fc}{ev} &= B \end{aligned}$$

10. $$\begin{aligned} 5[y-2(3-2y)+6] &= 5[y-6+4y+6] \\ &= 5[5y] \\ &= 25y \end{aligned}$$

11. $\{-4, 0\}$

12. $\{x|x\le 3\}\cap\{x|x>-1\}$

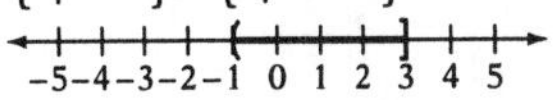

13. $$\begin{aligned} Ax+By+C &= 0 \\ By &= -C-Ax \\ \frac{By}{B} &= \frac{-C-Ax}{B} \\ y &= \frac{-C-Ax}{B} \end{aligned}$$

14. $$\begin{aligned} -\frac{5}{6}b &= -\frac{5}{12} \\ \left(-\frac{6}{5}\right)\left(-\frac{5}{6}\right)b &= \left(-\frac{6}{5}\right)\left(-\frac{5}{12}\right) \\ b &= \frac{1}{2} \end{aligned}$$

15. $$\begin{aligned} 2x+5 &= 5x+2 \\ 2x+5-5x &= 5x+2-5x \\ -3x+5 &= 2 \\ -3x+5-5 &= 2-5 \\ -3x &= -3 \\ \frac{-3x}{-3} &= \frac{-3}{-3} \\ x &= 1 \end{aligned}$$

16. $$\begin{aligned} \frac{5}{12}x-3 &= 7 \\ \frac{5}{12}x-3+3 &= 7+3 \\ \frac{5}{12}x &= 10 \\ \left(\frac{12}{5}\right)\left(\frac{5}{12}\right)x &= \left(\frac{12}{5}\right)10 \\ x &= 24 \end{aligned}$$

17.
$$\begin{aligned}2[3-2(3-2x)]&=2(3+x)\\2[3-6+4x]&=6+2x\\2[-3+4x]&=6+2x\\-6+8x&=6+2x\\-6+8x-2x&=6+2x-2x\\-6+6x+6&=6+6\\6x&=12\\\frac{6x}{6}&=\frac{12}{6}\\x&=2\end{aligned}$$

18.
$$\begin{aligned}3[2x-3(4-x)]&=2(1-2x)\\3[2x-12+3x]&=2-4x\\3[5x-12]&=2-4x\\15x-36&=2-4x\\15x-36+4x&=2-4x+4x\\19x-36&=2\\19x-36+36&=2+36\\19x&=38\\\frac{19x}{19}&=\frac{38}{19}\\x&=2\end{aligned}$$

19.
$$\begin{aligned}\frac{1}{2}y-\frac{2}{3}y+\frac{5}{12}&=\frac{3}{4}y-\frac{1}{2}\\12\left(\frac{1}{2}y-\frac{2}{3}y+\frac{5}{12}\right)&=12\left(\frac{3}{4}y-\frac{1}{2}\right)\\6y-8y+5&=9y-6\\-2y+5&=9y-6\\-2y+5-9y&=9y-6-9y\\-11y+5&=-6\\-11y+5-5&=-6-5\\-11y&=-11\\\frac{-11y}{-11}&=\frac{-11}{-11}\\y&=1\end{aligned}$$

20.
$$\begin{aligned}\frac{3x-1}{4}-\frac{4x-1}{12}&=\frac{3+5x}{8}\\24\left(\frac{3x-1}{4}-\frac{4x-1}{12}\right)&=24\left(\frac{3+5x}{8}\right)\\\frac{24(3x-1)}{4}-\frac{24(4x-1)}{12}&=\frac{24(3+5x)}{8}\\6(3x-1)-2(4x-1)&=3(3+5x)\\18x-6-8x+2&=9+15x\\10x-4&=9+15x\\10x-4-15x&=9+15x-15x\\-5x-4&=9\\-5x-4+4&=9+4\\-5x&=13\\\frac{-5x}{-5}&=\frac{13}{-5}\\x&=-\frac{13}{5}\end{aligned}$$

21.
$$\begin{aligned}3-2(2x-1)&\ge 3(2x-2)+1\\3-4x+2&\ge 6x-6+1\\-4x+5&\ge 6x-5\\-4x+5-6x&\ge 6x-5-6x\\-10x+5&\ge -5\\-10x+5-5&\ge -5-5\\-10x&\ge -10\\\frac{-10x}{-10}&\le\frac{-10}{-10}\\x&\le 1\end{aligned}$$

$\{x|x\le 1\}$

22.
$3x+2\le 5$ and $x+5>1$

$$\begin{aligned}3x+2-2&\le 5-2\\3x&\le 3\\\frac{3x}{3}&\le\frac{3}{3}\\x&\le 1\end{aligned}\qquad\begin{aligned}x+5-5&>1-5\\x&>-4\end{aligned}$$

$\{x|x\le 1\}$ $\quad\{x|x>-4\}$

$\{x|x\le 1\}\cap\{x|x>-4\}=\{x|-4\le x\le 1\}$

23. $|3-2x|=5$

$$\begin{aligned}3-2x&=5\\-2x&=2\\x&=-1\end{aligned}\quad\text{or}\quad\begin{aligned}3-2x&=-5\\-2x&=-8\\x&=4\end{aligned}$$

The solutions are −1 and 4.

24.
$$\begin{aligned}3-|2x-3|&=-8\\-|2x-3|&=-11\\|2x-3|&=11\end{aligned}$$

$$\begin{aligned}2x-3&=11\\2x&=14\\x&=7\end{aligned}\qquad\begin{aligned}2x-3&=-11\\2x&=-8\\x&=-4\end{aligned}$$

The solutions are 7 and −4.

25. $|3x-1|>5$

$$\begin{aligned}3x-1&<-5\\3x&<-4\\x&<-\frac{4}{3}\end{aligned}\quad\text{or}\quad\begin{aligned}3x-1&>5\\3x&>6\\x&>2\end{aligned}$$

$\left\{x\middle|x<-\frac{4}{3}\right\}$ $\quad\{x|x>2\}$

$\left\{x\middle|x<-\frac{4}{3}\right\}\cup\{x|x>2\}=\left\{x\middle|x<-\frac{4}{3}\text{ or }x>2\right\}$

26. $|2x-4|<8$

$$\begin{aligned}-8<2x-4&<8\\-8+4<2x-4+4&<8+4\\-4<2x&<12\\\frac{-4}{2}<\frac{2x}{2}&<\frac{12}{2}\\-2<x&<6\end{aligned}$$

$\{x|-2<x<6\}$

27. Strategy To find the number of checks, write and solve an inequality using c to represent the number of checks.
$5.00 + 0.04c > 2.00 + 0.10c$

Solution
$$\begin{aligned} 5.00+0.04c &> 2.00+0.10c \\ 5+0.04c-0.10c &> 2+0.10c-0.10c \\ 5-0.06c &> 2 \\ 5-0.06c-5 &> 2-5 \\ -0.06c &> -3 \\ \frac{-0.06c}{-0.06} &< \frac{-3}{-0.06} \\ c &< 50 \end{aligned}$$

The second account is cheaper if the customer writes fewer than 50 checks.

28. Strategy
- First odd integer: n
  Second odd integer: $n+2$
  Third odd integer: $n+4$
- Four times the sum of the first and third integer is one less than seven times the second.
  $4(n + n + 4) = 7(n + 2) - 1$

Solution
$$\begin{aligned} 4(n+n+4) &= 7(n+2)-1 \\ 4(2n+4) &= 7n+14-1 \\ 8n+16 &= 7n+13 \\ 8n+16-7n &= 7n+13-7n \\ n+16 &= 13 \\ n+16-16 &= 13-16 \\ n &= -3 \end{aligned}$$

The first integer is –3.

29. Strategy
- Number of quarters: x
  Number of dimes: $2x-5$

Coin	Number	Value	Total Value
Quarter	x	25	$25x$
Dime	$2x-5$	10	$10(2x-5)$

- The sum of the total values of each denomination of coin equals the total value of all the coins (400 cents).

Solution
$$\begin{aligned} 25x+10(2x-5) &= 400 \\ 25x+20x-50 &= 400 \\ 45x-50 &= 400 \\ 45x &= 450 \\ x &= 10 \\ 2x-5 = 2(10)-5 &= 15 \end{aligned}$$

The number of dimes is 15.

30. Strategy
- Ounces of pure silver: x
  Ounces of silver alloy: 100

	Amount	Cost	Value
Silver	x	8.50	$8.50x$
Alloy	100	4.00	100(4.00)
Mixture	$100+x$	6.00	$(100+x)6.00$

- The sum of the values before mixing equals the value after mixing.

Solution
$$\begin{aligned} 8.5x+100(4) &= (100+x)6 \\ 8.5x+400 &= 600+6x \\ 2.5x+400 &= 600 \\ 2.5x &= 200 \\ x &= 80 \end{aligned}$$

80 oz of pure silver are used in the mixture.

31. Strategy
- Slower plane: x
  Faster plane: $x+120$

	Rate	Time	Distance
Slower plane	x	2.5	$2.5x$
Faster plane	$x+120$	2.5	$2.5(x+120)$

- The two planes travel a total distance of 1400 miles.

Solution
$$\begin{aligned} 2.5x+2.5(x+120) &= 1400 \\ 2.5x+2.5x+300 &= 1400 \\ 5x+300 &= 1400 \\ 5x &= 1100 \\ x &= 220 \end{aligned}$$

32. Strategy Let b represent the diameter of the bushing, T the tolerance, and d the lower and upper limits of the diameter. Solve the absolute value inequality $|d-b| \le T$ for d.

Solution

$$|d-b| \le T$$
$$|d-2.45| \le 0.001$$
$$-0.001 \le d-2.45 \le 0.001$$
$$-0.001+2.45 \le d-2.45+2.45 \le 0.001+2.45$$
$$2.449 \le d \le 2.451$$

The lower and upper limits of the diameter of the bushing are 2.449 in. and 2.451 in.

33. Strategy

- Liters of 12% acid solution: x

	Amount	Percent	Quantity
12% solution	x	0.12	$0.12x$
5% solution	4	0.05	4(0.05)
8% solution	$x+4$	0.08	$0.08(x+4)$

- The sum of the quantities before mixing is equal to the quantity after mixing.

Solution

$$0.12x+4(0.05)=0.08(x+4)$$
$$0.12x+0.2=0.08x+0.32$$
$$0.04x+0.2=0.32$$
$$0.04x=0.12$$
$$x=3$$

3 L of 12% acid solution must be in the mixture.

Chapter 3: Linear Functions and Inequalities in Two Variables

SECTION 3.1

Objective A Exercises

1.

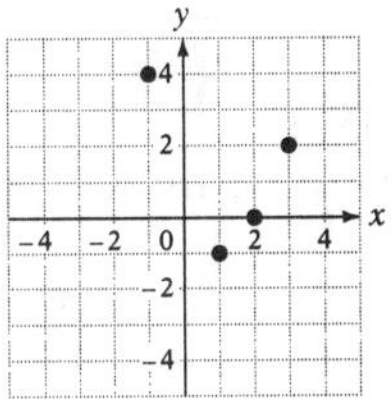

3. $A(0, 3)$, $B(1, 1)$, $C(3, -4)$, $D(-4, 4)$

5.

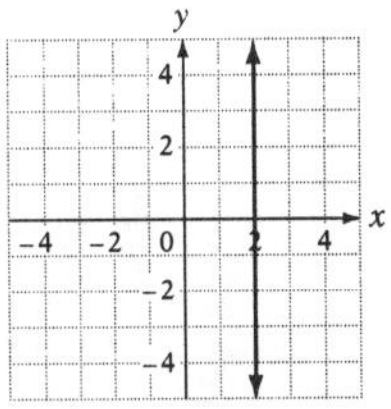

7.

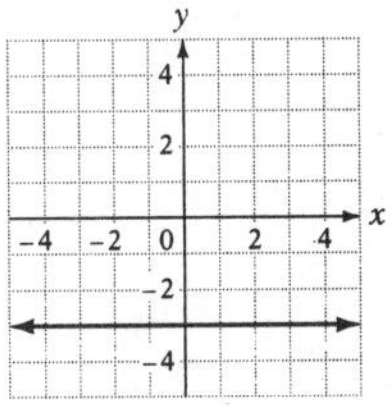

9.

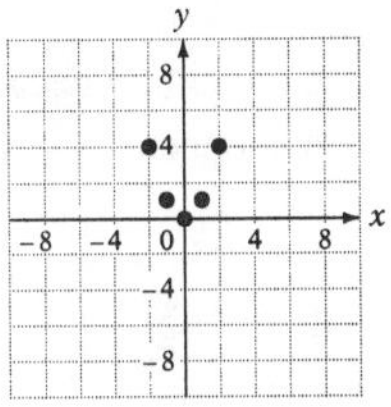

$y = x^2$
Ordered pairs: (–2, 4), (–1, 1), (0, 0), (1, 1), (2, 4)

11.

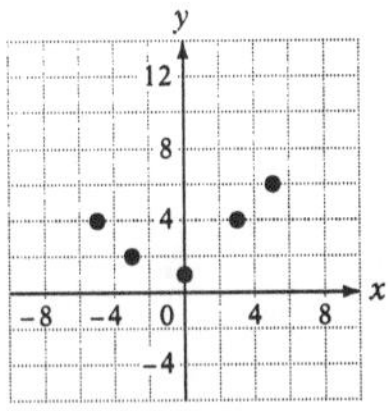

$y = |x+1|$
Ordered pairs: (–5, 4), (–3, 2), (0, 1), (3, 4), (5, 6)

13.

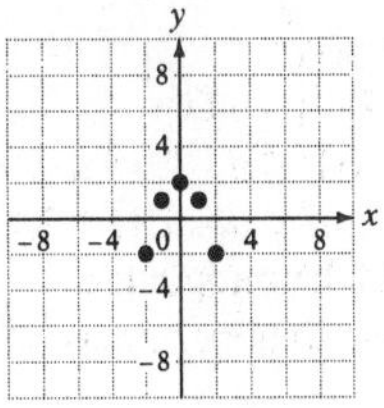

$y = -x^2 + 2$
Ordered pairs: (–2, –2), (–1, 1), (0, 2), (1, 1), (2, –2)

15.

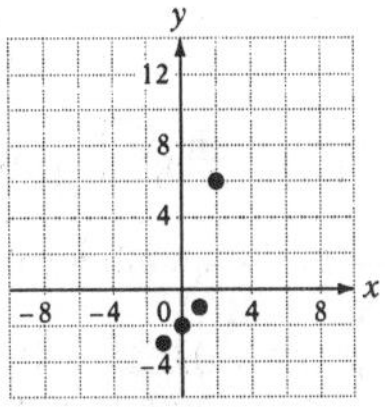

$y = x^3 - 2$
Ordered pairs: (–1, –3), (0, –2), (1, –1), (2, 6)

Objective B Exercises

17. $d = \sqrt{(5-3)^2 + (1-5)^2}$
$d = \sqrt{20} \approx 4.47$
$x_m = \dfrac{3+5}{2} = 4$
$y_m = \dfrac{1+5}{2} = 3$
The length is 4.47 and the midpoint is (4, 3).

19. $d = \sqrt{(-2-0)^2 + (4-3)^2}$
$d = \sqrt{5} \approx 2.24$
$x_m = \dfrac{0+(-2)}{2} = -1$
$y_m = \dfrac{3+4}{2} = \dfrac{7}{2}$
The length is 2.24 and the midpoint is $\left(-1, \dfrac{7}{2}\right)$.

21. $d = \sqrt{[2-(-3)]^2 + (-4-(-5))^2}$
$d = \sqrt{26} \approx 5.10$
$x_m = \dfrac{-3+2}{2} = -\dfrac{1}{2}$
$y_m = \dfrac{-5+(-4)}{2} = -\dfrac{9}{2}$
The length is 5.10 and the midpoint is $\left(-\dfrac{1}{2}, -\dfrac{9}{2}\right)$.

23. $d = \sqrt{(-2-5)^2 + [5-(-2)]^2}$
$d = \sqrt{98} \approx 9.90$
$x_m = \dfrac{5+(-2)}{2} = \dfrac{3}{2}$
$y_m = \dfrac{-2+5}{2} = \dfrac{3}{2}$
The length is 9.90 and the midpoint is $\left(\dfrac{3}{2}, \dfrac{3}{2}\right)$.

25. $d = \sqrt{(2-5)^2 + [-5-(-5)]^2}$
$d = 3$
$x_m = \dfrac{5+2}{2} = \dfrac{7}{2}$
$y_m = \dfrac{-5+(-5)}{2} = -5$
The length is 3 and the midpoint is $\left(\dfrac{7}{2}, -5\right)$.

27. $d = \sqrt{\left(-\dfrac{1}{2}-\dfrac{3}{2}\right)^2 + \left(\dfrac{7}{3}-\left(-\dfrac{4}{3}\right)\right)^2}$
$d = \sqrt{(-2)^2 + \left(\dfrac{11}{3}\right)^2}$
$d = \sqrt{\dfrac{157}{9}} \approx 4.18$
$x_m = \dfrac{-\frac{1}{2}+\frac{3}{2}}{2} = \dfrac{1}{2}$
$y_m = \dfrac{\frac{7}{3}+\left(-\frac{4}{3}\right)}{2} = \dfrac{1}{2}$
The length is 4.18 and the midpoint is $\left(\dfrac{1}{2}, \dfrac{1}{2}\right)$.

Objective C Exercises

29. a. 280°F
b. 50 min

31.

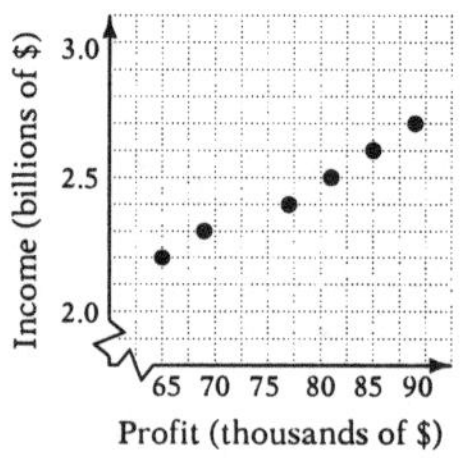

Applying the Concepts

33.

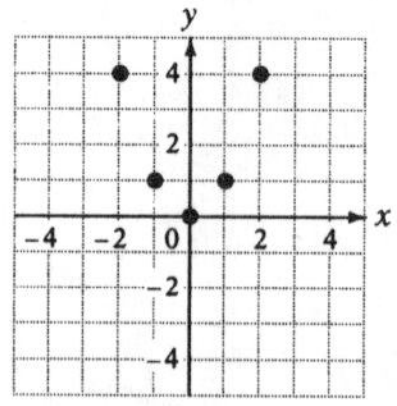

Ordered pairs: (−2, 4), (−1, 1), (0, 0), (1, 1), (2, 4)

35. The graph of all ordered pairs (x, y) that are 5 units from the origin is a circle of radius 5.

37.

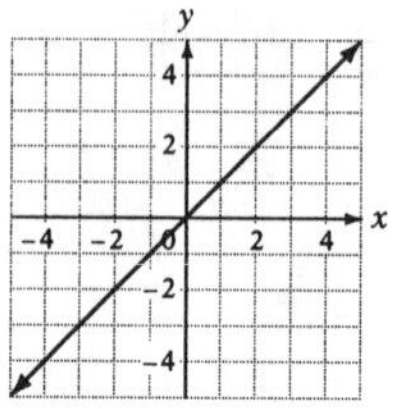

SECTION 3.2

Objective A Exercises

1. Function

3. Function

5. Function

7. Not a function

9. a. Yes, this table defines a function because no weight occurs more than once.
b. If $x = 2.75$ lb, then $y = \$22.25$.

11. $f(3) = 11$

13. $f(0) = -4$

15. $G(0) = 4$

17. $G(-2) = 10$

19. $q(3) = 5$

21. $q(-2) = 0$

23. $F(4) = 24$

25. $F(-3) = -4$

27. $H(1) = 1$

29. $H(t) = \dfrac{3t}{t+2}$

31. $s(-1) = 6$

33. $s(a) = a^3 - 3a + 4$

35. $P(-2+h) - P(-2) = 4(-2+h) + 7 - [4(-2) + 7]$
$= -8 + 4h + 7 + 8 - 7$
$= 4h$

37. $f(-3+h) - f(-3) = 8 - 3(-3+h) - [8 - 3(-3)]$
$= 8 + 9 - 3h - 8 - 9$
$= -3h$

39. a. \$4.75

b. \$4.00

41. a. \$3000

b. \$950

43. Domain = {1, 2, 3, 4, 5}
Range = {1, 4, 7, 10, 13}

45. Domain = {0, 2, 4, 6}
Range = {1, 2, 3, 4}

47. Domain = {1, 3, 5, 7, 9}
Range = {0}

49. Domain = {–2, –1, 0, 1, 2}
Range = {0, 1, 2}

51. Domain = {–2, –1, 0, 1, 2}
Range = {–3, 3, 6, 7, 9}

53. $x = 1$

55. $x = -8$

57. No values are excluded.

59. No values are excluded.

61. $x = 0$

63. No values are excluded.

65. No values are excluded.

67. $x = -2$

69. No values are excluded.

71. Range = {–3, 1, 5, 9}

73. Range = {–23, –13, –8, –3, 7}

75. Range = {0, 1, 4}

77. Range = {2, 14, 26, 42}

79. Range = $\left\{-5, \frac{5}{3}, 5\right\}$

81. Range = $\left\{-1, -\frac{1}{2}, -\frac{1}{3}, 1\right\}$

83. Range = {–38, –8, 2}

Applying the Concepts

85. A relation is a set of ordered pairs. A function is a relation in which no two ordered pairs have the same first coordinate and different second coordinates. A function is always a relation, but a relation is not always a function.

87. Set of ordered pairs:
{(–2, –8), (–1, –1), (0, 0), (1, 1), (2, 8)}.
Yes, this set of ordered pairs defines a function because no x-coordinate appears twice with different y-coordinates.

89. Find the value of the function
$s = f(v) = 0.017v^2$ when $v = 60$
$s = 0.017v^2$
$s = 0.017(60)^2$
$s = 61.2$
The car will skid for 61.2 feet.

91. a. 20 ft/s

b. 30 ft/s

93. a. 64°F

b. 52°F

SECTION 3.3

Objective A Exercises

1.

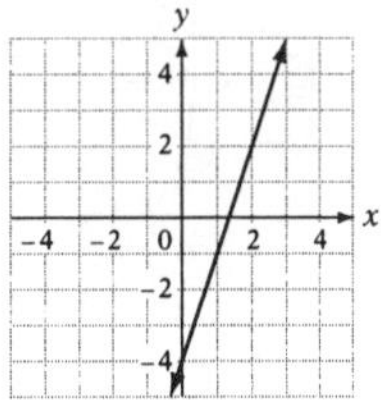

3.

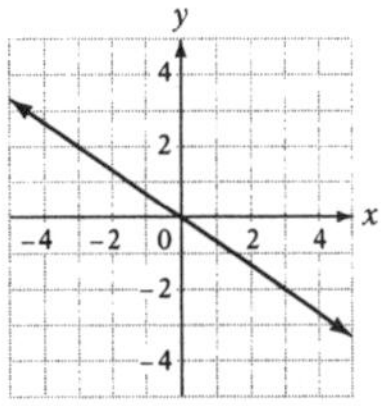

5.

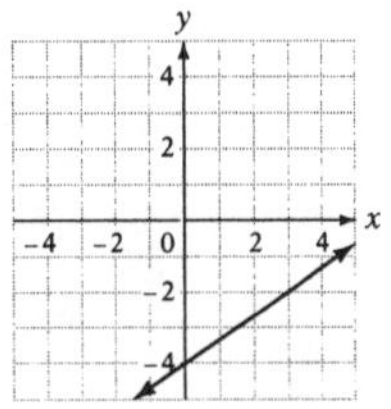

7.

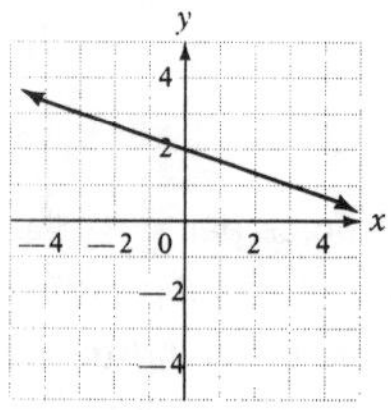

9.

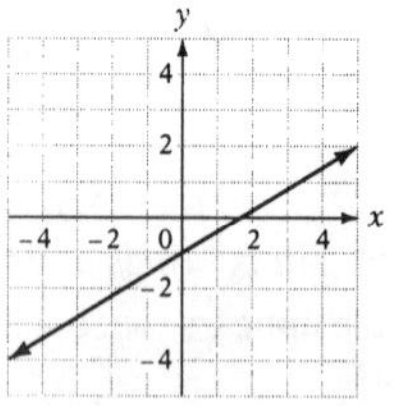

Objective B Exercises

11. $2x + y = -3$

$y = -2x - 3$

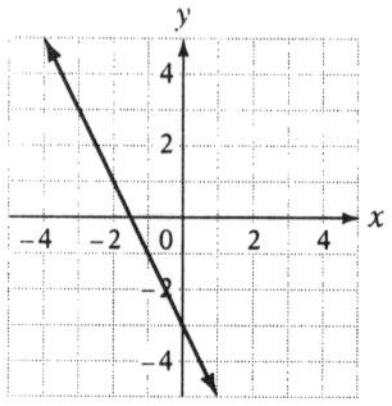

13. $x - 4y = 8$

$-4y = -x + 8$

$y = \frac{1}{4}x - 2$

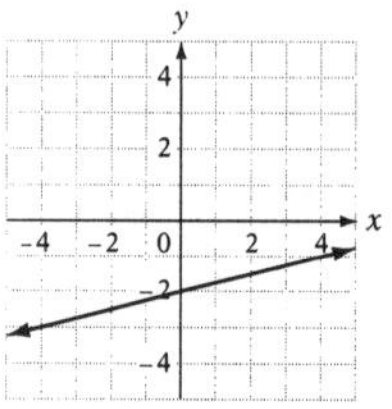

15. $y = \frac{1}{3}x$

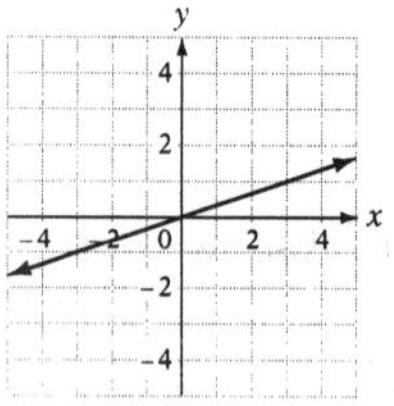

17. $3x - y = -2$

$-y = -3x - 2$

$y = 3x + 2$

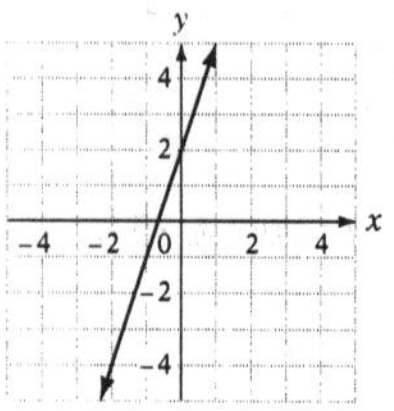

Objective C Exercises

19. x-intercept:

$x - 2y = -4$

$x - 2(0) = -4$

$x = -4$

$(-4, 0)$

y-intercept:

$x - 2y = -4$

$0 - 2y = -4$

$-2y = -4$

$y = 2$

$(0, 2)$

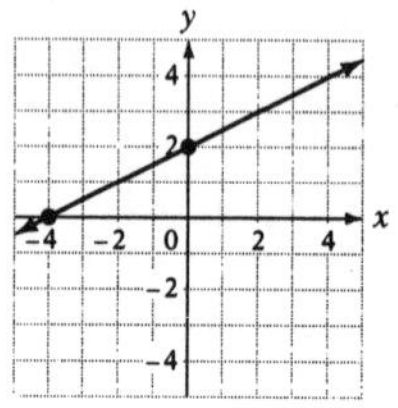

21. x-intercept:

$2x - 3y = 9$

$2x - 3(0) = 9$

$2x = 9$

$x = \frac{9}{2}$

$\left(\frac{9}{2}, 0\right)$

y-intercept:

$2x - 3y = 9$

$2(0) - 3y = 9$

$-3y = 9$

$y = -3$

$(0, -3)$

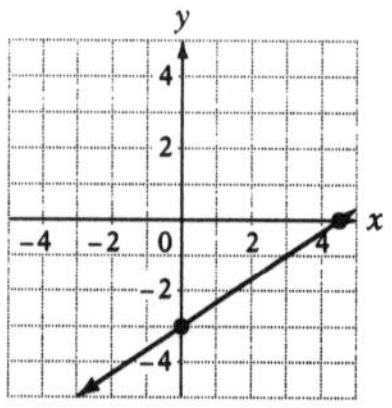

23. x-intercept:

$$\begin{aligned} 2x - y &= 4 \\ 2x - 0 &= 4 \\ 2x &= 4 \\ x &= 2 \end{aligned}$$

$(2, 0)$

y-intercept:

$$\begin{aligned} 2x - y &= 4 \\ 2(0) - y &= 4 \\ -y &= 4 \\ y &= -4 \end{aligned}$$

$(0, -4)$

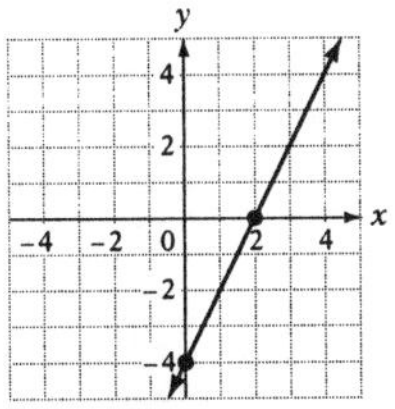

25. x-intercept:

$$\begin{aligned} 3x + 2y &= 5 \\ 3x + 2(0) &= 5 \\ 3x &= 5 \\ x &= \frac{5}{3} \end{aligned}$$

$\left(\frac{5}{3}, 0\right)$

y-intercept:

$$\begin{aligned} 3x + 2y &= 5 \\ 3(0) + 2y &= 5 \\ 2y &= 5 \\ y &= \frac{5}{2} \end{aligned}$$

$\left(0, \frac{5}{2}\right)$

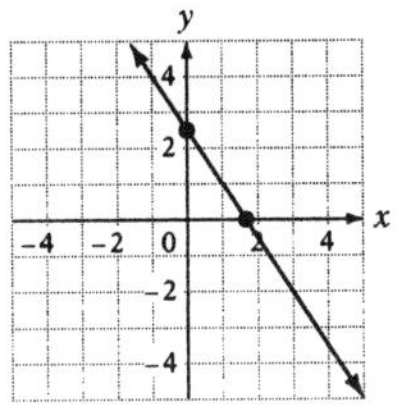

27. x-intercept:

$$\begin{aligned} 3x + 2y &= 4 \\ 3x + 2(0) &= 4 \\ 3x &= 4 \\ x &= \frac{4}{3} \end{aligned}$$

$\left(\frac{4}{3}, 0\right)$

y-intercept:

$$\begin{aligned} 3x + 2y &= 4 \\ 3(0) + 2y &= 4 \\ 2y &= 4 \\ y &= 2 \end{aligned}$$

$(0, 2)$

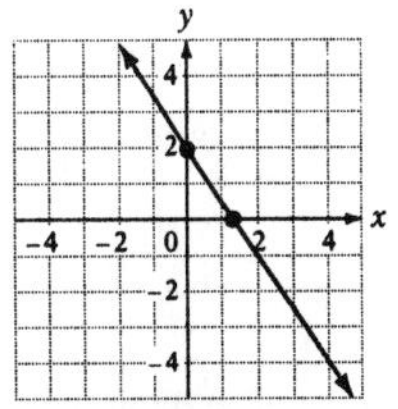

29. x-intercept:

$$\begin{aligned} 3x - 5y &= 9 \\ 3x - 5(0) &= 9 \\ 3x &= 9 \\ x &= 3 \end{aligned}$$

$(3, 0)$

y-intercept:

$$\begin{aligned} 3x - 5y &= 9 \\ 3(0) - 5y &= 9 \\ -5y &= 9 \\ y &= -\frac{9}{5} \end{aligned}$$

$\left(0, -\frac{9}{5}\right)$

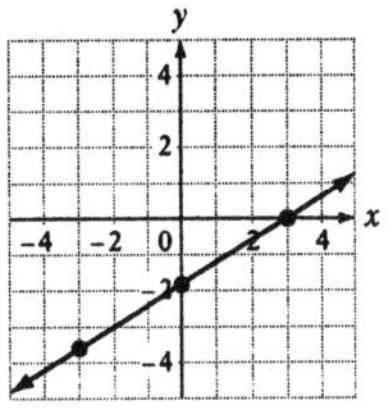

Objective D Application Problems

31.

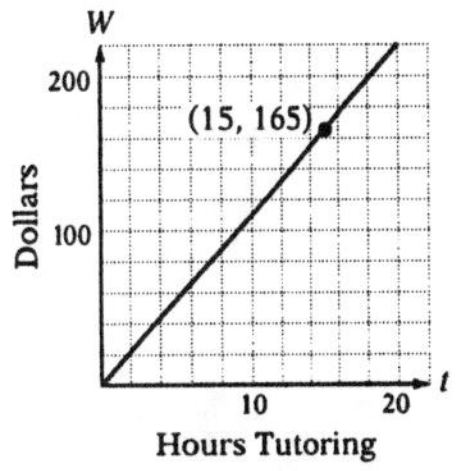

Marlys received \$165 for tutoring 15 h.

33.

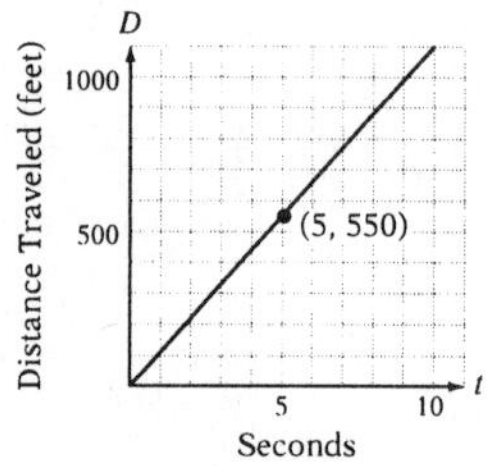

The roller coaster travels 550 ft in 5 s.

35.

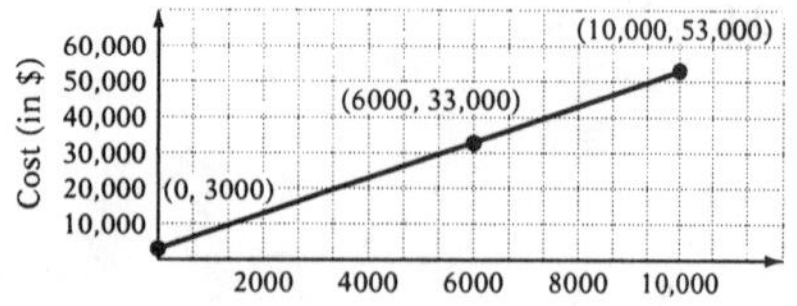

The cost of manufacturing 6000 compact discs is $33,000.

Applying the Concepts

37. The graph of an equation visually depicts the range of the function for continuous portions of the domain.

39. First plot the points (0, y-intercept) and (x-intercept, 0) on the x-y plane. Then draw a line between the two points.

41.

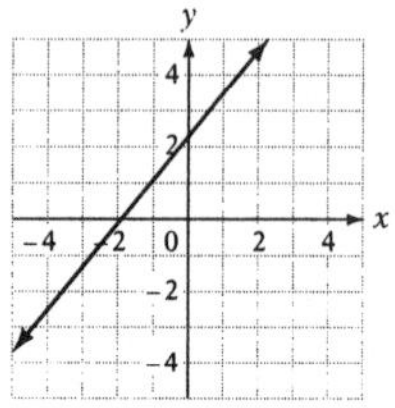

43.

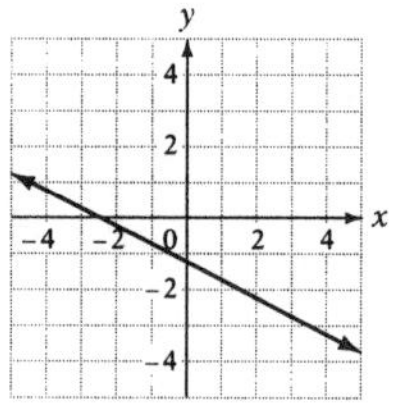

45.

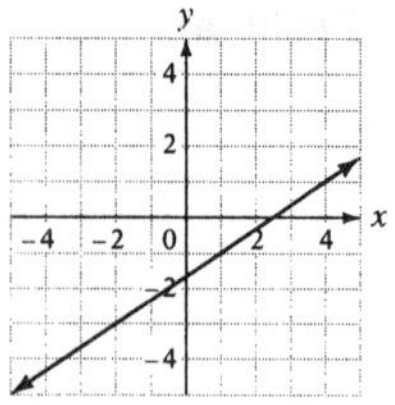

47.

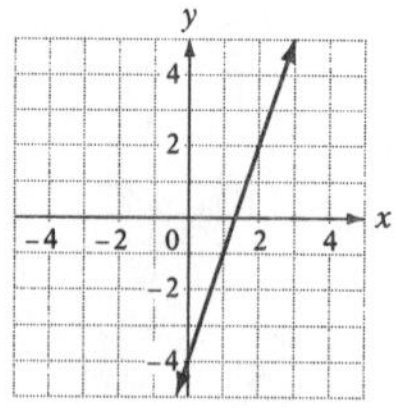

49.

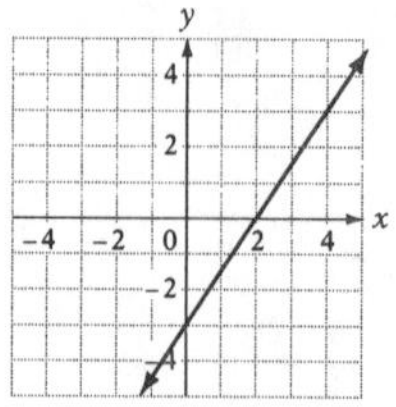

51.

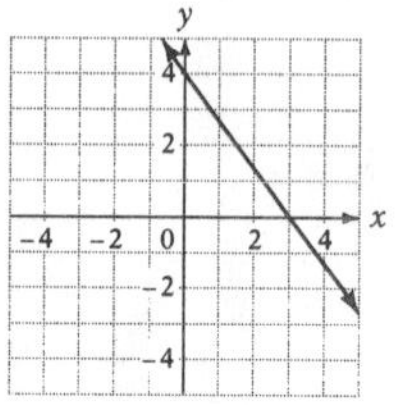

53.

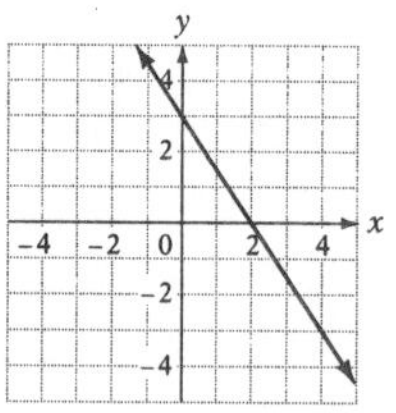

55.

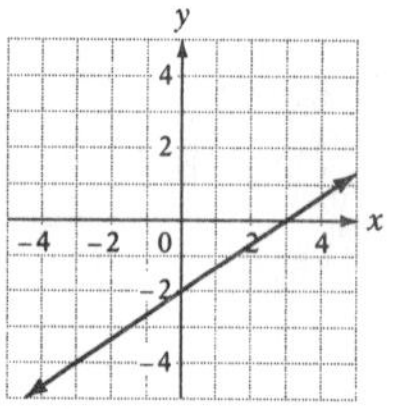

57.

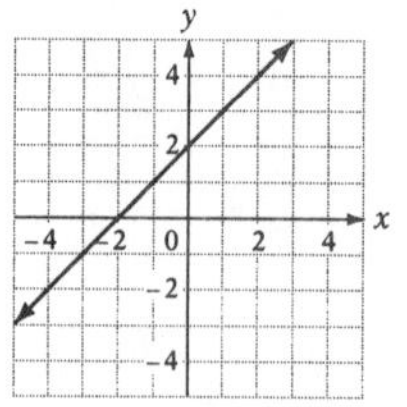

SECTION 3.4

Objective A Exercises

1. $P_1(1, 3)$, $P_2(3, 1)$

$$m = \frac{y_2 - y_1}{x_2 - x_1} = \frac{1-3}{3-1} = \frac{-2}{2} = -1$$

The slope is -1.

3. $P_1(-1, 4),\ P_2(2, 5)$

$m = \dfrac{y_2 - y_1}{x_2 - x_1} = \dfrac{5-4}{2-(-1)} = \dfrac{1}{3}$

The slope is $\dfrac{1}{3}$.

5. $P_1(-1, 3),\ P_2(-4, 5)$

$m = \dfrac{y_2 - y_1}{x_2 - x_1} = \dfrac{5-3}{-4-(-1)} = \dfrac{2}{-3} = -\dfrac{2}{3}$

The slope is $-\dfrac{2}{3}$.

7. $P_1(0, 3),\ P_2(4, 0)$

$m = \dfrac{y_2 - y_1}{x_2 - x_1} = \dfrac{0-3}{4-0} = \dfrac{-3}{4} = -\dfrac{3}{4}$

The slope is $-\dfrac{3}{4}$.

9. $P_1(2, 4),\ P_2(2, -2)$

$m = \dfrac{y_2 - y_1}{x_2 - x_1} = \dfrac{-2-4}{2-2} = \dfrac{-6}{0}$

The slope is undefined.

11. $P_1(2, 5),\ P_2(-3, -2)$

$m = \dfrac{y_2 - y_1}{x_2 - x_1} = \dfrac{-2-5}{-3-2} = \dfrac{-7}{-5} = \dfrac{7}{5}$

The slope is $\dfrac{7}{5}$.

13. $P_1(2, 3),\ P_2(-1, 3)$

$m = \dfrac{y_2 - y_1}{x_2 - x_1} = \dfrac{3-3}{-1-2} = \dfrac{0}{-3} = 0$

The line has zero slope.

15. $P_1(0, 4),\ P_2(-2, 5)$

$m = \dfrac{y_2 - y_1}{x_2 - x_1} = \dfrac{5-4}{-2-0} = \dfrac{1}{-2} = -\dfrac{1}{2}$

The slope is $-\dfrac{1}{2}$.

17. $P_1(-3, -1),\ P_2(-3, 4)$

$m = \dfrac{y_2 - y_1}{x_2 - x_1} = \dfrac{4-(-1)}{-3-(-3)} = \dfrac{5}{0}$

The slope is undefined.

19. $m = \dfrac{240-80}{6-2}$

$m = 40$

The average speed of the motorist was 40 mph.

21. $m = \dfrac{11-2}{97-78} \approx 0.5$

The slope is the increase in the number of gallons of bottled water sold per year.

23. $m = \dfrac{5000}{12.97} = 385.5$

Said Aouita's average speed was 385.5 meters per minute.

Objective B Exercises

25.

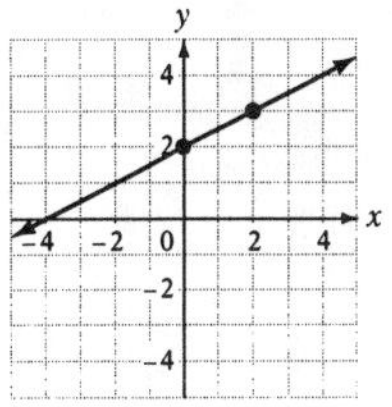

27.

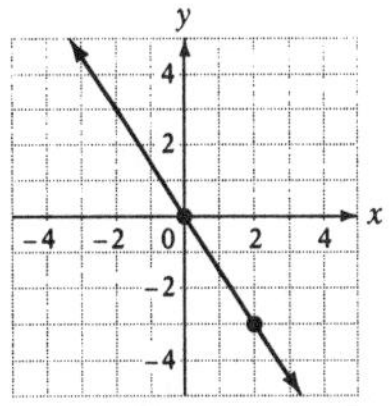

29.

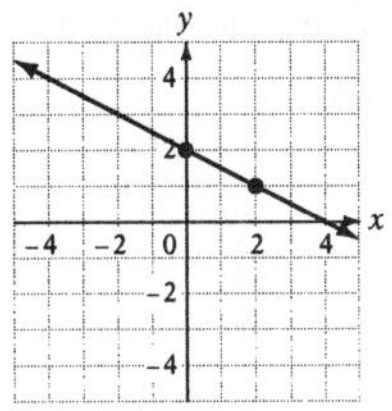

31.

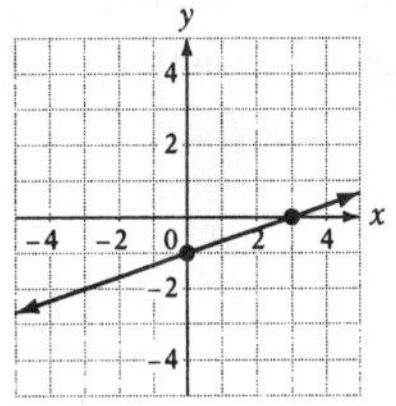

33.

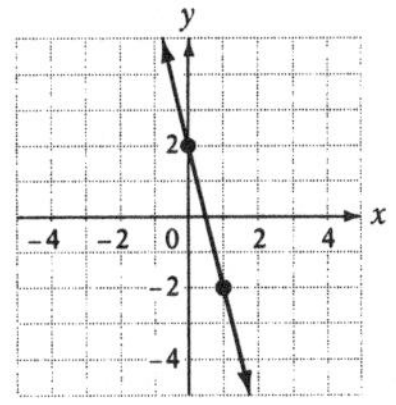

35.

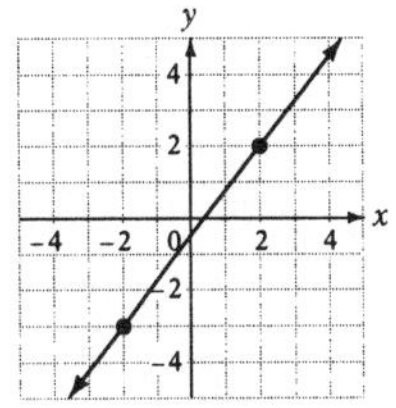

37.

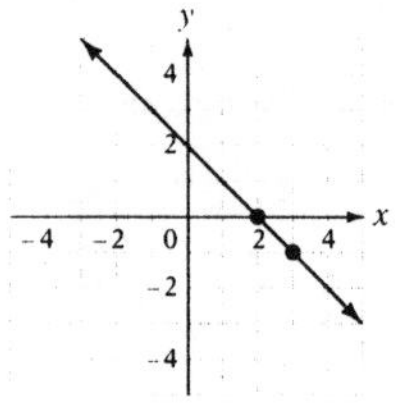

Applying the Concepts

39. $m(150) = 0.25(150) = 37.5$
The markup is \$37.50.

41. $f(21) = 8$

43. decreases by 3

45. decreases by 3

47. decreases by $\frac{2}{3}$

49. $y = mx + b$ is the slope-intercept form of the equation of a line because m is the slope and b is the y-intercept of the line.

51. $P_1 = (3, 2)$
$P_2 = (4, 6)$
$P_3 = (5, k)$
P_1 to P_2: $m = 4$
The slope from P_1 to P_3 and that from P_2 to P_3 must also be 4. Set the slope from P_1 to P_3 equal to 4.
$$\frac{2-k}{-2} = 4$$
$$2-k = -8$$
$$k = 10$$
This checks out against P_2 to P_3, so $k = 10$.

53. $P_1 = (k, 1)$
$P_2 = (0, -1)$
$P_3 = (2, -2)$
P_2 to P_3: $m = \frac{1}{-2}$
The slope from P_1 to P_2 and that from P_1 to P_3 must also be $-\frac{1}{2}$. Set the slope from P_1 to P_2 equal to $-\frac{1}{2}$.
$$\frac{2}{k} = -\frac{1}{2}$$
$$k = -4$$
This checks out against P_1 to P_3, so $k = -4$.

SECTION 3.5

Objective A Exercises

1. $m = 2,\ b = 5$
$$y = mx + b$$
$$y = 2x + 5$$
The equation of the line is $y = 2x + 5$.

3. $m = \frac{1}{2}\quad (x_1, y_1) = (2, 3)$
$$y - y_1 = m(x - x_1)$$
$$y - 3 = \frac{1}{2}(x-2)$$
$$y - 3 = \frac{1}{2}x - 1$$
$$y = \frac{1}{2}x + 2$$
The equation of the line is $y = \frac{1}{2}x + 2$.

5. $m = \frac{5}{4}\quad (x_1, y_1) = (-1, 4)$
$$y - y_1 = m(x - x_1)$$
$$y - 4 = \frac{5}{4}[x - (-1)]$$
$$y - 4 = \frac{5}{4}(x+1)$$
$$y - 4 = \frac{5}{4}x + \frac{5}{4}$$
$$y = \frac{5}{4}x + \frac{21}{4}$$
The equation of the line is $y = \frac{5}{4}x + \frac{21}{4}$.

7. $m = -\frac{5}{3}\quad (x_1, y_1) = (3, 0)$
$$y - y_1 = m(x - x_1)$$
$$y - 0 = -\frac{5}{3}(x-3)$$
$$y = -\frac{5}{3}x + 5$$
The equation of the line is $y = -\frac{5}{3}x + 5$.

9. $m = -3\quad (x_1, y_1) = (2, 3)$
$$y - y_1 = m(x - x_1)$$
$$y - 3 = -3(x-2)$$
$$y - 3 = -3x + 6$$
$$y = -3x + 9$$
The equation of the line is $y = -3x + 9$.

11. $m = -3\quad (x_1, y_1) = (-1, 7)$
$$y - y_1 = m(x - x_1)$$
$$y - 7 = -3[x - (-1)]$$
$$y - 7 = -3(x+1)$$
$$y - 7 = -3x - 3$$
$$y = -3x + 4$$
The equation of the line is $y = -3x + 4$.

13. $m = \frac{2}{3}$ $(x_1, y_1) = (-1, -3)$

$$y - y_1 = m(x - x_1)$$
$$y - (-3) = \frac{2}{3}[x - (-1)]$$
$$y + 3 = \frac{2}{3}(x + 1)$$
$$y + 3 = \frac{2}{3}x + \frac{2}{3}$$
$$y = \frac{2}{3}x - \frac{7}{3}$$

The equation of the line is $y = \frac{2}{3}x - \frac{7}{3}$.

15. $m = \frac{1}{2}$ $(x_1, y_1) = (0, 0)$

$$y - y_1 = m(x - x_1)$$
$$y - 0 = \frac{1}{2}(x - 0)$$
$$y = \frac{1}{2}x$$

The equation of the line is $y = \frac{1}{2}x$.

17. $m = 3$ $(x_1, y_1) = (2, -3)$

$$y - y_1 = m(x - x_1)$$
$$y - (-3) = 3(x - 2)$$
$$y + 3 = 3x - 6$$
$$y = 3x - 9$$

The equation of the line is $y = 3x - 9$.

19. $m = -\frac{2}{3}$ $(x_1, y_1) = (3, 5)$

$$y - y_1 = m(x - x_1)$$
$$y - 5 = -\frac{2}{3}(x - 3)$$
$$y - 5 = -\frac{2}{3}x + 2$$
$$y = -\frac{2}{3}x + 7$$

The equation of the line is $y = -\frac{2}{3}x + 7$.

21. $m = -1$ $(x_1, y_1) = (0, -3)$

$$y - y_1 = m(x - x_1)$$
$$y - (-3) = -1(x - 0)$$
$$y + 3 = -x + 0$$
$$y = -x - 3$$

The equation of the line is $y = -x - 3$.

23. $m = \frac{7}{5}$ $(x_1, y_1) = (1, -4)$

$$y - y_1 = m(x - x_1)$$
$$y - (-4) = \frac{7}{5}(x - 1)$$
$$y + 4 = \frac{7}{5}x - \frac{7}{5}$$
$$y = \frac{7}{5}x - \frac{27}{5}$$

The equation of the line is $y = \frac{7}{5}x - \frac{27}{5}$.

25. $m = -\frac{2}{5}$ $(x_1, y_1) = (4, -1)$

$$y - y_1 = m(x - x_1)$$
$$y - (-1) = -\frac{2}{5}(x - 4)$$
$$y + 1 = -\frac{2}{5}x + \frac{8}{5}$$
$$y = -\frac{2}{5}x + \frac{3}{5}$$

The equation of the line is $y = -\frac{2}{5}x + \frac{3}{5}$.

27. slope is undefined; $(x_1, y_1) = (3, -4)$
The line is a vertical line. All points on the line have an abscissa of 3. The equation of the line is $x = 3$.

29. $m = -\frac{5}{4}$ $(x_1, y_1) = (-2, -5)$

$$y - y_1 = m(x - x_1)$$
$$y - (-5) = -\frac{5}{4}[x - (-2)]$$
$$y + 5 = -\frac{5}{4}(x + 2)$$
$$y + 5 = -\frac{5}{4}x - \frac{5}{2}$$
$$y = -\frac{5}{4}x - \frac{15}{2}$$

The equation of the line is $y = -\frac{5}{4}x - \frac{15}{2}$.

31. $m = 0$ $(x_1, y_1) = (-2, -3)$

$$y - y_1 = m(x - x_1)$$
$$y - (-3) = 0[x - (-2)]$$
$$y + 3 = 0$$
$$y = -3$$

The equation of the line is $y = -3$.

33. $m = -2$ $(x_1, y_1) = (4, -5)$

$$y - y_1 = m(x - x_1)$$
$$y - (-5) = -2(x - 4)$$
$$y + 5 = -2x + 8$$
$$y = -2x + 3$$

The equation of the line is $y = -2x + 3$.

35. slope is undefined; $(x_1, y_1) = (-5, -1)$
The line is a vertical line. All points on the line have an abscissa of –5. The equation of the line is $x = -5$.

Objective B Exercises

37. $P_1(0, 2),\ P_2(3, 5)$

$$m = \frac{y_2 - y_1}{x_2 - x_1} = \frac{5-2}{3-0} = \frac{3}{3} = 1$$

$$\begin{aligned} y - y_1 &= m(x - x_1) \\ y - 2 &= 1(x - 0) \\ y - 2 &= x \\ y &= x + 2 \end{aligned}$$

The equation of the line is $y = x + 2$.

39. $P_1(0, -3),\ P_2(-4, 5)$

$$m = \frac{y_2 - y_1}{x_2 - x_1} = \frac{5-(-3)}{-4-0} = \frac{8}{-4} = -2$$

$$\begin{aligned} y - y_1 &= m(x - x_1) \\ y - (-3) &= -2(x - 0) \\ y + 3 &= -2x \\ y &= -2x - 3 \end{aligned}$$

The equation of the line is $y = -2x - 3$.

41. $P_1(2, 3),\ P_2(5, 5)$

$$m = \frac{y_2 - y_1}{x_2 - x_1} = \frac{5-3}{5-2} = \frac{2}{3}$$

$$\begin{aligned} y - y_1 &= m(x - x_1) \\ y - 3 &= \frac{2}{3}(x - 2) \\ y - 3 &= \frac{2}{3}x - \frac{4}{3} \\ y &= \frac{2}{3}x + \frac{5}{3} \end{aligned}$$

The equation of the line is $y = \frac{2}{3}x + \frac{5}{3}$.

43. $P_1(-1, 3),\ P_2(2, 4)$

$$m = \frac{y_2 - y_1}{x_2 - x_1} = \frac{4-3}{2-(-1)} = \frac{1}{3}$$

$$\begin{aligned} y - y_1 &= m(x - x_1) \\ y - 3 &= \frac{1}{3}[x - (-1)] \\ y - 3 &= \frac{1}{3}(x + 1) \\ y - 3 &= \frac{1}{3}x + \frac{1}{3} \\ y &= \frac{1}{3}x + \frac{10}{3} \end{aligned}$$

The equation of the line is $y = \frac{1}{3}x + \frac{10}{3}$.

45. $P_1(-1, -2),\ P_2(3, 4)$

$$m = \frac{y_2 - y_1}{x_2 - x_1} = \frac{4-(-2)}{3-(-1)} = \frac{6}{4} = \frac{3}{2}$$

$$\begin{aligned} y - y_1 &= m(x - x_1) \\ y - (-2) &= \frac{3}{2}[x - (-1)] \\ y + 2 &= \frac{3}{2}(x + 1) \\ y + 2 &= \frac{3}{2}x + \frac{3}{2} \\ y &= \frac{3}{2}x - \frac{1}{2} \end{aligned}$$

The equation of the line is $y = \frac{3}{2}x - \frac{1}{2}$.

47. $P_1(0, 3),\ P_2(2, 0)$

$$m = \frac{y_2 - y_1}{x_2 - x_1} = \frac{0-3}{2-0} = \frac{-3}{2} = -\frac{3}{2}$$

$$\begin{aligned} y - y_1 &= m(x - x_1) \\ y - 3 &= -\frac{3}{2}(x - 0) \\ y - 3 &= -\frac{3}{2}x \\ y &= -\frac{3}{2}x + 3 \end{aligned}$$

The equation of the line is $y = -\frac{3}{2}x + 3$.

49. $P_1(-3, -1),\ P_2(2, -1)$

$$m = \frac{y_2 - y_1}{x_2 - x_1} = \frac{-1-(-1)}{2-(-3)} = \frac{0}{5} = 0$$

$$\begin{aligned} y - y_1 &= m(x - x_1) \\ y - (-1) &= 0[x - (-3)] \\ y + 1 &= 0 \\ y &= -1 \end{aligned}$$

The equation of the line is $y = -1$.

51. $P_1(-2, -3),\ P_2(-1, -2)$

$$m = \frac{y_2 - y_1}{x_2 - x_1} = \frac{-2-(-3)}{-1-(-2)} = \frac{1}{1} = 1$$

$$\begin{aligned} y - y_1 &= m(x - x_1) \\ y - (-3) &= 1[x - (-2)] \\ y + 3 &= x + 2 \\ y &= x - 1 \end{aligned}$$

The equation of the line is $y = x - 1$.

53. $P_1(-2, 3),\ P_2(2, -1)$

$$m = \frac{y_2 - y_1}{x_2 - x_1} = \frac{-1-3}{2-(-2)} = \frac{-4}{4} = -1$$

$$\begin{aligned} y - y_1 &= m(x - x_1) \\ y - 3 &= -1[x - (-2)] \\ y - 3 &= -1(x + 2) \\ y - 3 &= -x - 2 \\ y &= -x + 1 \end{aligned}$$

The equation of the line is $y = -x + 1$.

55. $P_1(2, 3),\ P_2(5, -5)$

$$m = \frac{y_2 - y_1}{x_2 - x_1} = \frac{-5-3}{5-2} = -\frac{8}{3}$$

$$\begin{aligned} y - y_1 &= m(x - x_1) \\ y - 3 &= -\frac{8}{3}(x-2) \\ y - 3 &= -\frac{8}{3}x + \frac{16}{3} \\ y &= -\frac{8}{3}x + \frac{25}{3} \end{aligned}$$

The equation of the line is $y = -\frac{8}{3}x + \frac{25}{3}$.

57. $P_1(2, 0),\ P_2(0, -1)$

$$m = \frac{y_2 - y_1}{x_2 - x_1} = \frac{-1-0}{0-2} = \frac{-1}{-2} = \frac{1}{2}$$

$$\begin{aligned} y - y_1 &= m(x - x_1) \\ y - 0 &= \frac{1}{2}(x-2) \\ y &= \frac{1}{2}x - 1 \end{aligned}$$

The equation of the line is $y = \frac{1}{2}x - 1$.

59. $P_1(3, -4),\ P_2(-2, -4)$

$$m = \frac{y_2 - y_1}{x_2 - x_1} = \frac{-4-(-4)}{-2-3} = \frac{0}{-5} = 0$$

$$\begin{aligned} y - y_1 &= m(x - x_1) \\ y - (-4) &= 0(x-3) \\ y + 4 &= 0 \\ y &= -4 \end{aligned}$$

The equation of the line is $y = -4$.

61. $P_1(0, 0),\ P_2(4, 3)$

$$m = \frac{y_2 - y_1}{x_2 - x_1} = \frac{3-0}{4-0} = \frac{3}{4}$$

$$\begin{aligned} y - y_1 &= m(x - x_1) \\ y - 0 &= \frac{3}{4}(x-0) \\ y &= \frac{3}{4}x \end{aligned}$$

The equation of the line is $y = \frac{3}{4}x$.

63. $P_1(2, -1),\ P_2(-1, 3)$

$$m = \frac{y_2 - y_1}{x_2 - x_1} = \frac{3-(-1)}{-1-2} = \frac{4}{-3} = -\frac{4}{3}$$

$$\begin{aligned} y - y_1 &= m(x - x_1) \\ y - (-1) &= -\frac{4}{3}(x-2) \\ y + 1 &= -\frac{4}{3}x + \frac{8}{3} \\ y &= -\frac{4}{3}x + \frac{5}{3} \end{aligned}$$

The equation of the line is $y = -\frac{4}{3}x + \frac{5}{3}$.

65. $P_1(-2, 5),\ P_2(-2, -5)$

$$m = \frac{y_2 - y_1}{x_2 - x_1} = \frac{-5-5}{-2-(-2)} = \frac{-10}{0}$$

The slope is undefined. The line is a vertical line. All points on the line have an abscissa of −2. The equation of the line is $x = -2$.

67. $P_1(2, 1),\ P_2(-2, -3)$

$$m = \frac{y_2 - y_1}{x_2 - x_1} = \frac{-3-1}{-2-2} = \frac{-4}{-4} = 1$$

$$\begin{aligned} y - y_1 &= m(x - x_1) \\ y - 1 &= 1(x-2) \\ y - 1 &= x - 2 \\ y &= x - 1 \end{aligned}$$

The equation of the line is $y = x - 1$.

69. $P_1(-4, -3),\ P_2(2, 5)$

$$m = \frac{y_2 - y_1}{x_2 - x_1} = \frac{5-(-3)}{2-(-4)} = \frac{8}{6} = \frac{4}{3}$$

$$\begin{aligned} y - y_1 &= m(x - x_1) \\ y - (-3) &= \frac{4}{3}[x-(-4)] \\ y + 3 &= \frac{4}{3}(x+4) \\ y + 3 &= \frac{4}{3}x + \frac{16}{3} \\ y &= \frac{4}{3}x + \frac{7}{3} \end{aligned}$$

The equation of the line is $y = \frac{4}{3}x + \frac{7}{3}$.

71. $P_1(0, 3),\ P_2(3, 0)$

$$m = \frac{y_2 - y_1}{x_2 - x_1} = \frac{0-3}{3-0} = \frac{-3}{3} = -1$$

$$\begin{aligned} y - y_1 &= m(x - x_1) \\ y - 3 &= -1(x-0) \\ y - 3 &= -x \\ y &= -x + 3 \end{aligned}$$

The equation of the line is $y = -x + 3$.

Objective C Application Problems

73. Strategy
- Use the two given points along the line to find the slope.
- Use the point-slope form to find the equation of the line.

Solution

$(x_1, y_1) = (1990, 7.80)$

$(x_2, y_2) = (1998, 12.50)$

$$m = \frac{y_2 - y_1}{x_2 - x_1} = \frac{12.50 - 7.80}{1998 - 1990} = \frac{4.7}{8} = 0.5875$$

$$y - y_1 = m(x - x_1)$$
$$y - 7.80 = 0.5875(x - 1990)$$
$$y - 7.80 = 0.5875x - 1169.125$$
$$y = 0.5875x - 1161.325$$

The linear function is $y = 0.5875x - 1161.325$.

Evaluate the function when $x = 1995$.

$$y = 0.5875(1995) - 1161.325$$
$$y \approx 10.74$$

The predicted hourly wage in 1995 is \$10.74.

75. Strategy
- Use the two given points along the line to determine the slope.
- Use the point-slope form of an equation to determine the equation of the line.

Solution

$(x_1, y_1) = (1994, 600{,}000)$

$(x_2, y_2) = (2005, 1{,}100{,}000)$

$$m = \frac{y_2 - y_1}{x_2 - x_1} = \frac{1{,}100{,}000 - 600{,}000}{2005 - 1994} = \frac{500{,}000}{11} \approx 45{,}455$$

$$y - y_1 = m(x - x_1)$$
$$y - 600{,}000 = 45{,}455(x - 1994)$$
$$y - 600{,}000 = 45{,}455x - 90{,}637{,}270$$
$$y = 45{,}455x - 90{,}037{,}270$$

The linear function is $y = 45{,}455x - 90{,}037{,}270$.

Evaluate the function when $x = 2000$.

$$y = 45{,}455(2000) - 90{,}037{,}270$$
$$y = 872{,}730$$

There will be 872,730 health care jobs in 2000.

Applying the Concepts

77. The point-slope formula requires the slope of the line and one point on the line, while the slope-intercept formula requires the slope and the y-intercept of the line.

79. **a.** The slope is the rate at which the number of CD players sold (in millions) decreases per dollar increase in price.

b. The y-intercept represents the number of CD players that would be given away if the price were \$0.

c. The x-intercept represents the price at which no CD players would be sold.

81. To find the x-intercept, set y to 0.

$$0 = mx + b$$
$$-b = mx$$
$$-\frac{b}{m} = x$$

The x-intercept is $\left(-\frac{b}{m}, 0\right)$.

83. Find the equation of the line.

$$m = \frac{1-(-1)}{2-4} = \frac{2}{-2} = -1$$
$$y - (-1) = -1(x - 4)$$
$$y + 1 = -x + 4$$
$$y = -x + 3$$

$x = 0,\ y = -(0) + 3 = 3$

$x = 1,\ y = -1 + 3 = 2$

$x = 3,\ y = -3 + 3 = 0$

Three other points on the line are (0, 3), (1, 2), and (3, 0).

85. Find the equation of the line. The two points given are (–3, 2) and (2, 7).

$$m = \frac{7-2}{2-(-3)} = \frac{5}{5} = 1$$
$$y - 2 = 1(x - (-3))$$
$$y - 2 = x + 3$$
$$y = x + 5$$

The function is $f(x) = x + 5$, therefore, $f(0) = 0 + 5 = 5$

SECTION 3.6

Objective A Exercises

1. $x=-2$ is a vertical line
$y=3$ is a horizontal line
The lines are perpendicular.

3. $x=-3$ is a vertical line.
$y=\frac{1}{3}$ is a horizontal line.
The lines are not parallel.

5. $y=\frac{2}{3}x-4 \quad m_1=\frac{2}{3}$
$y=-\frac{3}{2}x-4 \quad m_2=-\frac{3}{2}$
$m_1 \neq m_2$
The lines are not parallel.

7. $y=\frac{4}{3}x-2 \quad m_1=\frac{4}{3}$
$y=-\frac{3}{4}x+2 \quad m_2=-\frac{3}{4}$
$m_1 \cdot m_2=\frac{4}{3}\left(-\frac{3}{4}\right)=-1$
The lines are perpendicular.

9. $2x+3y=2$
$3y=-2x+2$
$y=-\frac{2}{3}x+\frac{2}{3}$
$m_1=-\frac{2}{3}$
$2x+3y=-4$
$3y=-2x-4$
$y=-\frac{2}{3}x-\frac{4}{3}$
$m_2=-\frac{2}{3}$
$m_1=m_2=-\frac{2}{3}$
The lines are parallel.

11. $x-4y=2$
$-4y=-x+2$
$y=\frac{1}{4}x-\frac{1}{2}$
$m_1=\frac{1}{4}$
$4x+y=8$
$y=-4x+8$
$m_2=-4$
$m_1 \cdot m_2=\frac{1}{4}(-4)=-1$
The lines are perpendicular.

13. $m_1=\frac{6-2}{1-3}=\frac{4}{-2}=-2$
$m_2=\frac{-1-3}{-1-(-1)}=\frac{-4}{0}$
$m_1 \neq m_2$
The lines are not parallel.

15. $m_1=\frac{-1-2}{4-(-3)}=\frac{-3}{7}=-\frac{3}{7}$
$m_2=\frac{-4-3}{-2-1}=\frac{-7}{-3}=\frac{7}{3}$
$m_1 \cdot m_2=-\frac{3}{7}\left(\frac{7}{3}\right)=-1$
The lines are perpendicular.

17. $m_1=\frac{2-0}{0-(-5)}=\frac{2}{5}$
$m_2=\frac{-1-1}{0-5}=\frac{-2}{-5}=\frac{2}{5}$
$m_1=m_2=\frac{2}{5}$
The lines are parallel.

19. $2x-3y=2$
$-3y=-2x+2$
$y=\frac{2}{3}x-\frac{2}{3}$
$m=\frac{2}{3}$
$y-y_1=m(x-x_1)$
$y-(-4)=\frac{2}{3}[x-(-2)]$
$y+4=\frac{2}{3}(x+2)$
$y+4=\frac{2}{3}x+\frac{4}{3}$
$y=\frac{2}{3}x-\frac{8}{3}$
The equation of the line is $y=\frac{2}{3}x-\frac{8}{3}$.

21. $y=-3x+4$
$m_1=-3$
$m_1 \cdot m_2=-1$
$-3 \cdot m_2=-1$
$m_2=\frac{1}{3}$
$y-y_1=m(x-x_1)$
$y-1=\frac{1}{3}(x-4)$
$y-1=\frac{1}{3}x-\frac{4}{3}$
$y=\frac{1}{3}x-\frac{1}{3}$
The equation of the line is $y=\frac{1}{3}x-\frac{1}{3}$.

23. $3x-5y=2$

$-5y=-3x+2$

$y=\frac{3}{5}x-\frac{2}{5}$

$m_1=\frac{3}{5}$

$m_1\cdot m_2=-1$

$\frac{3}{5}\cdot m_2=-1$

$m_2=-\frac{5}{3}$

$y-y_1=m(x-x_1)$

$y-(-3)=-\frac{5}{3}[x-(-1)]$

$y+3=-\frac{5}{3}(x+1)$

$y+3=-\frac{5}{3}x-\frac{5}{3}$

$y=-\frac{5}{3}x-\frac{14}{3}$

The equation of the line is $y=-\frac{5}{3}x-\frac{14}{3}$.

Applying the Concepts

25. Two lines are parallel if they have the same slope and different y-intercepts.

27. Write the equation of the lines in slope-intercept form.

(1) $A_1x+B_1y=C_1$

$B_1y=C_1-A_1x$

$y=\frac{C_1}{B_1}-\frac{A_1}{B_1}x$

(2) $A_2x+B_2y=C_2$

$B_2y=C_2-A_2x$

$y=\frac{C_2}{B_2}-\frac{A_2}{B_2}x$

The slope of the second line must be the negative reciprocal of the first for the lines to be perpendicular, so $\frac{A_1}{B_1}=-\frac{B_2}{A_2}$.

29. Strategy

- Use one of the lines to find the slope of the line perpendicular to it.
- Use the slope-intercept form to define the line that makes a right triangle with the other two lines.

Solution For instance, choose the line

$y=-\frac{1}{2}x+2$

The slope is $-\frac{1}{2}$, so a line perpendicular to this line has a slope of 2. The y-intercept can be the same, or $b=2$.

$y=mx+b$

$y=2x+2$

An equation of the line is $y=2x+2$.

31. The equation of the tangent line is $y=-x+9$.

Slope $m=-1$

y-intercept: (0, 9)

x-intercept: (9, 0)

SECTION 3.7

Objective A Exercises

1. $3x-2y\geq 6$

$-2y\geq -3x+6$

$y\leq \frac{3}{2}x-3$

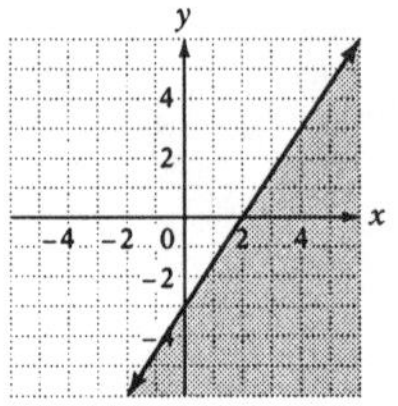

3. $x+3y<4$

$3y<-x+4$

$y<-\frac{1}{3}x+\frac{4}{3}$

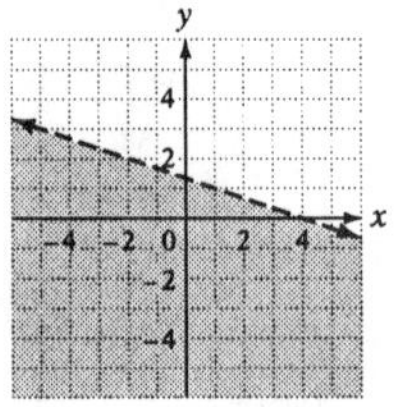

5. $4x - 5y > 10$

$-5y > -4x + 10$

$y < \frac{4}{5}x - 2$

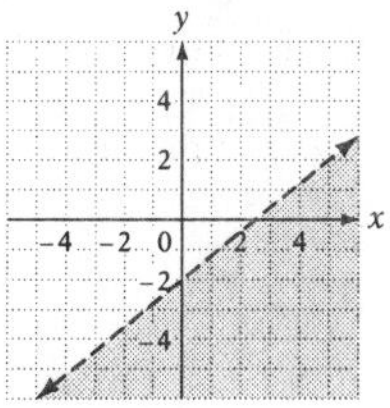

7. $x + 3y < 6$

$3y < -x + 6$

$y < -\frac{1}{3}x + 2$

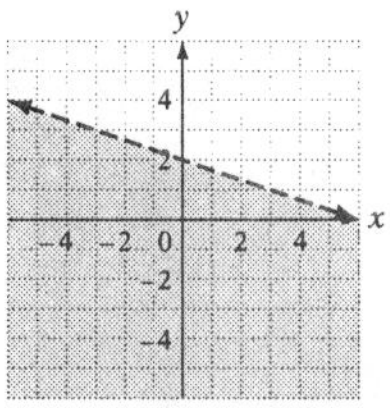

9. $2x + 3y \geq 6$

$3y \geq -2x + 6$

$y \geq -\frac{2}{3}x + 2$

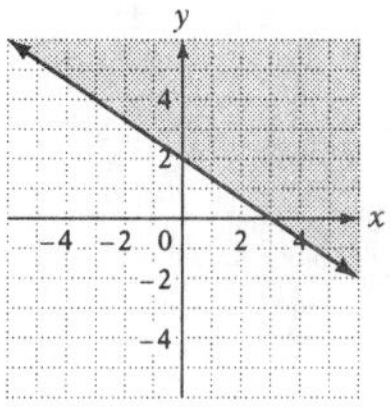

11. $-x + 2y > -8$

$2y > x - 8$

$y > \frac{1}{2}x - 4$

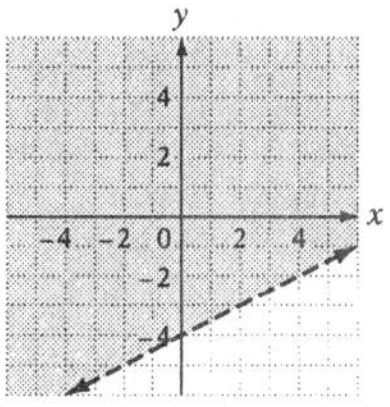

13. $y - 4 < 0$

$y < 4$

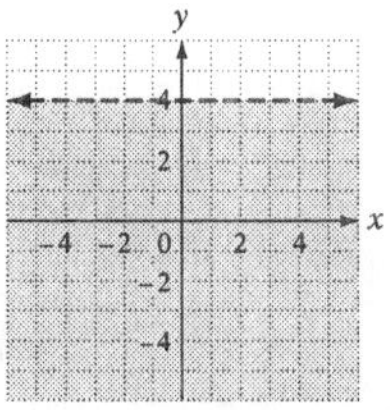

15. $6x + 5y < 15$

$5y < -6x + 15$

$y < -\frac{6}{5}x + 3$

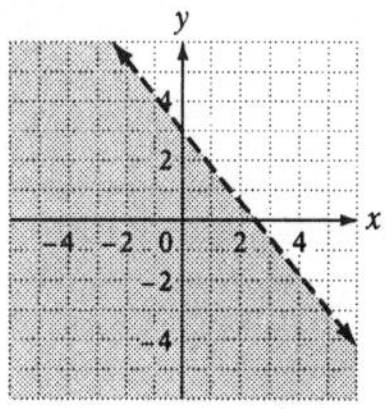

17. $-5x + 3y \geq -12$

$3y \geq 5x - 12$

$y \geq \frac{5}{3}x - 4$

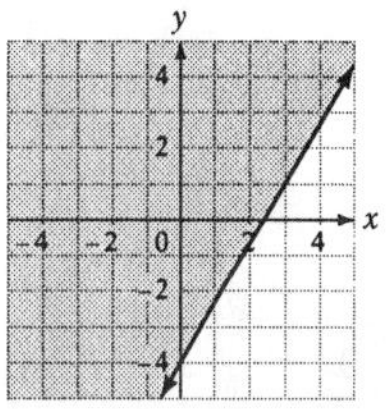

Applying the Concepts

19. No, it is not a function because for any x there can be many values of y. For example, when $x = 1$, $y < 2$, which is an infinite number of values.

21. Yes. Three examples are $P_1(0, 1)$, $P_2(0, 3)$, and $P_3(2, 0)$.

CHAPTER REVIEW

1. $y = \frac{x}{x-2}$

$y = \frac{4}{4-2}$

$y = 2$

The ordered pair is (4, 2).

2. $P(-2) = -2$

$P(a) = 3a + 4$

3. $y = 2x^2 - 5$

Ordered pairs: (–2, 3), (–1, –3), (0, –5), (1, –3), (2, 3)

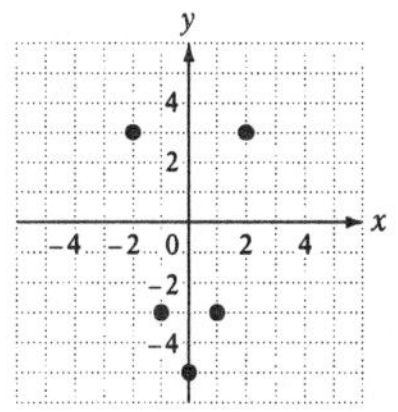

4.

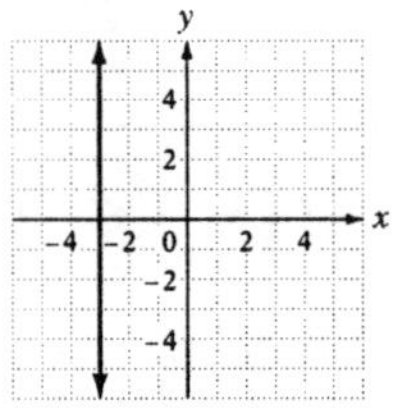

5. Evaluate the function at each element of the domain.

$f(x) = x^2 + x - 1$

$f(-2) = (-2)^2 + (-2) - 1 = 1$

$f(-1) = (-1)^2 + (-1) - 1 = -1$

$f(0) = 0^2 + 0 - 1 = -1$

$f(1) = 1^2 + 1 - 1 = 1$

$f(2) = 2^2 + 2 - 1 = 5$

Range = $\{-1, 1, 5\}$

6. Domain = $\{-1, 0, 1, 5\}$

Range = $\{0, 2, 4\}$

7. $y_m = \frac{y_1 + y_2}{2} = \frac{4+5}{2} = \frac{9}{2}$

$x_m = \frac{x_1 + x_2}{2} = \frac{-2+3}{2} = \frac{1}{2}$

Length $= \sqrt{(x_2 - x_1)^2 + (y_2 - y_1)^2}$

$= \sqrt{[3-(-2)]^2 + (5-4)^2}$

$= \sqrt{26} \approx 5.10$

The midpoint is $\left(\frac{1}{2}, \frac{9}{2}\right)$ and the length is 5.10.

8. $f(x) = \frac{x}{x+4}$

The function is not defined for zeros in the denominator.

$x + 4 = 0$

$x = -4$

$f(x)$ is not defined for $x = -4$.

9. x-intercept:

$y = -\frac{2}{3}x - 2$

$0 = -\frac{2}{3}x - 2$

$x = -3$

(–3, 0)

y-intercept:

$y = -\frac{2}{3}x - 2$

$y = -2$

(0, –2)

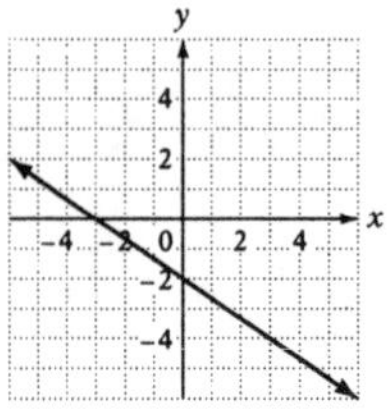

10. x-intercept:

$3x + 2y = -6$

$3x + 0 = -6$

$x = -2$

(–2, 0)

y-intercept:

$3x + 2y = -6$

$0 + 2y = -6$

$y = -3$

(0, –3)

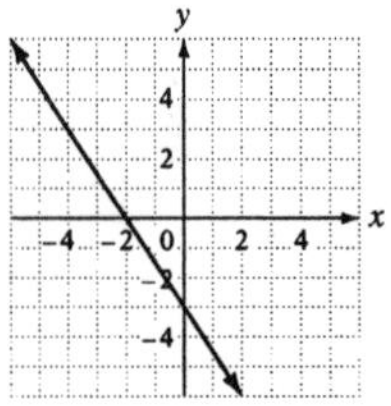

11.

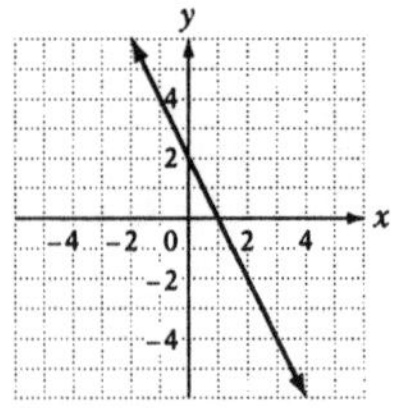

12.

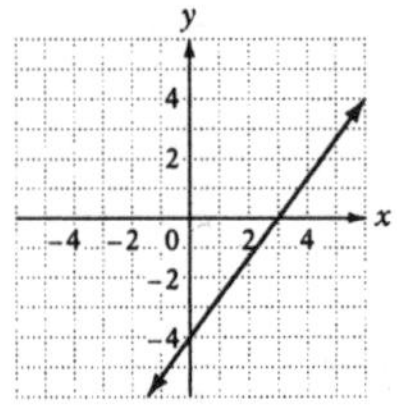

13. $m = \frac{y_2 - y_1}{x_2 - x_1}$

$m = \frac{2-(-2)}{-1-3} = \frac{4}{-4} = -1$

14. Use the point-slope form to find the equation of the line.

$$y - y_1 = m(x - x_1)$$
$$y - 4 = \frac{5}{2}[x - (-3)]$$
$$y - 4 = \frac{5}{2}x + \frac{15}{2}$$
$$y = \frac{5}{2}x + \frac{23}{2}$$

The equation of the line is $y = \frac{5}{2}x + \frac{23}{2}$.

15. $y \geq 2x - 3$

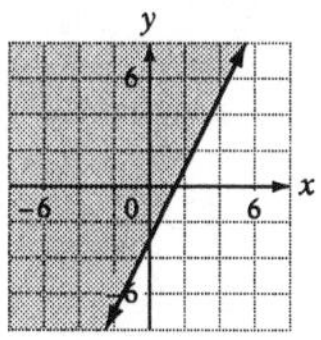

16. $3x - 2y \leq 6$

$$-2y \leq -3x + 6$$
$$y \geq \frac{3}{2}x - 3$$

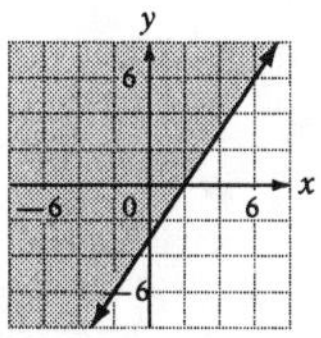

17. $P_1(-2, 4),\ P_2(4, -3)$

$$m = \frac{y_2 - y_1}{x_2 - x_1} = \frac{-3 - 4}{4 - (-2)} = \frac{-7}{6} = -\frac{7}{6}$$
$$y - y_1 = m(x - x_1)$$
$$y - 4 = -\frac{7}{6}(x - (-2))$$
$$y - 4 = -\frac{7}{6}(x + 2)$$
$$y - 4 = -\frac{7}{6}x - \frac{7}{3}$$
$$y = -\frac{7}{6}x + \frac{5}{3}$$

The equation of the line is $y = -\frac{7}{6}x + \frac{5}{3}$.

18. $4x - 2y = 7$

$$-2y = -4x + 7$$
$$y = 2x - \frac{7}{2}$$

The slope for a parallel line is $m = 2$.

$$y - y_1 = m(x - x_1)$$
$$y - (-4) = 2[x - (-2)]$$
$$y + 4 = 2x + 4$$
$$y = 2x$$

The equation of the parallel line is $y = 2x$.

19.

$$y - y_1 = m(x - x_1)$$
$$y - 4 = -\frac{1}{3}(x - (-1))$$
$$y - 4 = -\frac{1}{3}x - \frac{1}{3}$$
$$y = -\frac{1}{3}x + \frac{11}{3}$$

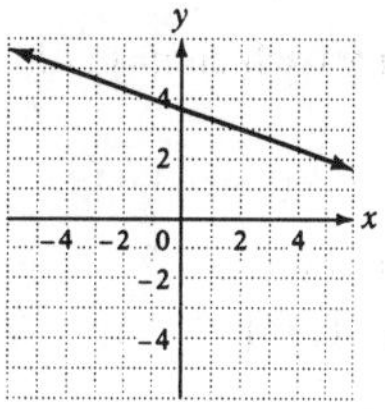

20. $y = -3x + 4$

$$m = -3$$
$$y - y_1 = m(x - x_1)$$
$$y - (-2) = -3(x - 3)$$
$$y + 2 = -3x + 9$$
$$y = -3x + 7$$

The equation of the line is $y = -3x + 7$.

21. $y = -\frac{2}{3}x + 6$

$$m_1 = -\frac{2}{3}$$
$$m_1 \cdot m_2 = -1$$
$$-\frac{2}{3}m_2 = -1$$
$$m_2 = \frac{3}{2}$$
$$y - y_1 = m(x - x_1)$$
$$y - 5 = \frac{3}{2}(x - 2)$$
$$y - 5 = \frac{3}{2}x - 3$$
$$y = \frac{3}{2}x + 2$$

The equation of the line is $y = \frac{3}{2}x + 2$.

22.

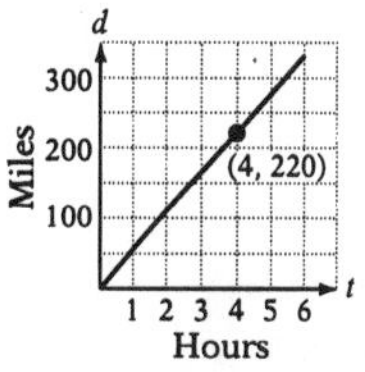

After 4 hours the car will have traveled 220 miles.

23.

$$m = \frac{y_2 - y_1}{x_2 - x_1} = \frac{12{,}000 - 6000}{500 - 200}$$
$$= \frac{6000}{300} = 20$$

The slope is 20. The slope represents the cost per calculator manufactured.

24. The y-intercept is (0, 25,000).
The slope is 80.
$y = mx + b$
$y = 80x + 25{,}000$
The linear function is $y = 80x + 25{,}000$.
Predict the cost of building a house with 2000 square feet.
$y = 80(2000) + 25{,}000$
$y = 185{,}000$
The house will cost $185,000 to build.

CHAPTER TEST

1. $P(s) = 2 - x^2$
ordered pairs: (–2, –2), (–1, 1), (0, 2), (1, 1), (2, –2)

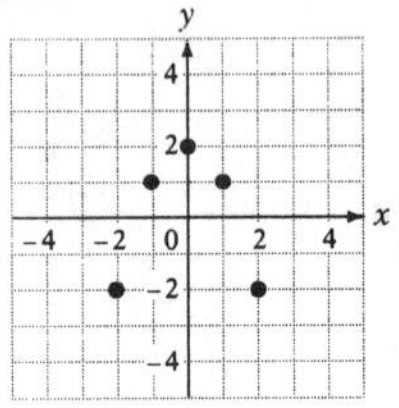

2. $y = 2x + 6$
$y = 2(-3) + 6$
$y = -6 + 6$
$y = 0$
The ordered-pair is (–3, 0).

3.

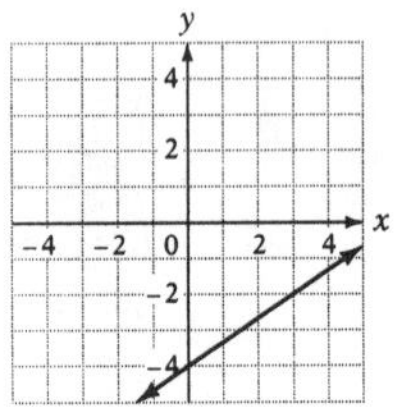

4. $2x + 3y = -3$
$3y = -2x - 3$
$y = -\frac{2}{3}x - 1$

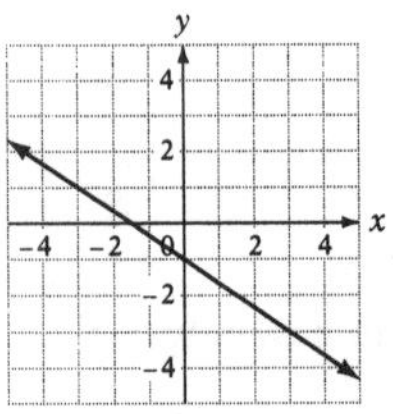

5. The equation of the vertical line that contains (–2, 3) is $x = -2$.

6. $x_m = \frac{x_1 + x_2}{2} = \frac{4 + (-5)}{2} = -\frac{1}{2}$

$y_m = \frac{y_1 + y_2}{2} = \frac{2 + 8}{2} = 5$

$\text{Length} = \sqrt{(x_2 - x_1)^2 + (y_2 - y_1)^2}$
$= \sqrt{(-5 - 4)^2 + (8 - 2)^2}$
$= \sqrt{81 + 36}$
$= \sqrt{117} \approx 10.82$

The midpoint is $\left(-\frac{1}{2}, 5\right)$ and the length is 10.82.

7. $P_1(-2, 3)$, $P_2(4, 2)$

$m = \frac{y_2 - y_1}{x_2 - x_1} = \frac{2 - 3}{4 - (-2)} = -\frac{1}{6}$

The slope of the line is $-\frac{1}{6}$.

8. $P(x) = 3x^2 - 2x + 1$
$P(2) = 3(2)^2 - 2(2) + 1$
$P(2) = 9$

9. x-intercept:
$2x - 3(0) = 6$
$x = 3$
(3, 0)
y-intercept:
$2x - 3y = 6$
$2(0) - 3y = 6$
$-3y = 6$
$y = -2$
(0, –2)

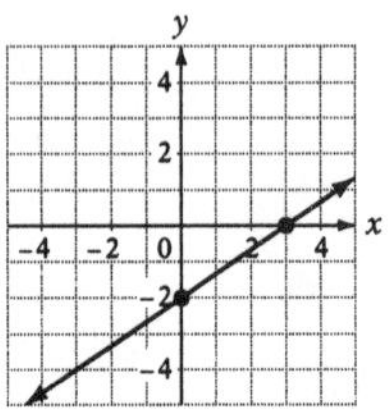

10.

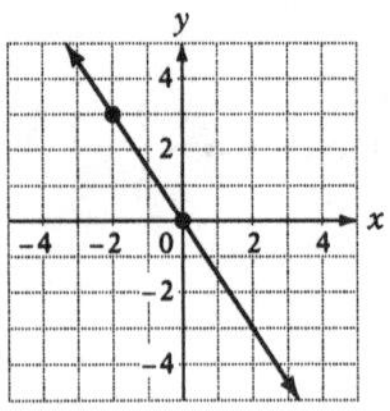

11. $m = \frac{2}{5}$ $(x_1, y_1) = (-5, 2)$

$$y - 2 = \frac{2}{5}(x - (-5))$$
$$y - 2 = \frac{2}{5}(x + 5)$$
$$y - 2 = \frac{2}{5}x + 2$$
$$y = \frac{2}{5}x + 4$$

The equation of the line is $y = \frac{2}{5}x + 4$.

12. $x = 0$

13. $P_1(3, -4)$, $P_2(-2, 3)$

$$m = \frac{y_2 - y_1}{x_2 - x_1} = \frac{3-(-4)}{-2-3} = \frac{3+4}{-5} = -\frac{7}{5}$$
$$y - y_1 = m(x - x_1)$$
$$y - (-4) = -\frac{7}{5}(x - 3)$$
$$y + 4 = -\frac{7}{5}x + \frac{21}{5}$$
$$y = -\frac{7}{5}x + \frac{1}{5}$$

The equation of the line is $y = -\frac{7}{5}x + \frac{1}{5}$.

14. A horizontal line has a slope of 0.

$$y - y_1 = m(x - x_1)$$
$$y - (-3) = 0(x - 4)$$
$$y + 3 = 0$$
$$y = -3$$

The equation of the line is $y = -3$.

15. Domain = {–4, –2, 0, 3}
Range = {0, 2, 5}

16. $y = -\frac{3}{2}x - 6$

$$m = -\frac{3}{2}$$
$$y - y_1 = m(x - x_1)$$
$$y - 2 = -\frac{3}{2}(x - 1)$$
$$y - 2 = -\frac{3}{2}x + \frac{3}{2}$$
$$y = -\frac{3}{2}x + \frac{7}{2}$$

The equation of the line is $y = -\frac{3}{2}x + \frac{7}{2}$.

17. $y = -\frac{1}{2}x - 3$

$$m_1 = -\frac{1}{2}$$
$$m_1 \cdot m_2 = -1$$
$$-\frac{1}{2}m_2 = -1$$
$$m_2 = 2$$
$$y - y_1 = m(x - x_1)$$
$$y - (-3) = 2(x - (-2))$$
$$y + 3 = 2(x + 2)$$
$$y + 3 = 2x + 4$$
$$y = 2x + 1$$

The equation of the line is $y = 2x + 1$.

18. $3x - 4y > 8$

$$-4y > -3x + 8$$
$$y < \frac{3}{4}x - 2$$

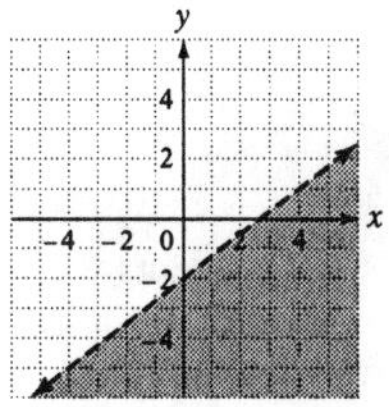

19. Strategy • Use two points on the graph to find the slope of the line.

Solution $(x_1, y_1) = (3, 40{,}000)$
$(x_2, y_2) = (12, 10{,}000)$

$$m = \frac{y_2 - y_1}{x_2 - x_1}$$
$$= \frac{10{,}000 - 40{,}000}{12 - 3}$$
$$= -\frac{10{,}000}{3}$$

The value of the house decreases by $\$\frac{10{,}000}{3}$ per year.

20. Dependent variable: number of students (y)
Independent variable: tuition cost (x)

$$m = \frac{\text{change of } y}{\text{change of } x} = \frac{-6}{20} = -\frac{3}{10}$$

$P_1(250, 100)$

Use the point-slope form to find the equation.

$$\begin{aligned} y - y_1 &= m(x - x_1) \\ y - 100 &= -\frac{3}{10}(x - 250) \\ y - 100 &= -\frac{3}{10}x + 75 \\ y &= -\frac{3}{10}x + 175 \end{aligned}$$

The equation that predicts the number of students for a certain tuition is $y = -\frac{3}{10}x + 175$. Predict the number of students when the tuition is \$300.

$$\begin{aligned} y &= -\frac{3}{10}x + 175 \\ y &= -\frac{3}{10}(300) + 175 \\ y &= 85 \end{aligned}$$

When the tuition is \$300, 85 students will enroll.

CUMULATIVE REVIEW

1. The Commutative Property of Multiplication

2.
$$\begin{aligned} 3 - \frac{x}{2} &= \frac{3}{4} \\ 4\left(3 - \frac{x}{2}\right) &= \frac{3}{4}(4) \\ 12 - 2x &= 3 \\ 12 - 2x - 12 &= 3 - 12 \\ -2x &= -9 \\ x &= \frac{9}{2} \end{aligned}$$

The solution is $\frac{9}{2}$.

3.
$$\begin{aligned} 2[y - 2(3 - y) + 4] &= 4 - 3y \\ 2(y - 6 + 2y + 4) &= 4 - 3y \\ 2(3y - 2) &= 4 - 3y \\ 6y - 4 &= 4 - 3y \\ 9y - 4 &= 4 \\ 9y &= 8 \\ y &= \frac{8}{9} \end{aligned}$$

The solution is $\frac{8}{9}$.

4.
$$\begin{aligned} \frac{1-3x}{2} + \frac{7x-2}{6} &= \frac{4x+2}{9} \\ 18\left(\frac{1-3x}{2} + \frac{7x-2}{6}\right) &= 18\left(\frac{4x+2}{9}\right) \\ 9(1-3x) + 3(7x-2) &= 2(4x+2) \\ 9 - 27x + 21x - 6 &= 8x + 4 \\ -6x + 3 &= 8x + 4 \\ -14x &= 1 \\ x &= -\frac{1}{14} \end{aligned}$$

The solution is $-\frac{1}{14}$.

5. $x - 3 < -4$ or $2x + 2 > 3$

$x < -1$ $\qquad$ $2x > 1$

$\qquad\qquad\quad$ $x > \frac{1}{2}$

$\{x|x < -1\}$ $\qquad$ $\left\{x\middle|x > \frac{1}{2}\right\}$

$\{x|x < -1\}$ or $\left\{x\middle|x > \frac{1}{2}\right\}$

$\left\{x\middle|x < -1 \text{ or } x > \frac{1}{2}\right\}$

6.
$$\begin{aligned} 8 - |2x - 1| &= 4 \\ -|2x - 1| &= -4 \\ |2x - 1| &= 4 \end{aligned}$$

$2x - 1 = 4$ or $2x - 1 = -4$

$2x = 5$ $\qquad$ $2x = -3$

$x = \frac{5}{2}$ $\qquad$ $x = -\frac{3}{2}$

The solutions are $\frac{5}{2}$ and $-\frac{3}{2}$.

7.
$$\begin{aligned} |3x - 5| &< 5 \\ -5 < 3x &- 5 < 5 \\ -5 + 5 < 3x - 5 &+ 5 < 5 + 5 \\ 0 < 3x &< 10 \\ \frac{1}{3}(0) < \frac{1}{3}(3x) &< 10\left(\frac{1}{3}\right) \\ 0 < x &< \frac{10}{3} \end{aligned}$$

$\left\{x\middle|0 < x < \frac{10}{3}\right\}$

8.
$$\begin{aligned} 4 - 2(4-5)^3 + 2 &= 4 - 2(-1)^3 + 2 \\ &= 4 + 2 + 2 = 8 \end{aligned}$$

9. $(a - b)^2 \div (ab)$ for $a = 4$ and $b = -2$

$$\begin{aligned} [4 - (-2)]^2 \div 4(-2) &= 6^2 \div -8 \\ &= 36 \div -8 \\ &= -4.5 \end{aligned}$$

10. $\{x|x < -2\} \cup \{x|x > 0\}$

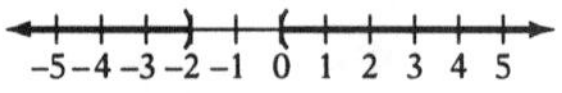

11. $P = \frac{R-C}{n}$

$P \cdot n = \frac{R-C}{n} \cdot n$

$P \cdot n = R - C$

$C = R - Pn$

12. $2x + 3y = 6$

$2x = 6 - 3y$

$x = 3 - \frac{3}{2}y$

13. Solve each inequality.

$3x - 1 < 4 \qquad x - 2 > 2$

$3x < 5 \qquad x > 4$

$x < \frac{5}{3}$

$\left\{x \middle| x < \frac{5}{3}\right\} \cap \{x | x > 4\} = \varnothing$

14. $P(x) = x^2 + 5$

$P(-3) = (-3)^2 + 5$

$P(-3) = 14$

15. $y = -\frac{5}{4}x + 3$

$y = -\frac{5}{4}(-8) + 3$

$y = 10 + 3$

$y = 13$

The ordered-pair solution is (–8, 13).

16. $P_1(-1, 3),\ P_2(3, -4)$

$m = \frac{y_2 - y_1}{x_2 - x_1} = \frac{-4-3}{3-(-1)} = \frac{-7}{4} = -\frac{7}{4}$

17. $m = \frac{3}{2},\ (x_1, y_1) = (-1, 5)$

$y - y_1 = m(x - x_1)$

$y - 5 = \frac{3}{2}(x - (-1))$

$y - 5 = \frac{3}{2}(x + 1)$

$y - 5 = \frac{3}{2}x + \frac{3}{2}$

$y = \frac{3}{2}x + \frac{13}{2}$

The equation of the line is $y = \frac{3}{2}x + \frac{13}{2}$.

18. $(x_1, y_1) = (4, -2),\ (x_2, y_2) = (0, 3)$

$m = \frac{y_2 - y_1}{x_2 - x_1} = \frac{3-(-2)}{0-4} = \frac{3+2}{-4} = -\frac{5}{4}$

$y - y_1 = m(x - x_1)$

$y - (-2) = -\frac{5}{4}(x - 4)$

$y + 2 = -\frac{5}{4}(x - 4)$

$y + 2 = -\frac{5}{4}x + 5$

$y = -\frac{5}{4}x + 3$

The equation of the line is $y = -\frac{5}{4}x + 3$.

19. $y = -\frac{3}{2}x + 2,\ m = -\frac{3}{2}$

$y - y_1 = m(x - x_1)$

$y - 4 = -\frac{3}{2}(x - 2)$

$y - 4 = -\frac{3}{2}x + 3$

$y = -\frac{3}{2}x + 7$

The equation of the line is $y = -\frac{3}{2}x + 7$.

20. $3x - 2y = 5$

$y = \frac{3}{2}x - \frac{5}{2}$

$m_1 = \frac{3}{2}$

$m_1 \cdot m_2 = -1$

$\frac{3}{2}m_2 = -1$

$m_2 = -\frac{2}{3}$

$y - y_1 = m(x - x_1)$

$y - 0 = -\frac{2}{3}(x - 4)$

$y = -\frac{2}{3}x + \frac{8}{3}$

The equation of the line is $y = -\frac{2}{3}x + \frac{8}{3}$.

21. Strategy

- Number of dimes: $17 - 5x$
  Number of nickels: $4x$
  Number of quarters: x

Coin	Number	Value	Total Value
Dimes	$17-5x$	10	$10(17-5x)$
Nickels	$4x$	5	$4x(5)$
Quarters	x	25	$25x$

- The sum of the total values of each denomination of coin equals the total value of all the coins (160 cents).

Solution

$$10(17-5x)+4x(5)+25x=160$$
$$170-50x+20x+25x=160$$
$$170-5x=160$$
$$-5x=-10$$
$$x=2$$
$$17-5x=17-5(2)=7$$

There are 7 dimes in the coin purse.

22. Strategy

- Rate of first plane: x
  Rate of second plane: $2x$

	Rate	Time	Distance
1st plane	x	3	$3x$
2nd plane	$2x$	3	$3(2x)$

- The total distance traveled by the two planes is 1800 mi.

Solution

$$3x+3(2x)=1800$$
$$3x+6x=1800$$
$$9x=1800$$
$$x=200$$
$$2x=400$$

The first plane is traveling at 200 mph and the second plane is traveling at 400 mph.

23. Strategy

- Pounds of coffee costing \$9.00: x
  Pounds of coffee costing \$6.00: $60 - x$

	Amount	Cost	Value
\$9 coffee	x	9	$9x$
\$6 coffee	$60-x$	6	$6(60-x)$
Mixture	60	8	$8(60)$

- The sum of the values before mixing equals the value after mixing.

Solution

$$9x+6(60-x)=8(60)$$
$$9x+360-6x=480$$
$$3x+360=480$$
$$3x=120$$
$$x=40$$
$$60-x=60-40=20$$

The mixture consists of 40 lb of \$9.00 coffee and 20 lb of \$6.00 coffee.

24. x-intercept:

$$3x-5(0)=15$$
$$3x=15$$
$$x=5$$

(5, 0)

y-intercept:

$$3(0)-5y=15$$
$$-5y=15$$
$$y=-3$$

(0, –3)

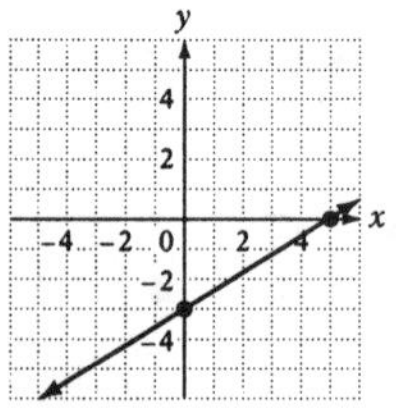

25.

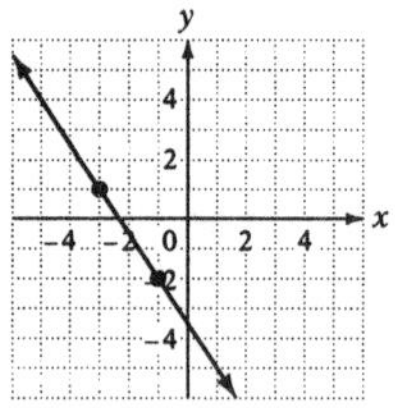

26.

$$3x-2y\ge 6$$
$$-2y\ge -3x+6$$
$$y\le \frac{3}{2}x-3$$

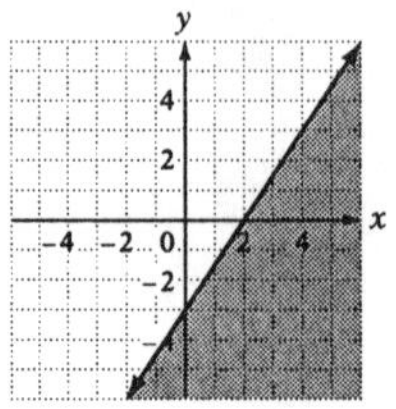

27. Strategy To write the equation:

- Use points on the graph to find the slope of the line.
- Locate the y-intercept of the line on the graph.
- Use the slope-intercept form of an equation to write the equation of the line.

Solution $(x_1, y_1) = (0, 15{,}000)$, $(x_2, y_2) = (6, 0)$

$$m = \frac{y_2 - y_1}{x_2 - x_1} = \frac{0 - 15{,}000}{6 - 0} = -2500$$

The y-intercept is (0, 15,000).

$y = mx + b$

$y = -2500x + 15{,}000$

The value of the truck decreases by \$2500 each year.

Chapter 4: Systems of Linear Equations and Inequalities

SECTION 4.1

Objective A Exercises

1.

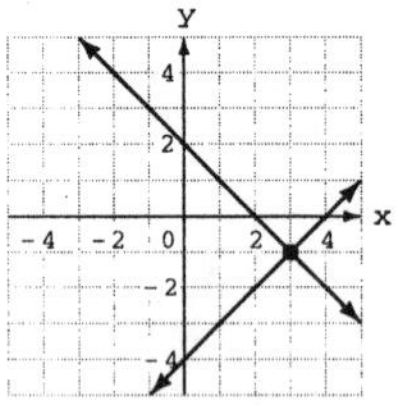

The solution is 3, –1.

3.

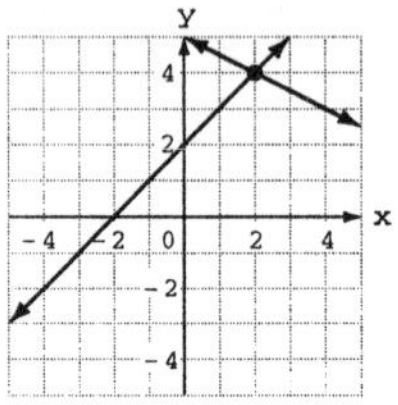

The solution is 2, 4.

5.

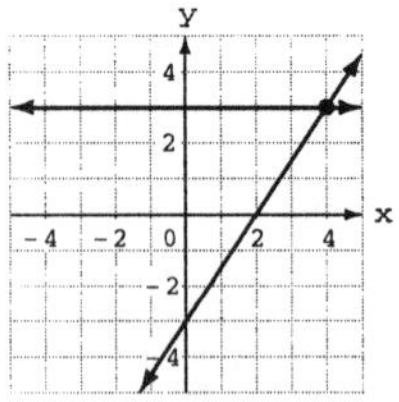

The solution is 4, 3.

7.

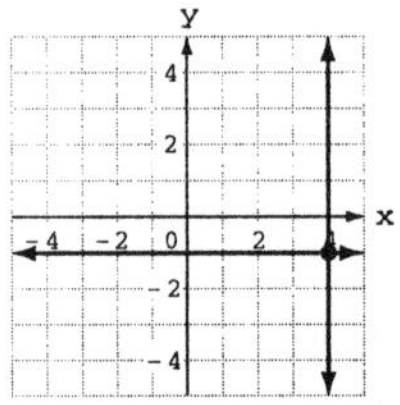

The solution is 4, –1.

9.

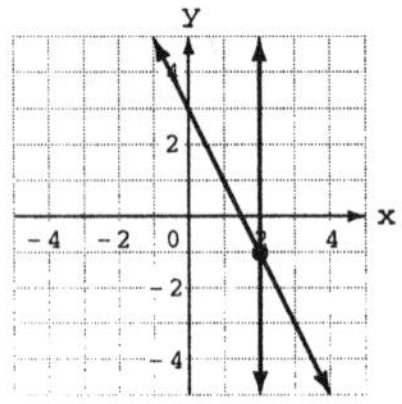

The solution is 2, –1.

11.

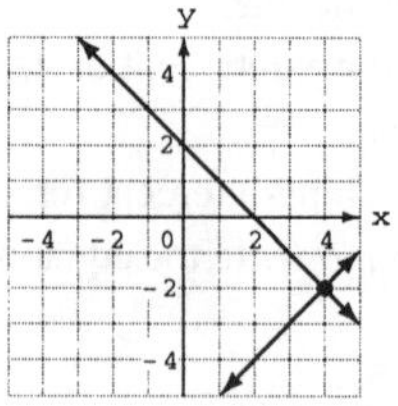

The solution is 4, –2.

13.

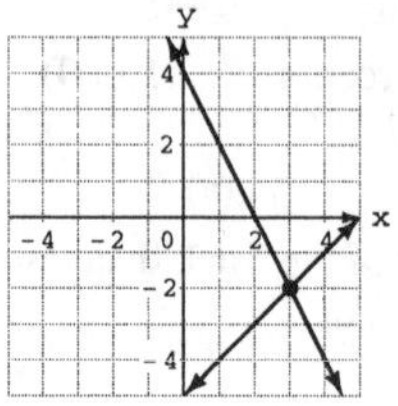

The solution is 3, –2.

15.

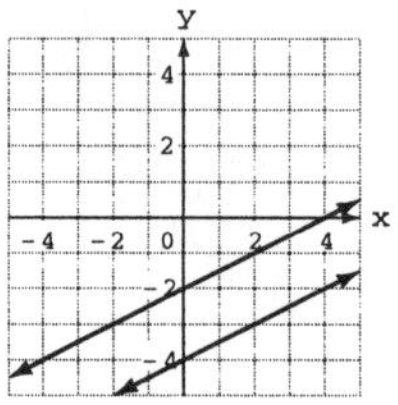

The lines are parallel and therefore do not intersect. The system of equations has no solution.

17.

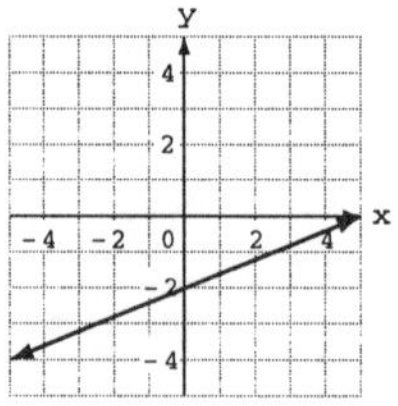

The two equations represent the same line. The solutions are the ordered pairs $\left(x, \frac{2}{5}x-2\right)$.

19.

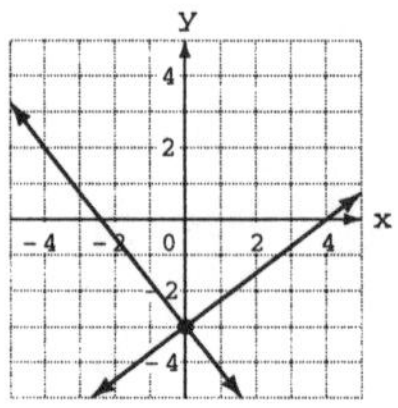

The solution is 0, –3.

21.

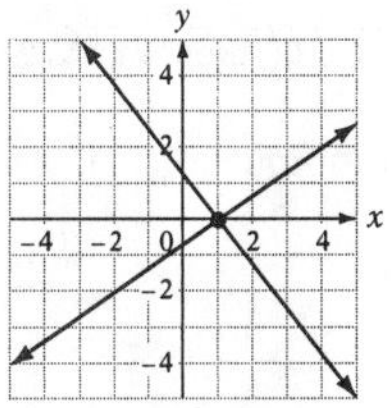

The solution is 1, 0.

Objective B Exercises

23. (1) $y=-2$

(2) $2x+3y=4$

Substitute the value of y into Equation (2).

$$\begin{aligned}2x+3y&=4\\2x+3(-2)&=4\\2x-6&=4\\2x&=10\\x&=5\end{aligned}$$

The solution is (5, –2).

25. (1) $y=-x+1$

(2) $2x-y=5$

Substitute $-x+1$ for y in Equation (2).

$$\begin{aligned}2x-y&=5\\2x-(-x+1)&=5\\2x+x-1&=5\\3x-1&=5\\3x&=6\\x&=2\end{aligned}$$

Substitute into Equation (1).

$$\begin{aligned}y&=-x+1\\y&=-2+1\\y&=-1\end{aligned}$$

The solution is (2, –1).

27. (1) $x=2y-3$

(2) $3x+y=5$

Substitute $2y-3$ for x in Equation (2).

$$\begin{aligned}3x+y&=5\\3(2y-3)+y&=5\\6y-9+y&=5\\7y-9&=5\\7y&=14\\y&=2\end{aligned}$$

Substitute into Equation (1).

$$\begin{aligned}x&=2y-3\\x&=2(2)-3\\x&=4-3\\x&=1\end{aligned}$$

The solution is (1, 2).

29. (1) $3x+5y=-1$

(2) $y=2x-8$

Substitute $2x-8$ for y in Equation (1).

$$\begin{aligned}3x+5y&=-1\\3x+5(2x-8)&=-1\\3x+10x-40&=-1\\13x-40&=-1\\13x&=39\\x&=3\end{aligned}$$

Substitute into Equation (2).

$$\begin{aligned}y&=2x-8\\y&=2(3)-8\\y&=6-8\\y&=-2\end{aligned}$$

The solution is (3, –2).

31. (1) $4x-3y=2$

(2) $y=2x+1$

Substitute $2x+1$ for y in equation (1).

$$\begin{aligned}4x-3(2x+1)&=2\\4x-6x-3&=2\\-2x-3&=2\\-2x&=5\\x&=-\frac{5}{2}\end{aligned}$$

Substitute into Equation 2.

$$\begin{aligned}y&=2\left(-\frac{5}{2}\right)+1\\y&=-5+1\\y&=-4\end{aligned}$$

The solution is $\left(-\frac{5}{2}, -4\right)$.

33. (1) $3x-2y=-11$

(2) $x=2y-9$

Substitute $2y-9$ for x in Equation (1).

$$\begin{aligned}3x-2y&=-11\\3(2y-9)-2y&=-11\\6y-27-2y&=-11\\4y-27&=-11\\4y&=16\\y&=4\end{aligned}$$

Substitute into Equation (2).

$$\begin{aligned}x&=2y-9\\x&=2(4)-9\\x&=8-9\\x&=-1\end{aligned}$$

The solution is (–1, 4).

35. (1) $3x+2y=4$

(2) $y=1-2x$

Substitute $1-2x$ for y in Equation (1).

$$\begin{aligned} 3x+2y&=4 \\ 3x+2(1-2x)&=4 \\ 3x+2-4x&=4 \\ -x+2&=4 \\ -x&=2 \\ x&=-2 \end{aligned}$$

Substitute into Equation (2).

$$\begin{aligned} y&=1-2x \\ y&=1-2(-2) \\ y&=1+4 \\ y&=5 \end{aligned}$$

The solution is $(-2, 5)$.

37. (1) $5x+2y=15$

(2) $x=6-y$

Substitute $6-y$ for x in Equation (1).

$$\begin{aligned} 5x+2y&=15 \\ 5(6-y)+2y&=15 \\ 30-5y+2y&=15 \\ 30-3y&=15 \\ -3y&=-15 \\ y&=5 \end{aligned}$$

Substitute into Equation (1).

$$\begin{aligned} x&=6-y \\ x&=6-5 \\ x&=1 \end{aligned}$$

The solution is $(1, 5)$.

39. (1) $3x-4y=6$

(2) $x=3y+2$

Substitute $3y+2$ for x in Equation (1).

$$\begin{aligned} 3x-4y&=6 \\ 3(3y+2)-4y&=6 \\ 9y+6-4y&=6 \\ 5y+6&=6 \\ 5y&=0 \\ y&=0 \end{aligned}$$

Substitute into Equation (2).

$$\begin{aligned} x&=3y+2 \\ x&=3(0)+2 \\ x&=2 \end{aligned}$$

The solution is $(2, 0)$.

41. (1) $3x+7y=-5$

(2) $y=6x-5$

Substitute $6x-5$ for y in Equation (1).

$$\begin{aligned} 3x+7y&=-5 \\ 3x+7(6x-5)&=-5 \\ 3x+42x-35&=-5 \\ 45x-35&=-5 \\ 45x&=30 \\ x&=\frac{2}{3} \end{aligned}$$

Substitute into Equation (2).

$$\begin{aligned} y&=6x-5 \\ y&=6\left(\frac{2}{3}\right)-5 \\ y&=4-5 \\ y&=-1 \end{aligned}$$

The solution is $\left(\frac{2}{3}, -1\right)$.

43. (1) $3x-y=10$

(2) $6x-2y=5$

Solve Equation (1) for y.

$$\begin{aligned} 3x-y&=10 \\ -y&=-3x+10 \\ y&=3x-10 \end{aligned}$$

Substitute into Equation (2).

$$\begin{aligned} 6x-2(3x-10)&=5 \\ 6x-6x+20&=5 \\ 20&=5 \end{aligned}$$

This is not a true equation. The lines are parallel and the system is inconsistent.

45. (1) $3x+4y=14$

(2) $2x+y=1$

Solve Equation (2) for y.

$$\begin{aligned} 2x+y&=1 \\ y&=-2x+1 \end{aligned}$$

Substitute into Equation (1).

$$\begin{aligned} 3x+4y&=14 \\ 3x+4(-2x+1)&=14 \\ 3x-8x+4&=14 \\ -5x+4&=14 \\ -5x&=10 \\ x&=-2 \end{aligned}$$

Substitute into Equation (2).

$$\begin{aligned} 2x+y&=1 \\ 2(-2)+y&=1 \\ -4+y&=1 \\ y&=5 \end{aligned}$$

The solution is $(-2, 5)$.

47. (1) $3x+5y=0$

(2) $x-4y=0$

Solve Equation (2) for x.

$x-4y=0$
$x=4y$

Substitute into Equation (1).

$3x+5y=0$
$3(4y)+5y=0$
$12y+5y=0$
$17y=0$
$y=0$

Substitute into Equation (2).

$x-4y=0$
$x-4(0)=0$
$x=0$

The solution is (0, 0).

49. (1) $2x-4y=16$

(2) $-x+2y=-8$

Solve Equation (2) for x.

$-x=-2y-8$
$x=2y+8$

Substitute into Equation (1).

$2x-4y=16$
$2(2y+8)-4y=16$
$4y+16-4y=16$
$16=16$

This is a true equation. The equations are dependent. The solutions are the ordered pairs $\left(x, \frac{1}{2}x-4\right)$.

51. (1) $y=3x+2$

(2) $y=2x+3$

Substitute $2x+3$ for y in Equation (1).

$y=3x+2$
$2x+3=3x+2$
$2x=3x-1$
$-x=-1$
$x=1$

Substitute into Equation (2).

$y=2x+3$
$y=2(1)+3$
$y=2+3$
$y=5$

The solution is (1, 5).

53. (1) $y=3x+1$

(2) $y=6x-1$

Substitute $6x-1$ for y in Equation (1).

$y=3x+1$
$6x-1=3x+1$
$6x=3x+2$
$3x=2$
$x=\frac{2}{3}$

Substitute into Equation (2).

$y=6x-1$
$y=6\left(\frac{2}{3}\right)-1$
$y=4-1$
$y=3$

The solution is $\left(\frac{2}{3}, 3\right)$.

55. Strategy
- Amount invested at 3.5%: 2800
  Amount invested at 4.2%: x

	Principal	Rate	Interest
Amount at 3.5%	2800	0.035	0.035(2800)
Amount at 4.2%	x	0.042	$0.042x$

- The sum of the interest earned is $329.

Solution
$0.035(2800)+0.042x=329$
$98+0.042x=329$
$0.042x=231$
$x=5500$

The amount invested at 4.2% is $5500.

57. Strategy • Amount invested at 4%; 6000
Amount invested at 6.5%: x
Total amount invested at 5%: y

	Principal	Rate	Interest
Amount at 4%	6000	0.04	0.04(6000)
Amount at 6.5%	x	0.065	$0.065x$
Total invested	y	0.05	$0.05y$

• The total amount invested is y.
$y = 6000 + x$
The total interest earned is equal to 5% of the total investment.

Solution (1) $y = 6000 + x$
(2) $0.04(6000) + 0.065x = 0.05y$
Substitute $6000 + x$ for y in Equation (2).

$$0.04(6000) + 0.065x = 0.05(6000 + x)$$
$$240 + 0.065x = 300 + 0.05x$$
$$240 + 0.015x = 300$$
$$0.015x = 60$$
$$x = 4000$$

The amount invested at 6.5% must be $4000.

59. Strategy • Amount invested at 3.5%: x
Amount invested at 4.5%: y

	Principal	Rate	Interest
Amount at 3.5%	x	0.035	$0.035x$
Amount at 4.5%	y	0.045	$0.045y$

• The total amount invested is $42,000.
$x + y = 42{,}000$
The interest earned from the 3.5% investment is equal to the interest earned from the 4.5% investment.

Solution (1) $x + y = 42{,}000$
(2) $0.035x = 0.045y$
Solve for y in Equation (1) and substitute for y in Equation (2).
$y = 42{,}000 - x$

$$0.035x = 0.045(42{,}000 - x)$$
$$0.035x = 1890 - 0.045x$$
$$0.080x = 1890$$
$$x = 23{,}625$$

$42{,}000 - x = 42{,}000 - 23{,}625 = 18{,}375$
The amount invested at 3.5% is $23,625. The amount invested at 4.5% is $18,375.

61. Strategy • Amount invested at 4.5%: x
Amount invested at 8%: y

	Principal	Rate	Interest
Amount at 4.5%	x	0.045	$0.045x$
Amount at 8%	y	0.08	$0.08y$

• The total amount invested is $16,000.
$x + y = 16{,}000$
The total interest earned is $1070.

Solution (1) $x + y = 16{,}000$
(2) $0.045x + 0.08y = 1070$
Solve equation (1) for y and substitute for y in Equation (2).
$y = 16{,}000 - x$

$$0.045x + 0.08(16{,}000 - x) = 1070$$
$$0.045x + 1280 - 0.08x = 1070$$
$$-0.035x + 1280 = 1070$$
$$-0.035x = -210$$
$$x = 6000$$

There is $6000 invested in the mutual bond fund.

Applying the Concepts

63. (1) $y = -\frac{1}{2}x + 2$
(2) $y = 2x - 1$
Substitute $2x - 1$ for y in Equation (1).

$$y = -\frac{1}{2}x + 2$$
$$2x - 1 = -\frac{1}{2}x + 2$$
$$\frac{5}{2}x = 3$$
$$x = 3 \cdot \frac{2}{5} = \frac{6}{5}$$

Substitute into Equation (2).

$$y = 2x - 1$$
$$y = 2 \cdot \frac{6}{5} - 1$$
$$y = \frac{12}{5} - 1$$
$$y = \frac{7}{5}$$

The solution is $\left(\frac{6}{5}, \frac{7}{5}\right)$, or (1.20, 1.40).

65. (1) $y = \pi x - \frac{2}{3}$

(2) $y = -x + \frac{\pi}{2}$

Substitute $-x + \frac{\pi}{2}$ for y in Equation (1).

$$y = \pi x - \frac{2}{3}$$
$$-x + \frac{\pi}{2} = \pi x - \frac{2}{3}$$
$$-(1+\pi)x = -\frac{2}{3} - \frac{\pi}{2}$$
$$x = \frac{\frac{2}{3} + \frac{\pi}{2}}{1+\pi}$$
$$x = 0.54$$

Substitute into Equation (2).

$$y = -x + \frac{\pi}{2}$$
$$y = -0.54 + \frac{\pi}{2}$$
$$y = 1.03$$

The solution is (0.54, 1.03).

67. A dependent system of equations is geometrically represented by a single line. An inconsistent system of equations is geometrically represented by a set of parallel lines. A consistent (or independent) system of equations is geometrically represented by two lines that intersect in a point.

SECTION 4.2

Objective A Exercises

1. (1) $x - y = 5$

(2) $x + y = 7$

Eliminate y. Add the equations.

$$2x = 12$$
$$x = 6$$

Replace x in Equation (1).

$$x - y = 5$$
$$6 - y = 5$$
$$-y = -1$$
$$y = 1$$

The solution is (6, 1).

3. (1) $3x + y = 4$

(2) $x + y = 2$

Eliminate y.

$$3x + y = 4$$
$$-1(x + y) = -1(2)$$

$$3x + y = 4$$
$$-x - y = -2$$

Add the equations.

$$2x = 2$$
$$x = 1$$

Replace x in Equation (2).

$$x + y = 2$$
$$1 + y = 2$$
$$y = 1$$

The solution is (1, 1).

5. (1) $3x + y = 7$

(2) $x + 2y = 4$

Eliminate y.

$$-2(3x + y) = -2(7)$$
$$x + 2y = 4$$

$$-6x - 2y = -14$$
$$x + 2y = 4$$

Add the equations.

$$-5x = -10$$
$$x = 2$$

Replace x in Equation (2).

$$x + 2y = 4$$
$$2 + 2y = 4$$
$$2y = 2$$
$$y = 1$$

The solution is (2, 1).

7. (1) $2x + 3y = -1$

(2) $x + 5y = 3$

Eliminate x.

$$2x + 3y = -1$$
$$-2(x + 5y) = -2(3)$$

$$2x + 3y = -1$$
$$-2x - 10y = -6$$

Add the equations.

$$-7y = -7$$
$$y = 1$$

Replace y in Equation (2).

$$x + 5y = 3$$
$$x + 5(1) = 3$$
$$x + 5 = 3$$
$$x = -2$$

The solution is (–2, 1).

9. (1) $3x - y = 4$

(2) $6x - 2y = 8$

Eliminate y.

$-2(3x - y) = -2(4)$
$6x - 2y = 8$

$-6x + 2y = -8$
$6x - 2y = 8$

Add the equations.

$0 = 0$

This is a true equation. The equation are dependent. The solutions are the ordered pairs $(x, 3x - 4)$.

11. (1) $2x + 5y = 9$

(2) $4x - 7y = -16$

Eliminate x.

$-2(2x + 5y) = -2(9)$
$4x - 7y = -16$

$-4x - 10y = -18$
$4x - 7y = -16$

Add the equations.

$-17y = -34$
$y = 2$

Replace y in Equation (1).

$2x + 5y = 9$
$2x + 5(2) = 9$
$2x + 10 = 9$
$2x = -1$
$x = -\frac{1}{2}$

The solution is $\left(-\frac{1}{2}, 2\right)$.

13. (1) $4x - 6y = 5$

(2) $2x - 3y = 7$

Eliminate y.

$4x - 6y = 5$
$-2(2x - 3y) = -2(7)$

$4x - 6y = 5$
$-4x + 6y = -14$

Add the equations.

$0 = -9$

This is not a true equation. The system of equations is inconsistent and therefore has no solution.

15. (1) $3x - 5y = 7$

(2) $x - 2y = 3$

Eliminate x.

$3x - 5y = 7$
$-3(x - 2y) = -3(3)$

$3x - 5y = 7$
$-3x + 6y = -9$

Add the equations.

$y = -2$

Replace y in Equation (2).

$x - 2y = 3$
$x - 2(-2) = 3$
$x + 4 = 3$
$x = -1$

The solution is $(-1, -2)$.

17. (1) $x + 3y = 7$

(2) $-2x + 3y = 22$

Eliminate y.

$-1(x + 3y) = -1(7)$
$-2x + 3y = 22$

$-x - 3y = -7$
$-2x + 3y = 22$

Add the equations.

$-3x = 15$
$x = -5$

Replace x in Equation (1).

$x + 3y = 7$
$-5 + 3y = 7$
$3y = 12$
$y = 4$

The solution is $(-5, 4)$.

19. (1) $3x + 2y = 16$

(2) $2x - 3y = -11$

Eliminate y.

$3(3x + 2y) = 3(16)$
$2(2x - 3y) = 2(-11)$

$9x + 6y = 48$
$4x - 6y = -22$

Add the equations.

$13x = 26$
$x = 2$

Replace x in Equation (1).

$3x + 2y = 16$
$3(2) + 2y = 16$
$6 + 2y = 16$
$2y = 10$
$y = 5$

The solution is $(2, 5)$.

21. (1) $4x+4y=5$

(2) $2x-8y=-5$

Eliminate y.

$$2(4x+4y)=2(5)$$
$$2x-8y=-5$$

$$8x+8y=10$$
$$2x-8y=-5$$

Add the equations.

$$10x=5$$
$$x=\frac{1}{2}$$

Replace x in Equation (1).

$$4x+4y=5$$
$$4\left(\frac{1}{2}\right)+4y=5$$
$$2+4y=5$$
$$4y=3$$
$$y=\frac{3}{4}$$

The solution is $\left(\frac{1}{2}, \frac{3}{4}\right)$.

23. (1) $5x+4y=0$

(2) $3x+7y=0$

Eliminate x.

$$-3(5x+4y)=-3(0)$$
$$5(3x+7y)=5(0)$$

$$-15x-12y=0$$
$$15x+35y=0$$

Add the equations.

$$23y=0$$
$$y=0$$

Replace y in Equation (1).

$$5x+4y=0$$
$$5x+4(0)=0$$
$$5x=0$$
$$x=0$$

The solution is (0, 0).

25. (1) $5x+2y=1$

(2) $2x+3y=7$

Eliminate y.

$$-3(5x+2y)=-3(1)$$
$$2(2x+3y)=2(7)$$

$$-15x-6y=-3$$
$$4x+6y=14$$

Add the equations.

$$-11x=11$$
$$x=-1$$

Replace x in Equation (1).

$$5x+2y=1$$
$$5(-1)+2y=1$$
$$-5+2y=1$$
$$2y=6$$
$$y=3$$

The solution is (–1, 3).

27. (1) $3x-6y=6$

(2) $9x-3y=8$

Eliminate y.

$$3x-6y=6$$
$$-2(9x-3y)=-2(8)$$

$$3x-6y=6$$
$$-18x+6y=-16$$

Add the equations.

$$-15x=-10$$
$$x=\frac{2}{3}$$

Replace x in Equation (1).

$$3x-6y=6$$
$$3\left(\frac{2}{3}\right)-6y=6$$
$$2-6y=6$$
$$-6y=4$$
$$y=-\frac{2}{3}$$

The solution is $\left(\frac{2}{3}, -\frac{2}{3}\right)$.

29. (1) $\frac{3}{4}x+\frac{1}{3}y=-\frac{1}{2}$

(2) $\frac{1}{2}x-\frac{5}{6}y=-\frac{7}{2}$

Clear the fractions.

$$12\left(\frac{3}{4}x+\frac{1}{3}y\right)=12\left(-\frac{1}{2}\right)$$
$$6\left(\frac{1}{2}x-\frac{5}{6}y\right)=6\left(-\frac{7}{2}\right)$$

$9x+4y=-6$
$3x-5y=-21$

Eliminate x.

$9x+4y=-6$
$-3(3x-5y)=-3(-21)$

$9x+4y=-6$
$-9x+15y=63$

Add the equations.

$19y=57$
$y=3$

Replace y in Equation (1).

$$\frac{3}{4}x+\frac{1}{3}y=-\frac{1}{2}$$
$$\frac{3}{4}x+\frac{1}{3}(3)=-\frac{1}{2}$$
$$\frac{3}{4}x+1=-\frac{1}{2}$$
$$\frac{3}{4}x=-\frac{3}{2}$$
$$x=-2$$

The solution is (–2, 3).

31. (1) $\frac{5x}{6}+\frac{y}{3}=\frac{4}{3}$

(2) $\frac{2x}{3}-\frac{y}{2}=\frac{11}{6}$

Clear the fractions.

$$6\left(\frac{5x}{6}+\frac{y}{3}\right)=6\left(\frac{4}{3}\right)$$
$$6\left(\frac{2x}{3}-\frac{y}{2}\right)=6\left(\frac{11}{6}\right)$$

$5x+2y=8$
$4x-3y=11$

Eliminate y.

$3(5x+2y)=3(8)$
$2(4x-3y)=2(11)$

$15x+6y=24$
$8x-6y=22$

Add the equations.

$23x=46$
$x=2$

Replace x in Equation (1).

$$\frac{5}{6}x+\frac{1}{3}y=\frac{4}{3}$$
$$\frac{5}{6}(2)+\frac{1}{3}y=\frac{4}{3}$$
$$\frac{5}{3}+\frac{1}{3}y=\frac{4}{3}$$
$$\frac{1}{3}y=-\frac{1}{3}$$
$$y=-1$$

The solution is (2, –1).

33. (1) $\frac{2x}{5} - \frac{y}{2} = \frac{13}{2}$

(2) $\frac{3x}{4} - \frac{y}{5} = \frac{17}{2}$

Clear the fractions.

$$10\left(\frac{2x}{5} - \frac{y}{2}\right) = 10\left(\frac{13}{2}\right)$$
$$20\left(\frac{3x}{4} - \frac{y}{5}\right) = 20\left(\frac{17}{2}\right)$$

$$4x - 5y = 65$$
$$15x - 4y = 170$$

Eliminate y.

$$-4(4x - 5y) = -4(65)$$
$$5(15x - 4y) = 5(170)$$

$$-16x + 20y = -260$$
$$75x - 20y = 850$$

Add the equations.

$$59x = 590$$
$$x = 10$$

Replace x in Equation (1).

$$\frac{2}{5}x - \frac{1}{2}y = \frac{13}{2}$$
$$\frac{2}{5}(10) - \frac{1}{2}y = \frac{13}{2}$$
$$4 - \frac{1}{2}y = \frac{13}{2}$$
$$-\frac{1}{2}y = \frac{5}{2}$$
$$y = -5$$

The solution is (10, –5).

35. (1) $\frac{3x}{2} - \frac{y}{4} = -\frac{11}{12}$

(2) $\frac{x}{3} - y = -\frac{5}{6}$

Clear the fractions.

$$12\left(\frac{3x}{2} - \frac{y}{4}\right) = 12\left(-\frac{11}{12}\right)$$
$$6\left(\frac{x}{3} - y\right) = 6\left(-\frac{5}{6}\right)$$

$$18x - 3y = -11$$
$$2x - 6y = -5$$

Eliminate y.

$$-2(18x - 3y) = -2(-11)$$
$$2x - 6y = -5$$

$$-36x + 6y = 22$$
$$2x - 6y = -5$$

Add the equations.

$$-34x = 17$$
$$x = -\frac{1}{2}$$

Replace x in Equation (2).

$$\frac{x}{3} - y = -\frac{5}{6}$$
$$\frac{1}{3}\left(-\frac{1}{2}\right) - y = -\frac{5}{6}$$
$$-\frac{1}{6} - y = -\frac{5}{6}$$
$$-y = -\frac{4}{6}$$
$$y = \frac{2}{3}$$

The solution is $\left(-\frac{1}{2}, \frac{2}{3}\right)$.

37. (1) $4x-5y=3y+4$

(2) $2x+3y=2x+1$

Write the equations in the form $Ax+By=C$.

$4x-5y=3y+4$
$4x-8y=4$

$2x+3y=2x+1$
$3y=1$

Solve the system.

$4x-8y=4$
$3y=1$

Solve the equation $3y=1$ for y.

$3y=1$
$y=\frac{1}{3}$

Replace y in the equation $4x-8y=4$.

$4x-8y=4$
$4x-8\left(\frac{1}{3}\right)=4$
$4x-\frac{8}{3}=4$
$4x=\frac{20}{3}$
$x=\frac{5}{3}$

The solution is $\left(\frac{5}{3},\frac{1}{3}\right)$.

39. (1) $2x+5y=5x+1$

(2) $3x-2y=3y+3$

Write the equations in the form $Ax+By=C$.

$2x+5y=5x+1$
$-3x+5y=1$

$3x-2y=3y+3$
$3x-5y=3$

Solve the system.

$-3x+5y=1$
$3x-5y=3$

Add the equations.

$0=4$

This is not a true equation. The system of equations is inconsistent and therefore has no solution.

41. (1) $5x+2y=2x+1$

(2) $2x-3y=3x+2$

Write the equations in the form $Ax+By=C$.

$5x+2y=2x+1$
$3x+2y=1$

$2x-3y=3x+2$
$-x-3y=2$

Solve the system.

$3x+2y=1$
$-x-3y=2$

Eliminate x.

$3x+2y=1$
$3(-x-3y)=3(2)$

$3x+2y=1$
$-3x-9y=6$

Add the equations.

$-7y=7$
$y=-1$

Replace y in the equation $-x-3y=2$.

$-x-3y=2$
$-x-3(-1)=2$
$-x+3=2$
$-x=-1$
$x=1$

The solution is $(1,-1)$.

Objective B Exercises

43. (1) $x+2y-z=1$
(2) $2x-y+z=6$
(3) $x+3y-z=2$

Eliminate z. Add Equation (1) and (2).

$x+2y-z=1$
$2x-y+z=6$

(4) $3x+y=7$

Add equations (2) and (3).

$2x-y+z=6$
$x+3y-z=2$

(5) $3x+2y=8$

Multiply Equation (4) by –1 and add to Equation (5).

$-1(3x+y)=-1(7)$
$3x+2y=8$

$-3x-y=-7$
$3x+2y=8$

$y=1$

Replace y by 1 in Equation (4).

$3x+y=7$
$3x+1=7$
$3x=6$
$x=2$

Replace x by 2 and y by 1 in Equation (1).

$x+2y-z=1$
$2+2(1)-z=1$
$2+2-z=1$
$4-z=1$
$-z=-3$
$z=3$

The solution is (2, 1, 3).

45. (1) $2x-y+2z=7$
(2) $x+y+z=2$
(3) $3x-y+z=6$

Eliminate y. Add Equations (1) and (2).

$2x-y+2z=7$
$x+y+z=2$

$3x+3z=9$

Multiply both sides of the equation by $\frac{1}{3}$.

(4) $x+z=3$

Add Equations (2) and (3).

$x+y+z=2$
$3x-y+z=6$

$4x+2z=8$

Multiply both sides of the equation by $\frac{1}{2}$.

(5) $2x+z=4$

Multiply Equation (4) by –1 and add to Equation (5).

$-1(x+z)=-1(3)$
$2x+z=4$

$-x-z=-3$
$2x+z=4$
$x=1$

Replace x by 1 in Equation (4).

$x+z=3$
$1+z=3$
$z=2$

Replace x by 1 and z by 2 in Equation (2).

$x+y+z=2$
$1+y+2=2$
$3+y=2$
$y=-1$

The solution is (1, –1, 2).

47. (1) $3x + y = 5$

(2) $3y - z = 2$

(3) $x + z = 5$

Eliminate z. Add Equations (2) and (3).

$$3y - z = 2$$
$$x + z = 5$$

(4) $x + 3y = 7$

Multiply Equation (4) by –3 and add to Equation (1).

$$-3(x + 3y) = -3(7)$$
$$3x + y = 5$$

$$-3x - 9y = -21$$
$$3x + y = 5$$

$$-8y = -16$$
$$y = 2$$

Replace y by 2 in Equation (1).

$$3x + y = 5$$
$$3x + 2 = 5$$
$$3x = 3$$
$$x = 1$$

Replace x by 1 in Equation (3).

$$x + z = 5$$
$$1 + z = 5$$
$$z = 4$$

The solution is (1, 2, 4).

49. (1) $x - y + z = 1$

(2) $2x + 3y - z = 3$

(3) $-x + 2y - 4z = 4$

Eliminate z. Add Equations (1) and (2).

$$x - y + z = 1$$
$$2x + 3y - z = 3$$

(4) $3x + 2y = 4$

Multiply Equation (1) by 4 and add to Equation (3).

$$4(x - y + z) = 4(1)$$
$$-x + 2y - 4z = 4$$

$$4x - 4y + 4z = 4$$
$$-x + 2y - 4z = 4$$

(5) $3x - 2y = 8$

Multiply Equation (4) by –1 and add to Equation (5).

$$-1(3x + 2y) = -1(4)$$
$$3x - 2y = 8$$

$$-3x - 2y = -4$$
$$3x - 2y = 8$$

$$-4y = 4$$
$$y = -1$$

Replace y by –1 in Equation (5).

$$3x - 2y = 8$$
$$3x - 2(-1) = 8$$
$$3x + 2 = 8$$
$$3x = 6$$
$$x = 2$$

Replace x by 2 and y by –1 in Equation (1).

$$x - y + z = 1$$
$$2 - (-1) + z = 1$$
$$3 + z = 1$$
$$z = -2$$

The solution is (2, –1, –2).

51. (1) $2x+3z=5$

(2) $3y+2z=3$

(3) $3x+4y=-10$

Eliminate z. Multiply Equation (1) by –2 and Equation (2) by 3.
Then add the equations.

$-2(2x+3z)=-2(5)$
$3(3y+2z)=3(3)$

$-4x-6z=-10$
$9y+6z=9$

(4) $-4x+9y=-1$

Multiply Equation (3) by 4 and Equation (4) by 3.
Then add the equations.

$4(3x+4y)=4(-10)$
$3(-4x+9y)=3(-1)$

$12x+16y=-40$
$-12x+27y=-3$

$43y=-43$
$y=-1$

Replace y by –1 in Equation (3).

$3x+4y=-10$
$3x+4(-1)=-10$
$3x-4=-10$
$3x=-6$
$x=-2$

Replace x by –2 in Equation (1).

$2x+3z=5$
$2(-2)+3z=5$
$-4+3z=5$
$3z=9$
$z=3$

The solution is (–2, –1, 3).

53. (1) $2x+4y-2z=3$

(2) $x+3y+4z=1$

(3) $x+2y-z=4$

Eliminate x. Multiply Equation (2) by –2 and add to Equation (1).

$2x+4y-2z=3$
$-2(x+3y+4z)=-2(1)$

$2x+4y-2z=3$
$-2x-6y-8z=-2$

(4) $-2y-10z=1$

Multiply Equation (2) by –1 and add to Equation (3).

$-1(x+3y+4z)=-1(1)$
$x+2y-z=4$

$-x-3y-4z=-1$
$x+2y-z=4$

(5) $-y-5z=3$

Multiply Equation (5) by –2 and add to Equation (4).

$-2(-y-5z)=-2(3)$
$-2y-10z=1$

$2y+10z=-6$
$-2y-10z=1$

$0=-5$

This is not a true equation. The system of equations is inconsistent and therefore has no solution.

55. (1) $2x + y - z = 5$

(2) $x + 3y + z = 14$

(3) $3x - y + 2z = 1$

Eliminate z. Add Equations (1) and (2).

$$2x + y - z = 5$$
$$x + 3y + z = 14$$

(4) $3x + 4y = 19$

Multiply Equation (1) by 2 and add to Equation (3).

$$2(2x + y - z) = 2(5)$$
$$3x - y + 2z = 1$$

$$4x + 2y - 2z = 10$$
$$3x - y + 2z = 1$$

(5) $7x + y = 11$

Multiply Equation (5) by –4 and add to Equation (4).

$$-4(7x + y) = -4(11)$$
$$3x + 4y = 19$$

$$-28x - 4y = -44$$
$$3x + 4y = 19$$

$$-25x = -25$$
$$x = 1$$

Replace x by 1 in Equation (5).

$$7x + y = 11$$
$$7(1) + y = 11$$
$$7 + y = 11$$
$$y = 4$$

Replace x by 1 and y by 4 in Equation (1).

$$2x + y - z = 5$$
$$2(1) + 4 - z = 5$$
$$2 + 4 - z = 5$$
$$6 - z = 5$$
$$-z = -1$$
$$z = 1$$

The solution is (1, 4, 1).

57. (1) $3x + y - 2z = 2$

(2) $x + 2y + 3z = 13$

(3) $2x - 2y + 5z = 6$

Eliminate y. Multiply Equation (1) by –2 and add to Equation (2).

$$-2(3x + y - 2z) = -2(2)$$
$$x + 2y + 3z = 13$$

$$-6x - 2y + 4z = -4$$
$$x + 2y + 3z = 13$$

(4) $-5x + 7z = 9$

Add Equations (2) and (3).

$$x + 2y + 3z = 13$$
$$2x - 2y + 5z = 6$$

(5) $3x + 8z = 19$

Multiply Equation (4) by 3 and Equation (5) by 5. Then add the equations.

$$3(-5x + 7z) = 3(9)$$
$$5(3x + 8z) = 5(19)$$

$$-15x + 21z = 27$$
$$15x + 40z = 95$$

$$61z = 122$$
$$z = 2$$

Replace z by 2 in Equation (5).

$$3x + 8z = 19$$
$$3x + 8(2) = 19$$
$$3x + 16 = 19$$
$$3x = 3$$
$$x = 1$$

Replace x by 1 and z by 2 in Equation (1).

$$3x + y - 2z = 2$$
$$3(1) + y - 2(2) = 2$$
$$3 + y - 4 = 2$$
$$y - 1 = 2$$
$$y = 3$$

The solution is (1, 3, 2).

59. (1) $2x - y + z = 6$

(2) $3x + 2y + z = 4$

(3) $x - 2y + 3z = 12$

Eliminate y. Multiply Equation (1) by 2 and add to Equation (2).

$2(2x - y + z) = 2(6)$
$3x + 2y + z = 4$

$4x - 2y + 2z = 12$
$3x + 2y + z = 4$

(4) $7x + 3z = 16$

Add Equations (2) and (3).

$3x + 2y + z = 4$
$x - 2y + 3z = 12$

$4x + 4z = 16$

Multiply each side of the equation by $\frac{1}{4}$.

(5) $x + z = 4$

Multiply Equation (5) by −3 and add to Equation (4).

$7x + 3z = 16$
$-3(x + z) = -3(4)$

$7x + 3z = 16$
$-3x - 3z = -12$

$4x = 4$
$x = 1$

Replace x by 1 in Equation (5).

$x + z = 4$
$1 + z = 4$
$z = 3$

Replace x by 1 and z by 3 in Equation (1).

$2x - y + z = 6$
$2(1) - y + 3 = 6$
$2 - y + 3 = 6$
$5 - y = 6$
$-y = 1$
$y = -1$

The solution is (1, −1, 3).

61. (1) $3x - 2y + 3z = -4$

(2) $2x + y - 3z = 2$

(3) $3x + 4y + 5z = 8$

Eliminate y. Multiply Equation (2) by 2 and add to Equation (1).

$3x - 2y + 3z = -4$
$2(2x + y - 3z) = 2(2)$

$3x - 2y + 3z = -4$
$4x + 2y - 6z = 4$

(4) $7x - 3z = 0$

Multiply Equation (2) by −4 and add to Equation (3).

$-4(2x + y - 3z) = -4(2)$
$3x + 4y + 5z = 8$

$-8x - 4y + 12z = -8$
$3x + 4y + 5z = 8$

(5) $-5x + 17z = 0$

Multiply Equation (4) by 5 and Equation (5) by 7.

$5(7x - 3z) = 5(0)$
$7(-5x + 17z) = 7(0)$

$35x - 15z = 0$
$-35x + 119z = 0$

$104z = 0$
$z = 0$

Replace z by 0 in Equation (4).

$7x - 3z = 0$
$7x - 3(0) = 0$
$7x = 0$
$x = 0$

Replace x by 0 and z by 0 in Equation (2).

$2x + y - 3z = 2$
$2(0) + y - 3(0) = 2$
$y = 2$

The solution is (0, 2, 0).

63. (1) $3x - y + 2z = 0$

(2) $4x + 2y - 7z = 0$

(3) $2x + 3y - 5z = 7$

Eliminate y. Multiply Equation (1) by 2 and add to Equation (2).

$2(3x - y + 2z) = 2(2)$
$4x + 2y - 7z = 0$

$6x - 2y + 4z = 4$
$4x + 2y - 7z = 0$

(4) $10x - 3z = 4$

Multiply Equation (1) by 3 and add to Equation (3).

$3(3x - y + 2z) = 3(2)$
$2x + 3y - 5z = 7$

$9x - 3y + 6z = 6$
$2x + 3y - 5z = 7$

(5) $11x + z = 13$

Multiply Equation (5) by 3 and add to Equation (4).

$10x - 3z = 4$
$3(11x + z) = 3(13)$

$10x - 3z = 4$
$33x + 3z = 39$

$43x = 43$
$x = 1$

Replace x by 1 in Equation (4).

$10x - 3z = 4$
$10(1) - 3z = 4$
$10 - 3z = 4$
$-3z = -6$
$z = 2$

Replace x by 1 and z by 2 in Equation (1).

$3x - y + 2z = 2$
$3(1) - y + 2(2) = 2$
$3 - y + 4 = 2$
$7 - y = 2$
$-y = -5$
$y = 5$

The solution is (1, 5, 2).

65. (1) $2x - 3y + 7z = 0$

(2) $x + 4y - 4z = -2$

(3) $3x + 2y + 5z = 1$

Eliminate x. Multiply Equation (2) by –2 and add to Equation (1).

$2x - 3y + 7z = 0$
$-2(x + 4y - 4z) = -2(-2)$

$2x - 3y + 7z = 0$
$-2x - 8y + 8z = 0$

(4) $-11y + 15z = 4$

Multiply Equation (2) by –3 and add to Equation (3).

$-3(x + 4y - 4z) = -3(-2)$
$3x + 2y + 5z = 1$

$-3x - 12y + 12z = 6$
$3x + 2y + 5z = 1$

(5) $-10y + 17z = 7$

Multiply Equation (4) by –10 and Equation (5) by 11. Then add the equations.

$-10(-11y + 15z) = -10(4)$
$11(-10y + 17z) = 11(7)$

$110y - 150z = -40$
$-110y + 187z = 77$

$37z = 37$
$z = 1$

Replace z by 1 in Equation (4).

$-11y + 15z = 4$
$-11y + 15(1) = 4$
$-11y + 15 = 4$
$-11y = -11$
$y = 1$

Replace y by 1 and z by 1 in Equation (1).

$2x - 3y + 7z = 0$
$2x - 3(1) + 7(1) = 0$
$2x - 3 + 7 = 0$
$2x + 4 = 0$
$2x = -4$
$x = -2$

The solution is (–2, 1, 1).

Applying the Concepts

67. a. The system of equations has no solutions; it is inconsistent.

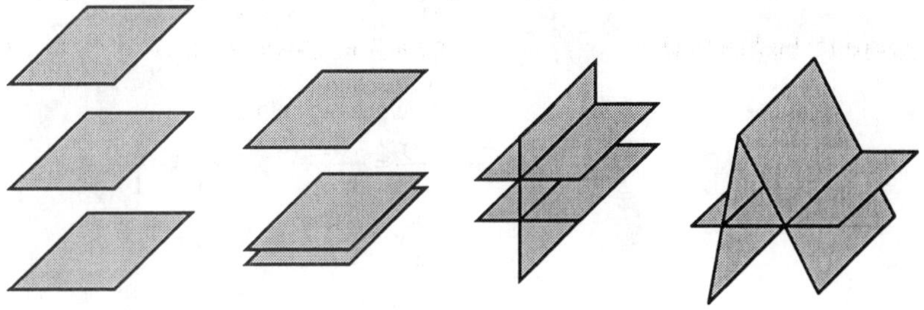

b. The system has exactly one solution. This is an independent system whose solution is a point in space.

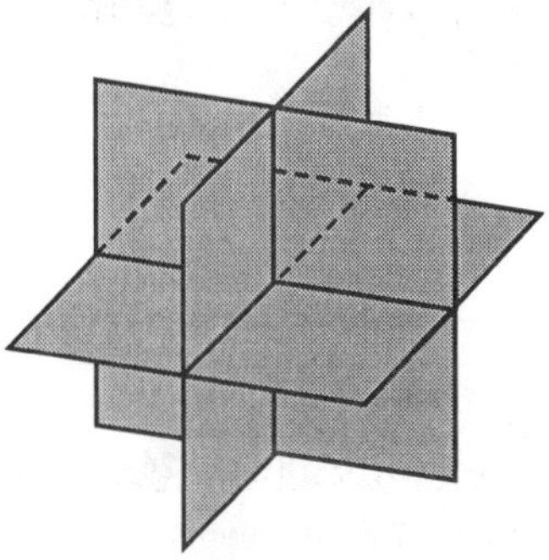

c. The system has infinitely many solutions. It is a dependent system.

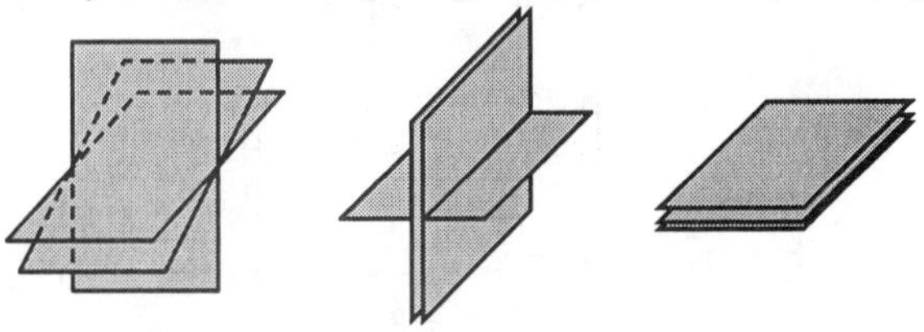

69. (1) $\frac{1}{x}-\frac{2}{y}=3$

(2) $\frac{2}{x}+\frac{3}{y}=-1$

Clear the fractions.

$$xy\left(\frac{1}{x}-\frac{2}{y}\right)=xy\cdot 3$$
$$xy\left(\frac{2}{x}+\frac{3}{y}\right)=xy\cdot(-1)$$
$$y-2x=3xy$$
$$2y+3x=-xy$$

Eliminate y.

$$-2y+4x=-6xy$$
$$2y+3x=-xy$$
$$7x=-7xy$$
$$y=-1$$

Substitute into Equation (2).

$$\frac{2}{x}+\frac{3}{y}=-1$$
$$\frac{2}{x}+\frac{3}{-1}=-1$$
$$\frac{2}{x}=2$$
$$x=1$$

The solution is $(1,-1)$.

71. (1) $\frac{3}{x}+\frac{2}{y}=1$

(2) $\frac{2}{x}+\frac{4}{y}=-2$

Clear fractions.

$$xy\left(\frac{3}{x}+\frac{2}{y}\right)=xy\cdot 1$$
$$xy\left(\frac{2}{x}+\frac{4}{y}\right)=xy\cdot(-2)$$
$$3y+2x=xy$$
$$2y+4x=-2xy$$

Eliminate x.

$$-6y-4x=-2xy$$
$$2y+4x=-2xy$$
$$-4y=-4xy$$
$$x=1$$

Substitute x into Equation (2).

$$\frac{2}{x}+\frac{4}{y}=-2$$
$$2+\frac{4}{y}=-2$$
$$\frac{4}{y}=-4$$
$$y=-1$$

The solution is $(1,-1)$.

73. Solve each equation for y.

$$\frac{1}{x}-\frac{2}{y}=3 \qquad \frac{2}{x}+\frac{3}{y}=-1$$
$$-\frac{2}{y}=3-\frac{1}{x} \qquad \frac{3}{y}=-1-\frac{2}{x}$$

Reciprocate both sides.

$$-\frac{y}{2}=\frac{1}{3-\frac{1}{x}} \qquad \frac{y}{3}=-\frac{1}{1+\frac{2}{x}}$$
$$y=\frac{-2}{3-\frac{1}{x}} \qquad y=-\frac{3}{1+\frac{2}{x}}$$

Reduce.

$$y=\frac{2x}{1-3x} \qquad y=\frac{-3x}{x+2}$$

SECTION 4.3

Objective A Exercises

1. $\begin{vmatrix} 2 & -1 \\ 3 & 4 \end{vmatrix}=2(4)-3(-1)=8+3=11$

3. $\begin{vmatrix} 6 & -2 \\ -3 & 4 \end{vmatrix}=6(4)-(-3)(-2)=24-6=18$

5. $\begin{vmatrix} 3 & 6 \\ 2 & 4 \end{vmatrix}=3(4)-2(6)=12-12=0$

7. $\begin{vmatrix} 1 & -1 & 2 \\ 3 & 2 & 1 \\ 1 & 0 & 4 \end{vmatrix}=1\begin{vmatrix} 2 & 1 \\ 0 & 4 \end{vmatrix}+1\begin{vmatrix} 3 & 1 \\ 1 & 4 \end{vmatrix}+2\begin{vmatrix} 3 & 2 \\ 1 & 0 \end{vmatrix}$

$$=1(8-0)+1(12-1)+2(0-2)$$
$$=8+11-4$$
$$=15$$

9. $\begin{vmatrix} 3 & -1 & 2 \\ 0 & 1 & 2 \\ 3 & 2 & -2 \end{vmatrix}=3\begin{vmatrix} 1 & 2 \\ 2 & -2 \end{vmatrix}+1\begin{vmatrix} 0 & 2 \\ 3 & -2 \end{vmatrix}+2\begin{vmatrix} 0 & 1 \\ 3 & 2 \end{vmatrix}$

$$=3(-2-4)+1(0-6)+2(0-3)$$
$$=3(-6)+1(-6)+2(-3)$$
$$=-18-6-6$$
$$=-30$$

11. $\begin{vmatrix} 4 & 2 & 6 \\ -2 & 1 & 1 \\ 2 & 1 & 3 \end{vmatrix}=4\begin{vmatrix} 1 & 1 \\ 1 & 3 \end{vmatrix}-2\begin{vmatrix} -2 & 1 \\ 2 & 3 \end{vmatrix}+6\begin{vmatrix} -2 & 1 \\ 2 & 1 \end{vmatrix}$

$$=4(3-1)-2(-6-2)+6(-2-2)$$
$$=4(2)-2(-8)+6(-4)$$
$$=8+16-24$$
$$=0$$

Objective B Exercises

13. $2x - 5y = 26$
$5x + 3y = 3$

$$D = \begin{vmatrix} 2 & -5 \\ 5 & 3 \end{vmatrix} = 31,\ D_x = \begin{vmatrix} 26 & -5 \\ 3 & 3 \end{vmatrix} = 93,$$

$$D_y = \begin{vmatrix} 2 & 26 \\ 5 & 3 \end{vmatrix} = -124$$

$$x = \frac{D_x}{D} = \frac{93}{31} = 3,\ y = \frac{D_y}{D} = \frac{-124}{31} = -4$$

The solution is (3, –4).

15. $x - 4y = 8$
$3x + 7y = 5$

$$D = \begin{vmatrix} 1 & -4 \\ 3 & 7 \end{vmatrix} = 19,\ D_x = \begin{vmatrix} 8 & -4 \\ 5 & 7 \end{vmatrix} = 76,$$

$$D_y = \begin{vmatrix} 1 & 8 \\ 3 & 5 \end{vmatrix} = -19$$

$$x = \frac{D_x}{D} = \frac{76}{19} = 4,\ y = \frac{D_y}{D} = \frac{-19}{19} = -1$$

The solution is (4, –1).

17. $2x + 3y = 4$
$6x - 12y = -5$

$$D = \begin{vmatrix} 2 & 3 \\ 6 & -12 \end{vmatrix} = -42,\ D_x = \begin{vmatrix} 4 & 3 \\ -5 & -12 \end{vmatrix} = -33,$$

$$D_y = \begin{vmatrix} 2 & 4 \\ 6 & -5 \end{vmatrix} = -34$$

$$x = \frac{D_x}{D} = \frac{-33}{-42} = \frac{11}{14},\ y = \frac{D_y}{D} = \frac{-34}{-42} = \frac{17}{21}$$

The solution is $\left(\frac{11}{14}, \frac{17}{21}\right)$.

19. $2x + 5y = 6$
$6x - 2y = 1$

$$D = \begin{vmatrix} 2 & 5 \\ 6 & -2 \end{vmatrix} = -34,\ D_x = \begin{vmatrix} 6 & 5 \\ 1 & -2 \end{vmatrix} = -17,$$

$$D_y = \begin{vmatrix} 2 & 6 \\ 6 & 1 \end{vmatrix} = -34$$

$$x = \frac{D_x}{D} = \frac{-17}{-34} = \frac{1}{2},\ y = \frac{D_y}{D} = \frac{-34}{-34} = 1$$

The solution is $\left(\frac{1}{2}, 1\right)$.

21. $-2x + 3y = 7$
$4x - 6y = 9$

$$D = \begin{vmatrix} -2 & 3 \\ 4 & -6 \end{vmatrix} = 0$$

Since $D = 0, \frac{D_x}{D}$ is undefined. Therefore, the system of equations does not have a unique solution. The equations are not independent.

23. $2x - 5y = -2$
$3x - 7y = -3$

$$D = \begin{vmatrix} 2 & -5 \\ 3 & -7 \end{vmatrix} = 1,\ D_x = \begin{vmatrix} -2 & -5 \\ -3 & -7 \end{vmatrix} = -1,$$

$$D_y = \begin{vmatrix} 2 & -2 \\ 3 & -3 \end{vmatrix} = 0$$

$$x = \frac{D_x}{D} = \frac{-1}{1} = -1,\ y = \frac{D_y}{D} = \frac{0}{1} = 0$$

The solution is (–1, 0).

25. $2x - y + 3z = 9$
$x + 4y + 4z = 5$
$3x + 2y + 2z = 5$

$$D = \begin{vmatrix} 2 & -1 & 3 \\ 1 & 4 & 4 \\ 3 & 2 & 2 \end{vmatrix} = -40,\ D_x = \begin{vmatrix} 9 & -1 & 3 \\ 5 & 4 & 4 \\ 5 & 2 & 2 \end{vmatrix} = -40,$$

$$D_y = \begin{vmatrix} 2 & 9 & 3 \\ 1 & 5 & 4 \\ 3 & 5 & 2 \end{vmatrix} = 40,\ D_z = \begin{vmatrix} 2 & -1 & 9 \\ 1 & 4 & 5 \\ 3 & 2 & 5 \end{vmatrix} = -80$$

$$x = \frac{D_x}{D} = \frac{-40}{-40} = 1,\ y = \frac{D_y}{D} = \frac{40}{-40} = -1$$

$$z = \frac{D_z}{D} = \frac{-80}{-40} = 2$$

The solution is (1, –1, 2).

27. $3x - y + z = 11$
$x + 4y - 2z = -12$
$2x + 2y - z = -3$

$$D = \begin{vmatrix} 3 & -1 & 1 \\ 1 & 4 & -2 \\ 2 & 2 & -1 \end{vmatrix} = -3,\ D_x = \begin{vmatrix} 11 & -1 & 1 \\ -12 & 4 & -2 \\ -3 & 2 & -1 \end{vmatrix} = -6,$$

$$D_y = \begin{vmatrix} 3 & 11 & 1 \\ 1 & -12 & -2 \\ 2 & -3 & -1 \end{vmatrix} = 6,\ D_z = \begin{vmatrix} 3 & -1 & 11 \\ 1 & 4 & -12 \\ 2 & 2 & -3 \end{vmatrix} = -9$$

$$x = \frac{D_x}{D} = \frac{-6}{-3} = 2,\ y = \frac{D_y}{D} = \frac{6}{-3} = -2$$

$$z = \frac{D_z}{D} = \frac{-9}{-3} = 3$$

The solution is (2, –2, 3).

29. $4x - 2y + 6z = 1$
$3x + 4y + 2z = 1$
$2x - y + 3z = 2$

$$D = \begin{vmatrix} 4 & -2 & 6 \\ 3 & 4 & 2 \\ 2 & -1 & 3 \end{vmatrix} = 0$$

Since $D = 0$, $\frac{D_x}{D}$ is undefined. Therefore, the system of equations does not have a unique solution. The equations are not independent.

Applying the Concepts

31. a. Sometimes true.

b. Always true.

c. Sometimes true.

33.
$$\begin{aligned}3x-7y+z&=2\\ x+y-z&=-1\\ -x+2y+3z&=0\end{aligned}$$

$$D=\begin{vmatrix}3 & -7 & 1\\ 1 & 1 & -1\\ -1 & 2 & 3\end{vmatrix}=32$$

$$D_x=\begin{vmatrix}2 & -7 & 1\\ -1 & 1 & -1\\ 0 & 2 & 3\end{vmatrix}=-13$$

$$D_y=\begin{vmatrix}3 & 2 & 1\\ 1 & -1 & -1\\ -1 & 0 & 3\end{vmatrix}=-14$$

$$D_z=\begin{vmatrix}3 & -7 & 2\\ 1 & 1 & -1\\ -1 & 2 & 0\end{vmatrix}=5$$

$$x=\frac{D_x}{D}=-\frac{13}{32}$$
$$y=\frac{D_y}{D}=-\frac{14}{32}=-\frac{7}{16}$$
$$z=\frac{D_z}{D}=\frac{5}{32}$$

The solution is $\left(-\frac{13}{32}, -\frac{7}{16}, \frac{5}{32}\right)$.

35.
$$\begin{aligned}x+2y+3z&=1\\ 4x+5y+6z&=2\\ 7x+8y+9z&=3\end{aligned}$$

$$D=\begin{vmatrix}1 & 2 & 3\\ 4 & 5 & 6\\ 7 & 8 & 9\end{vmatrix}=0$$

Since $D=0$, the system of equations does not have a unique solution. The equations are not independent.

SECTION 4.4

Objective A Application Problems

1. Strategy
- Rate of the motorboat in calm water: x
  Rate of the current: y

	Rate	Time	Distance
With current	$x+y$	2	$2(x+y)$
Against current	$x-y$	3	$3(x-y)$

- The distance traveled with the current is 36 mi.
  The distance traveled against the current is 36 mi.

$$2(x+y)=36$$
$$3(x-y)=36$$

Solution
$$2(x+y)=36$$
$$3(x-y)=36$$

$$\frac{1}{2}\cdot 2(x+y)=\frac{1}{2}\cdot 36$$
$$\frac{1}{3}\cdot 3(x-y)=\frac{1}{3}\cdot 36$$

$$x+y=18$$
$$x-y=12$$

$$2x=30$$
$$x=15$$

$$x+y=18$$
$$15+y=18$$
$$y=3$$

The rate of the motorboat in calm water is 15 mph. The rate f the current is 3 mph.

3. Strategy • Rate of the plane is calm air: p
Rate of the wind: w

	Rate	Time	Distance
With wind	$p+w$	4	$4(p+w)$
Against wind	$p-w$	4	$4(p-w)$

• The distance traveled with the wind is 2200 mi.
The distance traveled against the wind is 1820 mi.

$$4(p+w)=2200$$
$$4(p-w)=1820$$

Solution

$$4(p+w)=2200$$
$$4(p-w)=1820$$

$$\frac{1}{4}\cdot 4(p+w)=\frac{1}{4}\cdot 2200$$
$$\frac{1}{4}\cdot 4(p-w)=\frac{1}{4}\cdot 1820$$

$$p+w=550$$
$$p-w=455$$

$$2p=1005$$
$$p=502.5$$

$$p+w=550$$
$$502.5+w=550$$
$$w=47.5$$

The rate of the plane in calm air is 502.5 mph. The rate of the wind is 47.5 mph.

5. Strategy • The rate of the team in calm water: x
The rate of the current: y

	Rate	Time	Distance
With current	$x+y$	2	$2(x+y)$
Against current	$x-y$	2	$2(x-y)$

• The distance traveled with the current is 20 km.
The distance traveled against the current is 12 km.

$$2(x+y)=20$$
$$2(x-y)=12$$

Solution

$$2(x+y)=20$$
$$2(x-y)=12$$

$$\frac{1}{2}\cdot 2(x+y)=\frac{1}{2}\cdot 20$$
$$\frac{1}{2}\cdot 2(x-y)=\frac{1}{2}\cdot 12$$

$$x+y=10$$
$$x-y=6$$

$$2x=16$$
$$x=8$$

$$x+y=10$$
$$8+y=10$$
$$y=2$$

The rate of the team in calm water is 8 km/h. The rate of the current is 2 km/h.

7. Strategy • Rate of the plane in calm air: x
Rate of the wind: y

	Rate	Time	Distance
With wind	$x+y$	4	$4(x+y)$
Against wind	$x-y$	5	$5(x-y)$

• The distance traveled with the wind is 800 mi.
The distance traveled against the wind is 800 mi.

$4(x+y)=800$
$5(x-y)=800$

Solution $4(x+y)=800$
$5(x-y)=800$

$$\frac{1}{4}\cdot 4(x+y)=\frac{1}{4}\cdot 800$$
$$\frac{1}{5}\cdot 5(x-y)=\frac{1}{5}\cdot 800$$

$x+y=200$
$x-y=160$

$2x=360$
$x=180$

$x+y=200$
$180+y=200$
$y=20$

The rate of the plane in calm air is 180 mph. The rate of the wind is 20 mph.

9. Strategy • Rate of the plane in calm air: x
Rate of the wind: y

	Rate	Time	Distance
With wind	$x+y$	5	$5(x+y)$
Against wind	$x-y$	6	$6(x-y)$

• The distance traveled with the wind is 600 mi.
The distance traveled against the wind is 600 mi.

$5(x+y)=600$
$6(x-y)=600$

Solution $5(x+y)=600$
$6(x-y)=600$

$$\frac{1}{5}\cdot 5(x+y)=\frac{1}{5}\cdot 600$$
$$\frac{1}{6}\cdot 6(x-y)=\frac{1}{6}\cdot 600$$

$x+y=120$
$x-y=100$

$2x=220$
$x=110$

$x+y=120$
$110+y=120$
$y=10$

The rate of the plane in calm air is 110 mph. The rate of the wind is 10 mph.

Objective B Application Problems

11. Strategy • Number of nickels in the bank: n
Number of dimes in the bank: d
Coins in the bank now:

Coin	Number	Value	Total Value
Nickel	n	5	$5n$
Dime	d	10	$10d$

Coins in the bank if the nickels were dimes and the dimes were nickels:

Coin	Number	Value	Total Value
Nickel	d	5	$5d$
Dime	n	10	$10n$

• The value of the nickels and dimes in the bank is \$2.50. The value of the nickels and dimes in the bank would be \$3.50.

$$5n+10d=250$$
$$10n+5d=350$$

Solution

$$5n+10d=250$$
$$10n+5d=350$$

$$-1(5n+10d)=-1(250)$$
$$2(10n+5d)=2(350)$$

$$-5n-10d=-250$$
$$20n+10d=700$$

$$15n=450$$
$$n=30$$

There are 30 nickels in the bank.

13. Strategy • Cost of redwood: x
Cost of pine: y
First purchase:

	Amount	Rate	Total Value
Redwood	60	x	$60x$
Pine	80	y	$80y$

Second purchase:

	Amount	Rate	Total Value
Redwood	100	x	$100x$
Pine	60	y	$60y$

• The first purchase cost \$27.
The second purchase cost \$34.

$$60x+80y=27$$
$$100x+60y=34$$

Solution

$$60x+80y=27$$
$$100x+60y=34$$

$$3(60x+80y)=3(27)$$
$$-4(100x+60y)=-4(34)$$

$$180x+240y=81$$
$$-400x-240y=-136$$

$$-220x=-55$$
$$x=0.25$$

$$60x+80y=27$$
$$60(0.25)+80y=27$$
$$15+80y=27$$
$$80y=12$$
$$y=0.15$$

The cost of the pine is \$.15 per foot. The cost of the redwood is \$.25 per foot.

15. Strategy

- Cost per yard of nylon carpet: x
  Cost per yard of wool carpet: y

First purchase:

	Amount	Rate	Total Cost
Nylon	16	x	$16x$
Wool	20	y	$20y$

Second purchase:

	Amount	Rate	Total Cost
Nylon	18	x	$18x$
Wool	25	y	$25y$

- The first purchase cost \$920.
  The second purchase cost \$1100.

$$16x + 20y = 920$$
$$18x + 25y = 1100$$

Solution

$$16x + 20y = 920$$
$$18x + 25y = 1100$$

$$5(16x + 20y) = 5(920)$$
$$-4(18x + 25y) = -4(1100)$$

$$80x + 100y = 4600$$
$$-72x - 100y = -4400$$

$$8x = 200$$
$$x = 25$$

$$16x + 20y = 920$$
$$16(25) + 20y = 920$$
$$400 + 20y = 920$$
$$20y = 520$$
$$y = 26$$

The cost of the wool carpet is \$26/yd.

17. Strategy

- Number of 10-speed bicycles to be manufactured: t
  Number of standard model bicycles to be manufactured: s

Cost of materials:

Type	Number	Cost	Total Cost
10-speed	t	35	$35t$
Standard	s	25	$25s$

Cost of labor:

Type	Number	Cost	Total Cost
10-speed	t	40	$40t$
Standard	s	20	$20s$

- The company has budgeted \$1250 for materials. The company has budgeted \$1300 for labor.

$$35t + 25s = 1250$$
$$40t + 20s = 1300$$

Solution

$$35t + 25s = 1250$$
$$40t + 20s = 1300$$

$$4(35t + 25s) = 4(1250)$$
$$-5(40t + 20s) = -5(1300)$$

$$140t + 100s = 5000$$
$$-200t - 100s = -6500$$

$$-60t = -1500$$
$$t = 25$$

The company plans to manufacture twenty-five 10-speed bicycles during the week.

19. Strategy

- Amount of first alloy to be used: x
  Amount of second alloy to be used: y

Gold:

	Amount	Percent	Quantity
1st alloy	x	0.10	$0.10x$
2nd alloy	y	0.30	$0.30y$

Lead:

	Amount	Percent	Quantity
1st alloy	x	0.15	$0.15x$
2nd alloy	y	0.40	$0.40y$

- The resulting alloy contains 60 g of gold. The resulting alloy contains 88 g of lead.

$$0.10x + 0.30y = 60$$
$$0.15x + 0.40y = 88$$

Solution

$$0.10x + 0.30y = 60$$
$$0.15x + 0.40y = 88$$

$$3(0.10x + 0.30y) = 3(60)$$
$$-2(0.15x + 0.40y) = -2(88)$$

$$0.30x + 0.90y = 180$$
$$-0.30x - 0.80y = 176$$

$$0.10y = 4$$
$$y = 40$$

$$0.10x + 0.30y = 60$$
$$0.10x + 0.30(40) = 60$$
$$0.10x + 12 = 60$$
$$0.10x = 48$$
$$x = 480$$

The chemist should use 480 g of the first alloy and 40 g of the second alloy.

21. Strategy

- Cost of the Model II computer: x
  Cost of the Model VI computer: y
  Cost of the Model IX computer: z

First shipment:

	Number	Unit Cost	Value
Model II	4	x	$4x$
Model VI	6	y	$6y$
Model IX	10	z	$10z$

Second shipment:

	Number	Unit Cost	Value
Model II	8	x	$8x$
Model VI	3	y	$3y$
Model IX	5	z	$5z$

Third shipment:

	Number	Unit Cost	Value
Model II	2	x	$2x$
Model VI	9	y	$9y$
Model IX	5	z	$5z$

- The value of the first shipment is \$11,400. The value of the second is \$72,000. The value of the third shipment is \$81,000.

Solution

(1) $4x + 6y + 10z = 11,400$

(2) $8x + 3y + 5z = 72,000$

(3) $2x + 9y + 5z = 81,000$

- Equation (1)
- −2 times Equation (2)

$$4x + 6y + 10z = 114,000$$
$$-16x - 6y - 10z = -144,000$$

(4) $-12x = -30,000$

$$x = 2500$$

- Equation (2)
- −1 times Equation (3)

$$8x + 3y + 5z = 72,000$$
$$-2x - 9y - 5z = -81,000$$

(5) $6x - 6y = -9000$

Substitute 2500 for x in Equation (5).

$$6(2500) - 6y = -9000$$
$$-6y = -24,000$$
$$y = 4000$$

The model VI computer costs \$4000.

23. Strategy

- Number of regular admission tickets: x
  Number of member tickets: y
  Number of student tickets: z

	Number	Unit Cost	Amount
Regular	x	10	$10x$
Member	y	7	$7y$
Student	z	5	$5z$

- 20 more student tickets than regular tickets were sold. The total number of tickets sold was 750. The total receipts for Saturday was $5400.

Solution

(1) $z = x + 20$

(2) $x + y + z = 750$

(3) $10x + 7y + 5z = 5400$

Multiply Equation (2) by –7 and add to Equation (3).

$-7x - 7y - 7z = -5250$

$10x + 7y + 5z = 5400$

(4) $3x - 2z = 150$

Substitute $x + 20$ for z in Equation (4).

$3x - 2(x + 20) = 150$

$3x - 2x - 40 = 150$

$x = 190$

Substitute 190 for x in Equation (1).

$z = 190 + 20$

$z = 210$

Substitute 190 for x and 210 for z in Equation (2).

$190 + y + 210 = 750$

$y = 350$

There were 190 regular tickets, 350 member tickets, and 210 student tickets sold for the Saturday performance.

25. Strategy

- Amount deposited in the 8% account: x
  Amount deposited in the 6% account: y
  Amount deposited in the 4% account: z

	Principal	Rate	Interest
8% account	x	0.08	$0.08x$
6% account	y	0.06	$0.06y$
4% account	z	0.04	$0.04z$

- The amount deposited in the 8% account is twice the amount deposited in the 6% account. The total amount invested is $25,000. The total interest earned is $1520.

Solution

(1) $x = 2y$

(2) $x + y + z = 25{,}000$

(3) $0.08x + 0.06y + 0.04z = 1520$

Substitute $2y$ for x in Equation (2).

$2y + y + z = 25{,}000$

(4) $3y + z = 25{,}000$

Substitute $2y$ for x in Equation (3).

$0.08(2y) + 0.06y + 0.04z = 1520$

(5) $0.22y + 0.04z = 1520$

Solve Equation (4) for z and substitute for z in Equation (5).

$z = 25{,}000 - 3y$

$0.22y + 0.04(25{,}000 - 3y) = 1520$

$0.22y + 1000 - 0.12y = 1520$

$0.10y = 520$

$y = 5200$

Substitute 5200 for y in Equation (4).

$3(5200) + z = 25{,}000$

$z = 9400$

Substitute 5200 for y in Equation (1) and solve for x.

$x = 2(5200)$

$x = 10{,}400$

The investor placed $10,400 in the 8% account, $5200 in the 6% account and $9400 in the 4% account.

Applying the Concepts

27. Strategy • Measure of the smaller angle: n
Measure of the larger angle: m
First relationship: $m + n = 180$
Second relationship: $m = 3n + 40$

Solution Solve for m by substitution.

$$n = 180 - m$$
$$m = 3(180 - m) + 40$$
$$m = 540 - 3m + 40$$
$$4m = 580$$
$$m = 145$$

Substitute m into the equation $m + n = 180$ and solve for n.

$$145 + n = 180$$
$$n = 35$$

The measures of the two angles are 35° and 145°.

29. Strategy • Age of oil painting: x
Age of watercolor: y
First relationship: $x - y = 35$
Second relationship:

$$x + 5 = 2(y - 5)$$
$$x + 5 = 2y - 10$$
$$x = 2y - 15$$

Solution Solve for y by substitution.

$$x - y = 35$$
$$2y - 15 - y = 35$$
$$y - 15 = 35$$
$$y = 50$$

Substitute y into $x - y = 35$ and solve for x.

$$x - 50 = 35$$
$$x = 85$$

The age of the oil painting is 85 years, and the age of the watercolor is 50 years.

31. Strategy • Amount deposited in the 8% account: x
Amount deposited in the 6% account: y
Amount deposited in the 4% account: z

	Amount	Rate	Interest
8% account	x	0.08	$0.08x$
6% account	y	0.06	$0.06y$
4% account	z	0.04	$0.04z$

• The amount in the 8% account is \$1000 more than in the 4% account. The total of the three investments is \$25,000. The total interest earned from the three investments is \$1520.

Solution
(1) $x = 1000 + z$
(2) $x + y + z = 25,000$
(3) $0.08x + 0.06y + 0.04z = 1520$

Substitute $1000 + z$ for x in Equation (2) and in Equation (3).

$$1000 + z + y + z = 25,000$$
(4) $y + 2z = 24,000$

$$0.08(1000 + z) + 0.06y + 0.04z = 1520$$
$$80 + 0.08z + 0.06y + 0.04z = 1520$$
(5) $0.06y + 0.12z = 1440$

Solve Equation (4) for y and substitute for y in Equation (5).

$$y = 24,000 - 2z$$

$$0.06(24,000 - 2z) + 0.12z = 1440$$
$$1440 - 0.12z + 0.12z = 1440$$

The system of equations is dependent. The solutions are the numbers that satisfy the equations $x = z + 1000$ and $y = 24,000 - 2z$.

SECTION 4.5

Objective A Exercises

1. Solve each inequality.

$x - y \geq 3$
$-y \geq 3 - x$
$y \leq -3 + x$

$x + y \leq 5$
$y \leq 5 - x$

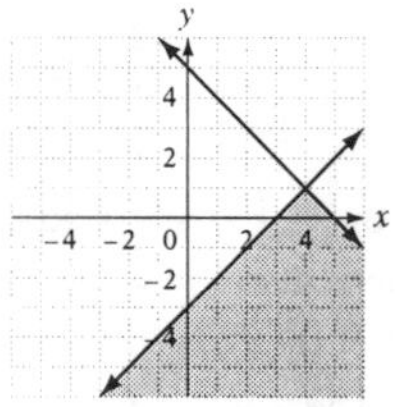

3. Solve each inequality.

$3x - y < 3$
$-y < 3 - 3x$
$y > -3 + 3x$

$2x + y \geq 2$
$y \geq 2 - 2x$

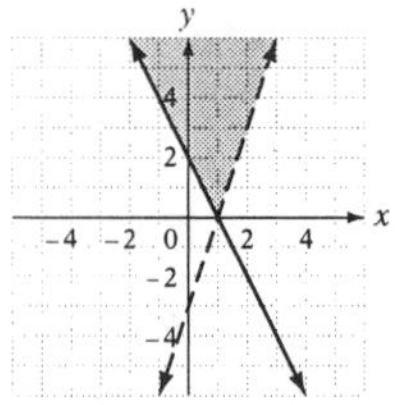

5. Solve each inequality.

$2x + y \geq -2$
$y \geq -2 - 2x$

$6x + 3y \leq 6$
$3y \leq 6 - 6x$
$y \leq 2 - 2x$

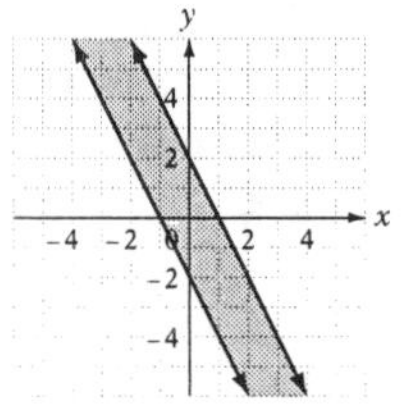

7. Solve each inequality.

$3x - 2y < 6$
$-2y < 6 - 3x$
$y > -3 + \frac{3}{2}x$

$y \leq 3$

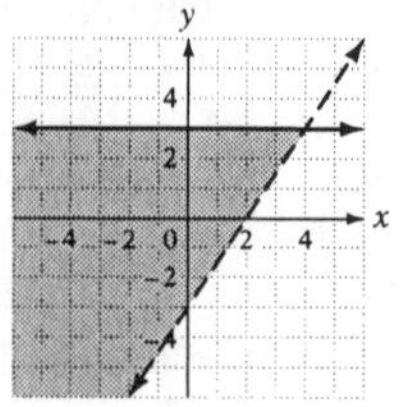

9. Solve each inequality.

$y > 2x - 6$

$x + y < 0$
$y < -x$

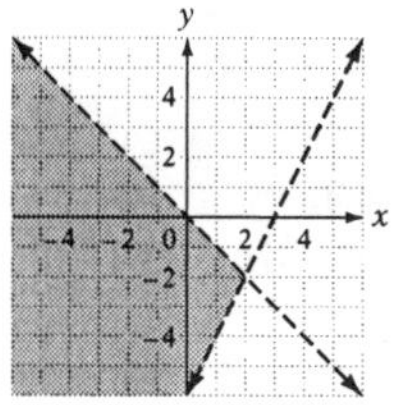

11. Solve each inequality.

$x + 1 \geq 0$
$x \geq -1$

$y - 3 \leq 0$
$y \leq 3$

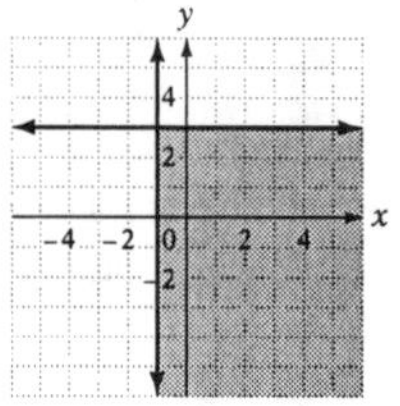

13. Solve each inequality.

$$2x + y \ge 4$$
$$y \ge -2x + 4$$

$$3x - 2y < 6$$
$$-2y < -3x + 6$$
$$y > \frac{3}{2}x - 3$$

$$y \ge -2x + 4$$
$$y > \frac{3}{2}x - 3$$

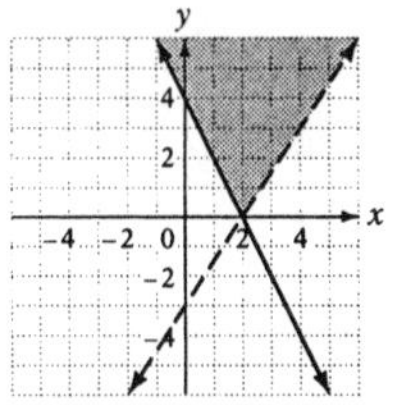

15. Solve each inequality.

$$x - 2y \le 6$$
$$-2y \le -x + 6$$
$$y \ge \frac{1}{2}x - 3$$

$$2x + 3y \le 6$$
$$3y \le -2x + 6$$
$$y \le -\frac{2}{3}x + 2$$

$$y \ge \frac{1}{2}x - 3$$
$$y \le -\frac{2}{3}x + 2$$

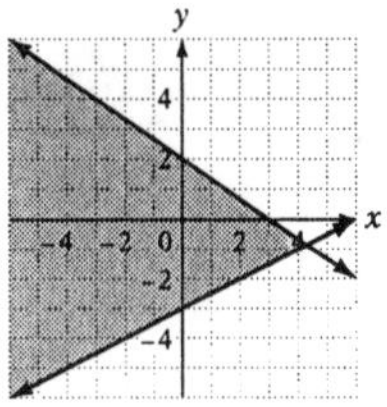

17. Solve each inequality.

$$x - 2y \le 4$$
$$-2y \le -x + 4$$
$$y \ge \frac{1}{2}x - 2$$

$$3x + 2y \le 8$$
$$2y \le -3x + 8$$
$$y \le -\frac{3}{2}x + 4$$

$$y \ge \frac{1}{2}x - 2$$
$$y \le -\frac{3}{2}x + 4$$
$$x > -1$$

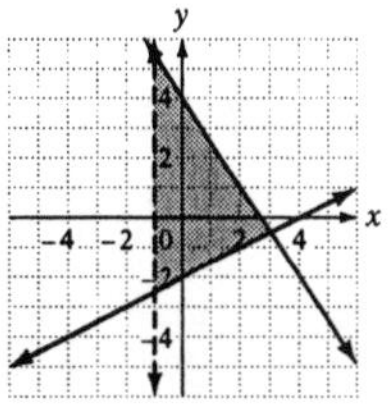

Applying the Concepts

19. Solve each inequality.

$$2x + 3y \le 15$$
$$3y \le -2x + 15$$
$$y \le -\frac{2}{3}x + 5$$

$$3x - y \le 6$$
$$-y \le -3x + 6$$
$$y \ge 3x - 6$$

$$y \le -\frac{2}{3}x + 5$$
$$y \ge 3x - 6$$
$$y \ge 0$$

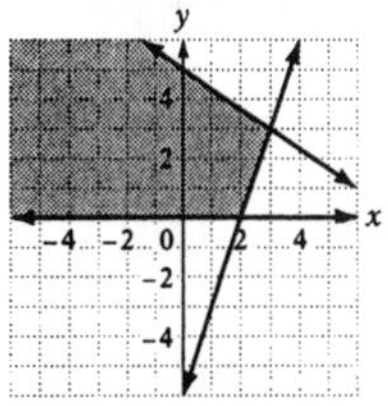

21. Solve each inequality.

$x - y \le 5$
$-y \le 5 - x$
$y \ge -5 + x$

$2x - y \ge 6$
$-y \ge 6 - 2x$
$y \le -6 + 2x$

$y \ge 0$

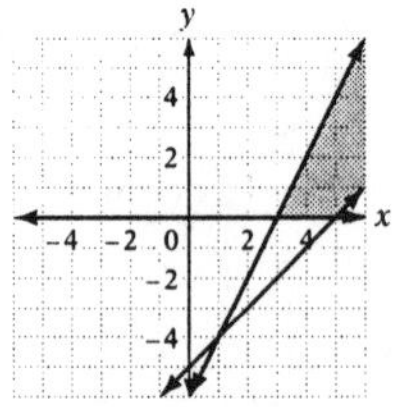

23. Solve each inequality.

$2x - y \le 4$
$-y \le 4 - 2x$
$y \ge -4 + 2x$

$3x + y < 1$
$y < 1 - 3x$

$y \le 0$

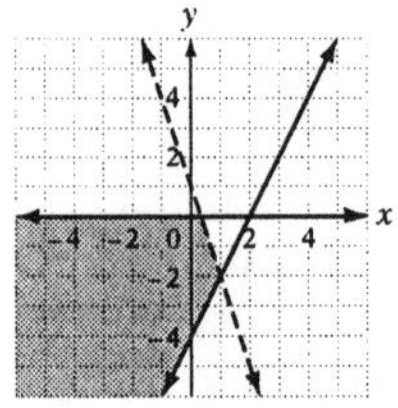

CHAPTER REVIEW

1. (1) $2x - 6y = 15$
(2) $x = 4y + 8$

Substitute $4y + 8$ for x in Equation (1).

$2(4y + 8) - 6y = 15$
$8y + 16 - 6y = 15$
$2y = -1$
$y = -\frac{1}{2}$

Substitute $-\frac{1}{2}$ for y in Equation (2).

$x = 4\left(-\frac{1}{2}\right) + 8$
$x = -2 + 8 = 6$

The solution is $\left(6, -\frac{1}{2}\right)$.

2. (1) $3x + 2y = 2$
(2) $x + y = 3$

Eliminate y. Multiply Equation (2) by -2 and add to Equation (1).

$3x + 2y = 2$
$-2(x + y) = 3(-2)$
$3x + 2y = 2$
$-2x - 2y = -6$

Add the equations.

$x = -4$

Replace x in Equation (2).

$x + y = 3$
$-4 + y = 3$
$y = 7$

The solution is $(-4, 7)$.

3.

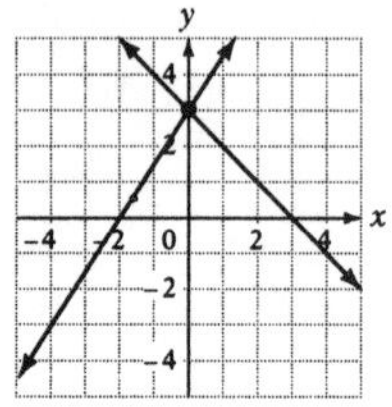

4.

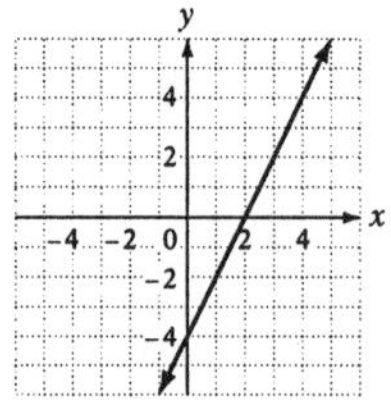

The two equations represent the same line. The solutions are the ordered pairs $(x, 2x - 4)$.

5. (1) $3x + 12y = 18$
(2) $x + 4y = 6$

Solve Equation (2) for x.

$x + 4y = 6$
$x = -4y + 6$

Substitute into Equation (1).

$3x + 12y = 18$
$3(-4y + 6) + 12y = 18$
$-12y + 18 + 12y = 18$
$18 = 18$

This is a true equation. The equations are dependent. The solutions are the ordered pairs $\left(x, -\frac{1}{4}x + \frac{3}{2}\right)$.

6. (1) $5x-15y=30$

(2) $x-3y=6$

Eliminate x. Multiply Equation (2) by –5 and add to Equation (1).

$5x-15y=30$
$-5(x-3y)=6(-5)$

$5x-15y=30$
$-5x+15y=-30$

Add the equations.

$0=0$

This is a true equation. The equations are dependent. The solutions are the ordered pairs $\left(x, \frac{1}{3}x-2\right)$.

7. (1) $3x-4y-2z=17$

(2) $4x-3y+5z=5$

(3) $5x-5y+3z=14$

Eliminate z. Multiply Equation (1) by 3 and Equation (3) by 2. Then add the equations.

$3(3x-4y-2z)=3(17)$
$2(5x-5y+3z)=2(14)$

$9x-12y-6z=51$
$10x-10y+6z=28$

(4) $19x-22y=79$

Multiply Equation (1) by 5 and Equation (2) by 2. Then add the equations.

$5(3x-4y-2z)=5(17)$
$2(4x-3y+5z)=2(5)$

$15x-20y-10z=85$
$8x-6y+10z=10$

(5) $23x-26y=95$

Multiply Equation (4) by 23 and Equation (5) by –19. Then add the equations.

$23(19x-22y)=23(79)$
$-19(23x-26y)=-19(95)$

$437x-506y=1817$
$-437x+494y=-1805$

$-12y=12$
$y=-1$

Replace y by –1 in Equation (4).

$19x-22y=79$
$19x-22(-1)=79$

$19x=57$
$x=3$

Replace x by 3 and y by –1 in Equation (1).

$3x-4y-2z=17$
$3(3)-4(-1)-2z=17$
$9+4-2z=17$
$-2z=4$
$z=-2$

The solution is (3, –1, –2).

8. (1) $3x+y=13$

(2) $2y+3z=5$

(3) $x+2z=11$

Eliminate y. Multiply Equation (1) by –2, then add to Equation (2).

$-2(3x+y)=-2(13)$
$2y+3z=5$

$-6x-2y=-26$
$2y+3z=5$

(4) $-6x+3z=-21$

Multiply Equation (3) by 6. Then add to Equation (4).

$6(x+2z)=6(11)$
$-6x+3z=-21$

$6x+12z=66$
$-6x+3z=-21$

$15z=45$
$z=3$

Replace z by 3 in Equation (3).

$x+2z=11$
$x+2(3)=11$
$x=5$

Replace x by 5 in Equation (1).

$3x+y=13$
$3(5)+y=13$
$y=-2$

The solution is (5, –2, 3).

9. $\begin{vmatrix} 6 & 1 \\ 2 & 5 \end{vmatrix} = 6(5)-2(1)=30-2=28$

10. $\begin{vmatrix} 1 & 5 & -2 \\ -2 & 1 & 4 \\ 4 & 3 & -8 \end{vmatrix} = 1\begin{vmatrix} 1 & 4 \\ 3 & -8 \end{vmatrix} - 5\begin{vmatrix} -2 & 4 \\ 4 & -8 \end{vmatrix} - 2\begin{vmatrix} -2 & 1 \\ 4 & 3 \end{vmatrix}$

$= 1(-8-12)-5(16-16)-2(-6-4)$
$= 1(-20)-5(0)-2(-10)$
$= -20-0+20$
$= 0$

11. $2x-y=7$
$3x+2y=7$

$D=\begin{vmatrix} 2 & -1 \\ 3 & 2 \end{vmatrix}=7$

$D_x=\begin{vmatrix} 7 & -1 \\ 7 & 2 \end{vmatrix}=21$

$D_y=\begin{vmatrix} 2 & 7 \\ 3 & 7 \end{vmatrix}=-7$

$x=\frac{D_x}{D}=\frac{21}{7}=3$

$y=\frac{D_y}{D}=\frac{-7}{7}=-1$

The solution is (3, –1).

12. $3x-4y=10$
$2x+5y=15$

$D=\begin{vmatrix} 3 & -4 \\ 2 & 5 \end{vmatrix}=23$

$D_x=\begin{vmatrix} 10 & -4 \\ 15 & 5 \end{vmatrix}=110$

$D_y=\begin{vmatrix} 3 & 10 \\ 2 & 15 \end{vmatrix}=25$

$x=\frac{D_x}{D}=\frac{110}{23}$

$y=\frac{D_y}{D}=\frac{25}{23}$

The solution is $\left(\frac{110}{23}, \frac{25}{23}\right)$.

13. $x+y+z=0$
$x+2y+3z=5$
$2x+y+2z=3$

$D=\begin{vmatrix} 1 & 1 & 1 \\ 1 & 2 & 3 \\ 2 & 1 & 2 \end{vmatrix}=2$

$D_x=\begin{vmatrix} 0 & 1 & 1 \\ 5 & 2 & 3 \\ 3 & 1 & 2 \end{vmatrix}=-2$

$D_y=\begin{vmatrix} 1 & 0 & 1 \\ 1 & 5 & 3 \\ 2 & 3 & 2 \end{vmatrix}=-6$

$D_z=\begin{vmatrix} 1 & 1 & 0 \\ 1 & 2 & 5 \\ 2 & 1 & 3 \end{vmatrix}=8$

$x=\frac{D_x}{D}=\frac{-2}{2}=-1$

$y=\frac{D_y}{D}=\frac{-6}{2}=-3$

$z=\frac{D_z}{D}=\frac{8}{2}=4$

The solution is (–1, –3, 4).

14. $x+3y+z=6$
$2x+y-z=12$
$x+2y-z=13$

$$D=\begin{vmatrix}1 & 3 & 1\\ 2 & 1 & -1\\ 1 & 2 & -1\end{vmatrix}=7$$

$$D_x=\begin{vmatrix}6 & 3 & 1\\ 12 & 1 & -1\\ 13 & 2 & -1\end{vmatrix}=14$$

$$D_y=\begin{vmatrix}1 & 6 & 1\\ 2 & 12 & -1\\ 1 & 13 & -1\end{vmatrix}=21$$

$$D_z=\begin{vmatrix}1 & 3 & 6\\ 2 & 1 & 12\\ 1 & 2 & 13\end{vmatrix}=-35$$

$$x=\frac{D_x}{D}=\frac{14}{7}=2$$
$$y=\frac{D_y}{D}=\frac{21}{7}=3$$
$$z=\frac{D_z}{D}=\frac{-35}{7}=-5$$

The solution is (2, 3, –5).

15. Solve each inequality.
$x+3y\le 6$
$3y\le 6-x$
$y\le 2-\frac{1}{3}x$

$2x-y\ge 4$
$-y\ge 4-2x$
$y\le -4+2x$

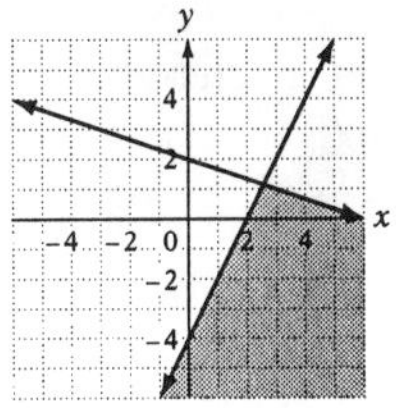

16. Solve each inequality.
$2x+4y\ge 8$
$4y\ge 8-2x$
$y\ge 2-\frac{1}{2}x$

$x+y\le 3$
$y\le 3-x$

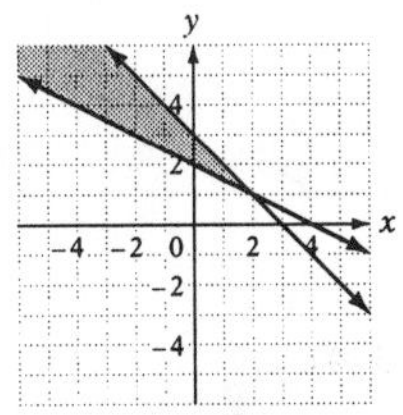

17. Strategy
- Rate of cabin cruiser in calm water: x
  Rate of the current: y

	Rate	Time	Distance
With current	$x+y$	3	$3(x+y)$
Against current	$x-y$	5	$5(x-y)$

- The distance traveled with the current is 60 mi. The distance traveled against the current is 60 mi.
  $3(x+y)=60$
  $5(x-y)=60$

Solution
$3(x+y)=60$
$5(x-y)=60$

$\frac{1}{3}\cdot 3(x+y)=\frac{1}{3}(60)$
$\frac{1}{5}\cdot 5(x-y)=\frac{1}{5}(60)$

$x+y=20$
$x-y=12$

$2x=32$
$x=16$

$x+y=20$
$16+y=20$
$y=4$

The rate of the cabin cruiser in calm water is 16 mph. The rate of the current is 4 mph.

18. Strategy

- Rate of the plane in calm air: p
  Rate of the wind: w

	Rate	Time	Distance
With wind	$p+w$	3	$3(p+w)$
Against wind	$p-w$	4	$4(p-w)$

- The distance traveled with the wind is 600 mi. The distance traveled against the wind is 600 mi.

$$3(p+w)=600$$
$$4(p-w)=600$$

Solution

$$3(p+w)=600$$
$$4(p-w)=600$$

$$\frac{1}{3}\cdot 3(p+w)=\frac{1}{3}(600)$$
$$\frac{1}{4}\cdot 4(p-w)=\frac{1}{4}(600)$$

$$p+w=200$$
$$p-w=150$$

$$2p=350$$
$$p=175$$

$$p+w=200$$
$$175+w=200$$
$$w=25$$

The rate of the plane in calm air is 175 mph. The rate of the wind is 25 mph.

19. Strategy

- Number of children's tickets sold Friday: x
  Number of adult's tickets sold Friday: y

	Amount	Rate	Quantity
Children	x	5	$5x$
Adults	y	8	$8y$

Saturday:

	Amount	Rate	Quantity
Children	$3x$	5	$5(3x)$
Adults	$\frac{1}{2}y$	8	$8(\frac{1}{2})y$

- The total receipts for Friday were \$2500. The total receipts for Saturday were \$2500.

$$5x+8y=2500$$
$$5(3x)+8\left(\frac{1}{2}y\right)=2500$$

Solution

$$5x+8y=2500$$
$$15x+4y=2500$$

$$5x+8y=2500$$
$$-2(15x+4y)=-2(2500)$$

$$5x+8y=2500$$
$$-30x-8y=-5000$$

$$-25x=-2500$$
$$x=100$$

The number of children attending on Friday was 100.

20. Strategy

- The amount invested at 3%: x
  The amount invested at 7%: y

	Principal	Rate	Interest
Amount at 3%	x	0.03	$0.03x$
Amount at 7%	y	0.07	$0.07y$

- The total amount invested is \$20,000. The total annual interest earned is \$1200.

Solution (1) $x+y=20,000$

(2) $0.03x+0.07y=1200$

Multiply Equation (1) by –0.07 and add to Equation (2).

$$-0.07x-0.07y=-1400$$
$$0.03x+0.07y=1200$$
$$-0.04x=-200$$
$$x=5000$$

Substitute 5000 for x in Equation (1).

$$5000+y=20,000$$
$$y=15,000$$

The amount invested at 3% is \$5000.
The amount invested at 7% is \$15,000.

CHAPTER TEST

1.

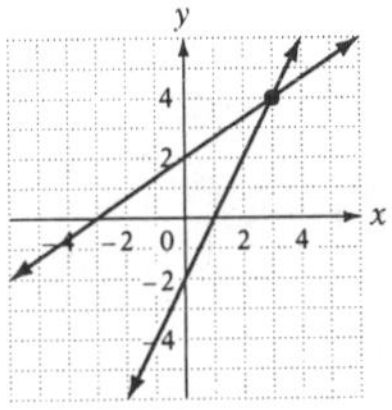

The solution is (3, 4).

2.

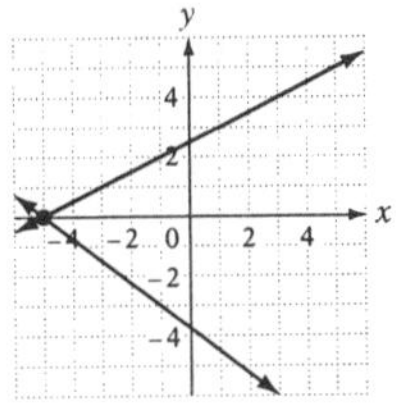

The solution is (–5, 0).

3. Solve each inequality.

$$2x-y<3$$
$$-y<3-2x$$
$$y>2x-3$$

$$4x+3y<11$$
$$3y<-4x+11$$
$$y<-\frac{4}{3}x+\frac{11}{3}$$

$$y>2x-3$$
$$y<-\frac{4}{3}x+\frac{11}{3}$$

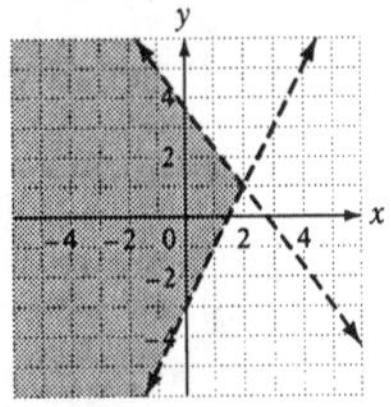

4. Solve each inequality.

$$x+y>2$$
$$y>2-x$$

$$2x-y<-1$$
$$-y<-1-2x$$
$$y>1+2x$$

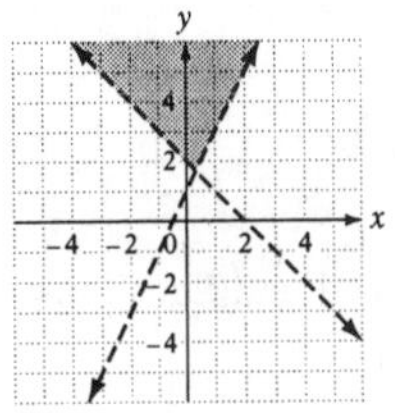

5. (1) $3x+2y=4$

(2) $x=2y-1$

Substitute $2y-1$ for x in Equation (1).

$$3(2y-1)+2y=4$$
$$6y-3+2y=4$$
$$8y=7$$
$$y=\frac{7}{8}$$

Substitute into Equation (2).

$$x=2y-1$$
$$x=2\left(\frac{7}{8}\right)-1$$
$$x=\frac{7}{4}-1=\frac{3}{4}$$

The solution is $\left(\frac{3}{4},\frac{7}{8}\right)$.

6. (1) $5x+2y=-23$

(2) $2x+y=-10$

Solve Equation (2) for y.

$2x+y=-10$

$y=-2x-10$

Substitute $-2x-10$ for y in Equation (1).

$5x+2y=-23$

$5x+2(-2x-10)=-23$

$5x-4x-20=-23$

$x-20=-23$

$x=-3$

Substitute into Equation (2).

$2x+y=-10$

$2(-3)+y=-10$

$-6+y=-10$

$y=-4$

The solution is $(-3, -4)$.

7. (1) $y=3x-7$

(2) $y=-2x+3$

Substitute Equation (2) into Equation (1).

$-2x+3=3x-7$

$-5x+3=-7$

$-5x=-10$

$x=2$

Substitute into Equation (1).

$y=3x-7$

$y=3(2)-7=6-7=-1$

The solution is $(2, -1)$.

8. (1) $3x+4y=-2$

(2) $2x+5y=1$

Multiply Equation (1) by -2 and Equation (2) by 3. Add the new equations.

$-2(3x+4y)=-2(-2)$

$3(2x+5y)=3(1)$

$-6x-8y=4$

$6x+15y=3$

$7y=7$

$y=1$

Substitute into Equation (2).

$2x+5y=1$

$2x+5(1)=1$

$2x+5=1$

$2x=-4$

$x=-2$

The solution is $(-2, 1)$.

9. (1) $4x-6y=5$

(2) $6x-9y=4$

Multiply Equation (1) by -3.

Multiply Equation (2) by 2. Add the new equations.

$-3(4x-6y)=-3(5)$

$2(6x-9y)=2(4)$

$-12x+18y=-15$

$12x-18y=8$

$0=-7$

This is not a true equation. The system of equations is inconsistent and therefore has no solution.

10. (1) $3x-y=2x+y-1$

(2) $5x+2y=y+6$

Write the equation in the form $Ax + By = C$.

(3) $x-2y=-1$

(4) $5x+y=6$

Multiply Equation (4) by 2 and add to Equation (3).

$x-2y=-1$

$2(5x+y)=2(6)$

$x-2y=-1$

$10x+2y=12$

$11x=11$

$x=1$

Substitute into Equation (4).

$5x+y=6$

$5(1)+y=6$

$y=1$

The solution is $(1, 1)$.

11. (1) $2x+4y-z=3$
(2) $x+2y+z=5$
(3) $4x+8y-2z=7$
Eliminate z. Add Equations (1) and (2).
$2x+4y-z=3$
$x+2y+z=5$

(4) $3x+6y=8$
Multiply Equation (2) by 2 and add to Equation (3).
$2(x+2y+z)=2(5)$
$4x+8y-2z=7$

$2x+4y+2z=10$
$4x+8y-2z=7$

(5) $6x+12y=17$
Multiply Equation (4) by –2 and add to Equation (5).
$-2(3x+6y)=-2(8)$
$6x+12y=17$

$-6x-12y=-16$
$6x+12y=17$
$0=1$
This is not a true equation. The system of equations is inconsistent and therefore has no solution.

12. (1) $x-y-z=5$
(2) $2x+z=2$
(3) $3y-2z=1$
Multiply Equation (1) by 3 and add to Equation (3).
$3(x-y-z)=3(5)$
$3y-2z=1$

$3x-3y-3z=15$
$3y-2z=1$

(4) $3x-5z=16$
Multiply Equation (2) by 5 and add to Equation (4).
$5(2x+z)=(2)5$
$3x-5z=16$

$10x+5z=10$
$3x-5z=16$

$13x=26$
$x=2$
Substitute into Equation (4).
$3x-5z=16$
$3(2)-5z=16$
$6-5z=16$
$-5z=10$
$z=-2$
Substitute into Equation (3).
$3y-2z=1$
$3y-2(-2)=1$
$3y+4=1$
$3y=-3$
$y=-1$
The solution is (2, –1, –2).

13. $\begin{vmatrix} 3 & -1 \\ -2 & 4 \end{vmatrix} = 3(4)-(-2)(-1)=12-2=10$

14. $\begin{vmatrix} 1 & -2 & 3 \\ 3 & 1 & 1 \\ 2 & -1 & -2 \end{vmatrix} = 1\begin{vmatrix} 1 & 1 \\ -1 & -2 \end{vmatrix} - (-2)\begin{vmatrix} 3 & 1 \\ 2 & -2 \end{vmatrix} + 3\begin{vmatrix} 3 & 1 \\ 2 & -1 \end{vmatrix}$
$=1(-2-(-1))+2(-6-2)+3(-3-2)$
$=1(-2+1)+2(-8)+3(-5)$
$=-1-16-15$
$=-32$

15. $x - y = 3$
$2x + y = -4$

$$D = \begin{vmatrix} 1 & -1 \\ 2 & 1 \end{vmatrix} = 3$$

$$D_x = \begin{vmatrix} 3 & -1 \\ -4 & 1 \end{vmatrix} = -1$$

$$D_y = \begin{vmatrix} 1 & 3 \\ 2 & -4 \end{vmatrix} = -10$$

$$x = \frac{D_x}{D} = -\frac{1}{3}$$

$$y = \frac{D_y}{D} = \frac{-10}{3}$$

The solution is $\left(-\frac{1}{3}, -\frac{10}{3}\right)$.

16. $5x + 2y = 9$
$3x + 5y = -7$

$$D = \begin{vmatrix} 5 & 2 \\ 3 & 5 \end{vmatrix} = 19$$

$$D_x = \begin{vmatrix} 9 & 2 \\ -7 & 5 \end{vmatrix} = 59$$

$$D_y = \begin{vmatrix} 5 & 9 \\ 3 & -7 \end{vmatrix} = -62$$

$$x = \frac{D_x}{D} = \frac{59}{19}$$

$$y = \frac{D_y}{D} = \frac{-62}{19}$$

The solution is $\left(\frac{59}{16}, -\frac{62}{19}\right)$.

17. $x - y + z = 2$
$2x - y - z = 1$
$x + 2y - 3z = -4$

$$D = \begin{vmatrix} 1 & -1 & 1 \\ 2 & -1 & -1 \\ 1 & 2 & -3 \end{vmatrix} = 5$$

$$D_x = \begin{vmatrix} 2 & -1 & 1 \\ 1 & -1 & -1 \\ -4 & 2 & -3 \end{vmatrix} = 1$$

$$D_y = \begin{vmatrix} 1 & 2 & 1 \\ 2 & 1 & -1 \\ 1 & -4 & -3 \end{vmatrix} = -6$$

$$D_z = \begin{vmatrix} 1 & -1 & 2 \\ 2 & -1 & 1 \\ 1 & 2 & -4 \end{vmatrix} = 3$$

$$x = \frac{D_x}{D} = \frac{1}{5}$$

$$y = \frac{D_y}{D} = -\frac{6}{5}$$

$$z = \frac{D_z}{D} = \frac{3}{5}$$

The solution is $\left(\frac{1}{5}, -\frac{6}{5}, \frac{3}{5}\right)$.

18. Strategy • Rate of plane in calm air: x
Rate of wind: y

	Rate	Time	Distance
With wind	$x+y$	2	$2(x+y)$
Against wind	$x-y$	2.8	$2.8(x-y)$

• The distance traveled with the wind is 350 mi. The distance traveled against the wind is 350 mi.

$$2(x+y)=350$$
$$2.8(x-y)=350$$

Solution

$$2(x+y)=350$$
$$2.8(x-y)=350$$

$$\frac{1}{2}\cdot 2(x+y)=\frac{1}{2}\cdot 350$$
$$\frac{1}{2.8}\cdot 2.8(x-y)=\frac{1}{2.8}\cdot 350$$

$$x+y=175$$
$$x-y=125$$

$$2x=300$$
$$x=150$$

$$x+y=175$$
$$150+y=175$$
$$y=25$$

The rate of the plane in calm air is 150 mph. The rate of the wind is 25 mph.

19. Strategy • Cost per yard of cotton: x
Cost per yard of wool: y
First purchase:

	Amount	Rate	Total Value
Cotton	60	x	$60x$
Wool	90	y	$90y$

Second purchase:

	Amount	Rate	Total Value
Cotton	80	x	$80x$
Wool	20	y	$20y$

• The total cost of the first purchase was \$900. The total cost of the second purchase was \$500.

$$60x+90y=900$$
$$80x+20y=500$$

Solution

$$-4(60x+90y)=-4(900)$$
$$3(80x+20y)=3(500)$$

$$-240x-360y=-3600$$
$$240x+60y=1500$$

$$-300y=-2100$$
$$y=7$$

$$60x+90(7)=900$$
$$60x+630=900$$
$$60x=270$$
$$x=4.5$$

The cost per yard of cotton is \$4.50. The cost per yard of wool is \$7.00.

20. Strategy • Amount invested at 2.7%: x
Amount invested at 5.1%: y

	Principal	Rate	Interest
Amount at 2.7%	x	0.027	$0.027x$
Amount at 5.1%	y	0.051	$0.051y$

• The total amount invested is \$15,000. The total annual interest earned is \$549.

Solution
(1) $x + y = 15{,}000$
(2) $0.027x + 0.051y = 549$

Multiply Equation (1) by –0.051 and add to Equation (2).

$$\begin{aligned} -0.051x - 0.051y &= -765 \\ 0.027x + 0.051y &= 549 \\ -0.024x &= -216 \\ x &= 9000 \end{aligned}$$

Substitute 9000 for x in Equation (1) and solve for y.

$$\begin{aligned} 9000 + y &= 15{,}000 \\ y &= 6000 \end{aligned}$$

The amount invested at 2.7% is \$9000.
The amount invested at 5.1% is \$6000.

CUMULATIVE REVIEW

1.
$$\begin{aligned} \frac{3}{2}x - \frac{3}{8} + \frac{1}{4}x &= \frac{7}{12}x - \frac{5}{6} \\ 24\left(\frac{3}{2}x - \frac{3}{8} + \frac{1}{4}x\right) &= 24\left(\frac{7}{12}x - \frac{5}{6}\right) \\ 36x - 9 + 6x &= 14x - 20 \\ 42x - 9 &= 14x - 20 \\ 28x - 9 &= -20 \\ 28x &= -11 \\ x &= -\frac{11}{28} \end{aligned}$$

The solution is $-\frac{11}{28}$.

2. $(x_1, y_1) = (2, -1), (x_2, y_2) = (3, 4)$

$$\begin{aligned} m = \frac{y_2 - y_1}{x_2 - x_1} &= \frac{4 - (-1)}{3 - 2} = \frac{5}{1} = 5 \\ y - y_1 &= m(x - x_1) \\ y - (-1) &= 5(x - 2) \\ y + 1 &= 5x - 10 \\ y &= 5x - 11 \end{aligned}$$

The equation of the line is $y = 5x - 11$.

3.
$$\begin{aligned} &3[x - 2(5 - 2x) - 4x] + 6 \\ &= 3(x - 10 + 4x - 4x) + 6 \\ &= 3(x - 10) + 6 \\ &= 3x - 30 + 6 \\ &= 3x - 24 \end{aligned}$$

4. $a + bc \div 2;\ a = 4,\ b = 8,\ c = -2$

$$\begin{aligned} 4 + 8(-2) \div 2 &= 4 - 16 \div 2 \\ &= 4 - 8 \\ &= -4 \end{aligned}$$

5. $2x - 3 < 9$ or $5x - 1 < 4$
Solve each inequality.

$$\begin{aligned} 2x - 3 &< 9 & \qquad 5x - 1 &< 4 \\ 2x &< 12 & 5x &< 5 \\ x &< 6 \quad \text{or} & x &< 1 \end{aligned}$$

$x < 6 \cup x < 1 = \{x|x < 6\}$.

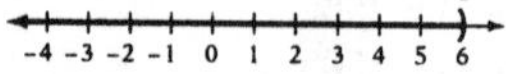

6.
$$\begin{aligned} |x - 2| - 4 &< 2 \\ |x - 2| &< 6 \\ -6 < x - 2 &< 6 \\ -6 + 2 < x - 2 + 2 &< 6 + 2 \\ -4 < x &< 8 \end{aligned}$$
$\{x|-4 < x < 8\}$

7. $|2x - 3| > 5$
Solve each inequality.

$$\begin{aligned} 2x - 3 < -5 &\quad \text{or} \quad 2x - 3 > 5 \\ 2x < -2 &\quad \text{or} \quad 2x > 8 \\ x < -1 &\quad \text{or} \quad x > 4 \end{aligned}$$

This is the set $\{x|x < -1\} \cup \{x|x > 4\}$ or $\{x|x < -1 \text{ or } x > 4\}$.

8.
$$\begin{aligned} f(x) &= 3x^3 - 2x^2 + 1 \\ f(-3) &= 3(-3)^3 - 2(-3)^2 + 1 \\ f(-3) &= 3 \cdot (-27) - 2(9) + 1 \\ f(-3) &= -98 \end{aligned}$$

9. The range is the set of numbers found by plugging in the set of numbers in the domain.

$$\begin{aligned} f(-2) &= 3(-2)^2 - 2(-2) = 16 \\ f(-1) &= 3(-1)^2 - 2(-1) = 5 \\ f(0) &= 3(0)^2 - 2(0) = 0 \\ f(1) &= 3(1)^2 - 2(1) = 1 \\ f(2) &= 3(2)^2 - 2(2) = 8 \end{aligned}$$

The range is {0, 1, 5, 8, 16}.

10.
$$\begin{aligned} F(x) &= x^2 - 3 \\ F(2) &= 2^2 - 3 = 1 \end{aligned}$$

11.
$$\begin{aligned} f(x) &= 3x - 4 \\ f(2 + h) &= 3(2 + h) - 4 \\ &= 6 + 3h - 4 \\ &= 2 + 3h \\ f(2) &= 3(2) - 4 = 2 \\ f(2 + h) - f(2) &= 2 + 3h - 2 \\ &= 3h \end{aligned}$$

12. $\{x|x \le 2\} \cap \{x|x > -3\}$

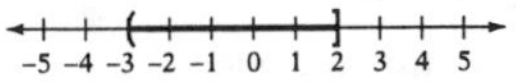

13. Slope $= -\dfrac{2}{3}$; Point = (–2, 3)

$$y-3 = \frac{-2}{3}[x-(-2)]$$
$$y-3 = \frac{-2}{3}(x+2)$$
$$y = \frac{-2}{3}x - \frac{4}{3} + 3$$
$$y = -\frac{2}{3}x + \frac{5}{3}$$

14. The slope of the line $2x - 3y = 7$ is found by rearranging the equation as follows:

$$-3y = 7 - 2x$$
$$y = \frac{-7}{3} + \frac{2}{3}x$$

Slope $= \dfrac{2}{3}$

The line is found using

$$y-2 = -\frac{3}{2}[x-(-1)]$$
$$y = -\frac{3}{2}(x+1)+2$$
$$y = -\frac{3}{2}x - \frac{3}{2} + 2$$
$$y = -\frac{3}{2}x + \frac{1}{2}$$

15. The distance between points is

$\sqrt{(x_2-x_1)^2+(y_2-y_1)^2}$.

$$\sqrt{[2-(-4)^2]+(0-2)^2} = \sqrt{6^2+(-2)^2}$$
$$= \sqrt{36+4}$$
$$= \sqrt{40} = 2\sqrt{10} \approx 6.32$$

16. The midpoint is found using $\left(\dfrac{x_1+x_2}{2}, \dfrac{y_1+y_2}{2}\right)$.

$$\text{Midpoint} = \left(\frac{-4+3}{2}, \frac{3+5}{2}\right)$$
$$= \left(-\frac{1}{2}, 4\right)$$

17. $2x - 5y = 10$

$$-5y = 10 - 2x$$
$$y = -2 + \frac{2}{5}x$$

The y-intercept is –2.

The slope is $\dfrac{2}{5}$.

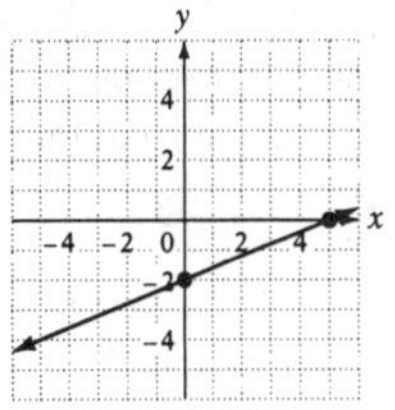

18. $3x - 4y \ge 8$

$$-4y \ge 8 - 3x$$
$$y \le -2 + \frac{3}{4}x$$

The y-intercept is –2.

The slope is $\dfrac{3}{4}$.

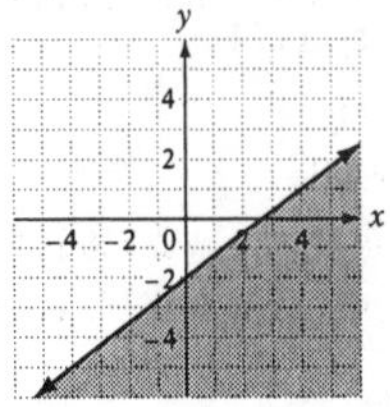

19.

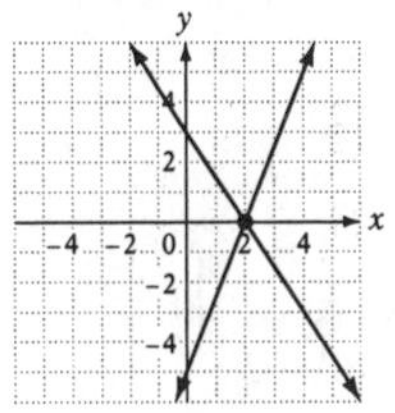

The solution is (2, 0).

20. Solve each inequality for y.

$3x - 2y \ge 4$

$$-2y \ge 4 - 3x$$
$$y \le -2 + \frac{3}{2}x$$

$x + y < 3$

$$y < 3 - x$$

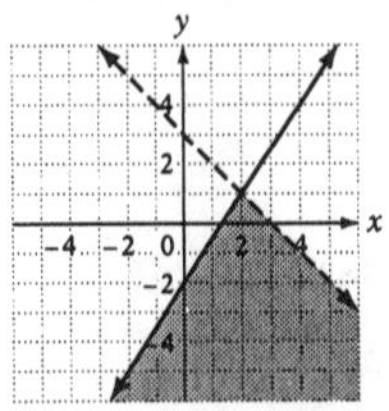

21. (1) $3x+2z=1$

(2) $2y-z=1$

(3) $x+2y=1$

Multiply Equation (2) by –1 and add to Equation (3).

$-1(2y-z)=-1(1)$
$x+2y=1$

$-2y+z=-1$
$x+2y=1$

(4) $x+z=0$

Multiply Equation (4) by –2 and add to Equation (1).

$(-2)(x+z)=-2(0)$
$3x+2z=1$

$-2x-2z=0$
$3x+2z=1$

$x=1$

Substitute 1 for x in Equation (4).

$x+z=0$
$1+z=0$
$z=-1$

Substitute 1 for x in Equation (4).

$x+2y=1$
$1+2y=1$
$2y=0$
$y=0$

The solution is (1, 0, –1).

22. $$\begin{vmatrix}2 & -5 & 1\\ 3 & 1 & 2\\ 6 & -1 & 4\end{vmatrix}=2\begin{vmatrix}1 & 2\\ -1 & 4\end{vmatrix}-3\begin{vmatrix}-5 & 1\\ -1 & 4\end{vmatrix}+6\begin{vmatrix}-5 & 1\\ 1 & 2\end{vmatrix}$$
$$=2(4+2)-3(-20+1)+6(-10-1)$$
$$=2(6)-3(-19)+6(-11)$$
$$=12+57-66$$
$$=3$$

23. $4x-3y=17$
$3x-2y=12$

$$D=\begin{vmatrix}4 & -3\\ 3 & -2\end{vmatrix}=4(-2)-3(-3)=1$$

$$D_x=\begin{vmatrix}17 & -3\\ 12 & -2\end{vmatrix}=17(-2)-12(-3)=2$$

$$D_y=\begin{vmatrix}4 & 17\\ 3 & 12\end{vmatrix}=4(12)-3(17)=-3$$

$$x=\frac{D_x}{D}=\frac{2}{1}=2$$

$$y=\frac{D_y}{D}=\frac{-3}{1}=-3$$

The solution is (2, –3).

24. (1) $3x-2y=7$

(2) $y=2x-1$

Solve by the substitution method.

$3x-2(2x-1)=7$
$3x-4x+2=7$
$-x+2=7$
$-x=5$
$x=-5$

Substitute –5 for x in Equation (2).

$y=2x-1$
$y=2(-5)-1=-10-1=-11$

The solution is (–5, –11).

25. Strategy

- The unknown number of quarters: x
  The unknown number of dimes: $3x$
  The unknown number of nickels: $40-(x+3x)$

	Amount	Rate	Total Value
Quarters	x	25	$25x$
Dimes	$3x$	10	$10(3x)$
Nickels	$40-4x$	5	$5(40-4x)$

- The sum of the total values of the denomination is \$4.10 (410 cents).

$25x+10(3x)+5(40-4x)=410$

Solution

$25x+10(3x)+5(40-4x)=410$
$25x+30x+200-20x=410$
$35x+200=410$
$35x=210$
$x=6$

$40-4x=40-24=16$

There are 16 nickels in the purse.

26. Strategy

- The unknown amount of pure water: x

	Amount	Percent	Quantity
Water	x	0	$0\cdot x$
4%	100	0.04	100(0.04)
2.5%	$100+x$	0.025	$(100+x)(0.025)$

- The sum of the quantities before mixing equals the quantity after mixing.

$0\cdot x+100(0.04)=(100+x)0.025$

Solution

$0\cdot x+100(0.04)=(100+x)0.025$
$0+4=2.5+0.025x$
$1.5=0.025x$
$60=x$

The amount of water that should be added is 60 ml.

27. Strategy • The rate of the plane in calm air: x
The rate of the wind: y

	Rate	Time	Distance
With wind	$x+y$	2	$2(x+y)$
Against wind	$x-y$	3	$3(x-y)$

• The distance traveled with the wind is 150 mi. The distance traveled against the wind is 150 mi.

$$2(x+y)=150$$
$$3(x-y)=150$$

Solution

$$2(x+y)=150$$
$$3(x-y)=150$$

$$\frac{1}{2}\cdot 2(x+y)=\frac{1}{2}\cdot 150$$
$$\frac{1}{3}\cdot 3(x-y)=\frac{1}{3}\cdot 150$$

$$x+y=75$$
$$x-y=50$$

$$2x=125$$
$$x=62.5$$

$$x+y=75$$
$$62.5+y=75$$
$$y=12.5$$

The rate of the wind is 12.5 mph.

28. Strategy • Cost per pound of hamburger: x
Cost per pound of steak: y
First purchase:

	Amount	Percent	Quantity
Hamburger	100	x	$100x$
Steak	50	y	$50y$

Second purchase:

	Amount	Percent	Quantity
Hamburger	150	x	$150x$
Steak	100	y	$100y$

• The total cost of the first purchase is \$270. The total cost of the second purchase is \$480.

$$100x+50y=270$$
$$150x+100y=480$$

Solution

$$100x+50y=270$$
$$150x+100y=480$$

$$3(100x+50y)=3(270)$$
$$-2(150x+100y)=-2(480)$$

$$300x+150y=810$$
$$-300x-200y=-960$$

$$-50y=-150$$
$$y=3$$

The cost per pound of steak is \$3.

29. Strategy • Let M be the number of ohms, T the tolerance, and r the given amount of the resistor. Find the tolerance and solve $|M-r|\le T$ for M.

Solution $T=0.15\cdot 12{,}000=1800$ ohms

$$|M-12{,}000|\le 1800$$
$$-1800\le M-12{,}000\le 1800$$
$$-1800+12{,}000\le M-12{,}000+12{,}000\le 1800+12{,}000$$
$$10{,}200\le M\le 13{,}800$$

The lower and upper limits of the resistor are 10,200 ohms and 13,800 ohms.

30. The slope of the line is $\frac{5000-1000}{100-0}=\frac{4000}{100}=40$. The slope represents the marginal income or the income generated per number of sales.

Chapter 5: Polynomials

SECTION 5.1

Objective A Exercises

1. $(ab^3)(a^3b) = a^4b^4$

3. $(9xy^2)(-2x^2y^2) = -18x^3y^4$

5. $(x^2y^4)^4 = x^8y^{16}$

7. $(-3x^2y^3)^4 = (-3)^4x^8y^{12} = 81x^8y^{12}$

9. $(3^3a^5b^3)^2 = 3^6a^{10}b^6 = 729a^{10}b^6$

11. $(x^2y^2)(xy^3)^3 = (x^2y^2)(x^3y^9) = x^5y^{11}$

13. $[(3x)^3]^2 = (3x)^6 = 3^6x^6 = 729x^6$

15. $[(ab)^3]^6 = (ab)^{18} = a^{18}b^{18}$

17. $[(2xy)^3]^4 = (2xy)^{12} = 2^{12}x^{12}y^{12} = 4096x^{12}y^{12}$

19. $[(2a^4b^3)^3]^2 = (2a^4b^3)^6 = 2^6a^{24}b^{18} = 64a^{24}b^{18}$

21. $x^n \cdot x^{n+1} = x^{n+n+1} = x^{2n+1}$

23. $y^{3n} \cdot y^{3n-2} = y^{3n+3n-2} = y^{6n-2}$

25. $(a^{n-3})^{2n} = a^{(n-3)2n} = a^{2n^2-6n}$

27. $(x^{3n+2})^5 = x^{(3n+2)5} = x^{15n+10}$

29. $(2xy)(-3x^2yz)(x^2y^3z^3) = -6x^5y^5z^4$

31. $(3b^5)(2ab^2)(-2ab^2c^2) = -12a^2b^9c^2$

33. $(-2x^2y^3z)(3x^2yz^4) = -6x^4y^4z^5$

35. $$\begin{aligned}(-3ab^3)^3(-2^2a^2b)^2 &= [(-3)^3a^3b^9][(-2^2)^2a^4b^2]\\ &= (-27a^3b^9)(16a^4b^2)\\ &= -432a^7b^{11}\end{aligned}$$

37. $$\begin{aligned}(-2ab^2)(-3a^4b^5)^3 &= (-2ab^2)[(-3)^3a^{12}b^{15}]\\ &= (-2ab^2)(-27a^{12}b^{15})\\ &= 54a^{13}b^{17}\end{aligned}$$

Objective B Exercises

39. $\frac{1}{3^{-5}} = 3^5 = 243$

41. $\frac{1}{y^{-3}} = y^3$

43. $\frac{a^3}{4b^{-2}} = \frac{a^3b^2}{4}$

45. $xy^{-4} = \frac{x}{y^4}$

47. $\frac{1}{2x^0} = \frac{1}{2}$

49. $\frac{-3^{-2}}{(2y)^0} = \frac{-1}{3^2} = -\frac{1}{9}$

51. $\frac{y^{-2}}{y^6} = y^{-2-6} = y^{-8} = \frac{1}{y^8}$

53. $(x^3y^5)^{-2} = x^{-6}y^{-10} = \frac{1}{x^6y^{10}}$

55. $\frac{x^4y^3}{x^{-1}y^{-2}} = x^5y^5$

57. $\frac{a^6b^{-4}}{a^{-2}b^5} = a^8b^{-9} = \frac{a^8}{b^9}$

59. $$\begin{aligned}(3a)^{-3}(9a^{-1})^{-2} &= (3a)^{-3}(3^2a^{-1})^{-2}\\ &= (3^{-3}a^{-3})(3^{-4}a^2)\\ &= 3^{-7}a^{-1}\\ &= \frac{1}{3^7a} = \frac{1}{2187a}\end{aligned}$$

61. $$\begin{aligned}(x^{-1}y^2)^{-3}(x^2y^{-4})^{-3} &= (x^3y^{-6})(x^{-6}y^{12})\\ &= x^{-3}y^6 = \frac{y^6}{x^3}\end{aligned}$$

63. $\frac{x^3y^6}{x^6y^2} = \frac{y^4}{x^3}$

65. $\frac{-6x^2y}{12x^4y} = -\frac{1}{2x^2}$

67. $\frac{-3ab^2}{(9a^2b^4)^3} = \frac{-3ab^2}{9^3a^6b^{12}} = \frac{-3ab^2}{729a^6b^{12}} = -\frac{1}{243a^5b^{10}}$

69. $\left(\frac{12x^3y^2z}{18xy^3z^4}\right)^4 = \left(\frac{2x^2}{3yz^3}\right)^4 = \frac{2^4x^8}{3^4y^4z^{12}} = \frac{16x^8}{81y^4z^{12}}$

71. $\frac{(3a^2b)^3}{(-6ab^3)^2} = \frac{3^3a^6b^3}{(-6)^2a^2b^6} = \frac{27a^6b^3}{36a^2b^6} = \frac{3a^4}{4b^3}$

73. $\frac{(-3a^2b^3)^2}{(-2ab^4)^3} = \frac{(-3)^2a^4b^6}{(-2)^3a^3b^{12}} = \frac{9a^4b^6}{-8a^3b^{12}} = \frac{-9a}{8b^6}$

75. $\frac{(-8x^2y^2)^4}{(16x^3y^7)^2} = \frac{(-8)^4x^8y^8}{16^2x^6y^{14}} = \frac{4096x^8y^8}{256x^6y^{14}} = \frac{16x^2}{y^6}$

77. $\frac{b^{6n}}{b^{10n}}=\frac{1}{b^{10n-6n}}=\frac{1}{b^{4n}}$

79. $\frac{y^{2n}}{-y^{8n}}=-\frac{1}{y^{8n-2n}}=-\frac{1}{y^{6n}}$

81. $\frac{y^{3n+2}}{y^{2n+4}}=y^{3n+2-(2n+4)}=y^{3n+2-2n-4}=y^{n-2}$

83. $\frac{x^n y^{3n}}{x^n y^{5n}}=\frac{1}{y^{5n-3n}}=\frac{1}{y^{2n}}$

85. $\frac{x^{2n-1}y^{n-3}}{x^{n+4}y^{n+3}}=x^{2n-1-(n+4)}y^{n-3-(n+3)}$

$=x^{2n-1-n-4}y^{n-3-n-3}$

$=x^{n-5}y^{-6}$

$=\frac{x^{n-5}}{y^6}$

87. $\left(\frac{9ab^{-2}}{8a^{-2}b}\right)^{-2}\left(\frac{3a^{-2}b}{2a^2b^{-2}}\right)^3$

$=\left(\frac{9a^3b^{-3}}{8}\right)^{-2}\left(\frac{3a^{-4}b^3}{2}\right)^3$

$=\frac{9^{-2}a^{-6}b^6}{8^{-2}}\cdot\frac{3^3a^{-12}b^9}{2^3}$

$=\frac{8^2\cdot 3^3a^{-18}b^{15}}{9^2\cdot 2^3}$

$=\frac{64\cdot 27b^{15}}{81\cdot 8a^{18}}$

$=\frac{8b^{15}}{3a^{18}}$

Objective C Exercises

89. $0.00000467=4.67\times 10^{-6}$

91. $0.00000000017=1.7\times 10^{-10}$

93. $200,000,000,000=2\times 10^{11}$

95. $1.23\times 10^{-7}=0.000000123$

97. $8.2\times 10^{15}=8,200,000,000,000,000$

99. $3.9\times 10^{-2}=0.039$

101. $(3\times 10^{-12})(5\times 10^{16})=(3)(5)\times 10^{-12+16}$

$=15\times 10^4$

$=150,000$

103. $(0.0000065)(3,200,000,000,000)$

$=(6.5\times 10^{-6})(3.2\times 10^{12})$

$=(6.5)(3.2)\times 10^{-6+12}$

$=20.8\times 10^6=20,800,000$

105. $\frac{9\times 10^{-3}}{6\times 10^5}=1.5\times 10^{-3-5}$

$=1.5\times 10^{-8}$

$=0.000000015$

107. $\frac{0.0089}{500,000,000}=\frac{8.9\times 10^{-3}}{5\times 10^8}$

$=1.78\times 10^{-3-8}$

$=1.78\times 10^{-11}$

$=0.0000000000178$

109. $\frac{0.00056}{0.000000000004}=\frac{5.6\times 10^{-4}}{4\times 10^{-12}}$

$=1.4\times 10^{-4-(-12)}$

$=1.4\times 10^8$

$=140,000,000$

111. $\frac{(3.2\times 10^{-11})(2.9\times 10^{15})}{8.1\times 10^{-3}}$

$=\frac{(3.2)(2.9)\times 10^{-11+15-(-3)}}{8.1}$

$=1.145679\times 10^7$

$=11,456,790$

113. $\frac{(0.00000004)(84,000)}{(0.0003)(1,400,000)}$

$=\frac{4\times 10^{-8}\times 8.4\times 10^4}{3\times 10^{-4}\times 1.4\times 10^6}$

$=\frac{(4)(8.4)\times 10^{-8+4-(-4)-6}}{3(1.4)}$

$=8\times 10^{-6}=0.000008$

Objective D Application Problems

115. Strategy To find the distance traveled:

- Write the speed of light in scientific notation.
- Write the number of seconds in one day in scientific notation.
- Use the equation $d=rt$, where r is the speed of light and t is the number of seconds in one day.

Solution $300,000=3\times 10^5$

$24\cdot 60\cdot 60=86,400=8.64\times 10^4$

$d=rt$

$d=(3\times 10^5)(8.64\times 10^4)$

$d=3\times 8.64\times 10^9$

$d=25.92\times 10^9$

$d=2.592\times 10^{10}$

Light travels 2.592×10^{10} km in one day.

117. Strategy To find the rate of the signals:
- Write the distance in scientific notation.
- Write 11 min in scientific notation.
- Use the equation $r = \frac{d}{t}$.

Solution
$$119{,}000{,}000 = 1.19 \times 10^8$$
$$11 = 1.1 \times 10^1$$
$$d = \frac{r}{t}$$
$$d = \frac{1.19 \times 10^8}{1.1 \times 10^1}$$
$$d = 1.0\overline{81} \times 10^7$$
The rate of the signals is $1.0\overline{81} \times 10^7$ mi/min.

119. Strategy To find the time for one revolution:
- Write the number of seconds in one minute (60) in scientific notation.
- Divide the number of revolutions per minute by the number of seconds in one minute.
- Find the reciprocal of the number of revolutions per second, which is the number of seconds per revolution.

Solution
$$60 = 6 \times 10$$
$$\frac{9 \times 10^7}{6 \times 10} = 1.5 \times 10^6$$
$$\frac{1}{1.5 \times 10^6} = \frac{1}{1.5} \times 10^{-6}$$
$$0.6\overline{6} \times 10^{-6} = 6.\overline{6} \times 10^{-7}$$
The high-speed centrifuge can make one revolution in $6.\overline{6} \times 10^{-7}$ s.

121. Strategy To find the number of times heavier the sun is:
- Divide the mass of the sun by the mass of the earth.

Solution
$$\frac{2 \times 10^{33}}{5.9 \times 10^{27}} = 0.338983 \times 10^6$$
$$= 3.38983 \times 10^5$$
The sun is 3.38983×10^5 times heavier than the earth.

123. Strategy To find the weight of one seed:
- Write the number of seeds per ounce in scientific notation.
- Find the reciprocal of the number of seeds per ounce, which is the number of ounces per seed.

Solution
$$31{,}000{,}000 = 3.1 \times 10^7$$
$$\frac{1}{3.1 \times 10^7} = 0.3225806 \times 10^{-7}$$
$$= 3.225806 \times 10^{-8}$$
The weight of one orchid seed is 3.225806×10^{-8} oz.

125. Strategy To find the distance, multiply the number of light years by the number of miles in one light year. (See Exercise 124).

Solution Distance
$$= (5.865696 \times 10^{12})(2.8 \times 10^8)$$
$$= 1.6423949 \times 10^{21}$$
The distance from the Coma cluster to Earth is 1.6423949×10^{21} mi.

Applying the Concepts

127. a.
$$\begin{aligned}1+(1+(1+2^{-1})^{-1})^{-1} &= 1+\left(1+\left(1+\frac{1}{2}\right)^{-1}\right)^{-1}\\ &= 1+\left(1+\left(\frac{3}{2}\right)^{-1}\right)^{-1}\\ &= 1+\left(1+\frac{2}{3}\right)^{-1}\\ &= 1+\left(\frac{5}{3}\right)^{-1}\\ &= 1+\frac{3}{5}\\ &= \frac{8}{5}\end{aligned}$$

b.
$$\begin{aligned}2-(2-(2-2^{-1})^{-1})^{-1} &= 2-\left(2-\left(2-\frac{1}{2}\right)^{-1}\right)^{-1}\\ &= 2-\left(2-\left(\frac{3}{2}\right)^{-1}\right)^{-1}\\ &= 2-\left(2-\frac{2}{3}\right)^{-1}\\ &= 2-\left(\frac{4}{3}\right)^{-1}\\ &= 2-\frac{3}{4}\\ &= \frac{5}{4}\end{aligned}$$

SECTION 5.2

Objective A Exercises

1. $P(3) = 3(3)^2 - 2(3) - 8$
$P(3) = 13$

3. $R(2) = 2(2)^3 - 3(2)^2 + 4(2) - 2$
$R(2) = 10$

5. $f(-1) = (-1)^4 - 2(-1)^2 - 10$
$f(-1) = -11$

7. Polynomial: (a) –1 (b) 8 (c) 2

9. Not a polynomial.

11. Not a polynomial.

13. Polynomial: (a) 3 (b) π (c) 5

15. Polynomial: (a) –5 (b) 2 (c) 3

17. Polynomial: (a) 14 (b) 14 (c) 0

19.

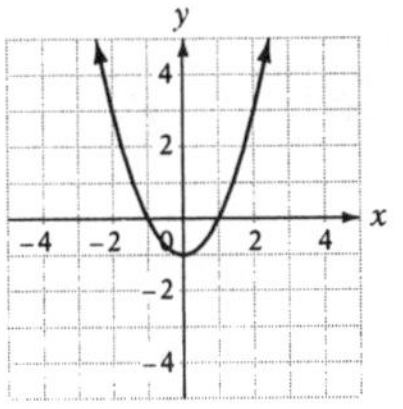

21.

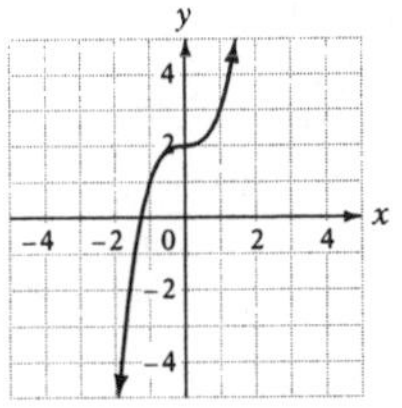

23.

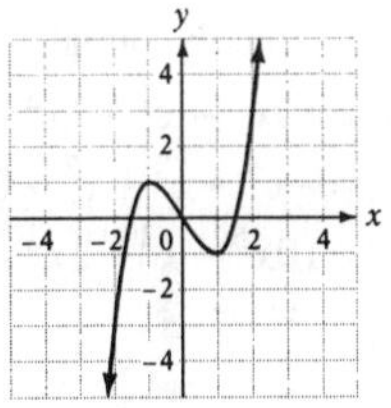

Objective B Exercises

25.
$$\begin{array}{r} 5x^2 + 2x - 7 \\ \underline{x^2 - 8x + 12} \\ 6x^2 - 6x + 5 \end{array}$$

27.
$$\begin{array}{r} x^2 - 3x + 8 \\ \underline{-2x^2 + 3x - 7} \\ -x^2 \qquad + 1 \end{array}$$

29. $(3y^2 - 7y) + (2y^2 - 8y + 2)$
$= (3y^2 + 2y^2) + (-7y - 8y) + 2$
$= 5y^2 - 15y + 2$

31. $(2a^2 - 3a - 7) - (-5a^2 - 2a - 9)$
$= (2a^2 + 5a^2) + (-3a + 2a) + (-7 + 9)$
$= 7a^2 - a + 2$

33. $P(x) + R(x) = (x^2 - 3xy + y^2) + (2x^2 - 3y^2)$
$= (x^2 + 2x^2) - 3xy + (y^2 - 3y^2)$
$= 3x^2 - 3xy - 2y^2$

35. $P(x) - R(x) = (3x^2 + 2y^2) - (-5x^2 + 2xy - 3y^2)$
$= (3x^2 + 5x^2) - 2xy + (2y^2 + 3y^2)$
$= 8x^2 - 2xy + 5y^2$

37. $S(x) = (3x^4 - 3x^3 - x^2) + (3x^3 - 7x^2 + 2x)$
$= 3x^4 + (-3x^3 + 3x^3) + (-x^2 - 7x^2) + 2x$
$S(x) = 3x^4 - 8x^2 + 2x$
$S(2) = 3(2)^4 - 8(2)^2 + 2(2)$
$S(2) = 20$

Applying the Concepts

39. a.
$$\begin{aligned} (2x^3 + 3x^2 + kx + 5) - (x^3 + 2x^2 + 3x + 7) &= x^3 + x^2 + 5x - 2 \\ (2x^3 - x^3) + (3x^2 - 2x^2) + (kx - 3x) + (5 - 7) &= x^3 + x^2 + 5x - 2 \\ x^3 + x^2 + (k-3)x - 2 &= x^3 + x^2 + 5x - 2 \\ (k-3)x &= 5x \\ k - 3 &= 5 \\ k &= 8 \end{aligned}$$

b.
$$\begin{aligned} (6x^3 + kx^2 - 2x - 1) - (4x^3 - 3x^2 + 1) &= 2x^3 - x^2 - 2x - 2 \\ (6x^3 - 4x^3) + (kx^2 + 3x^2) + (-2x) + (-1 - 1) &= 2x^3 - x^2 - 2x - 2 \\ 2x^3 + (k+3)x^2 - 2x - 2 &= 2x^3 - x^2 - 2x - 2 \\ (k+3)x^2 &= -x^2 \\ k + 3 &= -1 \\ k &= -4 \end{aligned}$$

41. $P(x) - Q(x)$ is a fifth-degree polynomial.

Example:
$$P(x) = 10x^5 - x^4 + 3x^2 - 1$$
$$Q(x) = -x^4 + x^3 + x^2 + 2x + 5$$
$$P(x) - Q(x) = 10x^5 - x^3 + 2x^2 - 2x - 6$$

SECTION 5.3

Objective A Exercises

1. $2x(x-3) = 2x^2 - 6x$

3. $3x^2(2x^2 - x) = 6x^4 - 3x^3$

5. $3xy(2x - 3y) = 6x^2y - 9xy^2$

7. $x^n(x+1) = x^{n+1} + x^n$

9. $x^n(x^n + y^n) = x^{2n} + x^n y^n$

11. $2b + 4b(2-b) = 2b + 8b - 4b^2 = -4b^2 + 10b$

13. $-2a^2(3a^2 - 2a + 3) = -6a^4 + 4a^3 - 6a^2$

15. $3b(3b^4 - 3b^2 + 8) = 9b^5 - 9b^3 + 24b$

17. $(-3y^2 - 4y + 2)(y^2) = -3y^4 - 4y^3 + 2y^2$

19. $-5x^2(4 - 3x + 3x^2 + 4x^3)$
$= -20x^2 + 15x^3 - 15x^4 - 20x^5$

21. $-2x^2y(x^2 - 3xy + 2y^2)$
$= -2x^4y + 6x^3y^2 - 4x^2y^3$

23. $x^n(x^{2n} + x^n + x)$
$= x^{3n} + x^{2n} + x^{n+1}$

25. $a^{n+1}(a^n - 3a + 2)$
$= a^{2n+1} - 3a^{n+2} + 2a^{n+1}$

27. $2y^2 - y[3 - 2(y-4) - y]$
$= 2y^2 - y[3 - 2y + 8 - y]$
$= 2y^2 - y[11 - 3y]$
$= 2y^2 - 11y + 3y^2$
$= 5y^2 - 11y$

29. $2y - 3[y - 2y(y-3) + 4y]$
$= 2y - 3[y - 2y^2 + 6y + 4y]$
$= 2y - 3[11y - 2y^2]$
$= 2y - 33y + 6y^2$
$= 6y^2 - 31y$

Objective B Exercises

31. $(x-2)(x+7) = x^2 + 7x - 2x - 14$
$= x^2 + 5x - 14$

33. $(2y-3)(4y+7) = 8y^2 + 14y - 12y - 21$
$= 8y^2 + 2y - 21$

35. $2(2x - 3y)(2x + 5y)$
$= 2(4x^2 + 10xy - 6xy - 15y^2)$
$= 2(4x^2 + 4xy - 15y^2)$
$= 8x^2 + 8xy - 30y^2$

37. $(xy+4)(xy-3) = x^2y^2 - 3xy + 4xy - 12$
$= x^2y^2 + xy - 12$

39. $(2x^2 - 5)(x^2 - 5) = 2x^4 - 10x^2 - 5x^2 + 25$
$= 2x^4 - 15x^2 + 25$

41. $(5x^2 - 5y)(2x^2 - y) = 10x^4 - 5x^2y - 10x^2y + 5y^2$
$= 10x^4 - 15x^2y + 5y^2$

43. $(x^n + 2)(x^n - 3) = x^{2n} - 3x^n + 2x^n - 6$
$= x^{2n} - x^n - 6$

45. $(2a^n - 3)(3a^n + 5) = 6a^{2n} + 10a^n - 9a^n - 15$
$= 6a^{2n} + a^n - 15$

47. $(2a^n - b^n)(3a^n + 2b^n)$
$= 6a^{2n} + 4a^nb^n - 3a^nb^n - 2b^{2n}$
$= 6a^{2n} + a^nb^n - 2b^{2n}$

49.
$$\begin{array}{r} x^3 \quad\quad -3x + 4 \\ \times \quad\quad\quad\quad x + 5 \\ \hline 5x^3 \quad\quad -15x + 20 \\ x^4 \quad\quad -3x^2 + 4x \quad\quad \\ \hline x^4 + 5x^3 - 3x^2 - 11x + 20 \end{array}$$

51.
$$\begin{array}{r} 5a^2 - 6ab + 4b^2 \\ \times \quad\quad 2a - 3b \\ \hline -15a^2b + 18ab^2 - 12b^3 \\ 10a^3 - 12a^2b + 8ab^2 \quad\quad\quad \\ \hline 10a^3 - 27a^2b + 26ab^2 - 12b^3 \end{array}$$

53.
$$\begin{array}{r} y^3 - 5y^2 - 3 \\ \times \quad\quad 2y^2 - 1 \\ \hline -y^3 + 5y^2 + 3 \\ 2y^5 - 10y^4 \quad - 6y^2 \quad\quad \\ \hline 2y^5 - 10y^4 - y^3 - y^2 + 3 \end{array}$$

55.
$$\begin{array}{r} 2x^4 - 3x^3 \quad\quad - 2x + 9 \\ \times \quad\quad\quad\quad 2x - 5 \\ \hline -10x^4 + 15x^3 \quad\quad + 10x - 45 \\ 4x^5 - 6x^4 \quad\quad - 4x^2 + 18x \quad\quad \\ \hline 4x^5 - 16x^4 + 15x^3 - 4x^2 + 28x - 45 \end{array}$$

57.

$$\begin{array}{r} x^2 + 2x - 3 \\ \times \qquad x^2 - 5x + 7 \\ \hline 7x^2 + 14x - 21 \\ -5x^3 - 10x^2 + 15x \quad \\ x^4 + 2x^3 - 3x^2 \qquad\qquad \\ \hline x^4 - 3x^3 - 6x^2 + 29x - 21 \end{array}$$

59. $(a-2)(2a-3)(a+7)$
$=(2a^2-3a-4a+6)(a+7)$
$=(2a^2-7a+6)(a+7)$

$$\begin{array}{r} 2a^2 - 7a + 6 \\ \times \qquad a + 7 \\ \hline 14a^2 - 49a + 42 \\ 2a^3 - 7a^2 + 6a \qquad \\ \hline 2a^3 + 7a^2 - 43a + 42 \end{array}$$

61.

$$\begin{array}{r} x^{2n} + x^n + 1 \\ \times \qquad x^n + 1 \\ \hline x^{2n} + x^n + 1 \\ x^{3n} + x^{2n} + x^n \qquad \\ \hline x^{3n} + 2x^{2n} + 2x^n + 1 \end{array}$$

63.

$$\begin{array}{r} x^n - 2x^ny^n + 3y^n \\ \times \qquad x^n + y^n \\ \hline x^ny^n - 2x^ny^{2n} + 3y^{2n} \\ x^{2n} - 2x^{2n}y^n + 3x^ny^n \qquad\qquad \\ \hline x^{2n} - 2x^{2n}y^n + 4x^ny^n - 2x^ny^{2n} + 3y^{2n} \end{array}$$

Objective C Exercises

65. $(3x-2)(3x+2)=9x^2-4$

67. $(6-x)(6+x)=36-x^2$

69. $(2a-3b)(2a+3b)=4a^2-9b^2$

71. $(x^2+1)(x^2-1)=x^4-1$

73. $(x^n+3)(x^n-3)=x^{2n}-9$

75. $(x-5)^2=x^2-10x+25$

77. $(3a+5b)^2=9a^2+30ab+25b^2$

79. $(x^2-3)^2=x^4-6x^2+9$

81. $(2x^2-3y^2)^2=4x^4-12x^2y^2+9y^4$

83. $(a^n-b^n)^2=a^{2n}-2a^nb^n+b^{2n}$

85. $y^2-(x-y)^2=y^2-(x^2-2xy+y^2)$
$=y^2-x^2+2xy-y^2$
$=-x^2+2xy$

87. $(x-y)^2-(x+y)^2$
$=(x^2-2xy+y^2)-(x^2+2xy+y^2)$
$=x^2-2xy+y^2-x^2-2xy-y^2$
$=-4xy$

Objective D Application Problems

89. Strategy To find the area, replace the variables L and W in the equation $A=L\cdot W$ by the given values and solve for A.

Solution $A=L\cdot W$
$A=(3x-2)(x+4)$
$A=3x^2+12x-2x-8$
$A=3x^2+10x-8$
The area is $(3x^2+10x-8)$ ft^2.

91. Strategy To find the area, add the area of the small rectangle to the area of the large rectangle.
Large rectangle:
Length = $L_1=x+5$
Width = $W_1=x-2$
Small rectangle:
Length = $L_2=5$
Width = $W_2=2$

Solution A = Area of the large rectangle + area of the small rectangle
$A=(L_1\cdot W_1)+(L_2\cdot W_2)$
$A=(x+5)(x-2)+(5)(2)$
$A=x^2-2x+5x-10+10$
$A=x^2+3x$
The area is (x^2+3x) m^2.

93. Strategy To find the volume, replace the variable s in the equation $V=s^3$ with its given value and solve for V.

Solution $V=s^3$
$V=(x+3)^3$
$V=(x+3)(x+3)(x+3)$
$V=(x^2+6x+9)(x+3)$
$V=x^3+9x^2+27x+27$
The volume is $(x^3+9x^2+27x+27)$ cm^3.

95. Strategy To find the volume, subtract the volume of the small rectangular solid from the volume of the large rectangular solid.

Large rectangular solid:
Length = $L_1 = x+2$
Width = $W_1 = 2x$
Height = $h_1 = x$
Small rectangular solid:
Length = $L_2 = x$
Width = $W_2 = 2x$
Height = $h_2 = x$

Solution
$$V = (L_1 \cdot W_1 \cdot h_1) - (L_2 \cdot W_2 \cdot h_2)$$
$$V = (x+2)(2x)(x) - (x)(2x)(2)$$
$$V = (2x^2+4x)(x) - (2x^2)(2)$$
$$V = 2x^3 + 4x^2 - 4x^2$$
$$V = 2x^3$$
The volume is $2x^3$ in.^{3}.

97. Strategy To find the area, replace the variable r in the equation $A = \pi r^2$ by the given value and solve for A.

Solution
$$A = \pi r^2$$
$$A = 3.14(25x^2+40x+16)$$
$$A = 78.5x^2 + 125.6x + 50.24$$
The area is $(78.5x^2+125.6x+50.24)$ in^2.

Applying the Concepts

99. a.
$$\begin{array}{r} a^2+ab+b^2 \\ \times \qquad a-b \\ \hline -a^2b-ab^2-b^3 \\ +\ a^3+a^2b+ab^2 \qquad \\ \hline a^3-b^3 \qquad \end{array}$$

b.
$$\begin{array}{r} x^2-xy+y^2 \\ \times \qquad x+y \\ \hline x^2y-xy^2+y^3 \\ x^3-x^2y+xy^2 \qquad \\ \hline x^3+y^3 \qquad \end{array}$$

101. a.
$$(3x-k)(2x+k) = 6x^2+5x-k^2$$
$$6x^2+xk-k^2 = 6x^2+5x-k^2$$
$$xk = 5x$$
$$k = 5$$

b.
$$(4x+k)^2 = 16x^2+8x+k^2$$
$$16x^2+8xk+k^2 = 16x^2+8x+k^2$$
$$8xk = 8x$$
$$k = 1$$

103. The product of $4a+b$ and $2a-b$ is
$(4a+b)(2a-b) = 8a^2-2ab-b^2$
Subtract $8a^2-2ab-b^2$ from $9a^2-2ab$.
$$\begin{array}{l} 9a^2-2ab \\ -(8a^2-2ab-b^2) \\ \hline \qquad a^2+b^2 \end{array}$$

SECTION 5.4

Objective A Exercises

1.
$$\begin{array}{r} x+8 \\ x-5\overline{)x^2+3x-40} \\ \underline{x^2-5x} \qquad \\ 8x-40 \\ \underline{8x-40} \\ 0 \end{array}$$
$(x^2+3x-40) \div (x-3) = x+8$

3.
$$\begin{array}{r} x^2+3x+6 \\ x-3\overline{)x^3+0x^2-3x+2} \\ \underline{x^3-3x^2} \qquad\qquad \\ 3x^2-3x \qquad \\ \underline{3x^2-9x} \qquad \\ 6x+\ 2 \\ \underline{6x-18} \\ 20 \end{array}$$
$(x^3-3x+2) \div (x-3) = x^2+3x+6+\dfrac{20}{x-3}$

5.
$$\begin{array}{r} 3x+5 \\ 2x+1\overline{)6x^2+13x+8} \\ \underline{6x^2+\ 3x} \qquad \\ 10x+8 \\ \underline{10x+5} \\ 3 \end{array}$$
$(6x^2+13x+8) \div (2x+1) = 3x+5+\dfrac{3}{2x+1}$

7.
$$\begin{array}{r} 5x+7 \\ 2x-1\overline{)10x^2+9x-5} \\ \underline{10x^2-5x} \qquad \\ 14x-5 \\ \underline{14x-7} \\ 2 \end{array}$$
$(10x^2+9x-5) \div (2x-1) = 5x+7+\dfrac{2}{2x-1}$

9.

$$\begin{array}{r} 4x^2+6x+9 \\ 2x-3\overline{)8x^3+0x^2+0x-9} \\ \underline{8x^3-12x^2} \\ 12x^2+0 \\ \underline{12x^2-18x} \\ 18x-9 \\ \underline{18x-27} \\ 18 \end{array}$$

$$(8x^3-9)\div(2x-3)=4x^2+6x+9+\frac{18}{2x-3}$$

11.

$$\begin{array}{r} 3x^2+1 \\ 2x^2-5\overline{)6x^4+0x^3-13x^2+0x-4} \\ \underline{6x^4-15x^2} \\ 2x^2+0x-4 \\ \underline{2x^2-5} \\ 1 \end{array}$$

$$(6x^4-13x^2-4)\div(2x^2-5)=3x^2+1+\frac{1}{2x^2-5}$$

13.

$$\begin{array}{r} x^2-3x-10 \\ 3x+1\overline{)3x^3-8x^2-33x-10} \\ \underline{3x^3+x^2} \\ -9x^2-33x \\ \underline{-9x^2-3x} \\ -30x-10 \\ \underline{-30x-10} \\ 0 \end{array}$$

$$\frac{3x^3-8x^2-33x-10}{3x+1}=x^2-3x-10$$

15.

$$\begin{array}{r} x^2-2x+1 \\ x-3\overline{)x^3-5x^2+7x-4} \\ \underline{x^3-3x^2} \\ -2x^2+7x \\ \underline{-2x^2+6x} \\ x-4 \\ \underline{x-3} \\ -1 \end{array}$$

$$\frac{x^3-5x^2+7x-4}{x-3}=x^2-2x+1-\frac{1}{x-3}$$

17.

$$\begin{array}{r} 2x^3-3x^2+x-4 \\ x-5\overline{)2x^4-13x^3+16x^2-9x+20} \\ \underline{2x^4-10x^3} \\ -3x^3+16x^2 \\ \underline{-3x^3+15x^2} \\ x^2-9x \\ \underline{x^2-5x} \\ -4x+20 \\ \underline{-4x+20} \\ 0 \end{array}$$

$$\frac{2x^4-13x^3+16x^2-9x+20}{x-5}=2x^3-3x^2+x-4$$

19.

$$\begin{array}{r} 2x \\ x^2+2x-1\overline{)2x^3+4x^2-x+2} \\ \underline{2x^3+4x^2-2x} \\ x+2 \end{array}$$

$$\frac{2x^3+4x^2-x+2}{x^2+2x-1}=2x+\frac{x+2}{x^2+2x-1}$$

21.

$$\begin{array}{r} x^2+4x+6 \\ x^2-2x-1\overline{)x^4+2x^3-3x^2-6x+2} \\ \underline{x^4-2x^3-x^2} \\ 4x^3-2x^2-6x \\ \underline{4x^3-8x^2-4x} \\ 6x^2-2x+2 \\ \underline{6x^2-12x-6} \\ 10x+8 \end{array}$$

$$\frac{x^4+2x^3-3x^2-6x+2}{x^2-2x-1}$$
$$=x^2+4x+6+\frac{10x+8}{x^2-2x-1}$$

23.

$$\begin{array}{r} x^2-2x+4 \\ x^2+2x+3\overline{)x^4+0x^3+3x^2-4x+5} \\ \underline{x^4+2x^3+3x^2} \\ -2x^3-4x \\ \underline{-2x^3-4x^2-6x} \\ 4x^2+2x+5 \\ \underline{4x^2+8x+12} \\ -6x-7 \end{array}$$

$$\frac{x^4+3x^2-4x+5}{x^2+2x+3}$$
$$=x^2-2x+4+\frac{-6x-7}{x^2+2x+3}$$

Objective B Exercises

25.

$$\begin{array}{r|rrr} -1 & 2 & -6 & -8 \\ & & -2 & 8 \\ \hline & 2 & -8 & 0 \end{array}$$

$(2x^2-6x-8)\div(x+1)=2x-8$

27.

$$\begin{array}{r|rrr} 2 & 3 & -14 & 16 \\ & & 6 & -16 \\ \hline & 3 & -8 & 0 \end{array}$$

$(3x^2-14x+16)\div(x-2)=3x-8$

29.

$$\begin{array}{r|rrr} 1 & 3 & 0 & -4 \\ & & 3 & 3 \\ \hline & 3 & 3 & -1 \end{array}$$

$(3x^2-4)\div(x-1)=3x+3-\dfrac{1}{x-1}$

31.

$$\begin{array}{r|rrrr} -1 & 2 & -1 & 6 & 9 \\ & & -2 & 3 & -9 \\ \hline & 2 & -3 & 9 & 0 \end{array}$$

$(2x^3-x^2+6x+9)\div(x+1)=2x^2-3x+9$

33.

$$\begin{array}{r|rrrr} 2 & 4 & 0 & -1 & -18 \\ & & 8 & 16 & 30 \\ \hline & 4 & 8 & 15 & 12 \end{array}$$

$(4x^3-x-18)\div(x-2)=4x^2+8x+15+\dfrac{12}{x-2}$

35.

$$\begin{array}{r|rrrr} -4 & 2 & 5 & -5 & 20 \\ & & -8 & 12 & -28 \\ \hline & 2 & -3 & 7 & -8 \end{array}$$

$(2x^3+5x^2-5x+20)\div(x+4)$
$=2x^2-3x+7-\dfrac{8}{x+4}$

37.

$$\begin{array}{r|rrrrr} 2 & 3 & -4 & 8 & -5 & -5 \\ & & 6 & 4 & 24 & 38 \\ \hline & 3 & 2 & 12 & 19 & 33 \end{array}$$

$\dfrac{3x^4-4x^3+8x^2-5x-5}{x-2}$
$=3x^3+2x^2+12x+19+\dfrac{33}{x-2}$

39.

$$\begin{array}{r|rrrrr} -1 & 3 & 3 & -1 & 3 & 2 \\ & & -3 & 0 & 1 & -4 \\ \hline & 3 & 0 & -1 & 4 & -2 \end{array}$$

$\dfrac{3x^4+3x^3-x^2+3x+2}{x+1}$
$=3x^3-x+4-\dfrac{2}{x+1}$

41.

$$\begin{array}{r|rrrrr} 3 & 2 & 0 & -1 & 0 & 2 \\ & & 6 & 18 & 51 & 153 \\ \hline & 2 & 6 & 17 & 51 & 155 \end{array}$$

$\dfrac{2x^4-x^2+2}{x-3}=2x^3+6x^2+17x+51+\dfrac{155}{x-3}$

Objective C Exercises

43.

$$\begin{array}{r|rrr} 3 & 2 & -3 & -1 \\ & & 6 & 9 \\ \hline & 2 & 3 & 8 \end{array}$$

$P(3)=8$

45.

$$\begin{array}{r|rrrr} 4 & 1 & -2 & 3 & -1 \\ & & 4 & 8 & 44 \\ \hline & 1 & 2 & 11 & 43 \end{array}$$

$R(4)=43$

47.

$$\begin{array}{r|rrrr} -2 & 2 & -4 & 3 & -1 \\ & & -4 & 16 & -38 \\ \hline & 2 & -8 & 19 & -39 \end{array}$$

$P(-2)=-39$

49.

$$\begin{array}{r|rrrr} -3 & 2 & -1 & 0 & 3 \\ & & -6 & 21 & -63 \\ \hline & 2 & -7 & 21 & -60 \end{array}$$

$Z(-3)=-60$

51.

$$\begin{array}{r|rrrrr} 2 & 1 & 3 & -2 & 4 & -9 \\ & & 2 & 10 & 16 & 40 \\ \hline & 1 & 5 & 8 & 20 & 31 \end{array}$$

$Q(2)=31$

53.

$$\begin{array}{r|rrrrr} -3 & 2 & -1 & 0 & 2 & -5 \\ & & -6 & 21 & -63 & 183 \\ \hline & 2 & -7 & 21 & -61 & 178 \end{array}$$

$F(-3)=178$

55.

5	1	0	0	−3
		5	25	125
	1	5	25	122

$P(5) = 122$

57.

−3	4	0	−3	0	5
		−12	36	−99	297
	4	−12	33	−99	302

$R(2) = 302$

59.

2	1	0	−4	−2	5	−2
		2	4	0	−4	2
	1	2	0	−2	1	0

$Q(2) = 0$

61.

−2	2	0	−1	0	4	−1
		−4	8	−14	28	−64
	2	−4	7	−14	32	−65

$R(-2) = -65$

Applying the Concepts

63. a.

$$\begin{array}{r|l} & a^2 - ab + b^2 \\ \hline a+b & a^3 \qquad\qquad + b^3 \\ & \underline{a^3 + a^2b} \\ & -a^2b \\ & \underline{-a^2b - ab^2} \\ & ab^2 + b^3 \\ & \underline{ab^2 + b^3} \\ & 0 \end{array}$$

$$\frac{a^3 + b^3}{a+b} = a^2 - ab + b^2$$

b.

$$\begin{array}{r|l} & x^4 - x^3y + x^2y^2 - xy^3 + y^4 \\ \hline x+y & x^5 \qquad\qquad\qquad\qquad + y^5 \\ & \underline{x^5 + x^4y} \\ & -x^4y \\ & \underline{-x^4y - x^3y^2} \\ & x^3y^2 \\ & \underline{x^3y^2 + x^2y^3} \\ & -x^2y^3 \\ & \underline{-x^2y^3 - xy^4} \\ & xy^4 + y^5 \\ & \underline{xy^4 + y^5} \\ & 0 \end{array}$$

$$\frac{x^5 + y^5}{x+y} = x^4 - x^3y + x^2y^2 - xy^3 + y^4$$

c.

$$\begin{array}{r|l} & x^5 - x^4y + x^3y^2 - x^2y^3 + xy^4 - y^5 \\ \hline x+y & x^6 \qquad\qquad\qquad\qquad\qquad - y^6 \\ & \underline{x^6 + x^5y} \\ & -x^5y \\ & \underline{-x^5y - x^4y^2} \\ & x^4y^2 \\ & \underline{x^4y^2 + x^3y^3} \\ & -x^3y^3 \\ & \underline{-x^3y^3 - x^2y^4} \\ & x^2y^4 \\ & \underline{x^2y^4 - xy^5} \\ & -xy^5 - y^6 \\ & \underline{-xy^5 - y^6} \\ & 0 \end{array}$$

$$\frac{x^6 - y^6}{x-y} = x^5 - x^4y + x^3y^2 - x^2y^3 + xy^4 - y^5$$

65. a.

$$\begin{array}{r} \tfrac{1}{2}x^2+\tfrac{3}{4}x-1 \\ 4x+8\overline{)2x^3+7x^2+2x-8} \\ \underline{2x^3+4x^2} \qquad\qquad \\ 3x^2+2x \qquad \\ \underline{3x^2+6x} \qquad \\ -4x-8 \\ \underline{-4x-8} \\ 0 \end{array}$$

$(2x^3+7x^2-2x-8)\div(4x+8)$
$=\frac{1}{2}x^2+\frac{3}{4}x-1$

b.

$$\begin{array}{r} \tfrac{2}{3}x^2+\tfrac{7}{2}x+\tfrac{10}{3} \\ 6x-12\overline{)4x^3+13x^2-22x+24} \\ \underline{4x^3-8x^2} \qquad\qquad \\ 21x^2-22x \qquad \\ \underline{21x^2-42x} \qquad \\ 20x+24 \\ \underline{20x-40} \\ 64 \end{array}$$

$(4x^3+13x^2-22x+24)\div(6x-12)$
$=\frac{2}{3}x^2+\frac{7}{2}x+\frac{10}{3}+\frac{64}{6x-12}$

c.

$$\begin{array}{r} 2x^2-x+1 \\ x^2-x+1\overline{)2x^4-3x^3+4x^2+x-10} \\ \underline{2x^4-2x^3+2x^2} \qquad\qquad \\ -x^3+2x^2+x \qquad \\ \underline{-x^3+x^2-x} \qquad \\ x^2+2x-10 \\ \underline{x^2-x+1} \\ 3x-11 \end{array}$$

$(2x^4-3x^3+4x^2+x-10)\div(x^2-x+1)$
$=2x^2-x+1+\frac{3x-11}{x^2-x+1}$

d.

$$\begin{array}{r} x^2+6x+17 \\ x^2-2x-3\overline{)x^4+4x^3+2x^2-x+5} \\ \underline{x^4-2x^3-3x^2} \qquad\qquad \\ 6x^3+5x^2-x \qquad \\ \underline{6x^3-12x^2-18x} \qquad \\ 17x^2+17x+5 \\ \underline{17x^2-34x-51} \\ 51x+56 \end{array}$$

$(x^4+4x^3+2x^2-x+5)\div(x^2-2x-3)$
$=x^2+6x+17+\frac{51x+56}{x^2-2x-3}$

SECTION 5.5

Objective A Exercises

1. The GCF of $6a^2$ and $15a$ is $3a$.
$6a^2-15a=3a(2a-5)$

3. The GCF of $4x^3$ and $3x^2$ is x^2.
$4x^3-3x^2=x^2(4x-3)$

5. There is no common factor.
$3a^2-10b^3$ is nonfactorable over the integers.

7. The GCF of x^5, x^3, and x is x.
$x^5-x^3-x=x(x^4-x^2-1)$

9. The GCF of $16x^2$, $12x$, and 24 is 4.
$16x^2-12+24=4(4x^2-3x+6)$

11. The GCF of $5b^2$, $10b^3$, and $25b^4$ is $5b^2$.
$5b^2-10b^3+25b^4=5b^2(1-2b+5b^2)$

13. The GCF of x^{2n} and x^n is x^n.
$x^{2n}-x^n=x^n(x^n-1)$

15. The GCF of x^{3n} and x^{2n} is x^{2n}.
$x^{3n}-x^{2n}=x^{2n}(x^n-1)$

17. The GCF of a^{2n+2} and a^2 is a^2.
$a^{2n+2}+a^2=a^2(a^{2n}+1)$

19. The GCF of $12x^2y^2$, $18x^3y$, and $24x^2y$ is $6x^2y$.
$12x^2y^2-18x^3y+24x^2y=6x^2y(2y-3x+4)$

21. The GCF of $24a^3b^2$, $4a^2b^2$, and $16a^2b^4$ is $4a^2b^2$.
$24a^3b^2-4a^2b^2-16a^2b^4$
$=4a^2b^2(6a-1-4b^2)$

23. The GCF of y^{2n+2}, y^{n+2}, and y^2 is y^2.
$y^{2n+2}+y^{n+2}-y^2=y^2(y^{2n}+y^n-1)$

Objective B Exercises

25. $x(a+2)-2(a+2)=(a+2)(x-2)$

27. $a(x-2)-b(2-x)=a(x-2)+b(x-2)$
$=(x-2)(a+b)$

29. $x(a-2b)+y(2b-a)=x(a-2b)-y(a-2b)$
$=(a-2b)(x-y)$

31. $xy+4y-2x-8=y(x+4)-2(x+4)$
$=(x+4)(y-2)$

33. $ax+bx-ay-by=x(a+b)-y(a+b)$
$=(a+b)(x-y)$

35. $x^2y - 3x^2 - 2y + 6 = x^2(y-3) - 2(y-3)$
$= (y-3)(x^2-2)$

37. $6 + 2y + 3x^2 + x^2y = 2(3+y) + x^2(3+y)$
$= (3+y)(2+x^2)$

39. $2ax^2 + bx^2 - 4ay - 2by = x^2(2a+b) - 2y(2a+b)$
$= (2a+b)(x^2-2y)$

41. $6xb + 3ax - 4by - 2ay = 3x(2b+a) - 2y(2b+a)$
$= (2b+a)(3x-2y)$

43. $x^ny - 5x^n + y - 5 = x^n(y-5) + (y-5)$
$= (y-5)(x^n+1)$

45. $2x^3 - x^2 + 4x - 2 = x^2(2x-1) + 2(2x-1)$
$= (2x-1)(x^2+1)$

Objective C Exercises

47. $x^2 + 12x + 20 = (x+10)(x+2)$

49. $a^2 + a - 72 = (a+9)(a-8)$

51. $a^2 + 7a + 6 = (a+1)(a+6)$

53. $y^2 - 18y + 72 = (y-6)(y-12)$

55. $x^2 + x - 132 = (x+12)(x-11)$

57. $x^2 + 15x + 50 = (x+5)(x+10)$

59. $b^2 - 6b - 16 = (b+2)(b-8)$

61. $a^2 - 3ab + 2b^2 = (a-b)(a-2b)$

63. $a^2 + 8ab - 33b^2 = (a+11b)(a-3b)$

65. $x^2 + 5xy + 6y^2 = (x+2y)(x+3y)$

67. $2 + x - x^2 = (1+x)(2-x)$

69. $5 + 4x - x^2 = (1+x)(5-x)$

71. $x^2 - 5x + 6 = (x-2)(x-3)$

Objective D Exercises

73. $2x^2 + 7x + 3 = (2x+1)(x+3)$

75. $6y^2 + 5y - 6 = (2y+3)(3y-2)$

77. $6b^2 - b - 35 = (3b+7)(2b-5)$

79. $3y^2 - 22y + 39 = (3y-13)(y-3)$

81. There are no binomial factors whose product is $6a^2 - 26a + 15$. The trinomial is nonfactorable over the integers.

83. $4a^2 - a - 5 = (a+1)(4a-5)$

85. $10x^2 - 29x + 10 = (5x-2)(2x-5)$

87. There are no binomial factors whose product is $4x^2 - 6x + 1$. The trinomial is nonfactorable over the integers.

89. $6x^2 + 41xy - 7y^2 = (x+7y)(6x-y)$

91. $7a^2 + 46ab - 21b^2 = (a+7b)(7a-3b)$

93. $18x^2 + 27xy + 10y^2 = (6x+5y)(3x+2y)$

95. $6 - 7x - 5x^2 = (2+x)(3-5x)$

97. There are no binomial factors whose product is $30 + 17a - 20a^2$. The trinomial is nonfactorable over the integers.

99. $35 - 6b - 8b^2 = (5+2b)(7-4b)$

101. The GCF of $5y^4$, $29y^3$, and $20y^2$ is y^2.
$5y^4 - 29y^3 + 20y^2 = y^2(5y^2 - 29y + 20)$
$= y^2(5y-4)(y-5)$

103. The GCF of $20x^2$, $38x^3$, and $30x^4$ is $2x^2$.
$20x^2 - 38x^3 - 30x^4 = 2x^2(10 - 19x - 15x^2)$
$= 2x^2(5+3x)(2-5x)$

105. The GCF of $a^4b^4, 3a^3b^3$ and $10a^2b^2$ is a^2b^2.
$a^4b^4 - 3a^3b^3 - 10a^2b^2 = a^2b^2(a^2b^2 - 3ab - 10)$
$= a^2b^2(ab+2)(ab-5)$

107. The GCF of $90a^2b^2$, $45ab$, and 10 is 5.
$90a^2b^2 + 45ab + 10 = 5(18a^2b^2 + 9ab + 2)$

109. There is no common factor.
$4x^4 - 45x^2 + 80$ is nonfactorable over the integers.

111. The GCF of $2a^5, 14a^3$, and $20a$ is $2a$
$2a^5 + 14a^3 + 20a = 2a(a^4 + 7a^2 + 10)$
$= 2a(a^2+2)(a^2+5)$

113. The GCF of $3x^4y^2, 39x^2y^2$, and $120y^2$ is $3y^2$.
$3x^4y^2 - 39x^2y^2 + 120y^2 = 3y^2(x^4 - 13x^2 + 40)$
$= 3y^2(x^2-5)(x^2-8)$

115. The GCF of $3x^3y^3, 6x^2y^2$, and $24xy$ is $3xy$.
$3x^3y^3 + 6x^2y^2 - 24xy = 3xy(x^2y^2 + 2xy - 8)$
$= 3xy(xy-2)(xy+4)$

117. The GCF of y^5, $8y^3$, and $15y$ is y.
$$y^5 - 8y^3 + 15y = y(y^4 - 8y^2 + 15) = y(y^2 - 3)(y^2 - 5)$$

119. The GCF of $3y$, $16y^2$, and $16y^3$ is y.
$$3y - 16y^2 + 16y^3 = y(16y^2 - 16y + 3) = y(4y - 3)(4y - 1)$$

121. The GCF of $12y^{2n}$, $51y^n$, and 45 is 3.
$$12y^{2n} - 51y^n + 45 = 3(4y^{2n} - 17y^n + 15) = 3(y^n - 3)(4y^n - 5)$$

123. The GCF of x^{3n}, $10x^{2n}$, and $16x^n$ is x^n.
$$x^{3n} + 10x^{2n} + 16x^n = x^n(x^{2n} + 10x^n + 16) = x^n(x^n + 2)(x^n + 8)$$

Applying the Concepts

125. **a.** $x^2 + kx + 8$
Find two positive or two negative factors of 8. Their sum is a value of k.

Factors	Sum
8, 1	9
2, 4	6
−1, −8	−9
−2, −4	−6

The values of k are −9, −6, 6, and 9.

b. $x^2 + kx - 6$
Find the factors of −6 with opposite signs. Their sum is a value of k.

Factors	Sum
−2, 3	1
−3, 2	−1
−6, 1	−5
−1, 6	5

The values of k are −5, −1, 1, and 5.

c. $2x^2 + kx + 3$
Find two positive or two negative factors of 6 $(2 \cdot 3)$. The sums of these factors are values of k.

Factors	Sum
2, 3	5
1, 6	7
−2, −3	−5
−1, −6	−7

The values of k are −7, −5, 5, and 7.

d. $2x^2 + kx - 5$
Find factors of −10 of opposite sign. The sums of these factors are values of k.

Factors	Sum
2, −5	−3
5, −2	3
−10, 1	−9
10, −1	9

The values of k are −9, −3, 3, and −9.

e. $3x^2 + kx + 5$
Find positive factors of 15. The sums of these factors are values of k.

Factors	Sum
3, 5	8
15, 1	16
−3, −5	−8
−15, −1	−16

The values of k are −16, −8, 8, and 16.

f. $2x^2 + kx - 3$
Find factors of −6 of opposite sign. The sums of these factors are values of k.

Factors	Sum
−3, 2	−1
3, −2	1
6, −1	5
−6, 1	−5

The values of k are −5, −1, 1, and 5.

SECTION 5.6

Objective A Exercises

1. $x^2 - 16 = x^2 - 4^2$
$= (x+4)(x-4)$

3. $4x^2 - 1 = (2x)^2 - 1^2$
$= (2x+1)(2x-1)$

5. $16x^2 - 121 = (4x)^2 - 11^2$
$= (4x+11)(4x-11)$

7. $1 - 9a^2 = 1^2 - (3a)^2$
$= (1+3a)(1-3a)$

9. $x^2y^2 - 100 = (xy)^2 - 10^2$
$= (xy+10)(xy-10)$

11. $x^2 + 4$ is nonfactorable over the integers.

13. $25 - a^2b^2 = 5^2 - (ab)^2$
$= (5+ab)(5-ab)$

15. $a^{2n} - 1 = (a^n)^2 - 1^2$
$= (a^n + 1)(a^n - 1)$

17. $x^2 - 12x + 36 = (x-6)^2$

19. $b^2 - 2b + 1 = (b-1)^2$

21. $16x^2 - 40x + 25 = (4x-5)^2$

23. $4a^2 + 4a - 1$ is nonfactorable over the integers.

25. $b^2 + 7b + 14$ is nonfactorable over the integers.

27. $x^2 + 6xy + 9y^2 = (x+3y)^2$

29. $25a^2 - 40ab + 16b^2 = (5a-4b)^2$

31. $x^{2n} + 6x^n + 9 = (x^n + 3)^2$

33. $(x-4)^2 - 9 = [(x-4)-3][(x-4)+3]$
$= (x-4-3)(x-4+3)$
$= (x-7)(x-1)$

35. $(x-y)^2 - (a+b)^2$
$= [(x-y)-(a+b)][(x-y)+(a+b)]$
$= (x-y-a-b)(x-y+a+b)$

Objective B Exercises

37. $x^3 - 27 = x^3 - 3^2$
$= (x-3)(x^2+3x+9)$

39. $8x^3 - 1 = (2x)^3 - 1^3$
$= (2x-1)(4x^2+2x+1)$

41. $x^3 - y^3 = (x-y)(x^2+xy+y^2)$

43. $m^3 + n^3 = (m+n)(m^2 - mn + n^2)$

45. $64x^3 + 1 = (4x)^3 + 1^3$
$= (4x+1)(16x^2 - 4x + 1)$

47. $27x^3 - 8y^3 = (3x)^3 - (2y)^3$
$= (3x-2y)(9x^2 + 6xy + 4y^2)$

49. $x^3y^3 + 64 = (xy)^3 + 4^3$
$= (xy+4)(x^2y^2 - 4xy + 16)$

51. $16x^3 - y^3$ is nonfactorable over the integers.

53. $8x^3 - 9y^3$ is nonfactorable over the integers.

55. $(a-b)^3 - b^3$
$= [(a-b)-b][(a-b)^2 + b(a-b) + b^2]$
$= (a-2b)(a^2 - 2ab + b^2 + ab - b^2 + b^2)$
$= (a-2b)(a^2 - ab + b^2)$

57. $x^{6n} + y^{3n} = (x^{2n})^3 + (y^n)^3$
$= (x^{2n} + y^n)(x^{4n} - x^{2n}y^n + y^{2n})$

59. $x^{3n} + 8 = (x^n)^3 + 2^3$
$= (x^n + 2)(x^{2n} - 2x^n + 4)$

Objective C Exercises

61. Let $u = xy$.
$x^2y^2 - 8xy + 15 = u^2 - 8u + 15$
$= (u-5)(u-3)$
$= (xy-5)(xy-3)$

63. Let $u = xy$.
$x^2y^2 - 17xy + 60 = u^2 - 17u + 60$
$= (u-12)(u-5)$
$= (xy-12)(xy-5)$

65. Let $u = x^2$.
$x^4 - 9x^2 + 18 = u^2 - 9u + 18$
$= (u-3)(u-6)$
$= (x^2-3)(x^2-6)$

67. Let $u = b^2$.
$b^4 - 13b^2 - 90 = u^2 - 13u - 90$
$= (u+5)(u-18)$
$= (b^2+5)(b^2-18)$

69. Let $u = x^2y^2$.
$x^4y^4 - 8x^2y^2 + 12 = u^2 - 8u + 12$
$= (u-2)(u-6)$
$= (x^2y^2 - 2)(x^2y^2 - 6)$

71. Let $u = x^n$.

$$\begin{aligned} x^{2n} + 3x^n + 2 &= u^2 + 3u + 2 \\ &= (u+1)(u+2) \\ &= (x^n + 1)(x^n + 2) \end{aligned}$$

73. Let $u = xy$.

$$\begin{aligned} 3x^2y^2 - 14xy + 15 &= 3u^2 - 14u + 15 \\ &= (3u-5)(u-3) \\ &= (3xy-5)(xy-3) \end{aligned}$$

75. Let $u = ab$.

$$\begin{aligned} 6a^2b^2 - 23ab + 21 &= 6u^2 - 23u + 21 \\ &= (2u-3)(3u-7) \\ &= (2ab-3)(3ab-7) \end{aligned}$$

77. Let $u = x^2$.

$$\begin{aligned} 2x^4 - 13x^2 - 15 &= 2u^2 - 13u - 15 \\ &= (u+1)(2u-15) \\ &= (x^2+1)(2x^2-15) \end{aligned}$$

79. Let $u = x^n$.

$$\begin{aligned} 2x^{2n} - 7x^n + 3 &= 2u^2 - 7u + 3 \\ &= (2u-1)(u-3) \\ &= (2x^n - 1)(x^n - 3) \end{aligned}$$

81. Let $u = a^n$.

$$\begin{aligned} 6a^{2n} + 19a^n + 10 &= 6u^2 + 19u + 10 \\ &= (2u+5)(3u+2) \\ &= (2a^n + 5)(3a^n + 2) \end{aligned}$$

Objective D Exercises

83. $$\begin{aligned} 12x^2 - 36x + 27 &= 3(4x^2 - 12x + 9) \\ &= 3(2x-3)^2 \end{aligned}$$

85. $$\begin{aligned} 27a^4 - a &= a(27a^3 - 1) \\ &= a(3a-1)(9a^2 + 3a + 1) \end{aligned}$$

87. $$\begin{aligned} 20x^2 - 5 &= 5(4x^2 - 1) \\ &= 5(2x+1)(2x-1) \end{aligned}$$

89. $$\begin{aligned} y^5 + 6y^4 - 55y^3 &= y^3(y^2 + 6y - 55) \\ &= y^3(y+11)(y-5) \end{aligned}$$

91. $$\begin{aligned} 16x^4 - 81 &= (4x^2+9)(4x^2-9) \\ &= (4x^2+9)(2x+3)(2x-3) \end{aligned}$$

93. $$\begin{aligned} 16a - 2a^4 &= 2a(8 - a^3) \\ &= 2a(2-a)(4 + 2a + a^2) \end{aligned}$$

95. $$\begin{aligned} a^3b^6 - b^3 &= b^3(a^3b^3 - 1) \\ &= b^3(ab-1)(a^2b^2 + ab + 1) \end{aligned}$$

97. $$\begin{aligned} 8x^4 - 40x^3 + 50x^2 &= 2x^2(4x^2 - 20x + 25) \\ &= 2x^2(2x-5)^2 \end{aligned}$$

99. $$\begin{aligned} x^4 - y^4 &= (x^2+y^2)(x^2-y^2) \\ &= (x^2+y^2)(x+y)(x-y) \end{aligned}$$

101. $$\begin{aligned} x^6 + y^6 &= (x^2)^3 + (y^2)^3 \\ &= (x^2+y^2)(x^4 - x^2y^2 + y^4) \end{aligned}$$

103. $a^4 - 25a^2 - 144$ is nonfactorable over the integers.

105. $$\begin{aligned} 16a^4 - 2a &= 2a(8a^3 - 1) \\ &= 2a(2a-1)(4a^2 + 2a + 1) \end{aligned}$$

107. $$\begin{aligned} a^4b^2 - 8a^3b^3 - 48a^2b^4 &= a^2b^2(a^2 - 8ab - 48b^2) \\ &= a^2b^2(a+4b)(a-12b) \end{aligned}$$

109. $$\begin{aligned} &24a^2b^2 - 14ab^3 - 90b^4 \\ &= 2b^2(12a^2 - 7ab - 45b^2) \\ &= 2b^2(3a+5b)(4a-9b) \end{aligned}$$

111. $$\begin{aligned} x^3 - 2x^2 - 4x + 8 &= x^2(x-2) - 4(x-2) \\ &= (x-2)(x^2-4) \\ &= (x-2)(x+2)(x-2) \\ &= (x-2)^2(x+2) \end{aligned}$$

113. $$\begin{aligned} &4x^4 - x^2 - 4x^2y^2 + y^2 \\ &= x^2(4x^2-1) - y^2(4x^2-1) \\ &= (4x^2-1)(x^2-y^2) \\ &= (2x+1)(2x-1)(x+y)(x-y) \end{aligned}$$

115. $$\begin{aligned} &x^6y^3 + x^3 - x^3y^3 - 1 \\ &= x^3(x^3y^3+1) - (x^3y^3+1) \\ &= (x^3y^3+1)(x^3-1) \\ &= (xy+1)(x^2y^2 - xy + 1)(x-1)(x^2+x+1) \end{aligned}$$

117. $$\begin{aligned} x^{2n+1} + 2x^{n+1} + x &= x(x^{2n} + 2x^n + 1) \\ &= x(x^n+1)^2 \end{aligned}$$

119. $$\begin{aligned} 3b^{n+2} + 4b^{n+1} - 4b^n &= b^n(3b^2 + 4b - 4) \\ &= b^n(b+2)(3b-2) \end{aligned}$$

Applying the Concepts

121. $$\begin{aligned} &x^2(x-3) - 3x(x-3) + 2(x-3) \\ &= (x-3)(x-3x+2) \\ &= (x-3)(x-2)(x-1) \end{aligned}$$

123. $$\begin{aligned} &x^4 + x^2y^2 + y^4 \\ &= (x^4 + 2x^2y^2 + y^4) - x^2y^2 \\ &= (x^2+y^2)(x^2+y^2) - x^2y^2 \\ &= (x^2+y^2)^2 - x^2y^2 \\ &= (x^2+y^2+xy)(x^2+y^2-xy) \end{aligned}$$

125. Divide out by synthetic division one of the first-degree factors. Then factor the remainder by grouping, using the other known factor as an aid.

3	1	6	–7	–60
		3	27	60
	1	9	20	0

$x^3 + 6x^2 - 7x - 60 = (x-3)(x^2 + 9x + 20)$
$= (x-3)(x+4)(x+5)$

The third first-degree factor is $(x + 5)$.

SECTION 5.7

Objective A Exercises

1. $(x-5)(x+3) = 0$
$x - 5 = 0 \quad x + 3 = 0$
$x = 5 \qquad x = -3$
The solutions are 5 and –3.

3. $(x+7)(x-8) = 0$
$x + 7 = 0 \quad x - 8 = 0$
$x = -7 \qquad x = 8$
The solutions are –7 and 8.

5. $2x(3x-2)(x+4) = 0$
$2x = 0 \quad 3x - 2 = 0 \quad x + 4 = 0$
$x = 0 \qquad 3x = 2 \qquad x = -4$
$x = \frac{2}{3}$
The solutions are 0, $\frac{2}{3}$, and –4.

7. $x^2 + 2x - 15 = 0$
$(x+5)(x-3) = 0$
$x + 5 = 0 \quad x - 3 = 0$
$x = -5 \qquad x = 3$
The solutions are –5 and 3.

9. $z^2 - 4z + 3 = 0$
$(z-3)(z-1) = 0$
$z - 3 = 0 \quad z - 1 = 0$
$z = 3 \qquad z = 1$
The solutions are 3 and 1.

11. $r^2 - 10 = 3r$
$r^2 - 3r - 10 = 0$
$(r-5)(r+2) = 0$
$r - 5 = 0 \quad r + 2 = 0$
$r = 5 \qquad r = -2$
The solutions are 5 and –2.

13. $4t^2 = 4t + 3$
$4t^2 - 4t - 3 = 0$
$(2t+1)(2t-3) = 0$
$2t + 1 = 0 \quad 2t - 3 = 0$
$2t = -1 \qquad 2t = 3$
$t = -\frac{1}{2} \qquad t = \frac{3}{2}$
The solutions are $-\frac{1}{2}$ and $\frac{3}{2}$.

15. $4v^2 - 4v + 1 = 0$
$(2v-1)(2v-1) = 0$
$2v - 1 = 0 \quad 2v - 1 = 0$
$2v = 1 \qquad 2v = 1$
$v = \frac{1}{2} \qquad v = \frac{1}{2}$
The solution is $\frac{1}{2}$.

17. $x^2 - 9 = 0$
$(x+3)(x-3) = 0$
$x + 3 = 0 \quad x - 3 = 0$
$x = -3 \qquad x = 3$
The solutions are –3 and 3.

19. $4y^2 - 1 = 0$
$(2y+1)(2y-1) = 0$
$2y + 1 = 0 \quad 2y - 1 = 0$
$2y = -1 \qquad 2y = 1$
$y = -\frac{1}{2} \qquad y = \frac{1}{2}$
The solutions are $-\frac{1}{2}$ and $\frac{1}{2}$.

21. $x + 15 = x(x-1)$
$x + 15 = x^2 - x$
$0 = x^2 - 2x - 15$
$0 = (x-5)(x+3)$
$x - 5 = 0 \quad x + 3 = 0$
$x = 5 \qquad x = -3$
The solutions are 5 and –3.

23. $v^2 + v + 5 = (3v+2)(v-4)$
$v^2 + v + 5 = 3v^2 - 10v - 8$
$0 = 2v^2 - 11v - 13$
$0 = (2v-13)(v+1)$
$2v - 13 = 0 \quad v + 1 = 0$
$2v = 13 \qquad v = -1$
$v = \frac{13}{2}$
The solutions are $\frac{13}{2}$ and –1.

25.
$$4x^2+x-10=(x-2)(x+1)$$
$$4x^2+x-10=x^2-x-2$$
$$3x^2+2x-8=0$$
$$(3x-4)(x+2)=0$$
$$3x-4=0 \quad x+2=0$$
$$3x=4 \quad x=-2$$
$$x=\frac{4}{3}$$
The solutions are $\frac{4}{3}$ and -2.

27.
$$c^3+3c^2-10c=0$$
$$c(c^2+3c-10)=0$$
$$c(c+5)(c-2)=0$$
$$c=0 \quad c+5=0 \quad c-2=0$$
$$c=-5 \quad c=2$$
The solutions are 0, –5, and 2.

29.
$$y^4-8y^2+16=0$$
$$(y^2-4)(y^2-4)=0$$
$$(y+2)(y-2)(y+2)(y-2)=0$$
$$y+2=0 \quad y-2=0 \quad y+2=0 \quad y-2=0$$
$$y=-2 \quad y=2 \quad y=-2 \quad y=2$$
The solutions are –2 and 2.

31.
$$a^3+a^2-9a-9=0$$
$$a^2(a+1)-9(a+1)=0$$
$$(a^2-9)(a+1)=0$$
$$(a+3)(a-3)(a+1)=0$$
$$a+3=0 \quad a-3=0 \quad a+1=0$$
$$a=-3 \quad a=3 \quad a=-1$$
The solutions are 3, –3, and –1.

33.
$$3x^3+2x^2-12x-8=0$$
$$x^2(3x+2)-4(3x+2)=0$$
$$(x^2-4)(3x+2)=0$$
$$(x+2)(x-2)(3x+2)=0$$
$$x+2=0 \quad x-2=0 \quad 3x+2=0$$
$$x=-2 \quad x=2 \quad 3x=-2$$
$$x=-\frac{2}{3}$$
The solutions are –2, 2, and $-\frac{2}{3}$.

35.
$$5x^3+2x^2-20x-8=0$$
$$x^2(5x+2)-4(5x+2)=0$$
$$(x^2-4)(5x+2)=0$$
$$(x+2)(x-2)(5x+2)=0$$
$$x+2=0 \quad x-2=0 \quad 5x+2=0$$
$$x=-2 \quad x=2 \quad 5x=-2$$
$$x=-\frac{2}{5}$$
The solutions are –2, 2, and $-\frac{2}{5}$.

Objective B Application Problems

37. Strategy
- Number: x
  Square of the number: x^2
- Sum of the number and its square is 210.

Solution
$$x+x^2=210$$
$$x^2+x-210=0$$
$$(x+15)(x-14)=0$$
$$x=-15 \quad x=14$$
The number is 14 or –15.

39. Strategy
- Width of the rectangle: w
  Length of the rectangle: $3w+8$
- Area of the rectangle is length · width = $w(3w+8)$.
  Area is 380 cm^2.

Solution
$$w(3w+8)=380$$
$$3w^2+8w-380=0$$
$$(3w+38)(w-10)=0$$
$$w=-\frac{38}{3} \quad w=10$$
The width of the rectangle is 10 cm and the length is 38 cm.

41. Strategy
- Length of one leg: x
  Length of other leg: $2x+2$
- Square of the hypotenuse of triangle is the sum of the squares of the other two legs and is equal to $(2x+2)+1=2x+3$.

Solution
$$x^2+(2x+2)^2=(2x+3)^2$$
$$x^2+4x^2+8x+4=4x^2+12x+9$$
$$x^2-4x-5=0$$
$$(x-5)(x+1)=0$$
$$x=5 \quad x=-1$$
The length of the hypotenuse is 13 ft.

43. Strategy
- Distance is d: 80 ft
  Speed is v: 8 ft/s

Solution
$$d=vt+16t^2$$
$$80=8t+16t^2$$
$$16t^2+8t-80=0$$
$$(16t+40)(t-2)=0$$
$$t=-2.5 \quad t=2$$
The stone will hit the bottom of the well in 2 seconds.

Applying the Concepts

45. Strategy
- Height of box: 2 in.
  Width of box: $w - 4$
  Length of box: $(w + 10) - 4 = w + 6$
- The volume of the box is length · width · height and is equal to 112 in^3.

Solution
$$(w+6)(w-4)\cdot 2 = 112$$
$$(w+6)(w-4) = 56$$
$$w^2 + 2w - 24 = 56$$
$$w^2 + 2w - 80 = 0$$
$$(w+10)(w-8) = 0$$
$$w = -10 \quad w = 8$$

Width cannot be negative, so the width of the cardboard is 8 inches and the length is 18 inches.

CHAPTER REVIEW

1. The GCF of $18a^5b^2 - 12a^3b^3 + 30a^2b$ is $6a^2b$.
$$18a^5b^2 - 12a^3b^3 + 30a^2b$$
$$= 6a^2b(3a^3b - 2ab^2 + 5)$$

2.
$$\begin{array}{r} 5x+4 \\ 3x-2\,\overline{)\,15x^2 + 2x - 2} \\ \underline{15x^2 - 10x} \\ 12x - 2 \\ \underline{12x - 8} \\ 6 \end{array}$$

$$\frac{15x^2 + 2x - 2}{3x - 2} = 5x + 4 + \frac{6}{3x - 2}$$

3.
$$(2x^{-1}y^2z^5)^4(-3x^3yz^{-3})^2$$
$$= (16x^{-4}y^8z^{20})(9x^6y^2z^{-6})$$
$$= 144x^2y^{10}z^{14}$$

4.
$$2ax + 4bx - 3ay - 6by = 2x(a+2b) - 3y(a+2b)$$
$$= (a+2b)(2x-3y)$$

5. $12 + x - x^2 = (4 - x)(3 + x)$

6.

2	1	–2	3	–5
		2	0	6
	1	0	3	1

$P(2) = 1$

7.
$$(5x^2 - 8xy + 2y^2) - (x^2 - 3y^2)$$
$$= (5x^2 - x^2) - 8xy + (2y^2 + 3y^2)$$
$$= 4x^2 - 8xy + 5y^2$$

8. $24x^2 + 38x + 15 = (6x+5)(4x+3)$

9. $4x^2 + 12xy + 9y^2 = (2x + 3y)^2$

10. $(-2a^2b^4)(3ab^2) = -6a^3b^6$

11.
$$64a^3 - 27b^3 = (4a)^3 - (3b)^3$$
$$= (4a - 3b)(16a^2 + 12ab + 9b^2)$$

12.

–6	4	27	10	2
		–24	–18	48
	4	3	–8	50

$$\frac{4x^3 + 27x^2 + 10x + 2}{x+6} = 4x^2 + 3x - 8 + \frac{50}{x+6}$$

13.
$$P(-2) = 2(-2)^3 - (-2) + 7$$
$$P(-2) = -16 + 2 + 7$$
$$P(2) = -7$$

14. $x^2 - 3x - 40 = (x - 8)(x + 5)$

15. Let $u = xy$.
$$x^2y^2 - 9 = u^2 - 9$$
$$= (u+3)(u-3)$$
$$= (xy+3)(xy-3)$$

16.
$$4x^2y(3x^3y^2 + 2xy - 7y^3)$$
$$= 12x^5y^3 + 8x^3y^2 - 28x^2y^4$$

17. Let $u = x^n$.
$$x^{2n} - 12x^n + 36 = u^2 - 12u + 36$$
$$= (u-6)^2$$
$$= (x^n - 6)^2$$

18.
$$6x^2 + 60 = 39x$$
$$6x^2 - 39x + 60 = 0$$
$$3(2x^2 - 13x + 20) = 0$$
$$3(2x-5)(x-4) = 0$$
$$2x - 5 = 0 \quad x - 4 = 0$$
$$2x = 5 \quad x = 4$$
$$x = \frac{5}{2}$$

The solutions are $\frac{5}{2}$ and 4.

19.
$$5x^2 - 4x[x - 3(3x+2) + x]$$
$$= 5x^2 - 4x(x - 9x - 6 + x)$$
$$= 5x^2 - 4x(-7x - 6)$$
$$= 5x^2 + 28x^2 + 24x$$
$$= 33x^2 + 24x$$

20.
$$3a^6 - 15a^4 - 18a^2 = 3a^2(a^4 - 5a^2 - 6)$$
$$= 3a^2(a^2 - 6)(a^2 + 1)$$

21. $(4x - 3y)^2 = 16x^2 - 24xy + 9y^2$

22.

4	1	0	0	0	–4
		4	16	64	256
	1	4	16	64	252

$$\frac{x^4-4}{x-4}=x^3+4x^2+16x+64+\frac{252}{x-4}$$

23. Let $u=x^2$.

$$\begin{aligned}15x^4+x^2-6&=15u^2+u-6\\&=(3u+2)(5u-3)\\&=(3x^2+2)(5x^2-3)\end{aligned}$$

24. $$\begin{aligned}\frac{(2a^4b^{-3}c^2)^3}{(2a^3b^2c^{-1})^4}&=\frac{8a^{12}b^{-9}c^6}{16a^{12}b^8c^{-4}}\\&=\frac{1}{2}a^{12-12}b^{-9-8}c^{6-(-4)}\\&=\frac{1}{2}b^{-17}c^{10}=\frac{c^{10}}{2b^{17}}\end{aligned}$$

25. $$\begin{aligned}&(x-4)(3x+2)(2x-3)\\&=(x-4)(6x^2-5x-6)\\&=6x^3-5x^2-6x-24x^2+20x+24\\&=6x^3-29x^2+14x+24\end{aligned}$$

26. Let $u=x^2y^2$.

$$\begin{aligned}21x^4y^4+23x^2y^2+6&=21u^2+23u+6\\&=(7u+3)(3u+2)\\&=(7x^2y^2+3)(3x^2y^2+2)\end{aligned}$$

27. $$\begin{aligned}x^3+16&=x(x+16)\\x^3+16&=x^2+16x\\x^3-x^2-16x+16&=0\\x^2(x-1)-16(x-1)&=0\\(x-1)(x^2-16)&=0\\(x-1)(x+4)(x-4)&=0\end{aligned}$$

$x-1=0 \quad x+4=0 \quad x-4=0$

$x=1 \quad x=-4 \quad x=4$

The solutions are 1, –4, and 4.

28. $(5a+2b)(5a-2b)=25a^2-4b^2$

29. $2.54\times10^{-3}=0.00254$

30. $6x^2-31x+18=(3x-2)(2x-9)$

31. $y=x^2+1$

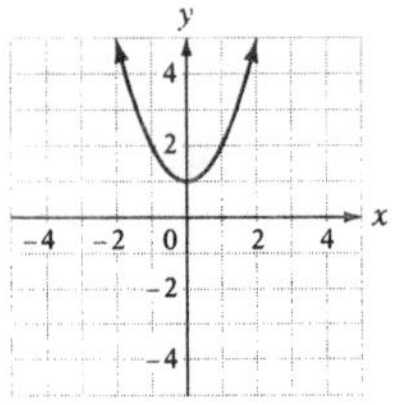

32. **a.** 3

b. 8

c. 5

33. Strategy To find the mass of the moon, multiply the mass of the sun $(2.19\times10^{27}$ tons) by 3.7×10^{-8}.

Solution $(2.19\times10^{27})(3.7\times10^{-8})$
$=8.103\times10^{19}$
The mass of the moon is 8.103×10^{19} tons.

34. Strategy The unknown number: x
The square of the number: x^2

Solution
$$\begin{aligned}x+x^2&=56\\x^2+x-56&=0\\(x+8)(x-7)&=0\end{aligned}$$

$x+8=0 \quad x-7=0$

$x=-8 \quad x=7$

The number is –8 or 7.

35. Strategy T is from the Great Galaxy of Andromeda, use the equation $d=rt$ where $r=6.7\times10^8$ mph and $t=2.2\times10^6$ years.
$2.2\times10^6\times24\times365$
$=1.9272\times10^{10}$ hours

Solution
$$\begin{aligned}d&=r\cdot t\\&=(6.7\times10^8)(1.9272\times10^{10})\\&=6.7\times1.9272\times10^{18}\\&=12.91224\times10^{18}\\&=1.291224\times10^{19}\end{aligned}$$
The distance from earth to the Great Galaxy of Andromeda is 1.291224×10^{19} miles.

36. Strategy To find the area, replace the variables *L* and *W* in the equation *A* = *LW* by the given values and solve for *A*.

Solution
$$\begin{aligned}A&=L\cdot W\\A&=(5x+3)(2x-7)\\&=10x^2-29x-21\end{aligned}$$
The area is $(10x^2-29x-21)$ cm^2.

CHAPTER TEST

1. $16t^2 + 24t + 9 = (4t + 3)^2$

2. $-6rs^2(3r - 2s - 3) = -18r^2s^2 + 12rs^3 + 18rs^2$

3. $P(2) = 3(2)^2 - 8(2) + 1$
$P(2) = 12 - 16 + 1$
$P(2) = -3$

4. $27x^3 - 8 = (3x)^3 - (2)^3 = (3x - 2)(9x^2 + 6x + 4)$

5. $16x^2 - 25 = (4x + 5)(4x - 5)$

6.
$$\begin{array}{rrrrrr} & & 3t^3 & -4t^2 & & +1 \\ \times & & & 2t^2 & & -5 \\ \hline & & -15t^3 & +20t^2 & & -5 \\ 6t^5 & -8t^4 & & +2t^2 & & \\ \hline 6t^5 & -8t^4 & -15t^3 & +22t^2 & & -5 \end{array}$$

7. $-5x[3 - 2(2x - 4) - 3x] = -5x[3 - 4x + 8 - 3x]$
$= -5x[-7x + 11]$
$= 35x^2 - 55x$

8. $12x^3 + 12x^2 - 45x = 3x(4x^2 + 4x - 15)$
$= 3x(2x - 3)(2x + 5)$

9. $6x^3 + x^2 - 6x - 1 = 0$
$x^2(6x + 1) - 1(6x + 1) = 0$
$(x^2 - 1)(6x + 1) = 0$
$(x + 1)(x - 1)(6x + 1) = 0$
$x + 1 = 0 \quad x - 1 = 0 \quad 6x + 1 = 0$
$x = -1 \quad x = 1 \quad 6x = -1$
$x = -\frac{1}{6}$

The solutions are -1, 1, and $-\frac{1}{6}$.

10. $(6x^3 - 7x^2 + 6x - 7) - (4x^3 - 3x^2 + 7)$
$= (6x^3 - 7x^2 + 6x - 7) + (-4x^3 + 3x^2 - 7)$
$= 2x^3 - 4x^2 + 6x - 14$

11. $0.000000501 = 5.01 \times 10^{-7}$

12.
$$\begin{array}{r} 2x + 1 \\ 7x - 3 \overline{)\, 14x^2 + x + 1} \\ \underline{14x^2 - 6x} \\ 7x + 1 \\ \underline{7x - 3} \\ 4 \end{array}$$

$\frac{14x^2 + x + 1}{7x - 3} = 2x + 1 + \frac{4}{7x - 3}$

13. $(7 - 5x)(7 + 5x) = 49 - 25x^2$

14. Let $u = a^2$.
$6a^4 - 13a^2 - 5 = 6u^2 - 13u - 5$
$= (2u - 5)(3u + 1)$
$= (2a^2 - 5)(3a^2 + 1)$

15. $(3a + 4b)(2a - 7b) = 6a^2 - 13ab - 28b^2$

16. $3x^4 - 23x^2 - 36 = (3x^2 + 4)(x^2 - 9)$
$= (3x^2 + 4)(x - 3)(x + 3)$

17. $(-4a^2b)^3(-ab^4) = -64a^6b^3(-ab^4)$
$= 64a^7b^7$

18. $6x^2 = x + 1$
$6x^2 - x - 1 = 0$
$(2x - 1)(3x + 1) = 0$
$2x - 1 = 0 \quad 3x + 1 = 0$
$2x = 1 \quad 3x = -1$
$x = \frac{1}{2} \quad x = -\frac{1}{3}$

The solutions are $\frac{1}{2}$ and $-\frac{1}{3}$.

19.
$$\begin{array}{r|rrrr} -2 & -1 & 0 & 4 & -8 \\ & & 2 & -4 & 0 \\ \hline & -1 & 2 & 0 & -8 \end{array}$$

$P(-2) = -8$

20. $\frac{(2a^{-4}b^2)^3}{4a^{-2}b^{-1}} = \frac{8a^{-12}b^6}{4a^{-2}b^{-1}}$
$= 2a^{-12-(-2)}b^{6-(-1)}$
$= 2a^{-10}b^7 = \frac{2b^7}{a^{10}}$

21.
$$\begin{array}{r|rrrr} -3 & 1 & -2 & -5 & 7 \\ & & -3 & 15 & -30 \\ \hline & 1 & -5 & 10 & -23 \end{array}$$

$\frac{x^3 - 2x^2 - 5x + 7}{x + 3} = x^2 - 5x + 10 - \frac{23}{x + 3}$

22. $12 - 17x + 6x^2 = (3 - 2x)(4 - 3x)$

23. $6x^2 - 4x - 3xa + 2a = 2x(3x - 2) - a(3x - 2)$
$= (3x - 2)(2x - a)$

24. Strategy To find the number of seconds in one week in scientific notation:

- Multiply the number of seconds in a minute (60) by the minutes in an hour (60) by the hours in a day (24) by the days in a week (7).
- Convert that product to scientific notation.

Solution $60\times60\times24\times7=604{,}800$

$=6.048\times10^5$

The number of seconds in a week is 6.048×10^5.

25. Strategy • The distance is h: 64 ft

Solution

$$h=32+48t-16t^2$$
$$64=32+48t-16t^2$$
$$16t^2-48t+32=0$$
$$t^2-3t+2=0$$
$$(t-1)(t-2)=0$$
$$t-1=0 \quad t-2=0$$
$$t=1 \quad t=2$$

The arrow will be 64 ft above the ground at 1 s and at 2 s after the arrow has been released.

26. Strategy To find the area, replace the variables L and W in the equation $A=L\cdot W$ by the given values and solve for A.

Solution $A=L\cdot W$

$A=(5x+1)(2x-1)$

$=10x^2-3x-1$

The area is $(10x^2-3x-1)\ \text{ft}^2$.

CUMULATIVE REVIEW

1. $8-2[-3-(-1)]^2+4=8-2[-3+1]^2+4$

$=8-2[-2]^2+4$

$=8-2(4)+4$

$=8-8+4$

$=0+4=4$

2. $\dfrac{2a-b}{b-c}=\dfrac{2(4)-(-2)}{-2-6}$

$=\dfrac{8+2}{-8}$

$=\dfrac{10}{-8}=-\dfrac{5}{4}$

3. The Inverse Property of Addition

4. $2x-4[x-2(3-2x)+4]=2x-4[x-6+4x+4]$

$=2x-4(5x-2)$

$=2x-20x+8$

$=-18x+8$

5.

$$\frac{2}{3}-y=\frac{5}{6}$$
$$\frac{2}{3}-y-\frac{2}{3}=\frac{5}{6}-\frac{2}{3}$$
$$-y=\frac{1}{6}$$
$$(-1)(-y)=(-1)\frac{1}{6}$$
$$y=-\frac{1}{6}$$

6.

$$8x-3-x=-6+3x-8$$
$$7x-3=3x-14$$
$$7x-3-3x=3x-14-3x$$
$$4x-3=-14$$
$$4x-3+3=-14+3$$
$$4x=-11$$
$$\frac{4x}{4}=-\frac{11}{4}$$
$$x=-\frac{11}{4}$$

7.

3	1	0	0	−3
		3	9	27
	1	3	9	24

$$\frac{x^3-3}{x-3}=x^2+3x+9+\frac{24}{x-3}$$

8. $3-|2-3x|=-2$

$-|2-3x|=-5$

$|2-3x|=5$

$2-3x=5 \quad 2-3x=-5$

$-3x=3 \quad -3x=-7$

$x=-1 \quad x=\dfrac{7}{3}$

The solutions are -1 and $\dfrac{7}{3}$.

9. $P(-2)=3(-2)^2-2(-2)+2$

$P(-2)=12+4+2$

$P(-2)=18$

10. $x=-2$

11. Range = $\{-4, -1, 8\}$

12. $M=\dfrac{y_2-y_1}{x_2-x_1}=\dfrac{2-3}{4-(-2)}=-\dfrac{1}{6}$

The slope is $-\dfrac{1}{6}$.

13. Use the point-slope form.

$$y-y_1=m(x-x_1)$$
$$y-2=-\frac{3}{2}[x-(-1)]$$
$$y-2=-\frac{3}{2}x-\frac{3}{2}$$
$$y=-\frac{3}{2}x+\frac{1}{2}$$

14. First find the x- and y-intercepts. Then use them to find the slope of the line.

$x\text{-intercept} = \left(\frac{4}{3}, 0\right)$

$y\text{-intercept} = (0, 2)$

$$m = \frac{y_2 - y_1}{x_2 - x_1} = \frac{2-0}{0-\frac{4}{3}} = -\frac{3}{2} \quad \left(-\frac{3}{2}\right)$$

The perpendicular line will have a slope that is the negative reciprocal of $-\frac{3}{2}$.

$$m = \frac{2}{3}$$

Now use the point-slope form of the equation to find the equation of the line.

$$y - y_1 = m(x - x_1)$$
$$y - 4 = \frac{2}{3}[x - (-2)]$$
$$y - 4 = \frac{2}{3}x + \frac{4}{3}$$
$$y = \frac{2}{3}x + \frac{16}{3}$$

The equation of the perpendicular line is $y = \frac{2}{3}x + \frac{16}{3}$.

15. $2x - 3y = 2$
$x + y = -3$

$$D = \begin{vmatrix} 2 & -3 \\ 1 & 1 \end{vmatrix} = 5$$
$$D_x = \begin{vmatrix} 2 & -3 \\ -3 & 1 \end{vmatrix} = -7$$
$$D_y = \begin{vmatrix} 2 & 2 \\ 1 & -3 \end{vmatrix} = -8$$
$$x = \frac{D_x}{D} = -\frac{7}{5}$$
$$y = \frac{D_y}{D} = -\frac{8}{5}$$

The solution is $\left(-\frac{7}{5}, -\frac{8}{5}\right)$.

16. (1) $x - y + z = 0$
(2) $2x + y - 3z = -7$
(3) $-x + 2y + 2z = 5$

Add Equations (1) and (3) to eliminate x.

$$\begin{array}{r} x - y + z = 0 \\ -x + 2y + 2z = 5 \\ \hline y + 3z = -5 \end{array}$$

Add –2 times Equation (1) and Equation (2) to eliminate x.

$$\begin{array}{r} -2x + 2y - 2z = 0 \\ 2x + y - 3z = -7 \\ \hline 3y - 5z = -7 \end{array}$$

Now solve the system in two variables.

$$y + 3z = 5$$
$$3y - 5z = -7$$

Add –3 times the first of these equations to the second.

$$\begin{array}{r} -3y - 9z = -15 \\ 3y - 5z = -7 \\ \hline -14z = -22 \end{array}$$

$$z = \frac{11}{7}$$

Next find y.

$$y + 3z = 5$$
$$y + 3\left(\frac{11}{7}\right) = 5$$
$$y = \frac{2}{7}$$

Replace y and z in Equation (1) and solve for x.

$$x - \frac{2}{7} + \frac{11}{7} = 0$$
$$x = -\frac{9}{7}$$

The solution is $\left(-\frac{9}{7}, \frac{2}{7}, \frac{11}{7}\right)$.

17.

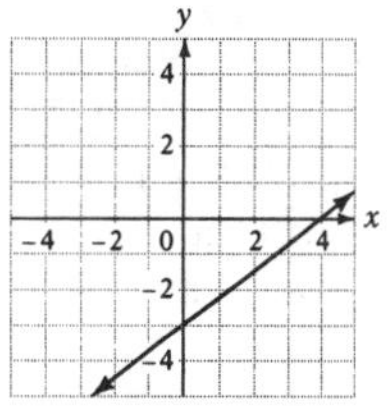

18.

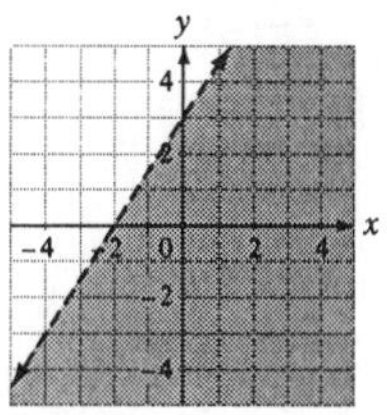

19.

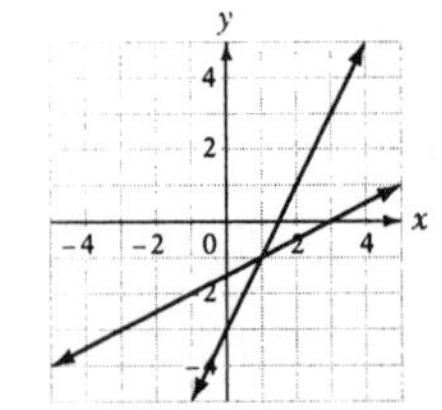

The lines intersect at $(1, -1)$.

20. Solve each inequality.

$$2x + y < 3$$
$$y < 3 - 2x$$

$$-6x + 3y \ge 4$$
$$3y \ge 4 + 6x$$
$$y \ge \frac{4}{3} + 2x$$

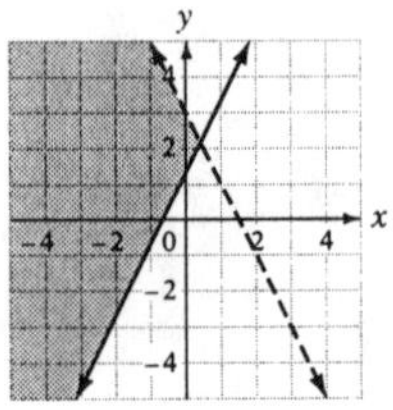

21. $$(4a^{-2}b^3)(2a^3b^{-1})^{-2} = 4a^{-2}b^3(2^{-2}a^{-6}b^2) = 4 \cdot 2^{-2}a^{-2-6}b^{3+2} = 4 \cdot \frac{1}{4}a^{-8}b^5 = \frac{b^5}{a^8}$$

22. $$\frac{(5x^3y^{-3}z)^{-2}}{y^4z^{-2}} = \frac{5^{-2}x^{-6}y^6z^{-2}}{y^4z^{-2}} = 5^{-2}x^{-6}y^{6-4}z^{-2-(-2)} = \frac{1}{25}x^{-6}y^2 = \frac{y^2}{25x^6}$$

23. $$3-(3-3^{-1})^{-1} = 3-\left(3-\frac{1}{3}\right)^{-1} = 3-\left(\frac{8}{3}\right)^{-1} = 3-\frac{3}{8} = \frac{21}{8}$$

24.

$$\begin{array}{r} 2x^2 - 3x + 1 \\ \times \qquad\qquad 2x + 3 \\ \hline 6x^2 - 9x + 3 \\ 4x^3 - 6x^2 + 2x \qquad \\ \hline 4x^3 \qquad\quad - 7x + 3 \end{array}$$

25. $$-4x^3 + 14x^2 - 12x = -2x(2x^2 - 7x + 6) = -2x(2x-3)(x-2)$$

26. $$a(x-y) - b(y-x) = a(x-y) + b(x-y) = (x-y)(a+b)$$

27. $$x^4 - 16 = (x^2+4)(x^2-4) = (x^2+4)(x+2)(x-2)$$

28. $$2x^2 - 16 = 2(x^3 - 8) = 2(x-2)(x^2+2x+4)$$

29. Strategy

- Smaller integer: x
  Larger integer: $24 - x$
- The difference between four times the smaller and nine is 3 less than twice the larger.

$$4x - 9 = 2(24 - x) - 3$$

Solution

$$4x - 9 = 2(24 - x) - 3$$
$$4x - 9 = 48 - 2x - 3$$
$$4x - 9 = 45 - 2x$$
$$6x - 9 = 45$$
$$6x = 54$$
$$x = 9$$
$$24 - x = 15$$

The integers are 9 and 15.

30. Strategy

- The number of ounces of pure gold: x

	Amount	Cost	Value
Pure gold	x	360	$360x$
Alloy	80	120	80(120)
Mixture	$x + 80$	200	$200(x + 80)$

- The sum of the values before mixing equals the value after mixing.

Solution

$$360x + 80(120) = 200(x + 80)$$
$$360x + 9600 = 200x + 16{,}000$$
$$160x + 9600 = 16{,}000$$
$$160x = 6400$$
$$x = 40$$

40 oz of pure gold must be mixed with the alloy.

31. Strategy • Faster cyclist: x

Slower cyclist: $\frac{2}{3}x$

	Rate	Time	Distance
Faster cyclist	x	2	$2x$
Slower cyclist	$\frac{2}{3}x$	2	$2\left(\frac{2}{3}x\right)$

• The sum of the distances is 25 miles.

Solution

$$2x+2\left(\frac{2}{3}x\right)=25$$
$$2x+\frac{4}{3}x=25$$
$$\frac{10}{3}x=25$$
$$x=7.5$$
$$\frac{2}{3}x=5$$

The slower cyclist travels at 5 mph, the faster cyclist at 7.5 mph.

32. Strategy To find the time:

• Use the equation $d=rt$, where r is the speed of the space vehicle and d is the distance from the earth to the moon.

Solution

$$d=rt$$
$$2.4\times10^5=(2\times10^4)t$$
$$\frac{2.4\times10^5}{2\times10^4}=t$$
$$1.2\times10^1=t$$

The vehicle will reach the moon in 12 h.

33. $m=\dfrac{y_2-y_1}{x_2-x_1}=\dfrac{300-100}{6-2}$

$m=50$

The slope represents the average speed of travel in miles per hour.

Chapter 6: Rational Expressions

SECTION 6.1

Objective A Exercises

1. $f(x) = \frac{2}{x-3}$

$f(4) = \frac{2}{4-3} = \frac{2}{1} = 2$

3. $f(x) = \frac{x-2}{x+4}$

$f(-2) = \frac{-2-2}{-2+4} = \frac{-4}{2} = -2$

5. $f(x) = \frac{1}{x^2 - 2x + 1}$

$f(-2) = \frac{1}{(-2)^2 - 2(-2) + 1} = \frac{1}{9}$

7. $f(x) = \frac{x-2}{2x^2 + 3x + 8}$

$f(-3) = \frac{3-2}{2(3)^2 + 3(3) + 8} = \frac{1}{35}$

9. $f(x) = \frac{x^2 - 2x}{x^3 - x + 4}$

$f(-1) = \frac{(-1)^2 - 2(-1)}{(-1)^3 - (-1) + 4} = \frac{3}{4}$

11. $f(x) = \frac{4}{x-3}$

$x - 3 = 0$

$x = 3$

The domain is $\{x | x \neq 3\}$.

13. $H(x) = \frac{x}{x+4}$

$x + 4 = 0$

$x = -4$

The domain is $\{x | x \neq -4\}$.

15. $h(x) = \frac{5x}{3x+9}$

$3x + 9 = 0$

$3x = -9$

$x = -3$

The domain is $\{x | x \neq -3\}$.

17. $q(x) = \frac{4-x}{(x-4)(3x-2)}$

$(x-4)(3x-2) = 0$

$x - 4 = 0 \quad 3x - 2 = 0$

$x = 4 \quad 3x = 2$

$x = \frac{2}{3}$

The domain is $\left\{x \middle| x \neq 4, \frac{2}{3}\right\}$.

19. $f(x) = \frac{2x-1}{x^2 + x - 6}$

$x^2 + x - 6 = 0$

$(x+3)(x-2) = 0$

$x + 3 = 0 \quad x - 2 = 0$

$x = -3 \quad x = 2$

The domain is $\{x | x \neq -3, 2\}$.

21. $f(x) = \frac{x+1}{x^2 + 1}$

The domain is $\{x | x \in \text{real numbers}\}$.

23. $\frac{4-8x}{4} = \frac{4(1-2x)}{4} = 1 - 2x$

25. $\frac{6x^2 - 2x}{2x} = \frac{2x(3x-1)}{2x} = 3x - 1$

27. $\frac{8x^2(x-3)}{4x(x-3)} = \frac{8x^2}{4x} = 2x$

29. $\frac{-36a^2 - 48a}{18a^3 + 24a^2} = \frac{-12a(3a+4)}{6a^2(3a+4)}$

$= \frac{-12a}{6a^2} = -\frac{2}{a}$

31. $\frac{3x-6}{x^2 + 2x} = \frac{3(x-2)}{x(x+2)}$

The expression is in simplest form.

33. $\frac{3x^3y^3 - 12x^2y^2 + 15xy}{3xy} = \frac{3xy(x^2y^2 - 4xy + 5)}{3xy}$

$= x^2y^2 - 4xy + 5$

35. $\frac{x^{2n} + x^n y^n}{x^{2n} - y^{2n}} = \frac{x^n(x^n + y^n)}{(x^n + y^n)(x^n - y^n)}$

$= \frac{x^n}{x^n - y^n}$

37. $\frac{x^2 - 7x + 12}{x^2 - 9x + 20} = \frac{(x-3)(x-4)}{(x-4)(x-5)}$

$= \frac{x-3}{x-5}$

39. $\frac{3x^2+10x-8}{8-14x+3x^2}=\frac{(3x-2)(x+4)}{(2-3x)(4-x)}$
$=-\frac{x+4}{4-x}=\frac{x+4}{x-4}$

41. $\frac{a^2-b^2}{a^3+b^3}=\frac{(a+b)(a-b)}{(a+b)(a^2-ab+b^2)}$
$=\frac{a-b}{a^2-ab+b^2}$

43. $\frac{8x^3-y^3}{4x^2-y^2}=\frac{(2x-y)(4x^2+2xy+y^2)}{(2x+y)(2x-y)}$
$=\frac{4x^2+2xy+y^2}{2x+y}$

45. $\frac{x^2(a-2)-a+2}{ax^2-ax}=\frac{x^2(a-2)-(a-2)}{ax(x-1)}$
$=\frac{(a-2)(x^2-1)}{ax(x-1)}$
$=\frac{(a-2)(x+1)(x-1)}{ax(x-1)}$
$=\frac{(a-2)(x+1)}{ax}$

47. $\frac{x^4-2x^2-3}{x^4+2x^2+1}=\frac{(x^2+1)(x^2-3)}{(x^2+1)(x^2+1)}$
$=\frac{x^2-3}{x^2+1}$

49. $\frac{6x^2y^2+11xy+4}{9x^2y^2+9xy-4}=\frac{(2xy+1)(3xy+4)}{(3xy+4)(3xy-1)}$
$=\frac{2xy+1}{3xy-1}$

51. $\frac{a^{2n}+a^n-12}{a^{2n}-2a^n-3}=\frac{(a^n+4)(a^n-3)}{(a^n+1)(a^n-3)}$
$=\frac{a^n+4}{a^n+1}$

53. $\frac{a^{2n}+2a^nb^n+b^{2n}}{a^{2n}-b^{2n}}=\frac{(a^n+b^n)(a^n+b^n)}{(a^n+b^n)(a^n-b^n)}$
$=\frac{a^n+b^n}{a^n-b^n}$

55. $\frac{x^2(a+b)+a+b}{x^4-1}=\frac{x^2(a+b)+1(a+b)}{(x^2+1)(x^2-1)}$
$=\frac{(a+b)(x^2+1)}{(x^2+1)(x+1)(x-1)}$
$=\frac{a+b}{(x+1)(x-1)}$

Objective B Exercises

57. $\frac{15x^2y^4}{24ab^3}\cdot\frac{28a^2b^4}{35xy^4}=\frac{15\cdot 28a^2b^4x^2y^4}{24\cdot 35ab^3xy^4}$
$=\frac{2^2\cdot 3\cdot 5\cdot 7a^2b^4x^2y^4}{2^3\cdot 3\cdot 5\cdot 7ab^3xy^4}$
$=\frac{abx}{2}$

59. $\frac{2x^2+4x}{8x^2-40x}\cdot\frac{6x^3-30x^2}{3x^2+6x}=\frac{2x(x+2)}{8x(x-5)}\cdot\frac{6x^2(x-5)}{3x(x+2)}$
$=\frac{2x(x+2)\cdot 6x^2(x-5)}{8x(x-5)\cdot 3x(x+2)}$
$=\frac{2x\cdot 6x^2}{8x\cdot 3x}$
$=\frac{x}{2}$

61. $\frac{2x^2-5x+3}{x^6y^3}\cdot\frac{x^4y^4}{2x^2-x-3}$
$=\frac{(2x-3)(x-1)}{x^6y^3}\cdot\frac{x^4y^4}{(2x-3)(x+1)}$
$=\frac{(2x-3)(x-1)\cdot x^4y^4}{x^6y^3(2x-3)(x+1)}$
$=\frac{(x-1)\cdot x^4y^4}{x^6y^3(x+1)}$
$=\frac{y(x-1)}{x^2(x+1)}$

63. $\frac{x^2+x-6}{12+x-x^2}\cdot\frac{x^2+x-20}{x^2-4x+4}$
$=\frac{(x+3)(x-2)}{(3+x)(4-x)}\cdot\frac{(x+5)(x-4)}{(x-2)(x-2)}$
$=\frac{(x+3)(x-2)(x+5)(x-4)}{(3+x)(4-x)(x-2)(x-2)}$
$=-\frac{x+5}{x-2}$

65. $\frac{x^{2n}+2x^n}{x^{n+1}+2x}\cdot\frac{x^2-3x}{x^{n+1}-3x^n}$
$=\frac{x^n(x^n+2)}{x(x^n+2)}\cdot\frac{x(x-3)}{x^n(x-3)}$
$=\frac{x^n(x^n+2)\cdot x(x-3)}{x(x^n+2)\cdot x^n(x-3)}$
$=\frac{x^n\cdot x}{x\cdot x^n}$
$=1$

67. $\dfrac{x^{2n}+3x^n+2}{x^{2n}-x^n-6}\cdot\dfrac{x^{2n}+x^n-12}{x^{2n}-1}$
$=\dfrac{(x^n+1)(x^n+2)}{(x^n+2)(x^n-3)}\cdot\dfrac{(x^n+4)(x^n-3)}{(x^n+1)(x^n-1)}$
$=\dfrac{(x^n+1)(x^n+2)(x^n+4)(x^n-3)}{(x^n+2)(x^n-3)(x^n+1)(x^n-1)}$
$=\dfrac{x^n+4}{x^n-1}$

69. $\dfrac{x^4-5x^2+4}{3x^2-4x-4}\cdot\dfrac{3x^2-10x-8}{x^2-4}$
$=\dfrac{(x^2-1)(x^2-4)}{(3x+2)(x-2)}\cdot\dfrac{(3x+2)(x-4)}{(x^2-4)}$
$=\dfrac{(x+1)(x-1)(x^2-4)(3x+2)(x-4)}{(3x+2)(x-2)(x^2-4)}$
$=\dfrac{(x+1)(x-1)(x-4)}{x-2}$

71. $\dfrac{x^2-y^2}{x^2+xy+y^2}\cdot\dfrac{x^2-xy}{3x^2-3xy}\cdot\dfrac{x^3-y^3}{x^2-2xy+y^2}$
$=\dfrac{(x+y)(x-y)}{(x^2+xy+y^2)}\cdot\dfrac{x(x-y)}{3x(x-y)}\cdot\dfrac{(x-y)(x^2+xy+y^2)}{(x-y)(x-y)}$
$=\dfrac{(x+y)(x-y)\cdot x(x-y)(x-y)(x^2+xy+y^2)}{(x^2+xy+y^2)\cdot 3x(x-y)(x-y)(x-y)}$
$=\dfrac{x+y}{3}$

Objective C Exercises

73. $\dfrac{12a^4b^7}{13x^2y^2}\div\dfrac{18a^5b^6}{26xy^3}$
$=\dfrac{12a^4b^7}{13x^2y^2}\cdot\dfrac{26xy^3}{18a^5b^6}$
$=\dfrac{12\cdot 26a^4b^7xy^3}{13\cdot 18a^5b^6x^2y^2}$
$=\dfrac{2^3\cdot 3\cdot 13a^4b^7xy^3}{2\cdot 3^2\cdot 13a^5b^6x^2y^2}$
$=\dfrac{2^2by}{3ax}=\dfrac{4by}{3ax}$

75. $\dfrac{4x^2-4y^2}{6x^2y^2}\div\dfrac{3x^2+3xy}{2x^2y-2xy^2}$
$=\dfrac{4x^2-4y^2}{6x^2y^2}\cdot\dfrac{2x^2y-2xy^2}{3x^3+3xy}$
$=\dfrac{4(x+y)(x-y)}{6x^2y^2}\cdot\dfrac{2xy(x-y)}{3x(x+y)}$
$=\dfrac{4(x+y)(x-y)\cdot 2xy(x-y)}{6x^2y^2\cdot 3x(x+y)}$
$=\dfrac{4(x-y)\cdot 2xy(x-y)}{6x^2y^2\cdot 3x}$
$=\dfrac{4(x-y)^2}{9x^2y}$

77. $\dfrac{8x^3+12x^2y}{4x^2-9y^2}\div\dfrac{16x^2y^2}{4x^2-12xy+9y^2}$
$=\dfrac{8x^3+12x^2y}{4x^2-9y^2}\cdot\dfrac{4x^2-12xy+9y^2}{16x^2y^2}$
$=\dfrac{4x^2(2x+3y)}{(2x+3y)(2x-3y)}\cdot\dfrac{(2x-3y)(2x-3y)}{16x^2y^2}$
$=\dfrac{4x^2(2x+3y)(2x-3y)(2x-3y)}{(2x+3y)(2x-3y)16x^2y^2}$
$=\dfrac{4x^2(2x-3y)}{16x^2y^2}$
$=\dfrac{2x-3y}{4y^2}$

79. $\dfrac{2x^2+13x+20}{8-10x-3x^2}\div\dfrac{6x^2-13x-5}{9x^2-3x-2}$
$=\dfrac{2x^2+13x+20}{8-10x-3x^2}\cdot\dfrac{9x^2-3x-2}{6x^2-13x-5}$
$=\dfrac{(2x+5)(x+4)}{(4+x)(2-3x)}\cdot\dfrac{(3x+1)(3x-2)}{(3x+1)(2x-5)}$
$=\dfrac{(2x+5)(x+4)(3x+1)(3x-2)}{(4+x)(2-3x)(3x+1)(2x-5)}$
$=-\dfrac{2x+5}{2x-5}$

81. $\dfrac{x^{2n}-4}{4x^n+8}\div\dfrac{x^{n+1}-2x}{4x^3-12x^2}$
$=\dfrac{x^{2n}-4}{4x^n+8}\cdot\dfrac{4x^3-12x^2}{x^{n+1}-2x}$
$=\dfrac{(x^n+2)(x^n-2)}{4(x^n+2)}\cdot\dfrac{4x^2(x-3)}{x(x^n-2)}$
$=\dfrac{(x^n+2)(x^n-2)\cdot 4x^2(x-3)}{4(x^n+2)\cdot x(x^n-2)}$
$=x(x-3)$

83. $\dfrac{16x^2-9}{6-5x-4x^2}\div\dfrac{16x^2+24x+9}{4x^2+11x+6}$
$=\dfrac{16x^2-9}{6-5x-4x^2}\cdot\dfrac{4x^2+11x+6}{16x^2+24x+9}$
$=\dfrac{(4x+3)(4x-3)}{(2+x)(3-4x)}\cdot\dfrac{(x+2)(4x+3)}{(4x+3)(4x+3)}$
$=\dfrac{(4x+3)(4x-3)(x+2)(4x+3)}{(2+x)(3-4x)(4x+3)(4x+3)}$
$=-1$

85. $\dfrac{x^{4n}-1}{x^{2n}+x^n-2}\div\dfrac{x^{2n}+1}{x^{2n}+3x^n+2}$
$=\dfrac{x^{4n}-1}{x^{2n}+x^n-2}\cdot\dfrac{x^{2n}+3x^n+2}{x^{2n}+1}$
$=\dfrac{(x^{2n}+1)(x^{2n}-1)}{(x^n+2)(x^n-1)}\cdot\dfrac{(x^n+1)(x^n+2)}{(x^{2n}+1)}$
$=\dfrac{(x^{2n}+1)(x^n+1)(x^n-1)}{(x^n+2)(x^n-1)}\cdot\dfrac{(x^n+1)(x^n+2)}{(x^{2n}+1)}$
$=(x^n+1)^2$

87. $\dfrac{x^3+y^3}{2x^3+2x^2y} \div \dfrac{3x^3-3x^2y+3xy^2}{6x^2-6y^2}$

$= \dfrac{x^3+y^3}{2x^3+2x^2y} \cdot \dfrac{6x^2-6y^2}{3x^3-3x^2y+3xy^2}$

$= \dfrac{(x+y)(x^2-xy+y^2)}{2x^2(x+y)} \cdot \dfrac{6(x^2-y^2)}{3x(x^2-xy+y^2)}$

$= \dfrac{(x+y)(x^2-xy+y^2)}{2x^2(x+y)} \cdot \dfrac{6(x+y)(x-y)}{3x(x^2-xy+y^2)}$

$= \dfrac{6(x+y)(x-y)}{2x^2 \cdot 3x}$

$= \dfrac{(x+y)(x+y)}{x^3}$

89. $\dfrac{3x^2+10x-8}{x^2+4x+3} \cdot \dfrac{x^2+6x+9}{3x^2-5x+2} \div \dfrac{x^2+x-12}{x^2-1}$

$= \dfrac{3x^2+10x-8}{x^2+4x+3} \cdot \dfrac{x^2+6x+9}{3x^2-5x+2} \cdot \dfrac{x^2-1}{x^2+x-12}$

$= \dfrac{(3x-2)(x+4)}{(x+3)(x+1)} \cdot \dfrac{(x+3)(x+3)}{(3x-2)(x-1)} \cdot \dfrac{(x+1)(x-1)}{(x+4)(x-3)}$

$= \dfrac{(3x-2)(x+4)(x+3)(x+3)(x+1)(x-1)}{(x+3)(x+1)(3x-2)(x-1)(x+4)(x-3)}$

$= \dfrac{x+3}{x-3}$

Applying the Concepts

91. a. $\dfrac{3x^2+6x}{4x^2-16} \cdot \dfrac{2x+8}{x^2+2x} \div \dfrac{3x-9}{5x-20}$

$= \dfrac{3x^2+6x}{4x^2-16} \cdot \dfrac{2x+8}{x^2+2x} \cdot \dfrac{5x-20}{3x-9}$

$= \dfrac{3x(x+2)}{4(x-2)(x+2)} \cdot \dfrac{2(x+4)}{x(x+2)} \cdot \dfrac{5(x-4)}{3(x-3)}$

$= \dfrac{3x(x+2) \cdot 2(x+4) \cdot 5(x-4)}{4(x-2)(x+2) \cdot x(x+2) \cdot 3(x-3)}$

$= \dfrac{5(x+4)(x-4)}{2(x-2)(x+2)(x-3)}$

b. $\dfrac{5y^2-20}{3y^2-12y} \cdot \dfrac{9y^3+6y}{2y^2-4y} \div \dfrac{y^3+2y^2}{2y^2-8y}$

$= \dfrac{5y^2-20}{3y^2-12y} \cdot \dfrac{9y^3+6y}{2y^2-4y} \cdot \dfrac{2y^2-8y}{y^3+2y^2}$

$= \dfrac{5(y-2)(y+2)}{3y(y-4)} \cdot \dfrac{3y(3y^2+2)}{2y(y-2)} \cdot \dfrac{2y(y-4)}{y^2(y+2)}$

$= \dfrac{5(y-2)(y+2) \cdot 3y(3y^2+2) \cdot 2y(y-4)}{3y(y-4) \cdot 2y(y-2) \cdot y^2(y+2)}$

$= \dfrac{5(3y^2+2)}{y^2}$

93. $\dfrac{14y^2+7y}{y} = \dfrac{7y(2y+1)}{y} = 7(2y+1)$ OK

95. $\dfrac{5b^2+3b}{b^2} = \dfrac{5\not{b}^2+3b}{\not{b}^2} = 3b+5$ Not OK

It should be $\dfrac{5b^2+3b}{b^2} = \dfrac{b(5b+3)}{b^2} = \dfrac{5b+3}{b}$

97. $\dfrac{x^2+3x-4}{x^2+3x+4} = \dfrac{1+1-1}{1+1+1} = \dfrac{1}{3}$ Not OK

This expression cannot be simplified further.

SECTION 6.2

Objective A Exercises

1. The LCM is $12x^2y^4$.

$\dfrac{3}{4x^2y} = \dfrac{3}{4x^2y} \cdot \dfrac{3y^3}{3y^3} = \dfrac{9y^3}{12x^2y^4}$

$\dfrac{17}{12xy^4} = \dfrac{17}{12xy^4} \cdot \dfrac{x}{x} = \dfrac{17x}{12x^2y^4}$

3. The LCM is $6x^2(x-2)$.

$\dfrac{x-2}{3x(x-2)} = \dfrac{x-2}{3x(x-2)} \cdot \dfrac{2x}{2x} = \dfrac{2x^2-4x}{6x^2(x-2)}$

$\dfrac{3}{6x^2} = \dfrac{3}{6x^2} \cdot \dfrac{x-2}{x-2} = \dfrac{3x-6}{6x^2(x-2)}$

5. The LCM is $2x(x-5)$.

$\dfrac{3x-1}{2x^2-10x} = \dfrac{3x-1}{2x(x-5)}$

$-3x = \dfrac{-3x}{1} \cdot \dfrac{2x(x-5)}{2x(x-5)} = -\dfrac{6x^3-30x^2}{2x(x-5)}$

7. The LCM is $(2x+3)(2x-3)$.

$\dfrac{3x}{2x-3} = \dfrac{3x}{2x-3} \cdot \dfrac{2x+3}{2x+3}$

$= \dfrac{6x^2+9x}{(2x+3)(2x-3)}$

$\dfrac{5x}{2x+3} = \dfrac{5x}{2x+3} \cdot \dfrac{2x-3}{2x-3}$

$= \dfrac{10x^2-15x}{(2x+3)(2x-3)}$

9. $x^2-9 = (x+3)(x-3)$

The LCM is $(x+3)(x-3)$.

$\dfrac{2x}{x^2-9} = \dfrac{2x}{(x+3)(x-3)}$

$\dfrac{x+1}{x-3} = \dfrac{x+1}{x-3} \cdot \dfrac{x+3}{x+3} = \dfrac{x^2+4x+3}{(x+3)(x-3)}$

11. $3x^2 - 12y^2 = 3(x+2y)(x-2y);$
$6x - 12y = 6(x-2y)$
The LCM is $6(x+2y)(x-2y)$.

$$\frac{3}{3x^2-12y^2} = \frac{3}{3(x+2y)(x-2y)} \cdot \frac{2}{2} = \frac{6}{6(x+2y)(x-2y)}$$

$$\frac{5}{6x-12y} = \frac{5}{6(x-2y)} \cdot \frac{x+2y}{x+2y} = \frac{5x+10y}{6(x+2y)(x-2y)}$$

13. $x^2 - 1 = (x+1)(x-1);$
$x^2 - 2x + 1 = (x-1)^2$
The LCM is $(x+1)(x-1)^2$.

$$\frac{3x}{x^2-1} = \frac{3x}{(x+1)(x-1)} \cdot \frac{x-1}{x-1} = \frac{3x^2-3x}{(x+1)(x-1)^2}$$

$$\frac{5x}{x^2-2x+1} = \frac{5x}{(x-1)(x-1)} \cdot \frac{x+1}{x+1} = \frac{5x^2+5x}{(x+1)(x-1)^2}$$

15. $8 - x^3 = -(x^3 - 8) = -(x-2)(x^2+2x+4)$
The LCM is $(x-2)(x^2+2x+4)$.

$$\frac{x-3}{8-x^3} = -\frac{x-3}{(x-2)(x^2+2x+4)}$$

$$\frac{2}{4+2x+x^2} = \frac{2}{4+2x+x^2} \cdot \frac{x-2}{x-2} = \frac{2x-4}{(x-2)(x^2+2x+4)}$$

17. $x^2 + 2x - 3 = (x+3)(x-1);$
$x^2 + 6x + 9 = (x+3)^2$
The LCM is $(x-1)(x+3)^2$.

$$\frac{2x}{x^2+2x-3} = \frac{2x}{(x+3)(x-1)} \cdot \frac{x+3}{x+3} = \frac{2x^2+6x}{(x-1)(x+3)^2}$$

$$\frac{-x}{x^2+6x+9} = \frac{-x}{(x+3)(x+3)} \cdot \frac{x-1}{x-1} = -\frac{x^2-x}{(x-1)(x+3)^2}$$

19. $4x^2 - 16x + 15 = (2x-3)(2x-5);$
$6x^2 - 19x + 10 = (2x-5)(3x-2)$
The LCM is $(2x-3)(2x-5)(3x-2)$.

$$\frac{-4x}{4x^2-16x+15} = -\frac{4x}{(2x-3)(2x-5)} \cdot \frac{3x-2}{3x-2} = -\frac{12x^2-8x}{(2x-3)(2x-5)(3x-2)}$$

$$\frac{3x}{6x^2-19x+10} = \frac{3x}{(2x-5)(3x-2)} \cdot \frac{2x-3}{2x-3} = \frac{6x^2-9x}{(2x-3)(2x-5)(3x-2)}$$

21. $6x^2 - 17x + 12 = (3x-4)(2x-3);$
$4 - 3x = -(3x-4)$
The LCM is $(3x-4)(2x-3)$.

$$\frac{5}{6x^2-17x+12} = \frac{5}{(3x-4)(2x-3)}$$

$$\frac{2x}{4-3x} = -\frac{2x}{3x-4} \cdot \frac{2x-3}{2x-3} = -\frac{4x^2-6x}{(3x-4)(2x-3)}$$

$$\frac{x+1}{2x-3} = \frac{x+1}{2x-3} \cdot \frac{3x-4}{3x-4} = \frac{3x^2-x-4}{(3x-4)(2x-3)}$$

23. $15 - 2x - x^2 = -(x^2 + 2x - 15)$
$= -(x+5)(x-3)$
The LCM is $(x+5)(x-3)$.

$$\frac{2x}{x-3} = \frac{2x}{x-3} \cdot \frac{x+5}{x+5} = \frac{2x^2+10x}{(x+5)(x-3)}$$

$$\frac{-2}{x+5} = -\frac{2}{x+5} \cdot \frac{x-3}{x-5} = -\frac{2x-6}{(x+5)(x-3)}$$

$$\frac{x-1}{15-2x-x^2} = -\frac{x-1}{(x+5)(x-3)}$$

25. $x^{2n} + 3x^n + 2 = (x^n+2)(x^n+1)$
The LCM is $(x^n+1)(x^n+2)$.

$$\frac{x-5}{x^{2n}+3x^n+2} = \frac{x-5}{(x^n+1)(x^n+2)}$$

$$\frac{2x}{x^n+2} = \frac{2x}{x^n+2} \cdot \frac{x^n+1}{x^n+1} = \frac{2x^{n+1}+2x}{(x^n+1)(x^n+2)}$$

Objective B Exercises

27. The LCM is $4x^2$.

$$-\frac{3}{4x^2} + \frac{8}{4x^2} - \frac{3}{4x^2} = \frac{-3+8-3}{4x^2} = \frac{2}{4x^2} = \frac{1}{2x^2}$$

29. The LCM is $3x^2 + x - 10$.

$$\frac{3x}{3x^2+x-10} - \frac{5}{3x^2+x-10} = \frac{3x-5}{3x^2+x-10} = \frac{1}{x+2}$$

31. The LCM is $30a^2b^2$.

$$\frac{2}{5ab} - \frac{3}{10a^2b} + \frac{4}{15ab^2} = \frac{2}{5ab} \cdot \frac{6ab}{6ab} - \frac{3}{10a^2b} \cdot \frac{3b}{3b} + \frac{4}{15ab^2} \cdot \frac{2a}{2a} = \frac{12ab-9b+8a}{30a^2b^2}$$

33. The LCM is $40ab$.

$$\frac{3}{4ab}-\frac{2}{5a}+\frac{3}{10b}-\frac{5}{8ab}$$
$$=\frac{3}{4ab}\cdot\frac{10}{10}-\frac{2}{5a}\cdot\frac{8b}{8b}+\frac{3}{10b}\cdot\frac{4a}{4a}-\frac{5}{8ab}\cdot\frac{5}{5}$$
$$=\frac{30-16b+12a-25}{40ab}$$
$$=\frac{5-16b+12a}{40ab}$$

35. The LCM is $12x$.

$$\frac{3x-4}{6x}-\frac{2x-5}{4x}=\frac{3x-4}{6x}\cdot\frac{2}{2}-\frac{2x-5}{4x}\cdot\frac{3}{3}$$
$$=\frac{(6x-8)-(6x-15)}{12x}$$
$$=\frac{6x-8-6x+15}{12x}=\frac{7}{12x}$$

37. The LCM is $10x^2y^2$.

$$\frac{2y-4}{5xy^2}+\frac{3-2x}{10x^2y}=\frac{2y-4}{5xy^2}\cdot\frac{2x}{2x}+\frac{3-2x}{10x^2y}\cdot\frac{y}{y}$$
$$=\frac{4xy-8x+(3y-2xy)}{10x^2y^2}$$
$$=\frac{4xy-8x+3y-2xy}{10x^2y^2}$$
$$=\frac{2xy-8x+3y}{10x^2y^2}$$

39. The LCM is $(a-2)(a+1)$.

$$\frac{3a}{a-2}-\frac{5a}{a+1}=\frac{3a}{a-2}\cdot\frac{a+1}{a+1}-\frac{5a}{a+1}\cdot\frac{a-2}{a-2}$$
$$=\frac{(3a^2+3a)-(5a^2-10a)}{(a-2)(a+1)}$$
$$=\frac{3a^2+3a-5a^2+10a}{(a+1)(a-2)}$$
$$=\frac{-2a^2+13a}{(a-2)(a+1)}$$
$$=\frac{-(2a^2-13a)}{(a+1)(a-2)}$$
$$=-\frac{a(2a-13)}{(a+1)(a-2)}$$

41. The LCM is $(2x-5)(5x-2)$.

$$\frac{x}{2x-5}-\frac{2}{5x-2}=\frac{x}{2x-5}\cdot\frac{5x-2}{5x-2}-\frac{2}{5x-2}\cdot\frac{2x-5}{2x-5}$$
$$=\frac{(5x^2-2x)-(4x-10)}{(2x-5)(5x-2)}$$
$$=\frac{5x^2-2x-4x+10}{(5x-2)(2x-5)}$$
$$=\frac{5x^2-6x+10}{(5x-2)(2x-5)}$$

43. The LCM is $b(a-b)$.

$$\frac{1}{a-b}+\frac{1}{b}=\frac{1}{a-b}\cdot\frac{b}{b}+\frac{1}{b}\cdot\frac{a-b}{a-b}$$
$$=\frac{b+(a-b)}{b(a-b)}$$
$$=\frac{b+a-b}{b(a-b)}$$
$$=\frac{a}{b(a-b)}$$

45. The LCM is $a(a-3)$.

$$\frac{6a}{a-3}-5+\frac{3}{a}=\frac{6a}{a-3}\cdot\frac{a}{a}-5\cdot\frac{a(a-3)}{a(a-3)}+\frac{3}{a}\cdot\frac{a-3}{a-3}$$
$$=\frac{6a^2-5a(a-3)+3a-9}{a(a-3)}$$
$$=\frac{6a^2-5a^2+15a+3a-9}{a(a-3)}$$
$$=\frac{a^2+18a-9}{a(a-3)}$$

47. $5-6x=-(6x-5)$

The LCM is $x(6x-5)$.

$$\frac{5}{x}-\frac{5x}{5-6x}+2$$
$$=\frac{5}{x}\cdot\frac{6x-5}{6x-5}-\frac{(-5x)}{6x-5}\cdot\frac{x}{x}+2\cdot\frac{x(6x-5)}{x(6x-5)}$$
$$=\frac{30x-25+5x^2+2x(6x-5)}{x(6x-5)}$$
$$=\frac{30x-25+5x^2+12x^2-10x}{x(6x-5)}$$
$$=\frac{17x^2+20x-25}{x(6x-5)}$$

49. $x^2-6x+9=(x-3)^2$

$x^2-9=(x+3)(x-3)$

The LCM is $(x+3)(x-3)^2$.

$$\frac{1}{x^2-6x+9}-\frac{1}{x^2-9}$$
$$=\frac{1}{(x-3)^2}\cdot\frac{x+3}{x+3}-\frac{1}{(x+3)(x-3)}\cdot\frac{x-3}{x-3}$$
$$=\frac{x+3-(x-3)}{(x+3)(x-3)^2}$$
$$=\frac{x+3-x+3}{(x-3)^2(x+3)}$$
$$=\frac{6}{(x-3)^2(x+3)}$$

51. $x^2+4x+4=(x+2)^2$

The LCM is $(x+2)^2$.

$$\frac{1}{x+2}-\frac{3x}{x^2+4x+4}=\frac{1}{x+2}\cdot\frac{x+2}{x+2}-\frac{3x}{(x+2)^2}$$
$$=\frac{x+2-3x}{(x+2)^2}$$
$$=\frac{-2x+2}{(x+2)^2}$$
$$=\frac{-(2x-2)}{(x+2)^2}=-\frac{2(x-1)}{(x+2)^2}$$

53. $x^2+2x-8=(x+4)(x-2)$

The LCM is $(x+4)(x-2)$.

$$\frac{-3x^2+8x+2}{x^2+2x-8}-\frac{2x-5}{x+4}$$
$$=\frac{-3x^2+8x+2}{(x+4)(x-2)}-\frac{2x-5}{x+4}\cdot\frac{x-2}{x-2}$$
$$=\frac{-3x^2+8x+2-(2x-5)(x-2)}{(x+4)(x-2)}$$
$$=\frac{-3x^2+8x+2-(2x^2-9x+10)}{(x+4)(x-2)}$$
$$=\frac{-3x^2+8x+2-2x^2+9x-10}{(x+4)(x-2)}$$
$$=\frac{-5x^2+17x-8}{(x+4)(x-2)}$$
$$=\frac{-(5x^2-17x+8)}{(x+4)(x-2)}$$
$$=-\frac{5x^2-17x+8}{(x+4)(x-2)}$$

55. $x^{2n}-1=(x^n+1)(x^n-1)$

The LCM is $(x^n+1)(x^n-1)$.

$$\frac{2}{x^n-1}+\frac{x^n}{x^{2n}-1}$$
$$=\frac{2}{x^n-1}\cdot\frac{x^n+1}{x^n+1}+\frac{x^n}{(x^n+1)(x^n-1)}$$
$$=\frac{2x^n+2+x^n}{(x^n+1)(x^n-1)}$$
$$=\frac{3x^n+2}{(x^n+1)(x^n-1)}$$

57. $x^{2n}-x^n-6=(x^n-3)(x^n+2)$

The LCM is $(x^n-3)(x^n+2)$.

$$\frac{2x^n-6}{x^{2n}-x^n-6}+\frac{x^n}{x^n+2}$$
$$=\frac{2x^n-6}{(x^n-3)(x^n+2)}+\frac{x^n}{x^n+2}\cdot\frac{x^n-3}{x^n-3}$$
$$=\frac{2x^n-6+x^{2n}-3x^n}{(x^n-3)(x^n+2)}$$
$$=\frac{x^{2n}-x^n-6}{(x^n-3)(x^n+2)}=1$$

59. $4x^2-36=4(x^2-9)=4(x+3)(x-3)$

The LCM is $4(x+3)(x-3)$.

$$\frac{x^2+4}{4x^2-36}-\frac{13}{x+3}$$
$$=\frac{x^2+4}{4(x+3)(x-3)}-\frac{13}{x+3}\cdot\frac{4(x-3)}{4(x-3)}$$
$$=\frac{x^2+4-52(x-3)}{4(x+3)(x-3)}$$
$$=\frac{x^2+4-52x+156}{4(x+3)(x-3)}$$
$$=\frac{x^2-52x+160}{4(x+3)(x-3)}$$

61. $4x^2+9x+2=(4x+1)(x+2)$

The LCM is $(4x+1)(x+2)$.

$$\frac{3x-4}{4x+1}+\frac{3x+6}{4x^2+9x+2}$$
$$=\frac{3x-4}{4x+1}\cdot\frac{x+2}{x+2}+\frac{3x+6}{(4x+1)(x+2)}$$
$$=\frac{3x^2+2x-8+3x+6}{(4x+1)(x+2)}$$
$$=\frac{3x^2+5x-2}{(4x+1)(x+2)}$$
$$=\frac{3x-1}{4x+1}$$

63. $x^2+x-12=(x+4)(x-3)$

$x^2+7x+12=(x+4)(x+3)$

The LCM is $(x+4)(x+3)(x-3)$.

$$\frac{x+1}{x^2+x-12}-\frac{x-3}{x^2+7x+12}$$
$$=\frac{x+1}{(x+4)(x-3)}\cdot\frac{x+3}{x+3}-\frac{x-3}{(x+4)(x+3)}\cdot\frac{x-3}{x-3}$$
$$=\frac{(x+1)(x+3)-(x-3)(x-3)}{(x+4)(x-3)(x+3)}$$
$$=\frac{(x^2+4x+3)-(x^2-6x+9)}{(x+4)(x-3)(x+3)}$$
$$=\frac{x^2+4x+3-x^2+6x-9}{(x+4)(x-3)(x+3)}$$
$$=\frac{2(5x-3)}{(x+4)(x-3)(x+3)}$$

65. $x^2-2x-15=(x-5)(x+3)$

$5-x=-(x-5)$

The LCM is $(x-5)(x+3)$.

$$\frac{2x^2-2x}{x^2-2x-15}-\frac{2}{x+3}+\frac{x}{5-x}$$
$$=\frac{2x^2-2x}{(x-5)(x+3)}-\frac{2}{x+3}\cdot\frac{x-5}{x-5}+\frac{-x}{x-5}\cdot\frac{x+3}{x+3}$$
$$=\frac{2x^2-2x-2x+10-x^2-3x}{(x-5)(x+3)}$$
$$=\frac{x^2-7x+10}{(x-5)(x+3)}$$
$$=\frac{x-2}{x+3}$$

67. $3x^2-11x-20=(3x+4)(x-5)$

The LCM is $(3x+4)(x-5)$.

$$\frac{x}{3x+4}+\frac{3x+2}{x-5}-\frac{7x^2+24x+28}{3x^2-11x-20}$$
$$=\frac{x}{3x+4}\cdot\frac{x-5}{x-5}+\frac{3x+2}{x-5}\cdot\frac{3x+4}{3x+4}-\frac{7x^2+24x+28}{(3x+4)(x-5)}$$
$$=\frac{x^2-5x+9x^2+18x+8-(7x^2+24x+28)}{(3x+4)(x-5)}$$
$$=\frac{x^2-5x+9x^2+18x+8-7x^2-24x-28}{(3x+4)(x-5)}$$
$$=\frac{3x^2-11x-20}{(3x+4)(x-5)}$$
$$=1$$

69. $1-2x=-(2x-1)$

$8x^2-10x+3=(2x-1)(4x-3)$

The LCM is $(2x-1)(4x-3)$.

$$\frac{x+1}{1-2x}-\frac{x+3}{4x-3}+\frac{10x^2+7x-9}{8x^2-10x+3}$$
$$=\frac{-(x+1)}{2x-1}\cdot\frac{4x-3}{4x-3}-\frac{x+3}{4x-3}\cdot\frac{2x-1}{2x-1}+\frac{10x^2+7x-9}{8x^2-10x+3}$$
$$=\frac{-(x+1)(4x-3)-(x+3)(2x-1)+10x^2+7x-9}{(2x-1)(4x-3)}$$
$$=\frac{-4x^2-x+3-2x^2-5x+3+10x^2+7x-9}{(2x-1)(4x-3)}$$
$$=\frac{4x^2+x-3}{(2x-1)(4x-3)}$$
$$=\frac{x+1}{2x-1}$$

71. $8x^3-1=(2x-1)(4x^2+2x+1)$

The LCM is $(2x-1)(4x^2+2x+1)$.

$$\frac{2x}{4x^2+2x+1}+\frac{4x+1}{8x^3-1}$$
$$=\frac{2x}{4x^2+2x+1}\cdot\frac{2x-1}{2x-1}+\frac{4x+1}{(2x-1)(4x^2+2x+1)}$$
$$=\frac{4x^2-2x+4x+1}{(2x-1)(4x^2+2x+1)}$$
$$=\frac{1}{2x-1}$$

73. $x^4-16=(x^2+4)(x+2)(x-2)$

$x^2-4=(x+2)(x-2)$

The LCM is $(x^2+4)(x+2)(x-2)$.

$$\frac{x^2-12}{x^4-16}+\frac{1}{x^2-4}-\frac{1}{x^2+4}$$
$$=\frac{x^2-12}{(x^2+4)(x+2)(x-2)}+\frac{1}{(x+2)(x-2)}\cdot\frac{x^2+4}{x^2+4}-\frac{1}{x^2+4}\cdot\frac{(x+2)(x-2)}{(x+2)(x-2)}$$
$$=\frac{x^2-12+x^2+4-(x^2-4)}{(x^2+4)(x+2)(x-2)}$$
$$=\frac{x^2-12+x^2+4-x^2+4}{(x^2+4)(x+2)(x-2)}$$
$$=\frac{x^2-4}{(x^2+4)(x+2)(x-2)}$$
$$=\frac{1}{x^2+4}$$

75. The LCM of $\frac{a-3}{a^2}$ and $\frac{a-3}{9}$ is $9a^2$.

$$\left[\frac{a-3}{a^2}-\frac{a-3}{9}\right]\div\frac{a^2-9}{3a}$$
$$=\left[\frac{a-3}{a^2}\cdot\frac{9}{9}-\frac{a-3}{9}\cdot\frac{a^2}{a^2}\right]\div\frac{a^2-9}{3a}$$
$$=\left[\frac{9(a-3)}{9a^2}-\frac{a^2(a-3)}{9a^2}\right]\div\frac{a^2-9}{3a}$$
$$=\frac{9(a-3)-a^2(a-3)}{9a^2}\div\frac{a^2-9}{3a}$$
$$=\frac{(9-a^2)(a-3)}{9a^2}\cdot\frac{3a}{a^2-9}$$
$$=\frac{(3-a)(3+a)(a-3)}{9a^2}\cdot\frac{3a}{(a-3)(a+3)}$$
$$=\frac{3-a}{3a}$$

77. $\dfrac{x^2-4x+4}{2x+1}\cdot\dfrac{2x^2+x}{x^3-4x}-\dfrac{3x-2}{x+1}$

$=\dfrac{(x-2)(x-2)}{2x+1}\cdot\dfrac{x(2x+1)}{x(x-2)(x+2)}-\dfrac{3x-2}{x+1}$

$=\dfrac{(x-2)(x-2)(x)(2x+1)}{(2x+1)(x)(x-2)(x+2)}-\dfrac{3x-2}{x+1}$

$=\dfrac{x-2}{x+2}-\dfrac{3x-2}{x+1}$

The LCM is $(x+2)(x+1)$.

$\dfrac{x-2}{x+2}-\dfrac{3x-2}{x+1}=\dfrac{x-2}{x+2}\cdot\dfrac{x+1}{x+1}-\dfrac{3x-2}{x+1}\cdot\dfrac{x+2}{x+2}$

$=\dfrac{x^2-x-2-(3x^2+4x-4)}{(x+2)(x+1)}$

$=\dfrac{x^2-x-2-3x^2-4x+4}{(x+2)(x+1)}$

$=\dfrac{-2x^2-5x+2}{(x+2)(x+1)}$

$=-\dfrac{2x^2+5x-2}{(x+2)(x+1)}$

79. The LCM is ab.

$\left[\dfrac{a-2b}{b}+\dfrac{b}{a}\right]\div\left[\dfrac{b+a}{a}-\dfrac{2a}{b}\right]$

$=\left[\dfrac{a-2b}{b}\cdot\dfrac{a}{a}+\dfrac{b}{a}\cdot\dfrac{b}{b}\right]\div\left[\dfrac{b+a}{a}\cdot\dfrac{b}{b}-\dfrac{2a}{b}\cdot\dfrac{a}{a}\right]$

$=\dfrac{a^2-2ab+b^2}{ab}\div\dfrac{b^2+ab-2a^2}{ab}$

$=\dfrac{a^2-2ab+b^2}{ab}\cdot\dfrac{ab}{b^2+ab-2a^2}$

$=\dfrac{(a-b)(a-b)ab}{ab(b+2a)(b-a)}$

$=\dfrac{a-b}{-(b+2a)}$

$=\dfrac{-(a-b)}{b+2a}=\dfrac{b-a}{b+2a}$

81. $\dfrac{2x}{x^2-x-6}-\dfrac{6x-6}{2x^2-9x+9}\div\dfrac{x^2+x-2}{2x-3}$

$=\dfrac{2x}{(x-3)(x+2)}-\dfrac{6(x-1)}{(2x-3)(x-3)}\div\dfrac{(x+2)(x-1)}{2x-3}$

$=\dfrac{2x}{(x-3)(x+2)}-\dfrac{6(x-1)}{(2x-3)(x-3)}\cdot\dfrac{2x-3}{(x+2)(x-1)}$

$=\dfrac{2x}{(x-3)(x+2)}-\dfrac{6(x-1)(2x-3)}{(2x-3)(x-3)(x+2)(x-1)}$

$=\dfrac{2x}{(x-3)(x+2)}-\dfrac{6}{(x-3)(x+2)}$

$=\dfrac{2x-6}{(x-3)(x+2)}$

$=\dfrac{2(x-3)}{(x-3)(x+2)}$

$=\dfrac{2}{x+2}$

Applying the Concepts

83. **a.** $\dfrac{3}{4}+\dfrac{x}{5}=\dfrac{3}{4}\cdot\dfrac{5}{5}+\dfrac{x}{5}\cdot\dfrac{4}{4}=\dfrac{15+4x}{20}$

b. $\dfrac{4x+5}{4}=x+\dfrac{5}{4}$

c. $\dfrac{1}{x}+\dfrac{1}{y}=\dfrac{1}{x}\cdot\dfrac{y}{y}+\dfrac{1}{y}\cdot\dfrac{x}{x}=\dfrac{y+x}{xy}$

85. **a.** $\dfrac{3x+6y}{xy}=\dfrac{3x}{xy}+\dfrac{6y}{xy}=\dfrac{3}{y}+\dfrac{6}{x}$

b. $\dfrac{4a^2+3ab}{a^2b^2}=\dfrac{4a^2}{a^2b^2}+\dfrac{3ab}{a^2b^2}=\dfrac{4}{b^2}+\dfrac{3}{ab}$

c. $\dfrac{3m^2n+2mn^2}{12m^3n^2}=\dfrac{3m^2n}{12m^3n^2}+\dfrac{2mn^2}{12m^3n^2}$

$=\dfrac{1}{4mn}+\dfrac{1}{6m^2}$

SECTION 6.3

Objective A Exercises

1. The LCM is 3.

$\dfrac{2-\frac{1}{3}}{4+\frac{11}{3}}=\dfrac{2-\frac{1}{3}}{4+\frac{11}{3}}\cdot\dfrac{3}{3}$

$=\dfrac{2\cdot3-\frac{1}{3}\cdot3}{4\cdot3+\frac{11}{3}\cdot3}$

$=\dfrac{6-1}{12+11}$

$=\dfrac{5}{23}$

3. The LCM is 6.

$\dfrac{3-\frac{2}{3}}{5+\frac{5}{6}}=\dfrac{3-\frac{2}{3}}{5+\frac{5}{6}}\cdot\dfrac{6}{6}$

$=\dfrac{3\cdot6-\frac{2}{3}\cdot6}{5\cdot6+\frac{5}{6}\cdot6}$

$=\dfrac{18-4}{30+5}$

$=\dfrac{14}{35}=\dfrac{2}{5}$

5. The LCM of x and x^2 is x^2.

$$\frac{1+\frac{1}{x}}{1-\frac{1}{x^2}}=\frac{1+\frac{1}{x}}{1-\frac{1}{x^2}}\cdot\frac{x^2}{x^2}$$
$$=\frac{1\cdot x^2+\frac{1}{x}\cdot x^2}{1\cdot x^2-\frac{1}{x^2}\cdot x^2}$$
$$=\frac{x^2+x}{x^2-1}$$
$$=\frac{x(x+1)}{(x+1)(x-1)}$$
$$=\frac{x}{x-1}$$

7. The LCM is a.

$$\frac{a-2}{\frac{4}{a}-a}=\frac{a-2}{\frac{4}{a}-a}\cdot\frac{a}{a}$$
$$=\frac{a\cdot a-2\cdot a}{\frac{4}{a}\cdot a-a\cdot a}$$
$$=\frac{a^2-2a}{4-a^2}$$
$$=\frac{a(a-2)}{(2+a)(2-a)}$$
$$=-\frac{a}{a+2}$$

9. The LCM of a^2 and a is a^2.

$$\frac{\frac{1}{a^2}-\frac{1}{a}}{\frac{1}{a^2}+\frac{1}{a}}=\frac{\frac{1}{a^2}-\frac{1}{a}}{\frac{1}{a^2}+\frac{1}{a}}\cdot\frac{a^2}{a^2}$$
$$=\frac{\frac{1}{a^2}\cdot a^2-\frac{1}{a}\cdot a^2}{\frac{1}{a^2}\cdot a^2+\frac{1}{a}\cdot a^2}$$
$$=\frac{1-a}{1+a}$$
$$=\frac{-(a-1)}{a+1}$$
$$=-\frac{a-1}{a+1}$$

11. The LCM is $x + 2$.

$$\frac{2-\frac{4}{x+2}}{5-\frac{10}{x+2}}=\frac{2-\frac{4}{x+2}}{5-\frac{10}{x+2}}\cdot\frac{x+2}{x+2}$$
$$=\frac{2(x+2)-\frac{4}{x+2}\cdot(x+2)}{5(x+2)-\frac{10}{x+2}\cdot(x+2)}$$
$$=\frac{2x+4-4}{5x+10-10}$$
$$=\frac{2x}{5x}=\frac{2}{5}$$

13. The LCM is $2a-3$.

$$\frac{\frac{3}{2a-3}+2}{\frac{-6}{2a-3}-4}=\frac{\frac{3}{2a-3}+2}{\frac{-6}{2a-3}-4}\cdot\frac{2a-3}{2a-3}$$
$$=\frac{\frac{3}{2a-3}\cdot(2a-3)+2(2a-3)}{\frac{-6}{2a-3}\cdot(2a-3)-4(2a-3)}$$
$$=\frac{3+4a-6}{-6-8a+12}$$
$$=\frac{4a-3}{-8a+6}$$
$$=-\frac{1}{2}$$

15. The LCM of x and $x + 1$ is $x(x+1)$.

$$\frac{\frac{x}{x+1}-\frac{1}{x}}{\frac{x}{x+1}+\frac{1}{x}}=\frac{\frac{x}{x+1}-\frac{1}{x}}{\frac{x}{x+1}+\frac{1}{x}}\cdot\frac{x(x+1)}{x(x+1)}$$
$$=\frac{\frac{x}{x+1}\cdot x(x+1)-\frac{1}{x}\cdot x(x+1)}{\frac{x}{x+1}\cdot x(x+1)+\frac{1}{x}\cdot x(x+1)}$$
$$=\frac{x^2-(x+1)}{x^2+(x+1)}$$
$$=\frac{x^2-x-1}{x^2+x+1}$$

17. The LCM of x and x^2 is x^2.

$$\frac{1-\frac{1}{x}-\frac{6}{x^2}}{1-\frac{4}{x}+\frac{3}{x^2}}=\frac{1-\frac{1}{x}-\frac{6}{x^2}}{1-\frac{4}{x}+\frac{3}{x^2}}\cdot\frac{x^2}{x^2}$$
$$=\frac{1\cdot x^2-\frac{1}{x}\cdot x^2-\frac{6}{x^2}\cdot x^2}{1\cdot x^2-\frac{4}{x}\cdot x^2+\frac{3}{x^2}\cdot x^2}$$
$$=\frac{x^2-x-6}{x^2-4x+3}$$
$$=\frac{(x+2)(x-3)}{(x-1)(x-3)}$$
$$=\frac{x+2}{x-1}$$

19. The LCM of x and x^2 is x^2.

$$\frac{1+\frac{1}{x}-\frac{12}{x^2}}{\frac{9}{x^2}+\frac{3}{x}-2}=\frac{1+\frac{1}{x}-\frac{12}{x^2}}{\frac{9}{x^2}+\frac{3}{x}-2}\cdot\frac{x^2}{x^2}$$
$$=\frac{1\cdot x^2+\frac{1}{x}\cdot x^2-\frac{12}{x^2}\cdot x^2}{\frac{9}{x^2}\cdot x^2+\frac{3}{x}\cdot x^2-2\cdot x^2}$$
$$=\frac{x^2+x-12}{9+3x-2x^2}$$
$$=\frac{(x+4)(x-3)}{(3+2x)(3-x)}$$
$$=-\frac{x+4}{2x+3}$$

21. $$a+\frac{a}{a+\frac{1}{a}}=a+\frac{a}{a+\frac{1}{a}}\cdot\frac{a}{a}$$
$$=a+\frac{a\cdot a}{a\cdot a+\frac{1}{a}\cdot a}$$
$$=a+\frac{a^2}{a^2+1}$$

The LCM is a^2+1.

$$a+\frac{a^2}{a^2+1}=a\cdot\frac{a^2+1}{a^2+1}+\frac{a^2}{a^2+1}$$
$$=\frac{a(a^2+1)+a^2}{a^2+1}$$
$$=\frac{a^3+a+a^2}{a^2+1}$$
$$=\frac{a(a^2+a+1)}{a^2+1}$$

23. $$\frac{1-\frac{1}{x-4}}{1-\frac{6}{x+1}}$$

The LCM is $(x-4)(x+1)$.

$$\frac{1-\frac{1}{x-4}}{1-\frac{6}{x+1}}\cdot\frac{(x-4)(x+1)}{(x-4)(x+1)}=\frac{(x-4)(x+1)-(x+1)}{(x-4)(x+1)-6(x-4)}$$
$$=\frac{x^2-3x-4-x-1}{x^2-3x-4-6x+24}$$
$$=\frac{x^2-4x-5}{x^2-9x+20}$$
$$=\frac{(x-5)(x+1)}{(x-5)(x-4)}$$
$$=\frac{x+1}{x-4}$$

25. $$\frac{x-\frac{1}{x}}{x+\frac{1}{x}}$$

The LCM is x.

$$\frac{x-\frac{1}{x}}{x+\frac{1}{x}}\cdot\frac{x}{x}=\frac{(x-1)(x+1)}{x^2+1}$$

27. $$\frac{\frac{1}{x+h}-\frac{1}{x}}{h}$$

The LCM is $x(x+h)$.

$$\frac{\frac{1}{x+h}-\frac{1}{x}}{h}\cdot\frac{x(x+h)}{x(x+h)}=\frac{x-(x+h)}{hx(x+h)}$$
$$=\frac{h}{hx(x+h)}$$
$$=-\frac{1}{x(x+h)}$$

29. $$\frac{1-\frac{2}{x-3}}{1+\frac{3}{2-x}}$$

The LCM is $(x-3)(2-x)$.

$$\frac{1-\frac{2}{x-3}}{1+\frac{3}{2-x}}\cdot\frac{(x-3)(2-x)}{(x-3)(2-x)}=\frac{(x-3)(2-x)-2(2-x)}{(x-3)(2-x)+3(x-3)}$$
$$=\frac{-x^2+5x-6-4+2x}{-x^2+5x-6+3x-9}$$
$$=\frac{-x^2+7x-10}{-x^2+8x-15}$$
$$=\frac{-(x^2-7x+10)}{-(x^2-8x+15)}$$
$$=\frac{(x-5)(x-2)}{(x-5)(x-3)}$$
$$=\frac{x-2}{x-3}$$

31. The LCM is $2x+3$.

$$\frac{x-4+\frac{9}{2x+3}}{x+3-\frac{5}{2x+3}}=\frac{x-4+\frac{9}{2x+3}}{x+3-\frac{5}{2x+3}}\cdot\frac{2x+3}{2x+3}$$
$$=\frac{(x-4)(2x+3)+\frac{9}{2x+3}\cdot(2x+3)}{(x+3)(2x+3)-\frac{5}{2x+3}\cdot(2x+3)}$$
$$=\frac{2x^2-5x-12+9}{2x^2+9x+9-5}$$
$$=\frac{2x^2-5x-3}{2x^2+9x+4}$$
$$=\frac{(2x+1)(x-3)}{(2x+1)(x+4)}$$
$$=\frac{x-3}{x+4}$$

33. The LCM is $2x-1$.

$$\frac{3x-2-\frac{5}{2x-1}}{x-6+\frac{9}{2x-1}}=\frac{3x-2-\frac{5}{2x-1}}{x-6+\frac{9}{2x-1}}\cdot\frac{2x-1}{2x-1}$$
$$=\frac{(3x-2)(2x-1)-\frac{5}{2x-1}\cdot(2x-1)}{(x-6)(2x-1)+\frac{9}{2x-1}\cdot(2x-1)}$$
$$=\frac{6x^2-7x+2-5}{2x^2-13x+6+9}$$
$$=\frac{6x^2-7x-3}{2x^2-13x+15}$$
$$=\frac{(3x+1)(2x-3)}{(2x-3)(x-5)}$$
$$=\frac{3x+1}{x-5}$$

35. The LCM is $a(a-2)$.

$$\frac{\frac{1}{a}-\frac{3}{a-2}}{\frac{2}{a}+\frac{5}{a-2}}=\frac{\frac{1}{a}-\frac{3}{a-2}}{\frac{2}{a}+\frac{5}{a-2}}\cdot\frac{a(a-2)}{a(a-2)}$$
$$=\frac{\frac{1}{a}\cdot a(a-2)-\frac{3}{a-2}\cdot a(a-2)}{\frac{2}{a}\cdot a(a-2)+\frac{5}{a-2}\cdot a(a-2)}$$
$$=\frac{a-2-3a}{2a-4+5a}$$
$$=\frac{-2a-2}{7a-4}$$
$$=\frac{-(2a+2)}{7a-4}$$
$$=-\frac{2a+2}{7a-4}$$

37. The LCM of y^2, xy, and x^2 is x^2y^2.

$$\frac{\frac{1}{y^2}-\frac{1}{xy}-\frac{2}{x^2}}{\frac{1}{y^2}-\frac{3}{xy}+\frac{2}{x^2}}=\frac{\frac{1}{y^2}-\frac{1}{xy}-\frac{2}{x^2}}{\frac{1}{y^2}-\frac{3}{xy}+\frac{2}{x^2}}\cdot\frac{x^2y^2}{x^2y^2}$$
$$=\frac{\frac{1}{y^2}\cdot x^2y^2-\frac{1}{xy}\cdot x^2y^2-\frac{2}{x^2}\cdot x^2y^2}{\frac{1}{y^2}\cdot x^2y^2-\frac{3}{xy}\cdot x^2y^2+\frac{2}{x^2}\cdot x^2y^2}$$
$$=\frac{x^2-xy-2y^2}{x^2-3xy+2y^2}$$
$$=\frac{(x+y)(x-2y)}{(x-y)(x-2y)}$$
$$=\frac{x+y}{x-y}$$

39. The LCM is $(x+1)(x-1)$.

$$\frac{\frac{x-1}{x+1}-\frac{x+1}{x-1}}{\frac{x-1}{x+1}+\frac{x+1}{x-1}}=\frac{\frac{x-1}{x+1}-\frac{x+1}{x-1}}{\frac{x-1}{x+1}+\frac{x+1}{x-1}}\cdot\frac{(x+1)(x-1)}{(x+1)(x-1)}$$
$$=\frac{\frac{x-1}{x+1}\cdot(x+1)(x-1)-\frac{x+1}{x-1}\cdot(x+1)(x-1)}{\frac{x-1}{x+1}\cdot(x+1)(x-1)+\frac{x+1}{x-1}\cdot(x+1)(x-1)}$$
$$=\frac{(x-1)(x-1)-(x+1)(x+1)}{(x-1)(x-1)+(x+1)(x+1)}$$
$$=\frac{x^2-2x+1-(x^2+2x+1)}{x^2-2x+1+x^2+2x+1}$$
$$=\frac{x^2-2x+1-x^2-2x-1}{2x^2+2}$$
$$=\frac{-4x}{2(x^2+1)}$$
$$=-\frac{2x}{x^2+1}$$

41. The LCM is $1-a$.

$$a-\frac{a}{1-\frac{a}{1-a}}=a-\frac{a}{1-\frac{a}{1-a}}\cdot\frac{1-a}{1-a}$$
$$=a-\frac{a\cdot(1-a)}{1\cdot(1-a)-\frac{a}{1-a}\cdot(1-a)}$$
$$=a-\frac{a-a^2}{1-a-a}$$
$$=a-\frac{a-a^2}{1-2a}$$

The LCM is $1-2a$.

$$a-\frac{a-a^2}{1-2a}=a\cdot\frac{1-2a}{1-2a}-\frac{a-a^2}{1-2a}$$
$$=\frac{a(1-2a)-(a-a^2)}{1-2a}$$
$$=\frac{a-2a^2-a+a^2}{1-2a}$$
$$=\frac{-a^2}{1-2a}$$
$$=-\frac{a^2}{1-2a}$$

43.

$$3-\frac{2}{1-\frac{2}{3-\frac{2}{x}}}=3-\frac{2}{1-\frac{2}{3-\frac{2}{x}}\cdot\frac{x}{x}}$$
$$=3-\frac{2}{1-\frac{2\cdot x}{3\cdot x-\frac{2}{x}\cdot x}}$$
$$=3-\frac{2}{1-\frac{2x}{3x-2}}$$

The LCM is $3x-2$.

$$3-\frac{2}{\frac{3x-2}{3x-2}-\frac{2x}{3x-2}}=3-\frac{2}{\frac{3x-2-2x}{3x-2}}$$
$$=3-\frac{2}{\frac{x-2}{3x-2}}$$
$$=3-\frac{2}{\frac{x-2}{3x-2}}\cdot\frac{3x-2}{3x-2}$$
$$=3-\frac{2(3x-2)}{x-2}$$

The LCM is $x-2$.

$$3\cdot\frac{x-2}{x-2}-\frac{2(3x-2)}{x-2}=\frac{3(x-2)-2(3x-2)}{x-2}$$
$$=\frac{3x-6-6x+4}{x-2}$$
$$=\frac{-3x-2}{x-2}$$
$$=-\frac{3x+2}{x-2}$$

Applying the Concepts

45. Strategy
- The first even integer: n
  The second consecutive even integer: $n+2$
  The third consecutive even integer: $n+4$
- Add the reciprocals of the three integers.

Solution

$$\frac{1}{n}+\frac{1}{n+2}+\frac{1}{n+4}=\frac{1}{n}\cdot\frac{(n+2)(n+4)}{(n+2)(n+4)}+\frac{1}{n+2}\cdot\frac{n(n+4)}{n(n+4)}+\frac{1}{n+4}\cdot\frac{n(n+2)}{n(n+2)}$$
$$=\frac{(n+2)(n+4)+n(n+4)+n(n+2)}{n(n+2)(n+4)}$$
$$=\frac{n^2+6n+8+n^2+4n+n^2+2n}{n(n+2)(n+4)}$$
$$=\frac{3n^2+12n+8}{n(n+2)(n+4)}$$

47. **a.** $\dfrac{x^{-1}}{x^{-1}+2^{-1}}=\dfrac{\frac{1}{x}}{\frac{1}{x}+\frac{1}{2}}$

The LCM is $2x$.

$$\frac{\frac{1}{x}}{\frac{1}{x}+\frac{1}{2}}=\frac{\frac{1}{x}}{\frac{1}{x}+\frac{1}{2}}\cdot\frac{2x}{2x}$$
$$=\frac{\frac{2x}{x}}{\frac{1}{x}(2x)+\frac{1}{2}(2x)}$$
$$=\frac{2}{2+x}$$

b. $\dfrac{-x^{-1}+x}{x^{-1}-x}=\dfrac{-\frac{1}{x}+x}{\frac{1}{x}-x}$

The LCM is x.

$$\frac{-\frac{1}{x}+x}{\frac{1}{x}-x}=\frac{-\frac{1}{x}+x}{\frac{1}{x}-x}\cdot\frac{x}{x}$$
$$=\frac{-\frac{1}{x}(x)+x\cdot x}{\frac{1}{x}(x)-x\cdot x}$$
$$=\frac{-1+x^2}{1-x^2}$$
$$=\frac{x^2-1}{-1\cdot(x^2-1)}$$
$$=\frac{1}{-1}=-1$$

c. $\dfrac{x^{-1}-x^{-2}-6x^{-3}}{x^{-1}-4x^{-3}}=\dfrac{\frac{1}{x}-\frac{1}{x^2}-\frac{6}{x^3}}{\frac{1}{x}-\frac{4}{x^3}}$

The LCM is x^3.

$$\frac{\frac{1}{x}-\frac{1}{x^2}-\frac{6}{x^3}}{\frac{1}{x}-\frac{4}{x^3}}=\frac{\frac{1}{x}-\frac{1}{x^2}-\frac{6}{x^3}}{\frac{1}{x}-\frac{4}{x^3}}\cdot\frac{x^3}{x^3}$$
$$=\frac{x^2-x-6}{x^2-4}$$
$$=\frac{(x-3)(x+2)}{(x-2)(x+2)}$$
$$=\frac{x-3}{x-2}$$

SECTION 6.4

Objective A Exercises

1.
$$\frac{x}{30}=\frac{3}{10}$$
$$\frac{x}{30}\cdot 30=\frac{3}{10}\cdot 30$$
$$x=3\cdot 3$$
$$x=9$$
The solution is 9.

3.
$$\frac{2}{x}=\frac{8}{30}$$
$$\frac{2}{x}\cdot 30x=\frac{8}{30}\cdot 30x$$
$$2\cdot 30=8x$$
$$60=8x$$
$$\frac{15}{2}=x$$
The solution is $\frac{15}{2}$.

5.
$$\frac{x+1}{10}=\frac{2}{5}$$
$$\frac{x+1}{10}\cdot 10=\frac{2}{5}\cdot 10$$
$$x+1=2\cdot 2$$
$$x+1=4$$
$$x=3$$
The solution is 3.

7.
$$\frac{4}{x+2}=\frac{3}{4}$$
$$\frac{4}{x+2}\cdot 4(x+2)=\frac{3}{4}\cdot 4(x+2)$$
$$4\cdot 4=3(x+2)$$
$$16=3x+6$$
$$10=3x$$
$$\frac{10}{3}=x$$
The solution is $\frac{10}{3}$.

9.
$$\frac{x}{4}=\frac{x-2}{8}$$
$$\frac{x}{4}\cdot 8=\frac{x-2}{8}\cdot 8$$
$$x\cdot 2=x-2$$
$$2x=x-2$$
$$x=-2$$
The solution is –2.

11.
$$\frac{16}{2-x}=\frac{4}{x}$$
$$\frac{16}{2-x}\cdot x(2-x)=\frac{4}{x}\cdot x(2-x)$$
$$16x=4(2-x)$$
$$16x=8-4x$$
$$20x=8$$
$$x=\frac{8}{20}$$
$$x=\frac{2}{5}$$
The solution is $\frac{2}{5}$.

13.
$$\frac{8}{x-2}=\frac{4}{x+1}$$
$$\frac{8}{x-2}\cdot(x-2)(x+1)=\frac{4}{x+1}\cdot(x-2)(x+1)$$
$$8(x+1)=4(x-2)$$
$$8x+8=4x-8$$
$$4x+8=-8$$
$$4x=-16$$
$$x=-4$$
The solution is –4.

15.
$$\frac{x}{3}=\frac{x+1}{7}$$
$$\frac{x}{3}\cdot 21=\frac{x+1}{7}\cdot 21$$
$$7x=(x+1)3$$
$$7x=3x+3$$
$$4x=3$$
$$x=\frac{3}{4}$$
The solution is $\frac{3}{4}$.

17.
$$\frac{8}{3x-2}=\frac{2}{2x+1}$$
$$\frac{8}{3x-2}\cdot(3x-2)(2x+1)=\frac{2}{2x+1}\cdot(3x-2)(2x+1)$$
$$8(2x+1)=2(3x-2)$$
$$16x+8=6x-4$$
$$10x=-12$$
$$x=\frac{-12}{10}$$
$$x=-\frac{6}{5}$$
The solution is $-\frac{6}{5}$.

19.

$$\frac{3x+1}{3x-4}=\frac{x}{x-2}$$
$$\frac{3x+1}{3x-4}\cdot(3x-4)(x-2)=\frac{x}{x-2}\cdot(3x-4)(x-2)$$
$$(3x+1)(x-2)=x(3x-4)$$
$$3x^2-5x-2=3x^2-4x$$
$$-5x-2=-4x$$
$$-2=x$$

The solution is –2.

Objective B Application Problems

21. Strategy: To find the number of doctors that would be expected to recommend Trident, write and solve a proportion using x to represent the number of doctors recommending Trident.

Solution

$$\frac{4}{5}=\frac{x}{8250}$$
$$\frac{4}{5}\cdot 8250=\frac{x}{8250}\cdot 8250$$
$$4\cdot 1650=x$$
$$6600=x$$

6600 dentists would be expected to recommend Trident.

23. Strategy: To find the number of squawfish, write and solve a proportion, using x to represent the number of squawfish in the area.

Solution

$$\frac{2400}{x}=\frac{9}{225}$$
$$\frac{2400}{x}=\frac{1}{25}$$
$$\frac{2400}{x}\cdot 25x=\frac{1}{25}\cdot 25x$$
$$2400\cdot 25=x$$
$$60{,}000=x$$

There would be 60,000 squawfish in the area.

25. Strategy: To find the number of defective CD-ROM drives, write and solve a proportion using x to represent the number of defective CD-ROM drives.

Solution

$$\frac{250}{45}=\frac{2800}{x}$$
$$\frac{50}{9}=\frac{2800}{x}$$
$$\frac{50}{9}\cdot 9x=\frac{2800}{x}\cdot 9x$$
$$50x=2800\cdot 9$$
$$50x=25{,}200$$
$$x=504$$

There were 504 defective CD-ROM drives.

27. Strategy: To find the dimensions of the room, write and solve two proportions using L to represent the length of the room and W to represent the width of the room.

Solution

$$\frac{\frac{1}{4}}{1}=\frac{4\frac{1}{2}}{W} \qquad \frac{\frac{1}{4}}{1}=\frac{6}{L}$$
$$\frac{\frac{1}{4}}{1}\cdot W=\frac{4\frac{1}{2}}{W}\cdot W \qquad \frac{\frac{1}{4}}{1}\cdot L=\frac{6}{L}\cdot L$$
$$\frac{1}{4}W=4\frac{1}{2} \qquad \frac{1}{4}L=6$$
$$W=18 \qquad L=24$$

The dimensions of the room are 18 ft by 24 ft.

29. Strategy: To find the additional amount of medicine, write and solve a proportion using x to represent the additional amount of medicine. Then, $x + 1.5$ is the total amount of medicine.

Solution

$$\frac{1.5}{140}=\frac{x+1.5}{210}$$
$$\frac{1.5}{140}\cdot 420=\frac{x+1.5}{210}\cdot 420$$
$$1.5\cdot 3=(x+1.5)2$$
$$4.5=2x+3$$
$$1.5=2x$$
$$0.75=x$$

An additional 0.75 oz of medicine is required.

31. Strategy: To find the number of pieces of mail the Postal Service handles in a year, write and solve a proportion using x to represent the number of pieces of mail.

Solution

$$\frac{3.5}{6}=\frac{x}{300}$$
$$\frac{3.5}{6}\cdot 300=\frac{x}{300}\cdot 300$$
$$3.5\cdot 50=x$$
$$175=x$$

The U.S. Postal Service handles about 175 billion pieces of mail in one year.

Applying the Concepts

33. $\frac{a}{b}=\frac{c}{d}$

Add 1 to each side.

$\frac{a}{b}+1=\frac{c}{d}+1$

Rationalize the expression.

$$\frac{a}{b}+1\cdot\frac{b}{b}=\frac{c}{d}+1\cdot\frac{d}{d}$$
$$\frac{a+b}{b}=\frac{c+d}{d}$$

35. Strategy Write a proportion expressing the equality of the ratio of the first person's cost to the total cost and the ratio of the first person's winnings to the total winnings.

Solution
$$\frac{20}{20+25+30}=\frac{x}{4.5\times10^6}$$
$$\frac{20}{75}=\frac{x}{4{,}500{,}000}$$
$$\frac{20}{75}\cdot4{,}500{,}000=\frac{x}{4{,}500{,}000}\cdot4{,}500{,}000$$
$$20\cdot60{,}000=x$$
$$1{,}200{,}000=x$$

The first person won \$1.2 million in the lottery.

SECTION 6.5

Objective A Exercises

1.
$$\frac{x}{2}+\frac{5}{6}=\frac{x}{3}$$
$$12\left(\frac{x}{2}+\frac{5}{6}\right)=12\left(\frac{x}{3}\right)$$
$$12\cdot\frac{x}{2}+12\cdot\frac{5}{6}=4x$$
$$6x+10=4x$$
$$10=-2x$$
$$-5=x$$

The solution is –5.

3.
$$\frac{8}{2x-1}=2$$
$$(2x-1)\cdot\frac{8}{2x-1}=(2x-1)2$$
$$8=4x-2$$
$$10=4x$$
$$\frac{5}{2}=x$$

The solution is $\frac{5}{2}$.

5.
$$1-\frac{3}{y}=4$$
$$y\left(1-\frac{3}{y}\right)=y\cdot4$$
$$y\cdot1-y\cdot\frac{3}{y}=4y$$
$$y-3=4y$$
$$-3=3y$$
$$-1=y$$

The solution is –1.

7.
$$\frac{3}{x-2}=\frac{4}{x}$$
$$x(x-2)\cdot\frac{3}{x-2}=x(x-2)\cdot\frac{4}{x}$$
$$3x=(x-2)4$$
$$3x=4x-8$$
$$-x=-8$$
$$x=8$$

The solution is 8.

9.
$$\frac{6}{2y+3}=\frac{6}{y}$$
$$y(2y+3)\cdot\frac{6}{2y+3}=y(2y+3)\cdot\frac{6}{y}$$
$$6y=(2y+3)6$$
$$6y=12y+18$$
$$-6y=18$$
$$y=-3$$

The solution is –3.

11.
$$\frac{5}{y+3}-2=\frac{7}{y+3}$$
$$(y+3)\left(\frac{5}{y+3}-2\right)=(y+3)\cdot\frac{7}{y+3}$$
$$(y+3)\cdot\frac{5}{y+3}-(y+3)2=7$$
$$5-2y-6=7$$
$$-2y-1=7$$
$$-2y=8$$
$$y=-4$$

The solution is –4.

13.
$$\frac{-4}{a-4}=3-\frac{a}{a-4}$$
$$(a-4)\frac{-4}{a-4}=(a-4)\left(3-\frac{a}{a-4}\right)$$
$$-4=(a-4)3-(a-4)\frac{a}{a-4}$$
$$-4=3a-12-a$$
$$-4=2a-12$$
$$8=2a$$
$$4=a$$

4 does not check as a solution.
The equation has no solution.

15.

$$\frac{2x}{x+2}+3x=\frac{-5}{x+2}$$
$$(x+2)\left(\frac{2x}{x+2}+3x\right)=\frac{-5}{x+2}(x+2)$$
$$2x+3x(x+2)=-5$$
$$2x+3x^2+6x=-5$$
$$3x^2+8x+5=0$$
$$(3x+5)(x+1)=0$$

$$3x+5=0 \qquad x+1=0$$
$$3x=-5 \qquad x=-1$$
$$x=-\frac{5}{3}$$

The solutions are $-\frac{5}{3}$ and -1.

17.

$$\frac{x}{2x-9}-3x=\frac{10}{9-2x}$$
$$(2x-9)\left(\frac{x}{2x-9}-3x\right)=\frac{10}{(9-2x)}(2x+9)$$
$$x-3x(2x-9)=-10$$
$$x-6x^2+27x=-10$$
$$-6x^2+28x+10=0$$
$$-2(3x^2-14x-5)=0$$
$$(3x+1)(x-5)=0$$

$$3x+1=0 \qquad x-5=0$$
$$3x=-1 \qquad x=5$$
$$x=-\frac{1}{3}$$

The solutions are $-\frac{1}{3}$ and 5.

19.

$$\frac{5}{x-2}-\frac{2}{x+2}=\frac{3}{x^2-4}$$
$$\frac{5}{x-2}-\frac{2}{x+2}=\frac{3}{(x+2)(x-2)}$$
$$(x+2)(x-2)\left(\frac{5}{x-2}-\frac{2}{x+2}\right)=(x+2)(x-2)\frac{3}{(x+2)(x-2)}$$
$$(x+2)(x-2)\frac{5}{x-2}-(x+2)(x-2)\frac{2}{x+2}=3$$
$$(x+2)5-(x-2)2=3$$
$$5x+10-2x+4=3$$
$$3x+14=3$$
$$3x=-11$$
$$x=-\frac{11}{3}$$

The solution is $-\frac{11}{3}$.

21.
$$\frac{9}{x^2+7x+10}=\frac{5}{x+2}-\frac{3}{x+5}$$
$$\frac{9}{(x+2)(x+5)}=\frac{5}{x+2}-\frac{3}{x+5}$$
$$(x+2)(x+5)\frac{9}{(x+2)(x+5)}=(x+2)(x+5)\left(\frac{5}{x+2}-\frac{3}{x+5}\right)$$
$$9=(x+2)(x+5)\frac{5}{x+2}-(x+2)(x+5)\frac{3}{x+5}$$
$$9=(x+5)5-(x+2)3$$
$$9=5x+25-3x-6$$
$$9=2x+19$$
$$-10=2x$$
$$-5=x$$

–5 does not check as a solution. The equation has no solution.

23.
$$\frac{P_1V_1}{T_1}=\frac{P_2V_2}{T_2}$$
$$\frac{P_1V_1T_2}{T_1}=P_2V_2$$
$$\frac{P_1V_1T_2}{V_2T_1}=P_2$$

25.
$$\frac{1}{f}=\frac{1}{a}+\frac{1}{b}$$
$$abf\left(\frac{1}{f}\right)=abf\left(\frac{1}{a}+\frac{1}{b}\right)$$
$$ab=abf\frac{1}{a}+abf\frac{1}{b}$$
$$ab=bf+af$$
$$ab-bf=af$$
$$b(a-f)=af$$
$$b=\frac{af}{a-f}$$

Objective B Application Problems

27. Strategy
- Time for the experienced bricklayer to do the job: t
  Time for the inexperienced bricklayer to do the job: $2t$

	Rate	Time	Part
Experienced Bricklayer	$\frac{1}{t}$	6	$\frac{6}{t}$
Inexperienced Bricklayer	$\frac{1}{2t}$	16	$\frac{16}{2t}$

- The sum of the parts of the task completed by each bricklayer must equal 1.

Solution
$$\frac{6}{t}+\frac{16}{2t}=1$$
$$2t\left(\frac{6}{t}+\frac{16}{2t}\right)=2t(1)$$
$$12+16=2t$$
$$28=2t$$
$$14=t$$

Working alone, the experienced bricklayer can do the job in 14 h.

29. Strategy

- Time for the slower machine to transmit the fax.

	Rate	Time	Part
Faster fax	$\frac{1}{40}$	35	$\frac{35}{40}$
Slower fax	$\frac{1}{t}$	20	$\frac{20}{t}$

- The sum of the part sent by the slower fax and the part sent by the faster fax is 1.

Solution

$$\frac{35}{40}+\frac{20}{t}=1$$
$$40t\left(\frac{35}{40}+\frac{20}{t}\right)=40t(1)$$
$$35t+40(20)=40t$$
$$35t+800=40t$$
$$800=5t$$
$$160=t$$

31. Strategy

- Unknown time to fill the bottles working together: t

	Rate	Time	Part
First machine	$\frac{1}{10}$	t	$\frac{t}{10}$
Second machine	$\frac{1}{12}$	t	$\frac{t}{12}$
Third machine	$\frac{1}{15}$	t	$\frac{t}{15}$

- The sum of the parts of the task completed by each machine must equal 1.

Solution

$$\frac{t}{10}+\frac{t}{12}+\frac{t}{15}=1$$
$$60\left(\frac{t}{10}+\frac{t}{12}+\frac{t}{15}\right)=60(1)$$
$$6t+5t+4t=60$$
$$15t=60$$
$$t=4$$

When all three machines are working, it would take 4 h to fill the bottles.

33. Strategy

- Unknown time to empty the tank working together: t

	Rate	Time	Part
Inlet pipe	$\frac{1}{45}$	t	$\frac{t}{45}$
Outlet pipe	$\frac{1}{30}$	t	$\frac{t}{30}$

- The part of the task completed by the outlet pipe minus the part of the task completed by the inlet pipe is 1.

Solution

$$\frac{t}{30}-\frac{t}{45}=1$$
$$90\left(\frac{t}{30}-\frac{t}{45}\right)=90(1)$$
$$3t-2t=90$$
$$t=90$$

It would take 90 min to empty the tank.

35. Strategy

- Time for the clowns to blow up 76 balloons: t

	Rate	Time	Part
First clown	$\frac{1}{2}$	t	$\frac{t}{2}$
Second clown	$\frac{1}{3}$	t	$\frac{t}{3}$
Balloon popping	$\frac{1}{5}$	t	$\frac{t}{5}$

- The sum of the tasks completed by the two clowns minus the part completed by the balloons popping is equal to 76. This is the number of balloons filled after t minutes.

Solution

$$\frac{t}{2}+\frac{t}{3}-\frac{t}{5}=76$$
$$30\left(\frac{t}{2}+\frac{t}{3}-\frac{t}{5}\right)=30(76)$$
$$15t+10t-6t=2280$$
$$19t=2280$$
$$t=120$$

It will take 120 minutes to have 76 balloons.

37. Strategy • Unknown time to address 140 envelopes: t

	Time to address envelope	Time to address 140 envelopes	Rate	Time	Part
First clerk	30 sec = $\frac{1}{2}$ min	70 min	$\frac{1}{70}$	t	$\frac{t}{70}$
Second clerk	40 sec = $\frac{2}{3}$ min	$\frac{280}{3}$ min	$\frac{3}{280}$	t	$\frac{3t}{280}$

• The sum of the parts of the task completed by the two clerks is 1.

$$\frac{t}{70}+\frac{3t}{280}=1$$

Solution

$$\frac{t}{70}+\frac{3t}{280}=1$$
$$280\left(\frac{t}{70}+\frac{3t}{280}\right)=(1)280$$
$$4t+3t=280$$
$$7t=280$$
$$t=40 \text{ min} = 2400 \text{ seconds}$$

The two clerks, working together, can complete the task in 40 minutes (or 2400 seconds).

Objective C Application Problems

39. Strategy • Rate of the runner: r
Rate of the bicyclist: $r+7$

	Distance	Rate	Time
Runner	16	r	$\frac{16}{r}$
Bicyclist	30	$r+7$	$\frac{30}{r+7}$

• The time the runner travels equals the time the bicyclist travels.

Solution

$$\frac{16}{r}=\frac{30}{r+7}$$
$$r(r+7)\frac{16}{r}=r(r+7)\frac{30}{r+7}$$
$$(r+7)(16)=30r$$
$$16r+112=30r$$
$$112=14r$$
$$8=r$$

The rate of the runner is 8 mph.

41. Strategy • Rate of the tortoise: r
Rate of the hare: $180r$

	Distance	Rate	Time
Tortoise	360	r	$\frac{360}{r}$
Hare	360	$180r$	$\frac{360}{180r}$

• The time for the tortoise is 14 min 55 s (895 s) more than the hare.

Solution

$$\frac{360}{180r}+895=\frac{360}{r}$$
$$\frac{2}{r}+895=\frac{360}{r}$$
$$r\left(\frac{2}{r}+895\right)=r\left(\frac{360}{r}\right)$$
$$2+895r=360$$
$$895r=358$$
$$r=0.4$$

$180r = 180(0.4) = 72$

The rate of the tortoise is 0.4 ft/s.

The rate of the hare is 72 ft/s.

43. Strategy • Rate of the jogger: r
Rate of the cyclist: $2r$

	Distance	Rate	Time
Jogger	30	r	$\frac{30}{r}$
Cyclist	30	$2r$	$\frac{30}{2r}$

• The time for the jogger is 3 h more than the time for the cyclist.

Solution

$$\frac{30}{2r}+3=\frac{30}{r}$$
$$2r\left(\frac{30}{2r}+3\right)=2r\left(\frac{30}{r}\right)$$
$$30+6r=60$$
$$6r=30$$
$$r=5$$
$$2r=2(5)=10$$

The rate of the cyclist is 10 mph.

45. Strategy • Rate of the current: r

	Distance	Rate	Time
With current	15	$8+r$	$\frac{15}{8+r}$
Against current	9	$8-r$	$\frac{9}{8-r}$

• The time traveling with the current equals the time traveling against the current.

Solution

$$\frac{15}{8+r}=\frac{9}{8-r}$$
$$(8+r)(8-r)\frac{15}{8+r}=(8+r)(8-r)\frac{9}{8-r}$$
$$(8-r)15=(8+r)9$$
$$120-15r=72+9r$$
$$120=72+24r$$
$$48=24r$$
$$2=r$$

The rate of the current is 2 mph.

47. Strategy • Rate of the wind: r

	Distance	Rate	Time
With wind	6150	$950+r$	$\frac{6150}{950+r}$
Against wind	5250	$950-r$	$\frac{5250}{950-r}$

• The time traveling with the wind equals the time traveling against the wind.

Solution

$$\frac{6150}{950+r}=\frac{5250}{950-r}$$
$$(950+r)(950-r)\frac{6160}{950+r}=(950+r)(950-r)\frac{5250}{950-r}$$
$$(950-r)(6150)=(950+r)(5250)$$
$$5{,}842{,}500-6150r=4{,}987{,}500+5250r$$
$$855{,}000-6150r=5250r$$
$$855{,}000=11{,}400r$$
$$75=r$$

The rate of the wind is 75 mph.

49. Strategy • Rate of the wind: r

	Distance	Rate	Time
With wind	3059	$550+r$	$\frac{3059}{550+r}$
Against wind	2450	$550-r$	$\frac{2450}{550-r}$

• The time flying with the wind equals the time flying against the wind.

Solution

$$\frac{3059}{550+r}=\frac{2450}{550-r}$$
$$(550+r)(550-r)\frac{3059}{550+r}=(550+r)(550-r)\frac{2450}{550-r}$$
$$(550+r)(3059)=(550+r)(2450)$$
$$1,682,450-3059r=1,347,500+2450r$$
$$1,682,450=1,347,500+5509r$$
$$334,950=5509r$$
$$60.80=r$$

The rate of the wind is 60.80 mph.

51. Strategy • Rate of the current: c

	Distance	Rate	Time
With current	16	$6+c$	$\frac{16}{6+c}$
Against current	16	$6-c$	$\frac{16}{6-c}$

• The sum of the times is 6 hours.

$$\frac{16}{6+c}+\frac{16}{6-c}=6$$

Solution

$$\frac{16}{6+c}+\frac{16}{6-c}=6$$
$$(6+c)(6-c)\left(\frac{16}{6+c}-\frac{16}{6-c}\right)=(6)(6+c)(6-c)$$
$$16(6-c)+16(6+c)=6(36-c^2)$$
$$96-16c+96+16c=216-6c^2$$
$$192=216-6c^2$$
$$0=24-6c^2$$
$$0=6(4-c^2)$$
$$0=6(2-c)(2+c)$$

$2-c=0 \quad 2+c=0$

$2=c \quad c=-2$

The rate of the current is 2 mph.

Applying the Concepts

53\. a.

$$\frac{x-2}{y}=\frac{x+2}{5y}$$
$$\frac{x-2}{y}\cdot 5y=\frac{x+2}{5y}\cdot 5y$$
$$(x-2)\cdot 5=x+2$$
$$5x-10=x+2$$
$$4x=12$$
$$x=3$$

b.

$$\frac{x}{x+y}=\frac{2x}{4y}$$
$$\frac{x}{x+y}\cdot 4y(x+y)=\frac{2x}{4y}\cdot 4y(x+y)$$
$$4xy=2x(x+y)$$
$$4xy=2x^2+2xy$$
$$2xy=2x^2$$
$$2x^2-2xy=0$$
$$x^2-xy=0$$
$$x(x-y)=0$$

$x=0 \quad x-y=0$

$\qquad x=y$

c.

$$\frac{x-y}{x}=\frac{2x}{9y}$$
$$\frac{x-y}{x}\cdot 9xy=\frac{2x}{9y}\cdot 9xy$$
$$(x-y)\cdot 9y=2x^2$$
$$9xy-9y^2=2x^2$$
$$2x^2-9xy+9y^2=0$$
$$(2x-3y)(x-3y)=0$$

$2x-3y=0 \qquad x-3y=0$

$2x=3y \qquad x=3y$

$x=\frac{3}{2}y$

55\. Strategy • Rate of the bus: r

	Distance	Rate	Time
Usual Conditions	165	r	$\frac{165}{r}$
Bad Weather	165	$r-5$	$\frac{165}{r-5}$

• The difference between the times is 15 minutes, or $\frac{1}{4}$ hr.

Solution

$$\frac{165}{r-5}-\frac{165}{r}=\frac{1}{4}$$
$$4r\cdot(r-5)\left(\frac{165}{r-5}-\frac{165}{r}\right)=\frac{1}{4}\cdot 4r(r-5)$$
$$660r-660(r-5)=r^2-5r$$
$$660r-660r+3300=r^2-5r$$
$$r^2-5r-3300=0$$
$$(r-60)(r+55)=0$$

$r-60=0 \qquad r+55=0$

$r=60 \qquad r=-55$

The rate of the bus cannot be negative, so the usual rate of the bus is 60 mph.

SECTION 6.6

Objective A Application Problems

1\. Strategy To find the profit:

- Write the basic direct variation equation, replace the variables by the given values, and solve for k.
- Write the direct variation equation, replacing k by its value. Substitute 5000 for s and solve for P.

Solution

$$P=ks$$
$$4000=k(250)$$
$$16=k$$
$$P=16s=16(5000)=80{,}000$$

When the company sells 5000 products, the profit is $80,000.

3\. Strategy To find the pressure:

- Write the basic direct variation equation, replace the variables by the given values, and solve for k.
- Write the direct variation equation, replacing k by its value. Substitute 15 for d and solve for p.

Solution

$$p=kd$$
$$4.5=k(10)$$
$$0.45=k$$
$$p=0.45d=0.45(15)=6.75$$

The pressure is 6.75 pounds per square inch.

5. Strategy To find how far the object will fall:

- Write the basic direct variation equation, replace the variables by the given values, and solve for k.
- Write the direct variation equation, replace k by its value. Substitute 10 for t and solve for d.

Solution

$$d = kt^2$$
$$144 = k(3)^2$$
$$144 = 9k$$
$$16 = k$$
$$d = 16t^2 = 16(10)^2 = 16(100) = 1600$$

In 10 s, the object will fall 1600 ft.

7. Strategy To find the distance:

- Write the basic direct variation equation, replace the variables by the given values, and solve for k.
- Write the direct variation equation, replacing k by its value. Substitute 3 for t and solve for s.

Solution

$$s = kt^2$$
$$6 = k(1)^2$$
$$6 = k$$
$$s = 6t^2 = 6(3)^2 = 6(9) = 54$$

In 3 s, the ball will roll 54 ft.

9. Strategy To find the length of the rectangle:

- Write the basic inverse variation equation, replace the variables by the given values, and solve for k.
- Write the inverse variation equation, replacing k by its value. Substitute 4 for w and solve for L.

Solution

$$L = \frac{k}{w}$$
$$8 = \frac{k}{5}$$
$$40 = k$$
$$L = \frac{40}{w} = \frac{40}{4} = 10$$

When the width is 4 ft, the length is 10 ft.

11. Strategy To find the speed:

- Write the basic inverse variation equation, replace the variables by the given values, and solve for k.
- Write the inverse variation equation, replacing k by its value. Substitute 36 for t and solve for v.

Solution

$$v = \frac{k}{t}$$
$$24 = \frac{k}{45}$$
$$1080 = k$$
$$v = \frac{1080}{t} = \frac{1080}{36} = 30$$

The gear which has 36 teeth will make 30 revolutions per minute.

13. Strategy To find the current:

- Write the basic combined variation equation, replace the variables by the given values, and solve for k.
- Write the combined variation equation, replacing k by its value. Substitute 180 for v and 24 for r.

Solution

$$I = \frac{kv}{r}$$
$$10 = \frac{k(110)}{11}$$
$$110 = 110k$$
$$1 = k$$
$$I = \frac{v}{r} = \frac{180}{24} = 7.5$$

The current is 7.5 amps.

15. Strategy To find the intensity:

- Write the basic inverse variation equation, replace the variables by the given values, and solve for k.
- Write the inverse variation equation, replacing k by its value. Substitute 5 for d and solve for I.

Solution

$$I = \frac{k}{d^2}$$
$$12 = \frac{k}{10^2}$$
$$12 = \frac{k}{100}$$
$$1200 = k$$
$$I = \frac{1200}{d^2} = \frac{1200}{5^2} = \frac{1200}{25} = 48$$

The intensity is 48 lumens when the distance is 5 ft.

Applying the Concepts

17. Strategy To find the effect on y, replace x with $2x$.

Solution $y = kx \quad y = k(2x)$

$y = 2kx$

If x is doubled, then y is doubled.

19. inversely

21. inversely

CHAPTER REVIEW

1. $$\frac{a^6b^4 + a^4b^6}{a^5b^4 - a^4b^4} \cdot \frac{a^2 - b^2}{a^4 - b^4}$$
$$= -\frac{a^4b^4(a^2 + b^2)}{a^4b^4(a-1)} \cdot \frac{(a+b)(a-b)}{(a^2+b^2)(a+b)(a-b)}$$
$$= \frac{a^4b^4(a^2+b)^2(a+b)(a-b)}{a^4b^4(a-1)(a^2+b^2)(a+b)(a-b)}$$
$$= \frac{1}{a-1}$$

2. The LCM is $(x-3)(x+2)$.
$$\frac{x}{x-3} - 4 - \frac{2x-5}{x+2}$$
$$= \frac{x}{x-3} \cdot \frac{x+2}{x+2} - 4 \cdot \frac{(x-3)(x+2)}{(x-3)(x+2)} - \frac{2x-5}{x+2} \cdot \frac{x-3}{x-3}$$
$$= \frac{x^2 + 2x - 4(x^2 - x - 6) - (2x^2 - 11x + 15)}{(x-3)(x+2)}$$
$$= \frac{x^2 + 2x - 4x^2 + 4x + 24 - 2x^2 + 11x - 15}{(x-3)(x+2)}$$
$$= \frac{-5x^2 + 17x + 9}{(x-3)(x+2)}$$
$$= \frac{-(5x^2 - 17x - 9)}{(x-3)(x+2)}$$
$$= -\frac{5x^2 - 17x - 9}{(x-3)(x+2)}$$

3. $$P(x) = \frac{x}{x-3}$$
$$P(4) = \frac{4}{4-3} = \frac{4}{1}$$
$$P(4) = 4$$

4. $$\frac{3x-2}{x+6} = \frac{3x+1}{x+9}$$
$$\frac{3x-2}{x+6} \cdot (x+6)(x+9) = \frac{3x+1}{x+9} \cdot (x+6)(x+9)$$
$$(3x-2)(x+9) = (3x+1)(x+6)$$
$$3x^2 + 25x - 18 = 3x^2 + 19x + 6$$
$$25x - 18 = 19x + 6$$
$$6x - 18 = 6$$
$$6x = 24$$
$$x = 4$$

The solution is 4.

5. $$\frac{\frac{3x+4}{3x-4} + \frac{3x-4}{3x+4}}{\frac{3x-4}{3x+4} - \frac{3x+4}{3x-4}}$$
The LCM is $(3x-4)(3x+4)$.
$$\frac{\frac{3x+4}{3x-4} + \frac{3x-4}{3x+4}}{\frac{3x-4}{3x+4} - \frac{3x+4}{3x-4}} \cdot \frac{(3x-4)(3x+4)}{(3x-4)(3x+4)}$$
$$= \frac{(3x+4)^2 + (3x-4)^2}{(3x-4)^2 - (3x+4)^2}$$
$$= \frac{9x^2 + 24x + 16 + 9x^2 - 24x + 16}{9x^2 - 24x + 16 - (9x^2 + 24x + 16)}$$
$$= \frac{18x^2 + 32}{9x^2 - 24x + 16 - 9x^2 - 24x - 16}$$
$$= \frac{18x^2 + 32}{-48x}$$
$$= \frac{2(9x^2 + 16)}{2(-24x)}$$
$$= -\frac{9x^2 + 16}{24x}$$

6. The LCM is $(4x-1)(4x+1)$.
$$\frac{4x}{4x-1} \cdot \frac{4x+1}{4x+1} = \frac{16x^2 + 4x}{(4x+1)(4x-1)}$$
$$\frac{3x-1}{4x+1} \cdot \frac{4x-1}{4x-1} = \frac{12x^2 - 7x + 1}{(4x+1)(4x-1)}$$

7. $$S = \frac{a}{1-r}$$
$$S(1-r) = \frac{a}{1-r}(1-r)$$
$$S - Sr = a$$
$$-Sr = a - S$$
$$r = \frac{a-S}{-S}$$
$$r = \frac{S-a}{S}$$

8. $$P(x) = \frac{x^2 - 2}{3x^2 - 2x + 5}$$
$$P(-2) = \frac{(-2)^2 - 2}{3(-2)^2 - 2(-2) + 5} = \frac{4-2}{12+4+5} = \frac{2}{21}$$
$$P(-2) = \frac{2}{21}$$

9.
$$\frac{10}{5x+3}=\frac{2}{10x-3}$$
$$\frac{10}{5x+3}\cdot(5x+3)(10x-3)=\frac{2}{10x-3}\cdot(5x+3)(10x-3)$$
$$10(10x-3)=2(5x+3)$$
$$100x-30=10x+6$$
$$90x-30=6$$
$$90x=36$$
$$x=\frac{36}{90}=\frac{2}{5}$$

The solution is $\frac{2}{5}$.

10. $f(x)=\frac{2x-7}{3x^2+3x-18}$
$$3x^2+3x-18=0$$
$$3(x^2+x-6)=0$$
$$3(x+3)(x-2)=0$$
$$x+3=0 \quad x-2=0$$
$$x=-3 \quad x=2$$
The domain is $\{x|x\neq -3, 2\}$.

11.
$$\frac{3x^4+11x^2-4}{3x^4+13x^2+4}=\frac{(3x^2-1)(x^2+4)}{(3x^2+1)(x^2+4)}=\frac{3x^2-1}{3x^2+1}$$

12. $q(x)=\frac{2x}{x-3}$
$$x-3=0$$
$$x=3$$
The domain is $\{x|x\neq 3\}$.

13.
$$\frac{x^3-8}{x^3+2x^2+4x}\cdot\frac{x^3+2x^2}{x^2-4}$$
$$=\frac{(x-2)(x^2+2x+4)}{x(x^2+2x+4)}\cdot\frac{x^2(x+2)}{(x+2)(x-2)}$$
$$=\frac{(x-2)(x^2+2x+4)x^2(x+2)}{x(x^2+2x+4)(x+2)(x-2)}=x$$

14.
$$\frac{3x^2+2}{x^2-4}-\frac{9x-x^2}{x^2-4}=\frac{3x^2+2-(9x-x^2)}{x^2-4}$$
$$=\frac{3x^2+2-9x+x^2}{x^2-4}$$
$$=\frac{4x^2-9x+2}{x^2-4}$$
$$=\frac{(4x-1)(x-2)}{(x+2)(x-2)}$$
$$=\frac{4x-1}{x+2}$$

15.
$$Q=\frac{N-S}{N}$$
$$Q\cdot N=\frac{N-S}{N}\cdot N$$
$$QN=N-S$$
$$QN-N=-S$$
$$N(Q-1)=-S$$
$$N=\frac{-S}{Q-1}$$
$$N=\frac{S}{1-Q}$$

16.
$$\frac{30}{x^2+5x+4}+\frac{10}{x+4}=\frac{4}{x+1}$$
$$\frac{30}{(x+4)(x+1)}+\frac{10}{x+4}=\frac{4}{x+1}$$
$$(x+4)(x+1)\left(\frac{30}{(x+4)(x+1)}+\frac{10}{x+4}\right)=\frac{4}{x+1}\cdot(x+4)(x+1)$$
$$30+10(x+1)=4(x+4)$$
$$30+10x+10=4x+16$$
$$10x+40=4x+16$$
$$6x+40=16$$
$$6x=-24$$
$$x=-4$$

-4 does not check as a solution. The equation has no solution.

17. $x+\dfrac{\frac{4}{x}-1}{\frac{1}{x}-\frac{3}{x^2}}=x+\dfrac{\frac{4}{x}-1}{\frac{1}{x}-\frac{3}{x^2}}\cdot\dfrac{x^2}{x^2}$

$=x+\dfrac{4x-x^2}{x-3}$

The LCM is –3.

$x\cdot\dfrac{x-3}{x-3}+\dfrac{4x-x^2}{x-3}=\dfrac{x^2-3x+4x-x^2}{x-3}$

$=\dfrac{x}{x-3}$

18. $x^2-9x+20=(x-5)(x-4);$

$4-x=-(x-4)$

The LCM is $(x-5)(x-4)$.

$\dfrac{x-3}{x-5}\cdot\dfrac{x-4}{x-4}=\dfrac{x^2-7x+12}{(x-5)(x-4)}$

$\dfrac{x}{x^2-9x+20}=\dfrac{x}{(x-5)(x-4)}$

$\dfrac{1}{4-x}=\dfrac{-1}{x-4}\cdot\dfrac{x-5}{x-5}=\dfrac{-x+5}{(x-5)(x-4)}$

$=\dfrac{-(x-5)}{(x-5)(x-4)}$

$=-\dfrac{x-5}{(x-5)(x-4)}$

19.
$$\frac{6}{2x-3}=\frac{5}{x+5}+\frac{5}{2x^2+7x-15}$$
$$\frac{6}{2x-3}=\frac{5}{x+5}+\frac{5}{(2x-3)(x+5)}$$
$$(2x-3)(x+5)\left(\frac{6}{2x-3}\right)=\left(\frac{5}{x+5}+\frac{5}{(2x-3)(x+5)}\right)(2x-3)(x+5)$$
$$6(x+5)=5(2x-3)+5$$
$$6x+30=10x-15+5$$
$$6x+30=10x-10$$
$$-4x=-40$$
$$x=10$$

The solution is 10.

20. $\dfrac{x^{n+1}+x}{x^{2n}-1}\div\dfrac{x^{n+2}-x^2}{x^{2n}-2x^n+1}=\dfrac{x^{n+1}+x}{x^{2n}-1}\cdot\dfrac{x^{2n}-2x^n+1}{x^{n+2}-x^2}$

$=\dfrac{x(x^n+1)}{(x^n+1)(x^n-1)}\cdot\dfrac{(x^n-1)(x^n-1)}{x^2(x^n-1)}$

$=\dfrac{x(x^n+1)(x^n-1)(x^n-1)}{(x^n+1)(x^n-1)(x^n-1)}=\dfrac{1}{x}$

21. $\dfrac{27x^3-8}{9x^3+6x^2+4x}\div\dfrac{9x^2-12x+4}{9x^2-4}=\dfrac{27x^3-8}{9x^3+6x^2+4x}\cdot\dfrac{9x^2-4}{9x^2-12x+4}$

$=\dfrac{(3x-2)(9x^2+6x+4)}{x(9x^2+6x+4)}\cdot\dfrac{(3x+2)(3x-2)}{(3x-2)(3x-2)}$

$=\dfrac{(3x-2)(9x^2+6x+4)(3x+2)(3x-2)}{x(9x^2+6x+4)(3x-2)(3x-2)}$

$=\dfrac{3x+2}{x}$

22. $3x^2 - 7x + 2 = (3x-1)(x-2)$

The LCM is $(3x-1)(x-2)$.

$$\frac{6x}{3x^2-7x+2} - \frac{2}{3x-1} + \frac{3x}{x-2}$$
$$= \frac{6x}{(3x-1)(x-2)} - \frac{2}{3x-1}\cdot\frac{x-2}{x-2} + \frac{3x}{x-2}\cdot\frac{3x-1}{3x-1}$$
$$= \frac{6x - 2(x-2) + 3x(3x-1)}{(3x-1)(x-2)}$$
$$= \frac{6x - 2x + 4 + 9x^2 - 3x}{(3x-1)(x-2)}$$
$$= \frac{9x^2 + x + 4}{(3x-1)(x-2)}$$

23. $$\frac{x^3-27}{x^2-9} = \frac{(x-3)(x^2+3x+9)}{(x-3)(x+3)}$$
$$= \frac{x^2+3x+9}{x+3}$$

24. The LCM is $24a^2b^4$.

$$\frac{5}{3a^2b^3} + \frac{7}{8ab^4} = \frac{5}{3a^2b^3}\cdot\frac{8b}{8b} + \frac{7}{8ab^4}\cdot\frac{3a}{3a}$$
$$= \frac{40b+21a}{24a^2b^4}$$

25. Strategy Rate of the helicopter: r

Rate of the airplane: $r + 20$

	Distance	Rate	Time
Helicopter	9	r	$\frac{9}{r}$
Airplane	10	$r+20$	$\frac{10}{r+20}$

- The time the helicopter travels equals the time the airplane travels.

Solution
$$\frac{9}{r} = \frac{10}{r+20}$$
$$\frac{9}{r}[r(r+20)] = \frac{10}{r+20}[r(r+20)]$$
$$9(r+20) = 10r$$
$$9r + 180 = 10r$$
$$180 = r$$

The rate of the helicopter is 180 mph.

26. Strategy To find how long it will take to do the reading, write and solve a proportion using x to represent the time.

Solution
$$\frac{2}{5} = \frac{150}{x}$$
$$\frac{2}{5}\cdot 5x = \frac{150}{x}\cdot 5x$$
$$2x = 750$$
$$x = 375$$

To read 150 pages, it will take 375 minutes.

27. Strategy To find the current:

- Write the basic inverse variation equation, replace the variables by the given values, and solve for k.
- Write the inverse variation equation, replacing k by its value. Substitute 100 for R and solve for I.

Solution
$$I = \frac{k}{R} \qquad I = \frac{k}{R}$$
$$4 = \frac{k}{50} \qquad = \frac{200}{R}$$
$$200 = k \qquad = \frac{200}{100}$$
$$= 2$$

The current is 2 amps.

28. Strategy To find the number of miles represented, write and solve a proportion using x to represent the number of miles.

Solution
$$\frac{2.5}{10} = \frac{12}{x}$$
$$\frac{2.5}{10}\cdot 10x = \frac{12}{x}\cdot 10x$$
$$2.5x = 120$$
$$x = 48$$

The number of miles is 48.

29. Strategy To find the stopping distance:

- Write the basic direct variation equation, replace the variables by the given values, and solve for k.
- Write the direct variation equation, replacing k by its value. Substitute 30 for v and solve for s.

Solution
$$s = kv^2 \qquad s = kv^2$$
$$170 = k(50)^2 \qquad = 0.068v^2$$
$$170 = k(2500) \qquad = 0.068(30)^2$$
$$0.068 = k \qquad = 0.068(900)$$
$$= 61.2$$

The stopping distance for a car traveling at 30 mph is 61.2 ft.

30. Strategy • Unknown time for apprentice, working alone, to install fan: t

	Rate	Time	Part
Electrician	$\frac{1}{65}$	40	$\frac{40}{65}$
Apprentice	$\frac{1}{t}$	40	$\frac{40}{t}$

• The sum of the part of the task completed by the electrician and the part of the task completed by the apprentice is 1.

Solution

$$\frac{40}{65}+\frac{40}{t}=1$$
$$65t\left(\frac{40}{65}+\frac{40}{t}\right)=1\cdot 65t$$
$$40t+2600=65t$$
$$2600=25t$$
$$104=t$$

The apprentice would take 104 minutes to complete the job alone.

CHAPTER TEST

1.
$$\frac{3}{x+1}=\frac{2}{x}$$
$$\frac{3}{x+1}\cdot x(x+1)=\frac{2}{x}\cdot x(x+1)$$
$$3x=2(x+1)$$
$$3x=2x+2$$
$$x=2$$

The solution is 2.

2.
$$\frac{x^2+x-6}{x^2+7x+12}\div\frac{x^2-3x+2}{x^2+6x+8}$$
$$=\frac{x^2+x-6}{x^2+7x+12}\cdot\frac{x^2+6x+8}{x^2-3x+2}$$
$$=\frac{(x+3)(x-2)}{(x+3)(x+4)}\cdot\frac{(x+4)(x+2)}{(x-2)(x-1)}$$
$$=\frac{(x+3)(x-2)(x+4)(x+2)}{(x+3)(x+4)(x-2)(x-1)}$$
$$=\frac{x+2}{x-1}$$

3. The LCM is $(x+2)(x-3)$.
$$\frac{2x-1}{x+2}-\frac{x}{x-3}=\frac{2x-1}{x+2}\cdot\frac{x-3}{x-3}-\frac{x}{x-3}\cdot\frac{x+2}{x+2}$$
$$=\frac{2x^2-7x+3-(x^2+2x)}{(x-3)(x+2)}$$
$$=\frac{x^2-9x+3}{(x-3)(x+2)}$$

4. $x^2+x-6=(x+3)(x-2)$
$x^2-9=(x+3)(x-3)$
The LCM is $(x+3)(x-3)(x-2)$.
$$\frac{x+1}{x^2+x-6}=\frac{x+1}{(x+3)(x-2)}\cdot\frac{x-3}{x-3}$$
$$=\frac{x^2-2x-3}{(x+3)(x-3)(x-2)}$$
$$\frac{2x}{x^2-9}=\frac{2x}{(x+3)(x-3)}\cdot\frac{x-2}{x-2}$$
$$=\frac{2x^2-4x}{(x+3)(x-3)(x-2)}$$

5.
$$\frac{4x}{2x-1}=2-\frac{1}{2x-1}$$
$$(2x-1)\frac{4x}{2x-1}=\left(2-\frac{1}{2x-1}\right)2x-1$$
$$4x=2(2x-1)-1$$
$$4x=4x-2-1$$
$$4x=4x-3$$
$$0=-3$$

There is no solution.

6.
$$\frac{v^3-4v}{2v^2-5v+2}=\frac{v(v^2-4)}{(2v-1)(v-2)}$$
$$=\frac{v(v+2)(v-2)}{(2v-1)(v-2)}$$
$$=\frac{v(v+2)}{2v-1}$$

7.
$$\frac{3x^2-12}{5x-15}\cdot\frac{2x^2-18}{x^2+5x+6}$$
$$=\frac{3(x+2)(x-2)}{5(x-3)}\cdot\frac{2(x+3)(x-3)}{(x+3)(x+2)}$$
$$=\frac{3(x+2)(x-2)2(x+3)(x-3)}{5(x-3)(x+3)(x+2)}$$
$$=\frac{6(x-2)}{5}$$

8.
$$f(x)=\frac{3x^2-x+1}{x^2-9}$$
$$x^2-9=0$$
$$(x+3)(x-3)=0$$
$$x+3=0 \quad x-3=0$$
$$x=-3 \quad x=3$$

The domain is $\{x|x\neq 3,-3\}$.

9.
$$\frac{1-\frac{1}{x}-\frac{12}{x^2}}{1+\frac{6}{x}+\frac{9}{x^2}}=\frac{1-\frac{1}{x}-\frac{12}{x^2}}{1+\frac{6}{x}+\frac{9}{x^2}}\cdot\frac{x^2}{x^2}$$
$$=\frac{x^2-x-12}{x^2+6x+9}$$
$$=\frac{(x-4)(x+3)}{(x+3)(x+3)}=\frac{x-4}{x+3}$$

10.
$$\frac{1-\frac{1}{x+2}}{1-\frac{3}{x+4}}=\frac{1-\frac{1}{x+2}}{1-\frac{3}{x+4}}\cdot\frac{(x+2)(x+4)}{(x+2)(x+4)}$$
$$=\frac{(x+2)(x+4)-(x+4)}{(x+2)(x+4)-3(x+2)}$$
$$=\frac{x^2+6x+8-x-4}{x^2+6x+8-3x-6}$$
$$=\frac{x^2+5x+4}{x^2+3x+2}$$
$$=\frac{(x+4)(x+1)}{(x+2)(x+1)}$$
$$=\frac{x+4}{x+2}$$

11.
$$\frac{2x^2-x-3}{2x^2-5x+3}\div\frac{3x^2-x-4}{x^2-1}$$
$$=\frac{2x^2-x-3}{2x^2-5x+3}\cdot\frac{x^2-1}{3x^2-x-4}$$
$$=\frac{(2x-3)(x+1)}{(2x-3)(x-1)}\cdot\frac{(x+1)(x-1)}{(3x-4)(x+1)}$$
$$=\frac{(2x-3)(x+1)(x+1)(x-1)}{(2x-3)(x-1)(3x-4)(x+1)}$$
$$=\frac{x+1}{3x-4}$$

12.
$$\frac{4x}{x+1}-x=\frac{2}{x+1}$$
$$(x+1)\left[\frac{4x}{x+1}-x\right]=\frac{2}{x+1}(x+1)$$
$$4x-x(x+1)=2$$
$$4x-x^2-x=2$$
$$3x-x^2=2$$
$$0=x^2-3x+2$$
$$0=(x-2)(x-1)$$

$0=x-2 \quad x-1=0$

$2=x \quad x=1$

The solutions are 2 and 1.

13.
$$\frac{2a^2-8a+8}{4+4a-3a^2}=\frac{2(a^2-4a+4)}{(2-a)(2+3a)}$$
$$=\frac{2(a-2)(a-2)}{(2-a)(2+3a)}$$
$$=-\frac{2(a-2)}{3a+2}$$

14.
$$\frac{1}{r}=\frac{1}{2}-\frac{2}{t}$$
$$2rt\left(\frac{1}{r}\right)=\left(\frac{1}{2}-\frac{2}{t}\right)2rt$$
$$2t=rt-4r$$
$$2t-rt=-4r$$
$$t(2-r)=-4r$$
$$t=\frac{-4r}{2-r}$$
$$t=\frac{4r}{r-2}$$

15.
$$f(x)=\frac{3-x^2}{x^3-2x^2+4}$$
$$f(-1)=\frac{3-(-1)^2}{(-1)^3-2(-1)^2+4}$$
$$f(-1)=2$$

16.
$$x^2+3x-4=(x+4)(x-1)$$
$$x^2-1=(x+1)(x-1)$$

The LCM is $(x+4)(x-1)(x+1)$.

$$\frac{x+2}{x^2+3x-4}-\frac{2x}{x^2-1}$$
$$=\frac{x+2}{(x+4)(x-1)}\cdot\frac{x+1}{x+1}-\frac{2x}{(x+1)(x-1)}\cdot\frac{x+4}{x+4}$$
$$=\frac{x^2+3x+2-2x(x+4)}{(x+4)(x-1)(x+1)}$$
$$=\frac{x^2+3x+2-2x^2-8x}{(x+4)(x-1)(x+1)}$$
$$=\frac{-x^2-5x+2}{(x+1)(x+4)(x-1)}$$

17. Strategy
- Rate of hiker: r
  Rate of cyclist: $r+7$

	Distance	Rate	Time
Hiker	6	r	$\frac{6}{r}$
Cyclist	20	$r+7$	$\frac{20}{r+7}$

- The time the hiker hikes equals the time the cyclist cycles.

Solution
$$\frac{6}{r}=\frac{20}{r+7}$$
$$\frac{6}{r}[r(r+7)]=\frac{20}{r+7}\cdot[r(r+7)]$$
$$6(r+7)=20r$$
$$6r+42=20r$$
$$42=14r$$
$$3=r$$
$$10=r+7$$

The rate of the cyclist is 10 mph.

18. Strategy To find the resistance:

- Write the basic combined variation equation, replace the variables with the given values, and solve for k.
- Write the combined variation equation, replacing k with its value. Substitute 8000 for l and d for $\frac{1}{2}$, and solve for r.

Solution

$$r = \frac{kl}{d^2}$$
$$3.2 = \frac{k \cdot 16{,}000}{\left(\frac{1}{4}\right)^2}$$
$$k = 0.0000125$$
$$r = \frac{0.0000125l}{d^2}$$
$$= \frac{0.00000125(8000)}{\left(\frac{1}{2}\right)^2}$$
$$r = 0.4$$

The resistance is 0.4 ohm.

19. Strategy To find the number of rolls of wallpaper, write and solve a proportion using x to represent the number of rolls.

Solution

$$\frac{2}{45} = \frac{x}{315}$$
$$\left(\frac{2}{45}\right) \cdot 315 = \frac{x}{315} \cdot 315$$
$$14 = x$$

The office requires 14 rolls of wallpaper.

20. Strategy

- Unknown time for both landscapers working together: t

	Rate	Time	Part
First landscaper	$\frac{1}{30}$	t	$\frac{t}{30}$
Second landscaper	$\frac{1}{15}$	t	$\frac{t}{15}$

- The sum of the part of the task completed by the first landscaper and the part of the task completed by the second landscaper is 1.

Solution

$$\frac{t}{30} + \frac{t}{15} = 1$$
$$30\left(\frac{t}{30} + \frac{t}{15}\right) = 1(30)$$
$$t + 2t = 30$$
$$3t = 30$$
$$t = 10$$

Working together, the landscapers can complete the task in 10 minutes.

CUMULATIVE REVIEW

1. $$8 - 4[-3-(-2)]^2 \div 5 = 8 - 4[-3+2]^2 \div 5$$
$$= 8 - 4[-1]^2 \div 5$$
$$= 8 - 4(1) \div 5$$
$$= 8 - 4 \div 5$$
$$= 8 - \frac{4}{5} = \frac{36}{5}$$

2. $$\frac{2x-3}{6} - \frac{x}{9} = \frac{x-4}{3}$$
$$18\left(\frac{2x-3}{6} - \frac{x}{9}\right) = \left(\frac{x-4}{3}\right)18$$
$$3(2x-3) - 2x = 6(x-4)$$
$$6x - 9 - 2x = 6x - 24$$
$$4x - 9 = 6x - 24$$
$$-2x = -15$$
$$x = \frac{15}{2} = 7\frac{1}{2}$$

3. $$5 - |x-4| = 2$$
$$-|x-4| = -3$$
$$|x-4| = 3$$
$$x - 4 = 3 \quad x - 4 = -3$$
$$x = 7 \qquad x = 1$$

The solutions are 7 and 1.

4. $$\frac{x}{x-3}$$
$$x - 3 = 0$$
$$x = 3$$

The domain is $\{x|x \neq 3\}$.

5. $$P(x) = \frac{x-1}{2x-3}$$
$$P(-2) = \frac{-2-1}{2(-2)-3} = \frac{-3}{-4-3} = \frac{-3}{-7}$$
$$P(-2) = \frac{3}{7}$$

6. $0.000000035 = 3.5 \times 10^{-8}$

7. $$\frac{(2a^{-2}b^3)^{-2}}{(4a)^{-1}} = \frac{2^{-2}a^4b^{-6}}{4^{-1}a^{-1}}$$
$$= 2^{-2}4a^{4-(-1)}b^{-6}$$
$$= \frac{1}{4}4a^5b^{-6} = \frac{a^5}{b^6}$$

8. $$x - 3(1-2x) \geq 1 - 4(2-2x)$$
$$x - 3 + 6x \geq 1 - 8 + 8x$$
$$7x - 3 \geq 8x - 7$$
$$-x - 3 \geq -7$$
$$-x \geq -4$$
$$(-1)(-x) \leq (-1)(-4)$$
$$x \leq 4$$
$$\{x|x \leq 4\}$$

9. $(2a^2 - 3a + 1)(-2a^2) = -4a^4 + 6a^3 - 2a^2$

10. Let $x^n = u$

$$2x^{2n} + 3x^n - 2 = 2u^2 + 3u - 2$$
$$= (2u - 1)(u + 2)$$
$$= (2x^n - 1)(x^n + 2)$$

11. $x^3y^3 - 27 = (xy)^3 - (3)^3$

$$= (xy - 3)(x^2y^2 + 3xy + 9)$$

12. $\dfrac{x^4 + x^3y - 6x^2y^2}{x^3 - 2x^2y} = \dfrac{x^2(x^2 + xy - 6y^2)}{x^2(x - 2y)}$

$$= \frac{x^2(x + 3y)(x - 2y)}{x^2(x - 2y)}$$
$$= x + 3y$$

13. $3x - 2y = 6$

$$-2y = -3x + 6$$
$$y = \frac{3}{2}x - 3$$
$$m = \frac{3}{2}$$
$$y - y_1 = m(x - x_1)$$
$$y - (-1) = \frac{3}{2}[x - (-2)]$$
$$y + 1 = \frac{3}{2}(x + 2)$$
$$y + 1 = \frac{3}{2}x + 3$$
$$y = \frac{3}{2}x + 2$$

The equation of the line is $y = \frac{3}{2}x + 2$.

14. $8x^2 - 6x - 9 = 0$

$$(4x + 3)(2x - 3) = 0$$
$$4x + 3 = 0 \qquad 2x - 3 = 0$$
$$4x = -3 \qquad 2x = 3$$
$$x = -\frac{3}{4} \qquad x = \frac{3}{2}$$

The solutions are $-\frac{3}{4}$ and $\frac{3}{2}$.

15. $\dfrac{4x^3 + 2x^2 - 10x + 1}{x - 2}$

2	4	2	−10	1
		8	20	20
	4	10	10	21

The simplified form is $4x^2 + 10x + 10 + \dfrac{21}{x - 2}$.

16. $\dfrac{16x^2 - 9y^2}{16x^2y - 12xy^2} \div \dfrac{4x^2 - xy - 3y^2}{12x^2y^2}$

$$= \frac{16x^2 - 9y^2}{16x^2y - 12xy^2} \cdot \frac{12x^2y^2}{4x^2 - xy - 3y^2}$$
$$= \frac{(4x - 3y)(4x + 3y)}{4xy(4x - 3y)} \cdot \frac{12x^2y^2}{(4x + 3y)(x - y)}$$
$$= \frac{(4x - 3y)(4x + 3y)12x^2y^2}{4xy(4x - 3y)(4x + 3y)(x - y)}$$
$$= \frac{3xy}{x - y}$$

17. $2x^2 + 2x = 2x(x + 1)$

$$2x^4 - 2x^3 - 4x^2 = 2x^2(x^2 - x - 2)$$
$$= 2x^2(x - 2)(x + 1)$$

The LCM = $2x^2(x - 2)(x + 1)$.

$$\frac{xy}{2x^2 + 2x} = \frac{xy}{2x(x + 1)} \cdot \frac{x(x - 2)}{x(x - 2)}$$
$$= \frac{x^2y(x - 2)}{2x^2(x + 1)(x - 2)}$$
$$= \frac{x^3y - 2x^2y}{2x^2(x + 1)(x - 2)}$$
$$= \frac{2}{2x^2(x + 1)(x - 2)}$$

18. $3x^2 - x - 2 = (3x + 2)(x - 1)$

$$x^2 - 1 = (x + 1)(x - 1)$$

The LCM is $(3x + 2)(x + 1)(x - 1)$.

$$\frac{5x}{3x^2 - x - 2} - \frac{2x}{x^2 - 1}$$
$$= \frac{5x}{(3x + 2)(x - 1)} \cdot \frac{x + 1}{x + 1} - \frac{2x}{(x + 1)(x - 1)} \cdot \frac{3x + 2}{3x + 2}$$
$$= \frac{5x^2 + 5x - (6x^2 + 4x)}{(3x + 2)(x - 1)(x + 1)}$$
$$= \frac{-x^2 + x}{(3x + 2)(x - 1)(x + 1)}$$
$$= \frac{-x(x - 1)}{(3x + 2)(x - 1)(x + 1)}$$
$$= -\frac{x}{(3x + 2)(x + 1)}$$

19. $-3x + 5y = -15$

x-intercept: (5, 0)

y-intercept: (0, −3)

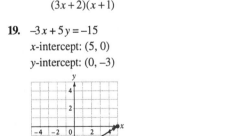

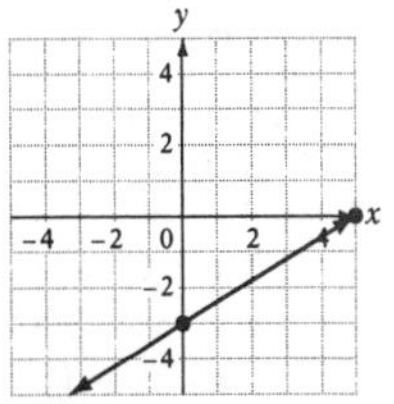

20. $x+y\le 3$ $\quad -2x+y>4$

$y\le 3-x \quad y>4+2x$

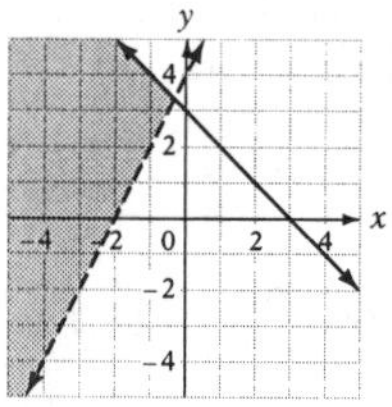

21. $\begin{vmatrix}6 & 5\\2 & -3\end{vmatrix}=6(-3)-5\cdot 2=-18-10=-28$

22.
$$\begin{aligned}\frac{x-4+\frac{5}{x+2}}{x+2-\frac{1}{x+2}}&=\frac{x-4+\frac{5}{x+2}}{x+2-\frac{1}{x+2}}\cdot\frac{x+2}{x+2}\\&=\frac{(x-4)(x+2)+5}{(x+2)^2-1}\\&=\frac{x^2-2x-8+5}{x^2+4x+4-1}\\&=\frac{x^2-2x-3}{x^2+4x+3}\\&=\frac{(x-3)(x+1)}{(x+3)(x+1)}\\&=\frac{x-3}{x+3}\end{aligned}$$

23.
$$\begin{aligned}x+y+z&=3\\-2x+y+3z&=2\\2x-4y+z&=-1\end{aligned}$$

$$D=\begin{vmatrix}1 & 1 & 1\\-2 & 1 & 3\\2 & -4 & 1\end{vmatrix}=27$$

$$D_x=\begin{vmatrix}3 & 1 & 1\\2 & 1 & 3\\-1 & -4 & 1\end{vmatrix}=27$$

$$D_y=\begin{vmatrix}1 & 3 & 1\\-2 & 2 & 3\\2 & -1 & 1\end{vmatrix}=27$$

$$D_z=\begin{vmatrix}1 & 1 & 3\\-2 & 1 & 2\\2 & -4 & -1\end{vmatrix}=27$$

$$x=\frac{D_x}{D}=\frac{27}{27}=1$$
$$y=\frac{D_y}{D}=\frac{27}{27}=1$$
$$z=\frac{D_z}{D}=\frac{27}{27}=1$$

The solution is (1, 1, 1).

24. $|3x-2|>4$

$3x-2<-4 \quad 3x-2>4$

$3x<-2 \quad 3x>6$

$x<-\frac{2}{3} \quad x>2$

$$\left\{x\middle|x<-\frac{2}{3}\right\}\cup\{x|x>2\}=\left\{x\middle|x<-\frac{2}{3}\text{ or }x>2\right\}$$

25.
$$\begin{aligned}\frac{2}{x-3}&=\frac{5}{2x-3}\\\left(\frac{2}{x-3}\right)(x-3)(2x-3)&=\left(\frac{5}{2x-3}\right)(x-3)(2x-3)\\2(2x-3)&=5(x-3)\\4x-6&=5x-15\\-x-6&=-15\\-x&=-9\\x&=9\end{aligned}$$

The solution is 9.

26.
$$\begin{aligned}\frac{3}{x^2-36}&=\frac{2}{x-6}-\frac{5}{x+6}\\\frac{3}{(x+6)(x-6)}&=\frac{2}{x-6}-\frac{5}{x+6}\\(x+6)(x-6)\left(\frac{3}{(x+6)(x-6)}\right)&=\left(\frac{2}{x-6}-\frac{5}{x+6}\right)(x+6)(x-6)\\3&=2(x+6)-5(x-6)\\3&=2x+12-5x+30\\3&=-3x+42\\-39&=-3x\\13&=x\end{aligned}$$

The solution is 13.

27.

$$I = \frac{E}{R+r}$$
$$I \cdot (R+r) = \frac{E}{R+r}(R+r)$$
$$IR + Ir = E$$
$$Ir = E - IR$$
$$r = \frac{E - IR}{I}$$

28. $(1 - x^{-1})^{-1} = \left(1 - \frac{1}{x}\right)^{-1}$

$$= \left(\frac{x-1}{x}\right)^{-1}$$
$$= \frac{x}{x-1}$$

29. Strategy

- Smaller integer: x
  Larger integer: $15 - x$

$5x = 5 + 2(15 - x)$

Solution

$$5x = 5 + 2(15 - x)$$
$$5x = 5 + 30 - 2x$$
$$7x = 35$$
$$x = 5$$
$$15 - x = 10$$

The smaller integer is 5 and the larger integer is 10.

30. Strategy

- The unknown number of pounds of almonds: x

	Amount	Cost	Value
Almonds	x	5.40	$5.40x$
Peanuts	50	2.60	50(2.60)
Mixture	$x + 50$	4.00	$4(x + 50)$

- The sum of the values before mixing equals the value after mixing.

$5.40x + 50(2.60) = 4(x + 50)$

Solution

$$5.40x + 50(2.60) = 4(x + 50)$$
$$5.4x + 130 = 4x + 200$$
$$1.4x + 130 = 200$$
$$1.4x = 70$$
$$x = 50$$

The number of pounds of almonds is 50.

31. Strategy

To find the number of people expected to vote, write and solve a proportion using x to represent the number of people expected to vote.

Solution

$$\frac{3}{5} = \frac{x}{125{,}000}$$
$$\frac{3}{5} \cdot 125{,}000 = \frac{x}{125{,}000} \cdot 125{,}000$$
$$75{,}000 = x$$

The number of people expected to vote is 75,000.

32. Strategy

- Time it takes older computer: $6r$
  Time it takes new computer: r

	Rate	Time	Part
Older computer	$\frac{1}{6r}$	12	$\frac{12}{6r}$
New Computer	$\frac{1}{r}$	12	$\frac{12}{r}$

- The sum of the part of the task completed by the older computer and the part of the task completed by the new computer is 1.

Solution

$$\frac{12}{6r} + \frac{12}{r} = 1$$
$$6r\left(\frac{12}{6r} + \frac{12}{r}\right) = (1)6r$$
$$12 + 72 = 6r$$
$$84 = 6r$$
$$14 = r$$

It takes the new computer 14 minutes to do the job working alone.

33. Strategy • Unknown rate of the wind: r

	Distance	Rate	Time
With the wind	900	$300+r$	$\frac{900}{300+r}$
Against the wind	600	$300-r$	$\frac{600}{300-r}$

• The time traveled with the wind equals the time traveled against the wind.

$$\frac{900}{300+r}=\frac{600}{300-r}$$

Solution

$$\frac{900}{300+r}=\frac{600}{300-r}$$
$$(300+r)(300-r)\left(\frac{900}{300+r}\right)=\left(\frac{600}{300-r}\right)(300+r)(300-r)$$
$$(300-r)(900)=600(300+r)$$
$$270{,}000-900r=180{,}000+600r$$
$$-1500r=-90{,}000$$
$$r=60$$

The rate of the wind is 60 mph.

34. Strategy • To find the distance apart, calculate the number of times around the track each person has gone and find the difference in distance.

Solution The walker travels 3 miles in 1 hour, or
3 miles ÷ 0.25 miles/cycle = 12 complete cycles

The jogger travels 5 miles in 1 hour, or
5 miles ÷ 0.25 miles/cycle = 20 complete cycles

Because the walker and the jogger have completed integer multiples of cycles, they are both at the starting point after 1 hour.

They have no distance between them after 1 hour.

Chapter 7: Exponents and Radicals

SECTION 7.1

Objective A Exercises

1. $8^{1/3} = (2^3)^{1/3} = 2$

3. $9^{3/2} = (3^2)^{3/2} = 3^3 = 27$

5. $27^{-2/3} = (3^3)^{-2/3} = 3^{-2} = \frac{1}{3^2} = \frac{1}{9}$

7. $32^{2/5} = (2^5)^{2/5} = 2^2 = 4$

9. $(-25)^{5/2}$
The base of the exponential expression is a negative number, while the denominator of the exponent is a positive even number.
Therefore, $(-25)^{5/2}$ is not a real number.

11. $$\left(\frac{25}{49}\right)^{-3/2} = \left(\frac{5^2}{7^2}\right)^{-3/2} = \left[\left(\frac{5}{7}\right)^2\right]^{-3/2} = \left(\frac{5}{7}\right)^{-3} = \frac{5^{-3}}{7^{-3}} = \frac{7^3}{5^3} = \frac{343}{125}$$

13. $x^{1/2}x^{1/2} = x$

15. $y^{-1/4}y^{3/4} = y^{1/2}$

17. $x^{-2/3} \cdot x^{3/4} = x^{1/12}$

19. $a^{1/3} \cdot a^{3/4} \cdot a^{-1/2} = a^{7/12}$

21. $\frac{a^{1/2}}{a^{3/2}} = a^{-1} = \frac{1}{a}$

23. $\frac{y^{-3/4}}{y^{1/4}} = y^{-1} = \frac{1}{y}$

25. $\frac{y^{2/3}}{y^{-5/6}} = y^{9/6} = y^{3/2}$

27. $(x^2)^{-1/2} = x^{-1} = \frac{1}{x}$

29. $(x^{-2/3})^6 = x^{-4} = \frac{1}{x^4}$

31. $(a^{-1/2})^{-2} = a$

33. $(x^{-3/8})^{-4/5} = x^{3/10}$

35. $(a^{1/2} \cdot a)^2 = (a^{3/2})^2 = a^3$

37. $(x^{-1/2}x^{3/4})^{-2} = (x^{1/4})^{-2} = x^{-1/2} = \frac{1}{x^{1/2}}$

39. $(y^{-1/2}y^{2/3})^{2/3} = (y^{1/6})^{2/3} = y^{1/9}$

41. $(x^8y^2)^{1/2} = x^4y$

43. $(x^4y^2z^6)^{3/2} = x^6y^3z^9$

45. $(x^{-3}y^6)^{-1/3} = xy^{-2} = \frac{x}{y^2}$

47. $(x^{-2}y^{1/3})^{-3/4} = x^{3/2}y^{-1/4} = \frac{x^{3/2}}{y^{1/4}}$

49. $\left(\frac{x^{1/2}}{y^2}\right)^4 = \frac{x^2}{y^8}$

51. $\frac{x^{1/4} \cdot x^{-1/2}}{x^{2/3}} = \frac{x^{-1/4}}{x^{2/3}} = x^{-11/12} = \frac{1}{x^{11/12}}$

53. $$\left(\frac{y^{2/3} \cdot y^{-5/6}}{y^{1/9}}\right)^9 = \left(\frac{y^{-1/6}}{y^{1/9}}\right)^9 = (y^{-5/18})^9 = y^{-5/2} = \frac{1}{y^{5/2}}$$

55. $$\left(\frac{b^2 \cdot b^{-3/4}}{b^{-1/2}}\right)^{-1/2} = \left(\frac{b^{5/4}}{b^{-1/2}}\right)^{-1/2} = (b^{7/4})^{-1/2} = b^{-7/8} = \frac{1}{b^{7/8}}$$

57. $(a^{2/3}b^2)^6(a^3b^3)^{1/3} = (a^4b^{12})(ab) = a^5b^{13}$

59. $$(16m^{-2}n^4)^{-1/2}(mn^{1/2}) = (2^4)^{-1/2}mn^{-2} \cdot mn^{1/2} = 2^{-2}m^2n^{-3/2} = \frac{m^2}{2^2n^{3/2}} = \frac{m^2}{4n^{3/2}}$$

61. $$\left(\frac{x^{1/2}y^{-3/4}}{y^{2/3}}\right)^{-6} = (x^{1/2}y^{-17/12})^{-6} = x^{-3}y^{17/2} = \frac{y^{17/2}}{x^3}$$

63. $\left(\dfrac{2^{-6}b^{-3}}{a^{-1/2}}\right)^{-2/3} = \dfrac{2^4b^2}{a^{1/3}} = \dfrac{16b^2}{a^{1/3}}$

65. $y^{3/2}(y^{1/2} - y^{-1/2}) = y^{4/2} - y^{2/2} = y^2 - y$

67. $a^{-1/4}(a^{5/4} - a^{9/4}) = a^1 - a^2 = a - a^2$

69. $x^n \cdot x^{3n} = x^{4n}$

71. $x^n \cdot x^{n/2} = x^{3n/2}$

73. $\dfrac{y^{n/2}}{y^{-n}} = y^{3n/2}$

75. $(x^{2n})^n = x^{2n^2}$

77. $(x^{n/4}y^{n/8})^8 = x^{2n}y^n$

79. $(x^{n/5}y^{n/10})^{20} = x^{4n}y^{2n}$

Objective B Exercises

81. $3^{1/4} = \sqrt[4]{3}$

83. $a^{3/2} = (a^3)^{1/2} = \sqrt{a^3}$

85. $(2t)^{5/2} = \sqrt{(2t)^5} = \sqrt{32t^5}$

87. $-2x^{2/3} = -2(x^2)^{1/3} = -2\sqrt[3]{x^2}$

89. $(a^2b)^{2/3} = \sqrt[3]{(a^2b)^2} = \sqrt[3]{a^4b^2}$

91. $(a^2b^4)^{3/5} = \sqrt[5]{(a^2b^4)^3} = \sqrt[5]{a^6b^{12}}$

93. $(4x-3)^{3/4} = \sqrt[4]{(4x-3)^3}$

95. $x^{-2/3} = \dfrac{1}{x^{2/3}} = \dfrac{1}{\sqrt[3]{x^2}}$

97. $\sqrt{14} = 14^{1/2}$

99. $\sqrt[3]{x} = x^{1/3}$

101. $\sqrt[3]{x^4} = x^{4/3}$

103. $\sqrt[5]{b^3} = b^{3/5}$

105. $\sqrt[3]{2x^2} = (2x^2)^{1/3}$

107. $-\sqrt{3x^5} = -(3x^5)^{1/2}$

109. $3x\sqrt[3]{y^2} = 3xy^{2/3}$

111. $\sqrt{a^2-2} = (a^2-2)^{1/2}$

Objective C Exercises

113. $\sqrt{x^{16}} = x^8$

115. $-\sqrt{x^8} = -x^4$

117. $\sqrt[3]{x^3y^9} = xy^3$

119. $-\sqrt[3]{x^{15}y^3} = -x^5y$

121. $\sqrt{16a^4b^{12}} = \sqrt{2^4a^4b^{12}} = 2^2a^2b^6 = 4a^2b^6$

123. $\sqrt{-16x^4y^2}$
The square root of a negative number is not a real number, since the square of a real number must be positive.

125. $\sqrt[3]{27x^9} = \sqrt[3]{3^3x^9} = 3x^3$

127. $\sqrt[3]{-64x^9y^{12}} = \sqrt[3]{(-4)^3x^9y^{12}} = -4x^3y^4$

129. $-\sqrt[4]{x^8y^{12}} = -x^2y^3$

131. $\sqrt[5]{x^{20}y^{10}} = x^4y^2$

133. $\sqrt[4]{81x^4y^{20}} = \sqrt[4]{3^4x^4y^{20}} = 3xy^5$

135. $\sqrt[5]{32a^5b^{10}} = \sqrt[5]{2^5a^5b^{10}} = 2ab^2$

Applying the Concepts

137. a. $\sqrt{(-2)^2} = -2$, false
$\sqrt{(-2)^2} = \sqrt{4} = 2$

b. $\sqrt[3]{(-3)^3} = -3$, true

c. $\sqrt[n]{a} = a^{1/n}$, true

d. $\sqrt[n]{a^n + b^n} = a + b$, false
$\sqrt[n]{a^n + b^n} = (a^n + b^n)^{1/n}$

e. $(a^{1/2} + b^{1/2})^2 = a + b$, false
$(a^{1/2} + b^{1/2})^2 = a + 2(ab)^{1/2} + b$

f. $\sqrt[m]{a^n} = a^{mn}$, false
$\sqrt[m]{a^n} = a^{n/m}$

139. Use a calculator to determine $\sqrt{2} = 1.41$.

SECTION 7.2

Objective A Exercises

1. $\sqrt{x^4y^3z^5} = \sqrt{x^4y^2z^4(yz)}$
$= \sqrt{x^4y^2z^4}\sqrt{yz}$
$= x^2yz^2\sqrt{yz}$

3. $\sqrt{8a^3b^8} = \sqrt{2^3a^3b^8}$
$= \sqrt{2^2a^2b^8(2a)}$
$= \sqrt{2^2a^2b^8}\sqrt{2a}$
$= 2ab^4\sqrt{2a}$

5. $\sqrt{45x^2y^3z^5} = \sqrt{3^2\cdot 5x^2y^3z^5}$
$= \sqrt{3^2x^2y^2z^4(5yz)}$
$= \sqrt{3^2x^2y^2z^4}\sqrt{5yz}$
$= 3xyz^2\sqrt{5yz}$

7. $\sqrt{-9x^3}$
The square root of a negative number is not a real number, since the square of a real number must be positive. Therefore, $\sqrt{-9x^3}$ is not a real number.

9. $\sqrt[3]{a^{16}b^8} = \sqrt[3]{a^{15}b^6(ab^2)}$
$= \sqrt[3]{a^{15}b^6}\sqrt[3]{ab^2}$
$= a^5b^2\sqrt[3]{ab^2}$

11. $\sqrt[3]{-125x^2y^4} = \sqrt[3]{(-5)^3x^2y^4}$
$= \sqrt[3]{(-5)^3y^3(x^2y)}$
$= \sqrt[3]{(-5)^3y^3}\sqrt[3]{x^2y}$
$= -5y\sqrt[3]{x^2y}$

13. $\sqrt[3]{a^4b^5c^6} = \sqrt[3]{a^3b^3c^6(ab^2)}$
$= \sqrt[3]{a^3b^3c^6}\sqrt[3]{ab^2}$
$= abc^2\sqrt[3]{ab^2}$

15. $\sqrt[4]{16x^9y^5} = \sqrt[4]{2^4x^9y^5}$
$= \sqrt[4]{2^4x^8y^4(xy)}$
$= \sqrt[4]{2^4x^8y^4}\sqrt[4]{xy}$
$= 2x^2y\sqrt[4]{xy}$

Objective B Exercises

17. $2\sqrt{x} - 8\sqrt{x} = -6\sqrt{x}$

19. $\sqrt{8} - \sqrt{32} = \sqrt{2^3} - \sqrt{2^5}$
$= \sqrt{2^2}\sqrt{2} - \sqrt{2^4}\sqrt{2}$
$= 2\sqrt{2} - 2^2\sqrt{2}$
$= 2\sqrt{2} - 4\sqrt{2}$
$= -2\sqrt{2}$

21. $\sqrt{18b} + \sqrt{75b} = \sqrt{2\cdot 3^2b} + \sqrt{3\cdot 5^2b}$
$= \sqrt{3^2}\sqrt{2b} + \sqrt{5^2}\sqrt{3b}$
$= 3\sqrt{2b} + 5\sqrt{3b}$

23. $3\sqrt{8x^2y^3} - 2x\sqrt{32y^3}$
$= 3\sqrt{2^3x^2y^3} - 2x\sqrt{2^5y^3}$
$= 3\sqrt{2^2x^2y^2}\sqrt{2y} - 2x\sqrt{2^4y^2}\sqrt{2y}$
$= 3\cdot 2xy\sqrt{2y} - 2x\cdot 2^2y\sqrt{2y}$
$= 6xy\sqrt{2y} - 8xy\sqrt{2y}$
$= -2xy\sqrt{2y}$

25. $2a\sqrt{27ab^5} + 3b\sqrt{3a^3b}$
$= 2a\sqrt{3^3ab^5} + 3b\sqrt{3a^3b}$
$= 2a\sqrt{3^2b^4}\sqrt{3ab} + 3b\sqrt{a^2}\sqrt{3ab}$
$= 2a\cdot 3b^2\sqrt{3ab} + 3ab\sqrt{3ab}$
$= 6ab^2\sqrt{3ab} + 3ab\sqrt{3ab}$

27. $\sqrt[3]{16} - \sqrt[3]{54} = \sqrt[3]{2^4} - \sqrt[3]{2\cdot 3^3}$
$= \sqrt[3]{2^3}\sqrt[3]{2} - \sqrt[3]{3^3}\sqrt[3]{2}$
$= 2\sqrt[3]{2} - 3\sqrt[3]{2}$
$= -\sqrt[3]{2}$

29. $2b\sqrt[3]{16b^2} + \sqrt[3]{128b^5}$
$= 2b\sqrt[3]{2^4b^2} + \sqrt[3]{2^7b^5}$
$= 2b\sqrt[3]{2^3}\sqrt[3]{2b^2} + \sqrt[3]{2^6b^3}\sqrt[3]{2b^2}$
$= 2b\cdot 2\sqrt[3]{2b^2} + 2^2b\sqrt[3]{2b^2}$
$= 4b\sqrt[3]{2b^2} + 4b\sqrt[3]{2b^2}$
$= 8b\sqrt[3]{2b^2}$

31. $3\sqrt[4]{32a^5} - a\sqrt[4]{162a}$
$= 3\sqrt[4]{2^5a^5} - a\sqrt[4]{2\cdot 3^4a}$
$= 3\sqrt[4]{2^4a^4}\sqrt[4]{2a} - a\sqrt[4]{3^4}\sqrt[4]{2a}$
$= 3\cdot 2a\sqrt[4]{2a} - 3a\sqrt[4]{2a}$
$= 6a\sqrt[4]{2a} - 3a\sqrt[4]{2a}$
$= 3a\sqrt[4]{2a}$

33. $2\sqrt{50}-3\sqrt{125}+\sqrt{98}$
$=2\sqrt{2\cdot 5^2}-3\sqrt{5^3}+\sqrt{2\cdot 7^2}$
$=2\sqrt{5^2}\sqrt{2}-3\sqrt{5^2}\sqrt{5}+\sqrt{7^2}\sqrt{2}$
$=2\cdot 5\sqrt{2}-3\cdot 5\sqrt{5}+7\sqrt{2}$
$=10\sqrt{2}-15\sqrt{5}+7\sqrt{2}$
$=17\sqrt{2}-15\sqrt{5}$

35. $\sqrt{9b^3}-\sqrt{25b^3}+\sqrt{49b^3}$
$=\sqrt{3^2b^3}-\sqrt{5^2b^3}+\sqrt{7^2b^3}$
$=\sqrt{3^2b^2}\sqrt{b}-\sqrt{5^2b^2}\sqrt{b}+\sqrt{7^2b^2}\sqrt{b}$
$=3b\sqrt{b}-5b\sqrt{b}+7b\sqrt{b}$
$=5b\sqrt{b}$

37. $2x\sqrt{8xy^2}-3y\sqrt{32x^3}+\sqrt{4x^3y^3}$
$=2x\sqrt{2^3xy^2}-3y\sqrt{2^5x^3}+\sqrt{2^2x^3y^3}$
$=2x\sqrt{2^2y^2}\sqrt{2x}-3y\sqrt{2^4x^2}\sqrt{2x}+\sqrt{2^2x^2y^2}\sqrt{xy}$
$=2x\cdot 2y\sqrt{2x}-3y\cdot 2^2x\sqrt{2x}+2xy\sqrt{xy}$
$=4xy\sqrt{2x}-12xy\sqrt{2x}+2xy\sqrt{xy}$
$=-8xy\sqrt{2x}+2xy\sqrt{xy}$

39. $\sqrt[3]{54xy^3}-5\sqrt[3]{2xy^3}+y\sqrt[3]{128x}$
$=\sqrt[3]{2\cdot 3^3xy^3}-5\sqrt[3]{2xy^3}+y\sqrt[3]{2^7x}$
$=\sqrt[3]{3^3y^3}\sqrt[3]{2x}-5\sqrt[3]{y^3}\sqrt[3]{2x}+y\sqrt[3]{2^6}\sqrt[3]{2x}$
$=3y\sqrt[3]{2x}-5y\sqrt[3]{2x}+2^2y\sqrt[3]{2x}$
$=3y\sqrt[3]{2x}-5y\sqrt[3]{2x}+4y\sqrt[3]{2x}$
$=2y\sqrt[3]{2x}$

41. $2a\sqrt[4]{32b^5}-3b\sqrt[4]{162a^4b}+\sqrt[4]{2a^4b^5}$
$=2a\sqrt[4]{2^5b^5}-3b\sqrt[4]{2\cdot 3^4a^4b}+\sqrt[4]{2a^4b^5}$
$=2a\sqrt[4]{2^4b^4}\sqrt[4]{2b}-3b\sqrt[4]{3^4a^4}\sqrt[4]{2b}+\sqrt[4]{a^4b^4}\sqrt[4]{2b}$
$=2a\cdot 2b\sqrt[4]{2b}-3b\cdot 3a\sqrt[4]{2b}+ab\sqrt[4]{2b}$
$=4ab\sqrt[4]{2b}-9ab\sqrt[4]{2b}+ab\sqrt[4]{2b}$
$=-4ab\sqrt[4]{2b}$

Objective C Exercises

43. $\sqrt{8}\sqrt{32}=\sqrt{256}=\sqrt{2^8}=2^4=16$

45. $\sqrt[3]{4}\sqrt[3]{8}=\sqrt[3]{32}=\sqrt[3]{2^5}=\sqrt[3]{2^3}\sqrt[3]{2^2}=2\sqrt[3]{4}$

47. $\sqrt{x^2y^5}\sqrt{xy}=\sqrt{x^3y^6}=\sqrt{x^2y^6}\sqrt{x}=xy^3\sqrt{x}$

49. $\sqrt{2x^2y}\sqrt{32xy}=\sqrt{64x^3y^2}$
$=\sqrt{2^6x^3y^2}$
$=\sqrt{2^6x^2y^2}\sqrt{x}$
$=2^3xy\sqrt{x}=8xy\sqrt{x}$

51. $\sqrt[3]{x^2y}\sqrt[3]{16x^4y^2}=\sqrt[3]{16x^6y^3}$
$=\sqrt[3]{2^4x^6y^3}$
$=\sqrt[3]{2^3x^6y^3}\sqrt[3]{2}$
$=2x^2y\sqrt[3]{2}$

53. $\sqrt[4]{12ab^3}\sqrt[4]{4a^5b^2}=\sqrt[4]{48a^6b^5}$
$=\sqrt[4]{2^4\cdot 3a^6b^5}$
$=\sqrt[4]{2^4a^4b^4}\sqrt[4]{3a^2b}$
$=2ab\sqrt[4]{3a^2b}$

55. $\sqrt{3}\left(\sqrt{27}-\sqrt{3}\right)=\sqrt{81}-\sqrt{9}$
$=\sqrt{3^4}-\sqrt{3^2}$
$=3^2-3$
$=9-3=6$

57. $\sqrt{x}\left(\sqrt{x}-\sqrt{2}\right)=\sqrt{x^2}-\sqrt{2x}=x-\sqrt{2x}$

59. $\sqrt{2x}\left(\sqrt{8x}-\sqrt{32}\right)=\sqrt{16x^2}-\sqrt{64x}$
$=\sqrt{2^4x^2}-\sqrt{2^6x}$
$=2^2x-2^3\sqrt{x}$
$=4x-8\sqrt{x}$

61. $\left(\sqrt{x}-3\right)^2=\left(\sqrt{x}\right)^2-3\sqrt{x}-3\sqrt{x}+9$
$=x-6\sqrt{x}+9$

63. $\left(4\sqrt{5}+2\right)^2=\left(4\sqrt{5}\right)^2+8\sqrt{5}+8\sqrt{5}+4$
$=16\cdot 5+16\sqrt{5}+4$
$=80+16\sqrt{5}+4$
$=84+16\sqrt{5}$

65. $2\sqrt{14xy}\cdot 4\sqrt{7x^2y}\cdot 3\sqrt{8xy^2}=24\sqrt{784x^4y^4}$
$=24\sqrt{2^4\cdot 7^2x^4y^4}$
$=24\cdot 2^2\cdot 7x^2y^2$
$=672x^2y^2$

67. $\sqrt[3]{2a^2b}\sqrt[3]{4a^3b^2}\sqrt[3]{8a^5b^6}=\sqrt[3]{64a^{10}b^9}$
$=\sqrt[3]{2^6a^{10}b^9}$
$=\sqrt[3]{2^6a^9b^9}\sqrt[3]{a}$
$=2^2a^3b^3\sqrt[3]{a}$
$=4a^3b^3\sqrt[3]{a}$

69. $\left(\sqrt{5}-5\right)\left(2\sqrt{5}+2\right)=2\sqrt{5^2}+2\sqrt{5}-10\sqrt{5}-10$
$=2\cdot 5-8\sqrt{5}-10$
$=10-8\sqrt{5}-10$
$=-8\sqrt{5}$

71. $\left(\sqrt{x}-y\right)\left(\sqrt{x}+y\right)=\sqrt{x^2}-y^2=x-y^2$

73. $\left(2\sqrt{3x}-\sqrt{y}\right)\left(2\sqrt{3x}+\sqrt{y}\right)=4\sqrt{3^2x^2}-\sqrt{y^2}$
$=4\cdot 3x-y$
$=12x-y$

Objective D Exercises

75. $\dfrac{\sqrt{60y^4}}{\sqrt{12y}}=\sqrt{\dfrac{60y^4}{12y}}$
$=\sqrt{5y^3}$
$=\sqrt{y^2}\sqrt{5y}$
$=y\sqrt{5y}$

77. $\dfrac{\sqrt{65ab^4}}{\sqrt{5ab}}=\sqrt{\dfrac{65ab^4}{5ab}}$
$=\sqrt{13b^3}$
$=\sqrt{b^2}\sqrt{13b}=b\sqrt{13b}$

79. $\dfrac{1}{\sqrt{2}}=\dfrac{1}{\sqrt{2}}\cdot\dfrac{\sqrt{2}}{\sqrt{2}}=\dfrac{\sqrt{2}}{\sqrt{2^2}}=\dfrac{\sqrt{2}}{2}$

81. $\dfrac{2}{\sqrt{3y}}=\dfrac{2}{\sqrt{3y}}\cdot\dfrac{\sqrt{3y}}{\sqrt{3y}}=\dfrac{2\sqrt{3y}}{\sqrt{3^2y^2}}=\dfrac{2\sqrt{3y}}{3y}$

83. $\dfrac{9}{\sqrt{3a}}=\dfrac{9}{\sqrt{3a}}\cdot\dfrac{\sqrt{3a}}{\sqrt{3a}}=\dfrac{9\sqrt{3a}}{\sqrt{3^2a^2}}=\dfrac{9\sqrt{3a}}{3a}=\dfrac{3\sqrt{3a}}{a}$

85. $\sqrt{\dfrac{y}{2}}=\dfrac{\sqrt{y}}{\sqrt{2}}=\dfrac{\sqrt{y}}{\sqrt{2}}\cdot\dfrac{\sqrt{2}}{\sqrt{2}}=\dfrac{\sqrt{2y}}{\sqrt{2^2}}=\dfrac{\sqrt{2y}}{2}$

87. $\dfrac{5}{\sqrt[3]{9}}=\dfrac{5}{\sqrt[3]{3^2}}\cdot\dfrac{\sqrt[3]{3}}{\sqrt[3]{3}}=\dfrac{5\sqrt[3]{3}}{\sqrt[3]{3^3}}=\dfrac{5\sqrt[3]{3}}{3}$

89. $\dfrac{5}{\sqrt[3]{3y}}=\dfrac{5}{\sqrt[3]{3y}}\cdot\dfrac{\sqrt[3]{3^2y^2}}{\sqrt[3]{3^2y^2}}=\dfrac{5\sqrt[3]{3^2y^2}}{\sqrt[3]{3^3y^3}}=\dfrac{5\sqrt[3]{9y^2}}{3y}$

91. $\dfrac{\sqrt{15a^2b^5}}{\sqrt{30a^5b^3}}=\sqrt{\dfrac{15a^2b^5}{30a^5b^3}}$
$=\sqrt{\dfrac{b^2}{2a^3}}$
$=\dfrac{b}{\sqrt{a^2}\sqrt{2a}}$
$=\dfrac{b}{a\sqrt{2a}}\cdot\dfrac{\sqrt{2a}}{\sqrt{2a}}$
$=\dfrac{b\sqrt{2a}}{a\sqrt{2^2a^2}}$
$=\dfrac{b\sqrt{2a}}{a\cdot 2a}=\dfrac{b\sqrt{2a}}{2a^2}$

93. $\dfrac{\sqrt{12x^3y}}{\sqrt{20x^4y}}=\sqrt{\dfrac{12x^3y}{20x^4y}}$
$=\sqrt{\dfrac{3}{5x}}$
$=\dfrac{\sqrt{3}}{\sqrt{5x}}\cdot\dfrac{\sqrt{5x}}{\sqrt{5x}}$
$=\dfrac{\sqrt{15x}}{\sqrt{5^2x^2}}=\dfrac{\sqrt{15x}}{5x}$

95. $\dfrac{-2}{1-\sqrt{2}}=\dfrac{-2}{1-\sqrt{2}}\cdot\dfrac{1+\sqrt{2}}{1+\sqrt{2}}$
$=\dfrac{-2-2\sqrt{2}}{1^2-\left(\sqrt{2}\right)^2}$
$=\dfrac{-2-2\sqrt{2}}{1-2}$
$=\dfrac{-2-2\sqrt{2}}{-1}=2+2\sqrt{2}$

97. $\dfrac{-4}{3-\sqrt{2}}=\dfrac{-4}{3-\sqrt{2}}\cdot\dfrac{3+\sqrt{2}}{3+\sqrt{2}}$
$=\dfrac{-12-4\sqrt{2}}{3^2-\left(\sqrt{2}\right)^2}$
$=\dfrac{-12-4\sqrt{2}}{9-2}$
$=\dfrac{-12-4\sqrt{2}}{7}=-\dfrac{12+4\sqrt{2}}{7}$

99. $\dfrac{5}{2-\sqrt{7}}=\dfrac{5}{2-\sqrt{7}}\cdot\dfrac{2+\sqrt{7}}{2+\sqrt{7}}$
$=\dfrac{10+5\sqrt{7}}{2^2-\left(\sqrt{7}\right)^2}$
$=\dfrac{10+5\sqrt{7}}{4-7}$
$=\dfrac{10+5\sqrt{7}}{-3}=-\dfrac{10+5\sqrt{7}}{3}$

101. $\dfrac{-7}{\sqrt{x}-3}=-\dfrac{7}{\sqrt{x}-3}\cdot\dfrac{\sqrt{x}+3}{\sqrt{x}+3}$
$=-\dfrac{7\sqrt{x}+21}{\left(\sqrt{x}\right)^2-3^2}$
$=-\dfrac{7\sqrt{x}+21}{x-9}$

103.
$$\frac{\sqrt{3}+\sqrt{4}}{\sqrt{2}+\sqrt{3}}=\frac{\sqrt{3}+\sqrt{2^2}}{\sqrt{2}+\sqrt{3}}=\frac{\sqrt{3}+2}{\sqrt{2}+\sqrt{3}}\cdot\frac{\sqrt{2}-\sqrt{3}}{\sqrt{2}-\sqrt{3}}$$
$$=\frac{\sqrt{6}-\sqrt{3^2}+2\sqrt{2}-2\sqrt{3}}{\left(\sqrt{2}\right)^2-\left(\sqrt{3}\right)^2}$$
$$=\frac{\sqrt{6}-3+2\sqrt{2}-2\sqrt{3}}{2-3}$$
$$=\frac{\sqrt{6}-3+2\sqrt{2}-2\sqrt{3}}{-1}$$
$$=-\sqrt{6}+3-2\sqrt{2}+2\sqrt{3}$$

105.
$$\frac{2+3\sqrt{5}}{1-\sqrt{5}}=\frac{2+3\sqrt{5}}{1-\sqrt{5}}\cdot\frac{1+\sqrt{5}}{1+\sqrt{5}}$$
$$=\frac{2+2\sqrt{5}+3\sqrt{5}+3\left(\sqrt{5}\right)^2}{1-\left(\sqrt{5}\right)^2}$$
$$=\frac{2+5\sqrt{5}+3(5)}{1-5}$$
$$=\frac{2+5\sqrt{5}+15}{-4}$$
$$=\frac{17+5\sqrt{5}}{-4}$$
$$=-\frac{17+5\sqrt{5}}{4}$$

107.
$$\frac{2\sqrt{a}-\sqrt{b}}{4\sqrt{a}+3\sqrt{b}}$$
$$=\frac{2\sqrt{a}-\sqrt{b}}{4\sqrt{a}+3\sqrt{b}}\cdot\frac{4\sqrt{a}-3\sqrt{b}}{4\sqrt{a}-3\sqrt{b}}$$
$$=\frac{8\left(\sqrt{a}\right)^2-6\sqrt{ab}-4\sqrt{ab}+3\left(\sqrt{b}\right)^2}{16\left(\sqrt{a}\right)^2-9\left(\sqrt{b}\right)^2}$$
$$=\frac{8a-10\sqrt{ab}+3b}{16a-9b}$$

109.
$$\frac{3\sqrt{y}-y}{\sqrt{y}+2y}=\frac{3\sqrt{y}-y}{\sqrt{y}+2y}\cdot\frac{\sqrt{y}-2y}{\sqrt{y}-2y}$$
$$=\frac{3\left(\sqrt{y}\right)^2-6y\sqrt{y}-y\sqrt{y}+2y^2}{\left(\sqrt{y}\right)^2-4y^2}$$
$$=\frac{3y-7y\sqrt{y}+2y^2}{y-4y^2}$$
$$=\frac{3-7\sqrt{y}+2y}{1-4y}$$

Applying the Concepts

111. a. $\sqrt[2]{3}\cdot\sqrt[3]{4}=\sqrt[5]{12}$, false
$\sqrt[2]{3}\cdot\sqrt[3]{4}=\sqrt[6]{432}$

b. $\sqrt{3}\cdot\sqrt{3}=3$, true

c. $\sqrt[3]{x}\cdot\sqrt[3]{x}=x$, false
$\sqrt[3]{x}\cdot\sqrt[3]{x}=x^{1/3}x^{1/3}=x^{2/3}=\sqrt[3]{x^2}$

d. $\sqrt{x}+\sqrt{y}=\sqrt{x+y}$, false
$\sqrt{x}+\sqrt{y}$ is in an irreducible form.

e. $\sqrt[2]{2}+\sqrt[3]{3}=\sqrt[5]{2+3}$, false
$\sqrt[2]{2}+\sqrt[3]{3}$ is an irreducible form.

f. $8\sqrt[5]{a}-2\sqrt[5]{a}=6\sqrt[5]{a}$, true

113. a.
$$\begin{aligned}(\sqrt{2}-2)^3&=(\sqrt{2}-2)(2-4\sqrt{2}+4)\\&=(\sqrt{2}-2)(6-4\sqrt{2})\\&=6\sqrt{2}-8-12+8\sqrt{2}\\&=14\sqrt{2}-20\end{aligned}$$

b.
$$\begin{aligned}\frac{2}{\sqrt{x+4}+2}&=\frac{2}{\sqrt{x+4}+2}\cdot\frac{\sqrt{x+4}-2}{\sqrt{x+4}-2}\\&=\frac{2\sqrt{x+4}-4}{(x+4)-4}\\&=\frac{2\sqrt{x+4}-4}{x}\end{aligned}$$

c.
$$\begin{aligned}\frac{\sqrt{b+9}-3}{\sqrt{b+9}+3}&=\frac{\sqrt{b+9}-3}{\sqrt{b+9}+3}\cdot\frac{\sqrt{b+9}-3}{\sqrt{b+9}-3}\\&=\frac{(b+9)-6\sqrt{b+9}+9}{(b+9)-9}\\&=\frac{b-6\sqrt{b+9}+18}{b}\end{aligned}$$

115. Rationalizing the denominator of a radical expression is a way of expressing the expression with no radicals in the denominator. It is accomplished by multiplying both the numerator and the denominator by an expression that removes radicals from the denominator of the original expression.

SECTION 7.3

Objective A Exercises

1. $\sqrt{-4}=i\sqrt{4}=i\sqrt{2^2}=2i$

3. $\sqrt{-98}=i\sqrt{98}=i\sqrt{2\cdot 7^2}=7i\sqrt{2}$

5. $\sqrt{-27}=i\sqrt{27}=i\sqrt{3^2\cdot 3}=3i\sqrt{3}$

7. $\sqrt{16}+\sqrt{-4}=\sqrt{16}+i\sqrt{4}=\sqrt{2^4}+i\sqrt{2^2}=4+2i$

9.
$$\begin{aligned}\sqrt{12}-\sqrt{-18}&=\sqrt{12}-i\sqrt{18}\\&=\sqrt{2^2\cdot 3}-i\sqrt{3^2\cdot 2}\\&=2\sqrt{3}-3i\sqrt{2}\end{aligned}$$

11.
$$\begin{aligned}\sqrt{160}-\sqrt{-147}&=\sqrt{160}-i\sqrt{147}\\&=\sqrt{2^4\cdot 2\cdot 5}-i\sqrt{7^2\cdot 3}\\&=4\sqrt{10}-7i\sqrt{3}\end{aligned}$$

Objective B Exercises

13. $(2+4i)+(6-5i)=8-i$

15. $(-2-4i)-(6-8i)=-8+4i$

17.
$$\begin{aligned}\left(8-\sqrt{-4}\right)-\left(2+\sqrt{-16}\right)&=(8-i\sqrt{4})-(2+i\sqrt{16})\\&=\left(8-i\sqrt{2^2}\right)-\left(2+i\sqrt{2^4}\right)\\&=(8-2i)-(2+4i)\\&=6-6i\end{aligned}$$

19.
$$\begin{aligned}&\left(12-\sqrt{-50}\right)+\left(7-\sqrt{-8}\right)\\&=\left(12-i\sqrt{50}\right)+\left(7-i\sqrt{8}\right)\\&=\left(12-i\sqrt{5^2\cdot 2}\right)+\left(7-i\sqrt{2^2\cdot 2}\right)\\&=\left(12-5i\sqrt{2}\right)+\left(7-2i\sqrt{2}\right)\\&=19-7i\sqrt{2}\end{aligned}$$

21.
$$\begin{aligned}&\left(\sqrt{8}+\sqrt{-18}\right)+\left(\sqrt{32}-\sqrt{-72}\right)\\&=\left(\sqrt{8}+i\sqrt{18}\right)+\left(\sqrt{32}-i\sqrt{72}\right)\\&=\left(\sqrt{2^2\cdot 2}+i\sqrt{3^2\cdot 2}\right)+\left(\sqrt{2^4\cdot 2}-i\sqrt{2^2\cdot 3^2\cdot 2}\right)\\&=\left(2\sqrt{2}+3i\sqrt{2}\right)+\left(4\sqrt{2}-6i\sqrt{2}\right)\\&=6\sqrt{2}-3i\sqrt{2}\end{aligned}$$

Objective C Exercises

23. $(7i)(-9i)=-63i^2=-63(-1)=63$

25. $\sqrt{-2}\sqrt{-8}=i\sqrt{2}\cdot i\sqrt{8}=i^2\sqrt{16}=-\sqrt{2^4}=-4$

27.
$$\begin{aligned}\sqrt{-3}\sqrt{-6}&=i\sqrt{3}\cdot i\sqrt{6}\\&=i^2\sqrt{18}\\&=-\sqrt{3^2\cdot 2}=-3\sqrt{2}\end{aligned}$$

29.
$$\begin{aligned}2i(6+2i)&=12i+4i^2\\&=12i+4(-1)\\&=-4+12i\end{aligned}$$

31. $\sqrt{-2}\left(\sqrt{8}+\sqrt{-2}\right)=i\sqrt{2}\left(\sqrt{8}+i\sqrt{2}\right)$
$=i\sqrt{16}+i^2\sqrt{2^2}$
$=i\sqrt{2^4}-\sqrt{2^2}$
$=4i-2=-2+4i$

33. $(5-2i)(3+i)=15+5i-6i-2i^2$
$=15-i-2i^2$
$=15-i-2(-1)$
$=17-i$

35. $(6+5i)(3+2i)=18+12i+15i+10i^2$
$=18+27i+10i^2$
$=18+27i+10(-1)$
$=8+27i$

37. $(1-i)\left(\frac{1}{2}+\frac{1}{2}i\right)=\frac{1}{2}+\frac{1}{2}i-\frac{1}{2}i-\frac{1}{2}i^2$
$=\frac{1}{2}-\frac{1}{2}i^2$
$=\frac{1}{2}-\frac{1}{2}(-1)$
$=\frac{1}{2}+\frac{1}{2}=1$

39. $\left(\frac{6}{5}+\frac{3}{5}i\right)\left(\frac{2}{3}-\frac{1}{3}i\right)=\frac{4}{5}-\frac{2}{5}i+\frac{2}{5}i-\frac{1}{5}i^2$
$=\frac{4}{5}-\frac{1}{5}i^2$
$=\frac{4}{5}-\frac{1}{5}(-1)$
$=\frac{4}{5}+\frac{1}{5}=1$

Objective D Exercises

41. $\frac{3}{i}=\frac{3}{i}\cdot\frac{i}{i}=\frac{3i}{i^2}=\frac{3i}{-1}=-3i$

43. $\frac{2-3i}{-4i}=\frac{2-3i}{-4i}\cdot\frac{i}{i}$
$=\frac{2i-3i^2}{-4i^2}$
$=\frac{2i-3(-1)}{-4(-1)}$
$=\frac{3+2i}{4}=\frac{3}{4}+\frac{1}{2}i$

45. $\frac{4}{5+i}=\frac{4}{5+i}\cdot\frac{5-i}{5-i}$
$=\frac{20-4i}{25+1}$
$=\frac{20-4i}{26}$
$=\frac{10-2i}{13}=\frac{10}{13}-\frac{2}{13}i$

47. $\frac{2}{2-i}=\frac{2}{2-i}\cdot\frac{2+i}{2+i}$
$=\frac{4+2i}{4+1}$
$=\frac{4+2i}{5}$
$=\frac{4}{5}+\frac{2}{5}i$

49. $\frac{1-3i}{3+i}=\frac{1-3i}{3+i}\cdot\frac{3-i}{3-i}$
$=\frac{3-i-9i+3i^2}{9+1}$
$=\frac{3-10i+3i^2}{10}$
$=\frac{3-10i+3(-1)}{10}$
$=\frac{-10i}{10}=-i$

51. $\frac{\sqrt{-10}}{\sqrt{8}-\sqrt{-2}}=\frac{i\sqrt{10}}{\sqrt{8}-i\sqrt{2}}$
$=\frac{i\sqrt{10}}{\sqrt{2^2\cdot 2}-i\sqrt{2}}$
$=\frac{i\sqrt{10}}{2\sqrt{2}-i\sqrt{2}}\cdot\frac{2\sqrt{2}+i\sqrt{2}}{2\sqrt{2}+i\sqrt{2}}$
$=\frac{2i\sqrt{20}+i^2\sqrt{20}}{(2\sqrt{2})^2+(\sqrt{2})^2}$
$=\frac{2i\sqrt{2^2\cdot 5}-\sqrt{2^2\cdot 5}}{8+2}$
$=\frac{2i\cdot 2\sqrt{5}-2\sqrt{5}}{10}$
$=\frac{-2\sqrt{5}+4i\sqrt{5}}{10}$
$=\frac{-\sqrt{5}+2i\sqrt{5}}{5}$
$=-\frac{\sqrt{5}}{5}+\frac{2\sqrt{5}}{5}i$

53. $\frac{2-3i}{3+i}=\frac{2-3i}{3+i}\cdot\frac{3-i}{3-i}$
$=\frac{6-2i-9i+3i^2}{9+1}$
$=\frac{6-11i+3i^2}{10}$
$=\frac{6-11i+3(-1)}{10}$
$=\frac{3-11i}{10}=\frac{3}{10}-\frac{11}{10}i$

55.
$$\begin{aligned}\frac{5+3i}{3-i} &= \frac{5+3i}{3-i}\cdot\frac{3+i}{3+i}\\ &= \frac{15+5i+9i+3i^2}{9+1}\\ &= \frac{15+14i+3i^2}{10}\\ &= \frac{15+14i+3(-1)}{10}\\ &= \frac{12+14i}{10}\\ &= \frac{6+7i}{5} = \frac{6}{5}+\frac{7}{5}i\end{aligned}$$

Applying the Concepts

57. a. $y^2+1=(y+i)(y-i)$

b. $49x^2+16=(7x+4i)(7x-4i)$

c. $9a^2+64=(3a+8i)(3a-8i)$

59.
$$\sqrt{i} = \frac{\sqrt{2}}{2}+i\frac{\sqrt{2}}{2}$$
$$i\cdot\sqrt{i} = \left(\frac{\sqrt{2}}{2}+i\frac{\sqrt{2}}{2}\right)\cdot i$$ Multiply both sides by i.
$$i\cdot\sqrt{i} = \frac{\sqrt{2}}{2}i-\frac{\sqrt{2}}{2}$$
$$\sqrt{-1}\cdot\sqrt{i} = \frac{\sqrt{2}}{2}i-\frac{\sqrt{2}}{2}$$ Let the i on the left side be $\sqrt{-1}$.
$$\sqrt{-i} = -\frac{\sqrt{2}}{2}+\frac{\sqrt{2}}{2}i$$ Combine the radicals on the left side.

SECTION 7.4

Objective A Exercises

1.
$$\begin{aligned}\sqrt[3]{4x} &= -2\\ \left(\sqrt[3]{4x}\right)^3 &= (-2)^3\\ 4x &= -8\\ x &= -2\end{aligned}$$

Check:

$\sqrt[3]{4x}$ =	-2
$\sqrt[3]{4(-2)}$	-2
$\sqrt[3]{-8}$	-2
-2 =	-2

The solution is –2.

3.
$$\begin{aligned}\sqrt{3x-2} &= 5\\ \left(\sqrt{3x-2}\right)^2 &= 5^2\\ 3x-2 &= 25\\ 3x &= 27\\ x &= 9\end{aligned}$$

Check:

$\sqrt{3x-2}$ =	5
$\sqrt{3(9)-2}$	5
$\sqrt{27-2}$	5
5 =	5

The solution is 9.

5.
$$\begin{aligned}\sqrt{4x-3}-5&=0\\ \sqrt{4x-3}&=5\\ \left(\sqrt{4x-3}\right)^2&=5^2\\ 4x-3&=25\\ 4x&=28\\ x&=7\end{aligned}$$

Check:

$\sqrt{4x-3}-5$	=	0
$\sqrt{4(7)-3}-5$		0
$\sqrt{28-3}-5$		0
$\sqrt{25}-5$		0
$5-5$		0
0	=	0

The solution is 7.

7.
$$\begin{aligned}\sqrt{2x+4}&=\sqrt{5x-9}\\ \left(\sqrt{2x+4}\right)^2&=\left(\sqrt{5x-9}\right)^2\\ 2x+4&=5x-9\\ -3x+4&=-9\\ -3x&=-13\\ x&=\frac{13}{3}\end{aligned}$$

Check:

$\sqrt{2x+4}$	=	$\sqrt{5x-9}$
$\sqrt{2\left(\frac{13}{3}\right)+4}$		$\sqrt{5\left(\frac{13}{3}\right)-9}$
$\sqrt{\frac{26}{3}+4}$		$\sqrt{\frac{65}{3}-9}$
$\sqrt{\frac{38}{3}}$	=	$\sqrt{\frac{38}{3}}$

The solution is $\frac{13}{3}$.

9.
$$\begin{aligned}\sqrt[3]{2x-6}&=4\\ \left(\sqrt[3]{2x-6}\right)^3&=4^3\\ 2x-6&=64\\ 2x&=70\\ x&=35\end{aligned}$$

Check:

$\sqrt[3]{2x-6}$	=	4
$\sqrt[3]{2(35)-6}$		4
$\sqrt[3]{70-6}$		4
$\sqrt[3]{64}$		4
4	=	4

The solution is 35.

11.
$$\begin{aligned}\sqrt[3]{x-12}&=\sqrt[3]{5x+16}\\ \left(\sqrt[3]{x-12}\right)^3&=\left(\sqrt[3]{5x+16}\right)^3\\ x-12&=5x+16\\ -4x-12&=16\\ -4x&=28\\ x&=-7\end{aligned}$$

Check:

$\sqrt[3]{x-12}$	=	$\sqrt[3]{5x+16}$
$\sqrt[3]{-7-12}$		$\sqrt[3]{5(-7)+16}$
$\sqrt[3]{-19}$		$\sqrt[3]{-35+16}$
$\sqrt[3]{-19}$	=	$\sqrt[3]{-19}$

The solution is –7.

13.
$$\begin{aligned}\sqrt[3]{2x-3}+5&=2\\ \sqrt[3]{2x-3}&=-3\\ \left(\sqrt[3]{2x-3}\right)^3&=(-3)^3\\ 2x-3&=-27\\ 2x&=-24\\ x&=-12\end{aligned}$$

Check:

$\sqrt[3]{2x-3}+5$	=	2
$\sqrt[3]{2(-12)-3}+5$		2
$\sqrt[3]{-24-3}+5$		2
$\sqrt[3]{-27}+5$		2
$-3+5$		2
2	=	2

The solution is –12.

15.

$$\sqrt{x}+\sqrt{x-5}=5$$
$$\sqrt{x}=5-\sqrt{x-5}$$
$$\left(\sqrt{x}\right)^2=\left(5-\sqrt{x-5}\right)^2$$
$$x=25-10\sqrt{x-5}+x-5$$
$$0=20-10\sqrt{x-5}$$
$$-20=-10\sqrt{x-5}$$
$$2=\sqrt{x-5}$$
$$(2)^2=\left(\sqrt{x-5}\right)^2$$
$$4=x-5$$
$$9=x$$

Check:

$\sqrt{x}+\sqrt{x-5}$ =	5
$\sqrt{9}+\sqrt{9-5}$	5
$3+\sqrt{4}$	5
$3+2$	5
5 =	5

The solution is 9.

17.

$$\sqrt{2x+5}-\sqrt{2x}=1$$
$$\sqrt{2x+5}=1+\sqrt{2x}$$
$$\left(\sqrt{2x+5}\right)^2=\left(1+\sqrt{2x}\right)^2$$
$$2x+5=1+2\sqrt{2x}+2x$$
$$5=1+2\sqrt{2x}$$
$$4=2\sqrt{2x}$$
$$2=\sqrt{2x}$$
$$2^2=\left(\sqrt{2x}\right)^2$$
$$4=2x$$
$$2=x$$

Check:

$\sqrt{2x+5}-\sqrt{2x}$ =	1
$\sqrt{2\cdot 2+5}-\sqrt{2\cdot 2}$	1
$\sqrt{9}-\sqrt{4}$	1
$3-2$	1
1 =	1

The solution is 2.

19.

$$\sqrt{2x}-\sqrt{x-1}=1$$
$$\sqrt{2x}=1+\sqrt{x-1}$$
$$\left(\sqrt{2x}\right)^2=\left(1+\sqrt{x-1}\right)^2$$
$$2x=1+2\sqrt{x-1}+x-1$$
$$x=2\sqrt{x-1}$$
$$(x)^2=\left(2\sqrt{x-1}\right)^2$$
$$x^2=4(x-1)$$
$$x^2=4x-4$$
$$x^2-4x+4=0$$
$$(x-2)(x-2)=0$$
$$x-2=0 \quad x-2=0$$
$$x=2 \quad x=2$$

Check:

$\sqrt{2x}-\sqrt{x-1}$ =	1
$\sqrt{2\cdot 2}-\sqrt{2-1}$	1
$\sqrt{4}-\sqrt{1}$	1
$2-1$	1
1 =	1

The solution is 2.

21.

$$\sqrt{2x+2}+\sqrt{x}=3$$
$$\sqrt{2x+2}=3-\sqrt{x}$$
$$\left(\sqrt{2x+2}\right)^2=\left(3-\sqrt{x}\right)^2$$
$$2x+2=9-6\sqrt{x}+x$$
$$x-7=-6\sqrt{x}$$
$$(x-7)^2=\left(-6\sqrt{x}\right)^2$$
$$x^2-14x+49=36x$$
$$x^2-50x+49=0$$
$$(x-49)(x-1)=0$$

$x-49=0 \qquad x-1=0$

$x=49 \qquad x=1$

Check:

$\sqrt{2x+2}+\sqrt{x}$ =	3
$\sqrt{2(49)+2}+\sqrt{49}$	3
$\sqrt{100}+\sqrt{49}$	3
$10+7$	3
$17 \neq$	3

Check:

$\sqrt{2x-5}+\sqrt{x+1}$ =	3
$\sqrt{2(1)+2}+\sqrt{1}$	3
$\sqrt{4}+\sqrt{1}$	3
$2+1$	3
$3 \neq$	3

The solution is 1.

Objective B Application Problems

23. Strategy To find the distance the object will fall, replace t and g in the equation with the given values and solve for d.

Solution

$$t=\sqrt{\frac{2d}{g}}$$
$$6=\sqrt{\frac{2d}{32}}$$
$$6=\sqrt{\frac{d}{16}}$$
$$6^2=\left(\sqrt{\frac{d}{16}}\right)^2$$
$$36=\frac{d}{16}$$
$$576=d$$

The object will fall 576 ft in 6 s.

25. Strategy To find the difference in width:

- Use the Pythagorean Theorem to find the width of the screen on the regular television. The hypotenuse is the diagonal. The height is one leg.
- Use the Pythagorean Theorem to find the width of the HDTV. The hypotenuse is the diagonal and the height is one leg.
- Subtract the width of the regular TV from the width of the HDTV.

Solution

$$c^2 = a^2 + b^2$$
$$27^2 = 16.2^2 + b^2$$
$$729 = 262.44 + b^2$$
$$466.56 = b^2$$
$$(466.56)^{1/2} = (b^2)^{1/2}$$
$$21.6 = b$$

$$33^2 = 16.2^2 + b^2$$
$$1089 = 262.44 + b^2$$
$$826.56 = b^2$$
$$(826.56)^{1/2} = (b^2)^{1/2}$$
$$28.75 \approx b$$

$28.75 - 21.6 = 7.15$

The HDTV is approximately 7.15 in. wider.

27. Strategy To find the length of the pendulum, replace T in the equation with the given value and solve for L.

Solution

$$T = 2\pi\sqrt{\frac{L}{32}}$$
$$3 = 2\pi\sqrt{\frac{L}{32}}$$
$$\frac{3}{2\pi} = \sqrt{\frac{L}{32}}$$
$$\left(\frac{3}{2\pi}\right)^2 = \left(\sqrt{\frac{L}{32}}\right)^2$$
$$\left(\frac{3}{2\pi}\right)^2 = \frac{L}{32}$$
$$32\left(\frac{3}{2\pi}\right)^2 = L$$
$$7.30 \approx L$$

The length of the pendulum is 7.30 ft.

Applying the Concepts

29.

$$\sqrt{3x-2} = \sqrt{2x-3} + \sqrt{x-1}$$
$$\left(\sqrt{3x-2}\right)^2 = \left(\sqrt{2x-3} + \sqrt{x-1}\right)^2$$
$$3x-2 = 2x-3+2\sqrt{2x-3}\cdot\sqrt{x-1}+x-1$$
$$3x-2 = 3x-4+2\sqrt{2x-3}\cdot\sqrt{x-1}$$
$$2 = 2\sqrt{2x-3}\cdot\sqrt{x-1}$$
$$(1)^2 = \left(\sqrt{2x-3}\cdot\sqrt{x-1}\right)^2$$
$$1 = (2x-3)(x-1)$$
$$1 = 2x^2-5x+3$$
$$2x^2-5x+2=0$$
$$(2x-1)(x-2)=0$$

$x = \frac{1}{2}$ $\quad x = 2$

Check:

$\sqrt{3x-2}$ =	$\sqrt{2x-3}+\sqrt{x-1}$
$\sqrt{3\left(\frac{1}{2}\right)-2}$	$\sqrt{2\left(\frac{1}{2}\right)-3}+\sqrt{\frac{1}{2}-1}$
$\sqrt{\frac{3}{2}-2}$	$\sqrt{1-3}+\sqrt{-\frac{1}{2}}$
$\sqrt{-\frac{1}{2}}$ =	$\sqrt{-1}+\sqrt{-\frac{1}{2}}$

Not real numbers

Check:

$\sqrt{3x-2}$ =	$\sqrt{2x-3}+\sqrt{x-1}$
$\sqrt{3(2)-2}$	$\sqrt{2(2)-3}+\sqrt{2-1}$
$\sqrt{4}$	$\sqrt{1}+\sqrt{1}$
2 =	1 + 1

The solution is 2.

31. Strategy First find a in terms of s by finding the hypotenuse of the triangle.

$$a^2 = \left(\frac{s}{2}\right)^2 + s^2$$
$$a^2 = \frac{s^2}{4} + s^2$$
$$a^2 = \frac{5s^2}{4}$$
$$a = \sqrt{5}\frac{s}{2}$$

Solution **a** Area = base · height

Base = $\frac{s}{2} + a = \frac{s}{2} + \sqrt{5}\frac{s}{2}$

Height = s

$$\text{Area} = \left(\frac{s}{2} + \sqrt{5}\frac{s}{2}\right)\cdot s$$
$$= (1+\sqrt{5})\frac{s^2}{2}$$
$$= \frac{s^2 + s^2\sqrt{5}}{2}$$

b
$$\frac{\text{Length}}{\text{Width}} = \frac{\frac{s}{2}+a}{s}$$
$$= \frac{\frac{s}{2}+\sqrt{5}\frac{s}{2}}{s}$$
$$= \frac{1+\sqrt{5}}{2}$$

33. Strategy Find the hypotenuse of the triangles in order, letting each become a leg of the next triangle.

Triangle 1: $a^2 = b^2 + c^2$

$a^2 = 1^2 + 1^2$

$a^2 = 2$

$a = \sqrt{2}$

Triangle 2: Let a become b. Then the new a is

$a^2 = \left(\sqrt{2}\right)^2 + 1^2$

$a^2 = 2 + 1$

$a^2 = 3$

$a = \sqrt{3}$

Triangle 3: Let a become b. Then the new a is

$a^2 = \left(\sqrt{3}\right)^2 + 1^2$

$a^2 = 3 + 1$

$a^2 = 4$

$a = 2$

Triangle 4: Let a become b. Then the new a is

$a^2 = (2)^2 + (1)^2$

$a^2 = 4 + 1$

$a^2 = 5$

$a = \sqrt{5}$

For the last triangle, let a become b. Then x is

$x^2 = \left(\sqrt{5}\right)^2 + 1^2$

$x^2 = 5 + 1$

$x^2 = 6$

$x = \sqrt{6}$

CHAPTER REVIEW

1. $(16x^{-4}y^{12})^{1/4}(100x^6y^{-2})^{1/2}$

$= (2^4)^{1/4}x^{-1}y^3 \cdot (10^2)^{1/2}x^3y^{-1}$

$= 20x^2y^2$

2. $\sqrt[4]{3x-5} = 2$

$\left(\sqrt[4]{3x-5}\right)^2 = 2$

$3x - 5 = 16$

$3x = 21$

$x = 7$

Check:

$\sqrt[4]{3x-5} =$	2
$\sqrt[4]{3 \cdot 7 - 5}$	2
$\sqrt[4]{21-5}$	2
$\sqrt[4]{16}$	2
$2 =$	2

The solution is 7.

3. $(6-5i)(4+3i) = 24 + 18i - 20i - 15i^2$

$= 24 - 2i - 15(-1)$

$= 24 + 15 - 2i$

$= 39 - 2i$

4. $7y\sqrt[3]{x^2} = 7yx^{2/3}$

5. $\left(\sqrt{3}+8\right)\left(\sqrt{3}-2\right) = \sqrt{3^2} + 6\sqrt{3} - 16$

$= 3 + 6\sqrt{3} - 16$

$= 6\sqrt{3} - 13$

6. $\sqrt{4x+9} + 10 = 11$

$\sqrt{4x+9} = 1$

$\left(\sqrt{4x+9}\right)^2 = 1^2$

$4x + 9 = 1$

$4x = -8$

$x = -2$

Check:

$\sqrt{4x+9} + 10 =$	11
$\sqrt{4(-2)+9} + 10$	11
$\sqrt{1} + 10$	11
$1 + 10$	11
$11 =$	11

The solution is −2.

7. $\dfrac{x^{-3/2}}{x^{7/2}} = x^{-10/2} = x^{-5} = \dfrac{1}{x^5}$

8. $\dfrac{8}{\sqrt{3y}} = \dfrac{8}{\sqrt{3y}} \cdot \dfrac{\sqrt{3y}}{\sqrt{3y}} = \dfrac{8\sqrt{3y}}{\sqrt{3^2y^2}} = \dfrac{8\sqrt{3y}}{3y}$

9. $\sqrt[3]{-8a^6b^{12}} = \sqrt[3]{(-2)^3a^6b^{12}} = -2a^2b^4$

10. $\sqrt{50a^4b^3} - ab\sqrt{18a^2b}$
$= \sqrt{5^2a^4b^2(2b)} - ab\sqrt{3^2a^2(2b)}$
$= 5a^2b\sqrt{2b} - 3a^2b\sqrt{2b}$
$= 2a^2b\sqrt{2b}$

11. $\dfrac{x+2}{\sqrt{x}+\sqrt{2}} = \dfrac{x+2}{\sqrt{x}+\sqrt{2}} \cdot \dfrac{\sqrt{x}-\sqrt{2}}{\sqrt{x}-\sqrt{2}}$
$= \dfrac{x\sqrt{x} - x\sqrt{2} + 2\sqrt{x} - 2\sqrt{2}}{\sqrt{x^2} - \sqrt{2^2}}$
$= \dfrac{x\sqrt{x} - x\sqrt{2} + 2\sqrt{x} - 2\sqrt{2}}{x-2}$

12. $\dfrac{5+2i}{3i} = \dfrac{5+2i}{3i} \cdot \dfrac{-3i}{-3i}$
$= \dfrac{-15i - 6i^2}{-9i^2}$
$= \dfrac{-15i - 6(-1)}{-9(-1)}$
$= \dfrac{-15i + 6}{9}$
$= \dfrac{6}{9} - \dfrac{15}{9}i$
$= \dfrac{2}{3} - \dfrac{5}{3}i$

13. $\sqrt{18a^3b^6} = \sqrt{3^2a^2b^6(2a)} = 3ab^3\sqrt{2a}$

14. $\left(\sqrt{50} + \sqrt{-72}\right) - \left(\sqrt{162} - \sqrt{-8}\right)$
$= \left(\sqrt{5^2 \cdot 2} + i\sqrt{6^2 \cdot 2}\right) - \left(\sqrt{9^2 \cdot 2} - i\sqrt{2^2 \cdot 2}\right)$
$= \left(5\sqrt{2} + 6i\sqrt{2}\right) - \left(9\sqrt{2} - 2i\sqrt{2}\right)$
$= -4\sqrt{2} + 8i\sqrt{2}$

15. $3x\sqrt[3]{54x^8y^{10}} - 2x^2y\sqrt[3]{16x^5y^7}$
$= 3x\sqrt[3]{3^3x^6y^9(2x^2y)} - 2x^2y\sqrt[3]{2^3x^3y^6(2x^2y)}$
$= 9x^3y^3\sqrt[3]{2x^2y} - 4x^3y^3\sqrt[3]{2x^2y}$
$= 5x^3y^3\sqrt[3]{2x^2y}$

16. $\sqrt[3]{16x^4y}\sqrt[3]{4xy^5} = \sqrt[3]{64x^5y^6}$
$= \sqrt[3]{4^3x^3y^6(x^2)}$
$= 4xy^2\sqrt[3]{x^2}$

17. $i(3-7i) = 3i - 7i^2$
$= 3i - 7(-1)$
$= 7 + 3i$

18. $3x^{3/4} = 3\sqrt[4]{x^3}$

19. $\sqrt[5]{-64a^8b^{12}} = \sqrt[5]{(-2)^5a^5b^{10}(2a^3b^2)}$
$= -2ab^2\sqrt[5]{2a^3b^2}$

20. $\dfrac{5+9i}{1-i} = \dfrac{5+9i}{1-i} \cdot \dfrac{1+i}{1+i}$
$= \dfrac{5+14i+9i^2}{1+1}$
$= \dfrac{5+14i-9}{2}$
$= \dfrac{-4+14i}{2}$
$= -2 + 7i$

21. $\sqrt{-12}\sqrt{-6} = i\sqrt{12} \cdot i\sqrt{6}$
$= i^2\sqrt{72}$
$= (-1)\sqrt{6^2 \cdot 2} = -6\sqrt{2}$

22. $\sqrt{x-5} + \sqrt{x+6} = 11$
$\sqrt{x-5} = 11 - \sqrt{x+6}$
$\left(\sqrt{x-5}\right)^2 = \left(11 - \sqrt{x+6}\right)^2$
$x - 5 = 121 - 22\sqrt{x+6} + x + 6$
$-11 = 121 - 22\sqrt{x+6}$
$-132 = -22\sqrt{x+6}$
$6 = \sqrt{x+6}$
$6^2 = \left(\sqrt{x+6}\right)^2$
$36 = x + 6$
$30 = x$

Check:

$\sqrt{x-5} + \sqrt{x+6}$	$=$ 11
$\sqrt{30-5} + \sqrt{30+6}$	11
$\sqrt{25} + \sqrt{36}$	11
$5 + 6$	11
$11 =$	11

The solution is 30.

23. $\sqrt[4]{81a^8b^{12}} = \sqrt[4]{3^4a^8b^{12}} = 3a^2b^3$

24. $\sqrt{-50} = i\sqrt{50} = i\sqrt{5^2 \cdot 2} = 5i\sqrt{2}$

25. $(-8+3i) - (4-7i) = -12 + 10i$

26. $\left(5 - \sqrt{6}\right)^2 = 25 - 10\sqrt{6} + \sqrt{6^2}$
$= 25 - 10\sqrt{6} + 6$
$= 31 - 10\sqrt{6}$

27. $4x\sqrt{12x^2y} + \sqrt{3x^4y} - x^2\sqrt{27y}$
$= 4x\sqrt{2^2x^2(3y)} + \sqrt{x^4(3y)} - x^2\sqrt{3^2(3y)}$
$= 8x^2\sqrt{3y} + x^2\sqrt{3y} - 3x^2\sqrt{3y}$
$= 6x^2\sqrt{3y}$

28. Strategy To find the amount of power, replace v in the equation with the given value and solve for P.

Solution
$$v = 4.05\sqrt[3]{P}$$
$$20 = 4.05\sqrt[3]{P}$$
$$4.94 \approx \sqrt[3]{P}$$
$$(4.94)^3 = \left(\sqrt[3]{P}\right)^3$$
$$120 \approx P$$
The amount of power is 120 watts.

29. Strategy To find the distance required, replace v and a in the equation with the given values and solve for s.

Solution
$$v = \sqrt{2as}$$
$$88 = \sqrt{2 \cdot 16s}$$
$$88^2 = \left(\sqrt{32s}\right)^2$$
$$7744 = 32s$$
$$242 = s$$
The distance required is 242 feet.

30. Strategy To find the distance, use the Pythagorean Theorem. The hypotenuse is the length of the ladder (12 ft). One leg is the height on the building that the ladder reaches (10 ft). The distance from the bottom of the ladder to the building is the other leg.

Solution
$$c^2 = a^2 + b^2$$
$$12^2 = 10^2 + b^2$$
$$144 = 100 + b^2$$
$$44 = b^2$$
$$44^{1/2} = (b^2)^{1/2}$$
$$\sqrt{44} = b$$
$$6.63 = b$$

The distance is 6.63 feet.

CHAPTER TEST

1. $\frac{1}{2}\sqrt[4]{x^3} = \frac{1}{2}x^{3/4}$

2. $\sqrt[3]{54x^7y^3} - x\sqrt[3]{128x^4y^3} - x^2\sqrt[3]{2xy^3}$
$= \sqrt[3]{3^3x^6y^3(2x)} - x\sqrt[3]{4^3x^3y^3(2x)} - x^2\sqrt[3]{y^3(2x)}$
$= 3x^2y\sqrt[3]{2x} - 4x^2y\sqrt[3]{2x} - x^2y\sqrt[3]{2x}$
$= -2x^2y\sqrt[3]{2x}$

3. $3y^{2/5} = 3\sqrt[5]{y^2}$

4. $(2+5i)(4-2i) = 8 - 4i + 20i - 10i^2$
$= 8 + 16i - 10(-1)$
$= 8 + 16i + 10$
$= 18 + 16i$

5. $\left(2\sqrt{x} + \sqrt{y}\right)^2 = 4\sqrt{x^2} + 4\sqrt{xy} + \sqrt{y^2}$
$= 4x + 4\sqrt{xy} + y$

6. $\dfrac{r^{2/3}r^{-1}}{r^{-1/2}} = \dfrac{r^{-1/3}}{r^{-1/2}} = r^{1/6}$

7.
$$\sqrt{x+12} - \sqrt{x} = 2$$
$$\sqrt{x+12} = 2 + \sqrt{x}$$
$$\left(\sqrt{x+12}\right)^2 = \left(2+\sqrt{x}\right)^2$$
$$x + 12 = 4 + 4\sqrt{x} + x$$
$$12 = 4 + 4\sqrt{x}$$
$$8 = 4\sqrt{x}$$
$$2 = \sqrt{x}$$
$$2^2 = \left(\sqrt{x}\right)^2$$
$$4 = x$$

Check:

$\sqrt{x+12} - \sqrt{x} =$	2
$\sqrt{4+12} - \sqrt{4}$	2
$\sqrt{16} - \sqrt{4}$	2
$4 - 2$	2
$2 =$	2

The solution is 4.

8. $\sqrt[3]{8x^3y^6} = \sqrt[3]{2^3x^3y^6} = 2xy^2$

9. $\sqrt{3x}\left(\sqrt{x} - \sqrt{25x}\right) = \sqrt{3x^2} - \sqrt{75x^2}$
$= \sqrt{x^2(3)} - \sqrt{5^2x^2(3)}$
$= x\sqrt{3} - 5x\sqrt{3} = -4x\sqrt{3}$

10. $(5-2i) - (8-4i) = -3 + 2i$

11. $\sqrt{32x^4y^7} = \sqrt{2^4x^4y^6(2y)} = 4x^2y^3\sqrt{2y}$

12. $\left(2\sqrt{3}+4\right)\left(3\sqrt{3}-1\right) = 6\sqrt{3^2} - 2\sqrt{3} + 12\sqrt{3} - 4$
$= 18 + 10\sqrt{3} - 4$
$= 14 + 10\sqrt{3}$

13. $(2+i) + (2-i)(3+2i) = 2 + i + 6 + 4i - 3i - 2i^2$
$= 8 + 2i - 2(-1)$
$= 8 + 2 + 2i$
$= 10 + 2i$

14.
$$\frac{4-2\sqrt{5}}{2-\sqrt{5}} = \frac{4-2\sqrt{5}}{2-\sqrt{5}} \cdot \frac{2+\sqrt{5}}{2+\sqrt{5}}$$
$$= \frac{8+4\sqrt{5}-4\sqrt{5}-2\sqrt{5^2}}{2^2-\sqrt{5^2}}$$
$$= \frac{8-2\cdot 5}{4-5}$$
$$= \frac{8-10}{-1} = \frac{-2}{-1} = 2$$

15.
$$\sqrt{18a^3} + a\sqrt{50a} = \sqrt{3^2a^2(2a)} + a\sqrt{5^2(2a)}$$
$$= 3a\sqrt{2a} + 5a\sqrt{2a}$$
$$= 8a\sqrt{2a}$$

16.
$$\left(\sqrt{a}-3\sqrt{b}\right)\left(2\sqrt{a}+5\sqrt{b}\right)$$
$$= 2\sqrt{a^2} + 5\sqrt{ab} - 6\sqrt{ab} - 15\sqrt{b^2}$$
$$= 2a - \sqrt{ab} - 15b$$

17.
$$\frac{(2x^{1/3}y^{-2/3})^6}{(x^{-4}y^8)^{1/4}} = \frac{2^6x^2y^{-4}}{x^{-1}y^2} = 2^6x^3y^{-6} = \frac{64x^3}{y^6}$$

18.
$$\frac{\sqrt{x}}{\sqrt{x}-\sqrt{y}} = \frac{\sqrt{x}}{\sqrt{x}-\sqrt{y}} \cdot \frac{\sqrt{x}+\sqrt{y}}{\sqrt{x}+\sqrt{y}}$$
$$= \frac{\sqrt{x^2}+\sqrt{xy}}{\sqrt{x^2}-\sqrt{y^2}}$$
$$= \frac{x+\sqrt{xy}}{x-y}$$

19.
$$\frac{2+3i}{1-2i} = \frac{2+3i}{1-2i} \cdot \frac{1+2i}{1+2i}$$
$$= \frac{2+4i+3i+6i^2}{1+4}$$
$$= \frac{2+7i+6(-1)}{5}$$
$$= \frac{2-6+7i}{5}$$
$$= \frac{-4+7i}{5} = -\frac{4}{5} + \frac{7}{5}i$$

20.
$$\sqrt[3]{2x-2} + 4 = 2$$
$$\sqrt[3]{2x-2} = -2$$
$$\left(\sqrt[3]{2x-2}\right)^3 = (-2)^3$$
$$2x-2 = -8$$
$$2x = -6$$
$$x = -3$$

Check:

$\sqrt[3]{2x-2}+4$	$=$ 2
$\sqrt[3]{2(-3)-2}+4$	2
$\sqrt[3]{-8}+4$	2
$-2+4$	2
$2 =$	2

The solution is –3.

21.
$$\left(\frac{4a^4}{b^2}\right)^{-3/2} = \frac{4^{-3/2}a^{-6}}{b^{-3}}$$
$$= (2^2)^{-3/2}a^{-6}b^3$$
$$= 2^{-3}a^{-6}b^3$$
$$= \frac{b^3}{8a^6}$$

22. $\sqrt[3]{27a^4b^3c^7} = \sqrt[3]{3^3a^3b^3c^6(ac)} = 3abc^2\sqrt[3]{ac}$

23. $\dfrac{\sqrt{32x^5y}}{\sqrt{2xy^3}} = \sqrt{\dfrac{32x^5y}{2xy^3}} = \sqrt{\dfrac{16x^4}{y^2}} = \sqrt{\dfrac{4^2x^4}{y^2}} = \dfrac{4x^2}{y}$

24. $\left(\sqrt{-8}\right)\left(\sqrt{-2}\right) = i\sqrt{8}\cdot i\sqrt{2} = i^2\sqrt{16} = -1\cdot 4 = -4$

25. Strategy To find the distance, replace v in the formula and solve for d.

Solution
$$v = \sqrt{64d}$$
$$192 = \sqrt{64d}$$
$$(192)^2 = \left(\sqrt{64d}\right)^2$$
$$36864 = 64d$$
$$576 = d$$
The distance is 576 feet.

CUMULATIVE REVIEW

1. The Distributive Property

2.
$$f(-3) = 3(-3)^2 - 2(-3) + 1$$
$$f(-3) = 3\cdot 9 + 6 + 1$$
$$f(-3) = 34$$

3.
$$5-\frac{2}{3}x=4$$
$$5-\frac{2}{3}x-5=4-5$$
$$-\frac{2}{3}x=-1$$
$$\left(-\frac{3}{2}\right)\left(-\frac{2}{3}\right)x=-1\left(-\frac{3}{2}\right)$$
$$x=\frac{3}{2}$$

The solution is $\frac{3}{2}$.

4.
$$2[4-2(3-2x)]=4(1-x)$$
$$2[4-6+4x]=4-4x$$
$$2[-2+4x]=4-4x$$
$$-4+8x=4-4x$$
$$-4+8x+4x=4-4x+4x$$
$$12x-4=4$$
$$12x-4+4=4+4$$
$$12x=8$$
$$\left(\frac{1}{12}\right)12x=\frac{1}{12}(8)$$
$$x=\frac{2}{3}$$

The solution is $\frac{2}{3}$.

5.
$$2+|4-3x|=5$$
$$|4-3x|=3$$
$$4-3x=3 \qquad 4-3x=-3$$
$$-3x=-1 \qquad -3x=-7$$
$$x=\frac{1}{3} \qquad x=\frac{7}{3}$$

The solutions are $\frac{1}{3}$ and $\frac{7}{3}$.

6.
$$6x-3(2x+2)>3-3(x+2)$$
$$6x-6x-6>3-3x-6$$
$$-6>-3-3x$$
$$-6+3x>-3-3x+3x$$
$$3x-6>-3$$
$$3x>3$$
$$\left(\frac{1}{3}\right)3x>\frac{1}{3}(3)$$
$$x>1$$

$\{x|x>1\}$

7.
$$|2x+3|\le 9$$
$$-9\le 2x+3\le 9$$
$$-9-3\le 2x+3-3\le 9-3$$
$$-12\le 2x\le 6$$
$$\frac{1}{2}(-12)\le\frac{1}{2}(2x)\le\frac{1}{2}(6)$$
$$-6\le x\le 3$$

$\{x|-6\le x\le 3\}$

8. $81x^2-y^2=(9x+y)(9x-y)$

9.
$$x^5+2x^3-3x=x(x^4+2x^2-3)$$
$$=x(x^2+3)(x^2-1)$$
$$=x(x^2+3)(x+1)(x-1)$$

10. First find the slope of the line.

$$m=\frac{y_2-y_1}{x_2-x_1}=\frac{2-3}{-1-2}=\frac{-1}{-3}=\frac{1}{3}$$

Use the point-slope form to find the equation of the line.

$$y-y_1=m(x-x_1)$$
$$y-3=\frac{1}{3}(x-2)$$
$$y-3=\frac{1}{3}x-\frac{2}{3}$$
$$y=\frac{1}{3}x+\frac{7}{3}$$

The equation of the line is $y=\frac{1}{3}x+\frac{7}{3}$.

11.
$$\begin{vmatrix}1 & 2 & -3\\ 0 & -1 & 2\\ 3 & 1 & -2\end{vmatrix}=1\cdot\begin{vmatrix}-1 & 2\\ 1 & -2\end{vmatrix}-2\begin{vmatrix}0 & 2\\ 3 & -2\end{vmatrix}-3\begin{vmatrix}0 & -1\\ 3 & 1\end{vmatrix}$$
$$=1\cdot 0-2(-6)-3\cdot 3$$
$$=3$$

12.
$$P=\frac{R-C}{n}$$
$$P\cdot n=\frac{R-C}{n}\cdot n$$
$$nP=R-C$$
$$nP+C=R$$
$$C=R-nP$$

13.
$$(2^{-1}x^2y^{-6})(2^{-1}y^{-4})^{-2}=(2^{-1}x^2y^{-6})(2^2y^8)$$
$$=2^{-1+2}x^2y^{-6+8}$$
$$=2^1x^2y^2$$
$$=2x^2y^2$$

14.
$$\frac{x^2y^3}{x^2+2x-8}\cdot\frac{2x^2-7x+6}{xy^4}$$
$$=\frac{x^2y^3}{(x+4)(x-2)}\cdot\frac{(2x-3)(x-2)}{xy^4}$$
$$=\frac{x^2y^3(2x-3)(x-2)}{(x+4)(x-2)xy^4}$$
$$=\frac{x(2x-3)}{y(x+4)}$$

15.
$$\sqrt{40x^3}-x\sqrt{90x}=\sqrt{2^2x^2(10x)}-x\sqrt{3^2(10x)}$$
$$=2x\sqrt{10x}-3x\sqrt{10x}$$
$$=-x\sqrt{10x}$$

16.
$$\frac{x}{x-2} - 2x = \frac{-3}{x-2}$$
$$(x-2)\left(\frac{x}{x-2} - 2x\right) = (x-2)\left(\frac{-3}{x-2}\right)$$
$$x - (x-2)(2x) = -3$$
$$x - 2x^2 + 4x = -3$$
$$-2x^2 + 5x + 3 = 0$$
$$2x^2 - 5x - 3 = 0$$
$$(2x+1)(x-3) = 0$$

$2x + 1 = 0 \qquad x - 3 = 0$

$2x = -1 \qquad x = 3$

$x = -\frac{1}{2}$

The solutions are $-\frac{1}{2}$ and 3.

17. Find the y-intercept at $x = 0$.
$3(0) - 2y = -6$
$y = 3$
The y-intercept is (0, 3).
To find the slope, find the x-intercept and use it to get the slope.
$3x - 2(0) = -6$
$x = -2$
The x-intercept is (–2, 0).
$$m = \frac{y_2 - y_1}{x_2 - x_1}$$
$$m = \frac{3-0}{0-(-2)} = \frac{3}{2}$$
The slope is $\frac{3}{2}$, and the y-intercept is (0, 3).

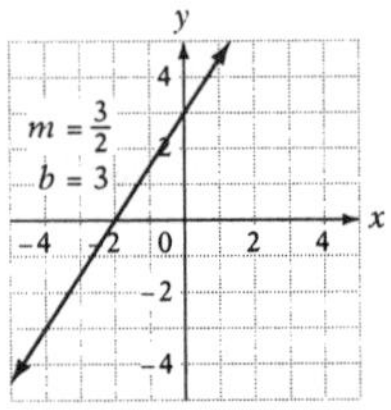

18. First graph the line $3x + 2y = 4$:
Find the y-intercept at $x = 0$.
$3(0) + 2y = 4$
$y = 2$
The y-intercept is (0, 2).
Find the x-intercept at $y = 0$.
$3x + 2(0) = 4$
$x = \frac{4}{3}$
The x-intercept is $\left(\frac{4}{3}, 0\right)$.
Determine the shading: (0, 0) is a solution, so shade below the line.

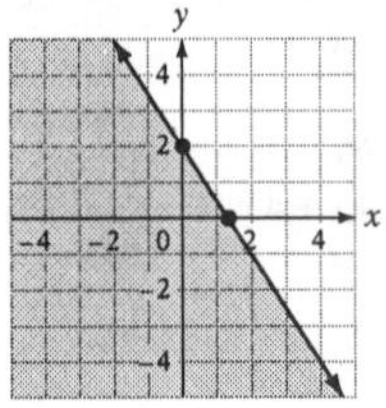

19.
$$\frac{2i}{3-i} = \frac{2i}{3-i} \cdot \frac{3+i}{3+i}$$
$$= \frac{6i + 2i^2}{9+1}$$
$$= \frac{6i + 2(-1)}{10}$$
$$= \frac{-2+6i}{10} = -\frac{1}{5} + \frac{3}{5}i$$

20.
$$\sqrt[3]{3x-4} + 5 = 1$$
$$\sqrt[3]{3x-4} = -4$$
$$\left(\sqrt[3]{3x-4}\right)^3 = (-4)^3$$
$$3x - 4 = -64$$
$$3x = -60$$
$$x = -20$$

Check:

$\sqrt[3]{3x-4} + 5$	= 1
$\sqrt[3]{3(-20)-4} + 5$	1
$\sqrt[3]{-64} + 5$	1
$-4 + 5$	1
1 =	1

The solution is –20.

21. The LCM is $(2x-3)(x+4)$.

$$\frac{x}{2x-3}+\frac{4}{x+4}=\frac{x}{2x-3}\cdot\frac{x+4}{x+4}+\frac{4}{x+4}\cdot\frac{2x-3}{2x-3}$$
$$=\frac{x(x+4)+4(2x-3)}{(2x-3)(x+4)}$$
$$=\frac{x^2+4x+8x-12}{(2x-3)(x+4)}$$
$$=\frac{x^2+12x-12}{(2x-3)(x+4)}$$

22. $2x-y=4$
$-2x+3y=5$

$$D=\begin{vmatrix}2 & -1\\ -2 & 3\end{vmatrix}=4$$
$$D_x=\begin{vmatrix}4 & -1\\ 5 & 3\end{vmatrix}=17$$
$$D_y=\begin{vmatrix}2 & 4\\ -2 & 5\end{vmatrix}=18$$
$$x=\frac{D_x}{D}=\frac{17}{4}$$
$$y=\frac{D_y}{D}=\frac{18}{4}=\frac{9}{2}$$

The solution is $\left(\frac{17}{4},\frac{9}{2}\right)$.

23. Strategy
- Number of 18¢ stamps: x
  Number of 13¢ stamps: $30-x$

Stamps	Number	Value	Total Value
18¢	x	18	$18x$
13¢	$30-x$	13	$13(30-x)$

- The sum of the total values of each type of stamp equals the total value of the stamps (485¢).
  $18x+13(30-x)=485$

Solution
$$18x+13(30-x)=485$$
$$18x+390-13x=485$$
$$5x+390=485$$
$$5x=95$$
$$x=19$$

The are nineteen 18¢ stamps.

24. Strategy
- Unknown rate of the car: x
  Unknown rate of the plane: $5x$

	Distance	Rate	Time
Car	25	x	$\frac{25}{x}$
Plane	625	$5x$	$\frac{625}{5x}$

- The total time of the trip was 3 h.
  $\frac{25}{x}+\frac{625}{5x}=3$

Solution
$$5x\left(\frac{25}{x}+\frac{625}{5x}\right)=3(5x)$$
$$125+625=15x$$
$$750=15x$$
$$50=x$$
$$250=5x$$

The rate of the plane is 250 mph.

25. Strategy
- To find the time it takes light to travel from the earth to the moon, use the formula $RT=D$, substituting for R and D and solving for T.

Solution
$$RT=D$$
$$1.86\times10^5\cdot T=232{,}500$$
$$1.86\times10^5\cdot T=2.325\times10^5$$
$$T=1.25\times10^0$$
$$T=1.25$$

The time is 1.25 seconds.

26. Strategy
- To find the height of the periscope, replace d in the given equation and solve for h.

Solution
$$d=\sqrt{1.5h}$$
$$7=\sqrt{1.5h}$$
$$7^2=\left(\sqrt{1.5h}\right)^2$$
$$49=1.5h$$
$$32.7=h$$

The height of the periscope is 32.7 ft.

27. Slope $m=\frac{y_2-y_1}{x_2-x_1}=\frac{400-0}{5000-0}=\frac{400}{5000}=0.08$

The slope represents the simple interest rate on an investment. The interest rate is 8%.

Chapter 8: Quadratic Equations

SECTION 8.1

Objective A Exercises

1. $x^2 - 4x = 0$
$x(x-4) = 0$
$x = 0 \quad x - 4 = 0$
$x = 4$
The solutions are 0 and 4.

3. $t^2 - 25 = 0$
$(t-5)(t+5) = 0$
$t - 5 = 0 \quad t + 5 = 0$
$t = 5 \quad t = -5$
The solutions are 5 and –5.

5. $s^2 - s - 6 = 0$
$(s-3)(s+2) = 0$
$s - 3 = 0 \quad s + 2 = 0$
$s = 3 \quad s = -2$
The solutions are 3 and –2.

7. $y^2 - 6y + 9 = 0$
$(y-3)(y-3) = 0$
$y - 3 = 0 \quad y - 3 = 0$
$y = 3 \quad y = 3$
The solution is 3.

9. $9z^2 - 18z = 0$
$9z(z-2) = 0$
$9z = 0 \quad z - 2 = 0$
$z = 0 \quad z = 2$
The solutions are 0 and 2.

11. $r^2 - 3r = 10$
$r^2 - 3r - 10 = 0$
$(r-5)(r+2) = 0$
$r - 5 = 0 \quad r + 2 = 0$
$r = 5 \quad r = -2$
The solutions are 5 and –2.

13. $v^2 + 10 = 7v$
$v^2 - 7v + 10 = 0$
$(v-2)(v-5) = 0$
$v - 2 = 0 \quad v - 5 = 0$
$v = 2 \quad v = 5$
The solutions are 2 and 5.

15. $2x^2 - 9x - 18 = 0$
$(x-6)(2x+3) = 0$
$x - 6 = 0 \quad 2x + 3 = 0$
$x = 6 \quad 2x = -3$
$x = -\frac{3}{2}$
The solutions are 6 and $-\frac{3}{2}$.

17. $4z^2 - 9z + 2 = 0$
$(z-2)(4z-1) = 0$
$z - 2 = 0 \quad 4z - 1 = 0$
$z = 2 \quad 4z = 1$
$z = \frac{1}{4}$
The solutions are 2 and $\frac{1}{4}$.

19. $3w^2 + 11w = 4$
$3w^2 + 11w - 4 = 0$
$(3w-1)(w+4) = 0$
$3w - 1 = 0 \quad w + 4 = 0$
$3w = 1 \quad w = -4$
$w = \frac{1}{3}$
The solutions are $\frac{1}{3}$ and –4.

21. $6x^2 = 23x + 18$
$6x^2 - 23x - 18 = 0$
$(2x-9)(3x+2) = 0$
$2x - 9 = 0 \quad 3x + 2 = 0$
$2x = 9 \quad 3x = -2$
$x = \frac{9}{2} \quad x = -\frac{2}{3}$
The solutions are $\frac{9}{2}$ and $-\frac{2}{3}$.

23. $4 - 15u - 4u^2 = 0$
$(1-4u)(4+u) = 0$
$1 - 4u = 0 \quad 4 + u = 0$
$-4u = -1 \quad u = -4$
$u = \frac{1}{4}$
The solutions are $\frac{1}{4}$ and –4.

25. $x + 18 = x(x-6)$
$x + 18 = x^2 - 6x$
$0 = x^2 - 7x - 18$
$0 = (x-9)(x+2)$
$x - 9 = 0 \quad x + 2 = 0$
$x = 9 \quad x = -2$
The solutions are 9 and –2.

27. $$\begin{aligned} 4s(s+3) &= s-6 \\ 4s^2+12s &= s-6 \\ 4s^2+11s+6 &= 0 \\ (s+2)(4s+3) &= 0 \end{aligned}$$
$s+2=0 \quad 4s+3=0$
$s=-2 \quad 4s=-3$
$s=-\frac{3}{4}$
The solutions are –2 and $-\frac{3}{4}$.

29. $$\begin{aligned} u^2-2u+4 &= (2u-3)(u+2) \\ u^2-2u+4 &= 2u^2+u-6 \\ 0 &= u^2+3u-10 \\ 0 &= (u-2)(u+5) \end{aligned}$$
$u-2=0 \quad u+5=0$
$u=2 \quad u=-5$
The solutions are 2 and –5.

31. $$\begin{aligned} (3x-4)(x+4) &= x^2-3x-28 \\ 3x^2+8x-16 &= x^2-3x-28 \\ 2x^2+11x+12 &= 0 \\ (x+4)(2x+3) &= 0 \end{aligned}$$
$x+4=0 \quad 2x+3=0$
$x=-4 \quad 2x=-3$
$x=-\frac{3}{2}$
The solutions are –4 and $-\frac{3}{2}$.

33. $x^2-9bx+14b^2=0$
$(x-2b)(x-7b)=0$
$x-2b=0 \quad x-7b=0$
$x=2b \quad x=7b$
The solutions are $2b$ and $7b$.

35. $x^2-6cx-7c^2=0$
$(x-7c)(x+c)=0$
$x-7c=0 \quad x+c=0$
$x=7c \quad x=-c$
The solutions are $7c$ and $-c$.

37. $2x^2+3bx+b^2=0$
$(2x+b)(x+b)=0$
$2x+b=0 \quad x+b=0$
$2x=-b \quad x=-b$
$x=-\frac{b}{2}$
The solutions are $-\frac{b}{2}$ and $-b$.

39. $3x^2-14ax+8a^2=0$
$(x-4a)(3x-2a)=0$
$x-4a=0 \quad 3x-2a=0$
$x=4a \quad 3x=2a$
$x=\frac{2a}{3}$
The solutions are $4a$ and $\frac{2a}{3}$.

41. $3x^2-8ax-3a^2=0$
$(3x+a)(x-3a)=0$
$3x+a=0 \quad x-3a=0$
$3x=-a \quad x=3a$
$x=-\frac{a}{3}$
The solutions are $-\frac{a}{3}$ and $3a$.

43. $4x^2+8xy+3y^2=0$
$(2x+3y)(2x+y)=0$
$2x+3y=0 \quad 2x+y=0$
$2x=-3y \quad 2x=-y$
$x=-\frac{3y}{2} \quad x=-\frac{y}{2}$
The solutions are $-\frac{3y}{2}$ and $-\frac{y}{2}$.

45. $6x^2+11ax+4a^2=0$
$(2x+a)(3x+4a)=0$
$2x+a=0 \quad 3x+4a=0$
$2x=-a \quad 3x=-4a$
$x=-\frac{a}{2} \quad x=-\frac{4a}{3}$
The solutions are $-\frac{a}{2}$ and $-\frac{4a}{3}$.

Objective B Exercises

47. $(x-r_1)(x-r_2)=0$
$(x-2)(x-5)=0$
$x^2-7x+10=0$

49. $(x-r_1)(x-r_2)=0$
$[x-(-2)][x-(-4)]=0$
$(x+2)(x+4)=0$
$x^2+6x+8=0$

51. $(x-r_1)(x-r_2)=0$
$(x-6)[x-(-1)]=0$
$(x-6)(x+1)=0$
$x^2-5x-6=0$

53. $(x-r_1)(x-r_2)=0$
$(x-3)[x-(-3)]=0$
$(x-3)(x+3)=0$
$x^2-9=0$

55. $(x-r_1)(x-r_2)=0$
$(x-4)(x-4)=0$
$x^2-8x+16=0$

57. $(x-r_1)(x-r_2)=0$
$(x-0)(x-5)=0$
$x(x-5)=0$
$x^2-5x=0$

59. $(x-r_1)(x-r_2)=0$
$(x-0)(x-3)=0$
$x(x-3)=0$
$x^2-3x=0$

61. $(x-r_1)(x-r_2)=0$
$(x-3)\left(x-\frac{1}{2}\right)=0$
$x^2-\frac{7}{2}x+\frac{3}{2}=0$
$2\left(x^2-\frac{7}{2}x+\frac{3}{2}\right)=2\cdot 0$
$2x^2-7x+3=0$

63. $(x-r_1)(x-r_2)=0$
$\left[x-\left(-\frac{3}{4}\right)\right](x-2)=0$
$\left(x+\frac{3}{4}\right)(x-2)=0$
$x^2-\frac{5}{4}x-\frac{3}{2}=0$
$4\left(x^2-\frac{5}{4}x-\frac{3}{2}\right)=4\cdot 0$
$4x^2-5x-6=0$

65. $(x-r_1)(x-r_2)=0$
$\left[x-\left(-\frac{5}{3}\right)\right][x-(-2)]=0$
$\left(x+\frac{5}{3}\right)(x+2)=0$
$x^2+\frac{11}{3}x+\frac{10}{3}=0$
$3\left(x^2+\frac{11}{3}x+\frac{10}{3}\right)=3\cdot 0$
$3x^2+11x+10=0$

67. $(x-r_1)(x-r_2)=0$
$\left[x-\left(-\frac{2}{3}\right)\right]\left(x-\frac{2}{3}\right)=0$
$\left(x+\frac{2}{3}\right)\left(x-\frac{2}{3}\right)=0$
$x^2-\frac{4}{9}=0$
$9\left(x^2-\frac{4}{9}\right)=9\cdot 0$
$9x^2-4=0$

69. $(x-r_1)(x-r_2)=0$
$\left(x-\frac{1}{2}\right)\left(x-\frac{1}{3}\right)=0$
$x^2-\frac{5}{6}x+\frac{1}{6}=0$
$6\left(x^2-\frac{5}{6}x+\frac{1}{6}\right)=6\cdot 0$
$6x^2-5x+1=0$

71. $(x-r_1)(x-r_2)=0$
$\left(x-\frac{6}{5}\right)\left[x-\left(-\frac{1}{2}\right)\right]=0$
$\left(x-\frac{6}{5}\right)\left(x+\frac{1}{2}\right)=0$
$x^2-\frac{7}{10}x-\frac{3}{5}=0$
$10\left(x^2-\frac{7}{10}x-\frac{3}{5}\right)=10\cdot 0$
$10x^2-7x-6=0$

73. $(x-r_1)(x-r_2)=0$
$\left[x-\left(-\frac{1}{4}\right)\right]\left[x-\left(-\frac{1}{2}\right)\right]=0$
$\left(x+\frac{1}{4}\right)\left(x+\frac{1}{2}\right)=0$
$x^2+\frac{3}{4}x+\frac{1}{8}=0$
$8\left(x^2+\frac{3}{4}x+\frac{1}{8}\right)=8\cdot 0$
$8x^2+6x+1=0$

75. $(x-r_1)(x-r_2)=0$
$\left(x-\frac{3}{5}\right)\left[x-\left(-\frac{1}{10}\right)\right]=0$
$\left(x-\frac{3}{5}\right)\left(x+\frac{1}{10}\right)=0$
$x^2-\frac{1}{2}x-\frac{3}{50}=0$
$50\left(x^2-\frac{1}{2}x-\frac{3}{50}\right)=50\cdot 0$
$50x^2-25x-3=0$

Objective C Exercises

77. $y^2=49$
$\sqrt{y^2}=\sqrt{49}$
$y=\pm\sqrt{49}=\pm 7$
The solutions are 7 and –7.

79. $z^2=-4$
$\sqrt{z^2}=\sqrt{-4}$
$z=\pm\sqrt{-4}=\pm 2i$
The solutions are $2i$ and $-2i$.

81. $s^2 - 4 = 0$
$s^2 = 4$
$\sqrt{s^2} = \sqrt{4}$
$s = \pm\sqrt{4} = \pm 2$
The solutions are 2 and –2.

83. $4x^2 - 81 = 0$
$4x^2 = 81$
$x^2 = \frac{81}{4}$
$\sqrt{x^2} = \sqrt{\frac{81}{4}}$
$x = \pm\sqrt{\frac{81}{4}} = \pm\frac{9}{2}$
The solutions are $\frac{9}{2}$ and $-\frac{9}{2}$.

85. $y^2 + 49 = 0$
$y^2 = -49$
$\sqrt{y^2} = \sqrt{-49}$
$y = \pm\sqrt{-49} = \pm 7i$
The solutions are $7i$ and $-7i$.

87. $v^2 - 48 = 0$
$v^2 = 48$
$\sqrt{v^2} = \sqrt{48}$
$v = \pm\sqrt{48} = \pm 4\sqrt{3}$
The solutions are $4\sqrt{3}$ and $-4\sqrt{3}$.

89. $r^2 - 75 = 0$
$r^2 = 75$
$\sqrt{r^2} = \sqrt{75}$
$r = \pm\sqrt{75} = \pm 5\sqrt{3}$
The solutions are $5\sqrt{3}$ and $-5\sqrt{3}$.

91. $z^2 + 18 = 0$
$z^2 = -18$
$\sqrt{z^2} = \sqrt{-18}$
$z = \pm\sqrt{-18} = \pm 3i\sqrt{2}$
The solutions are $3i\sqrt{2}$ and $-3i\sqrt{2}$.

93. $(x-1)^2 = 36$
$\sqrt{(x-1)^2} = \sqrt{36}$
$x - 1 = \pm\sqrt{36} = \pm 6$
$x - 1 = 6 \quad x - 1 = -6$
$x = 7 \quad x = -5$
The solutions are 7 and –5.

95. $3(y+3)^2 = 27$
$(y+3)^2 = 9$
$\sqrt{(y+3)^2} = \sqrt{9}$
$y + 3 = \pm\sqrt{9} = \pm 3$
$y + 3 = 3 \quad y + 3 = -3$
$y = 0 \quad y = -6$
The solutions are 0 and –6.

97. $5(z+2)^2 = 125$
$(z+2)^2 = 25$
$\sqrt{(z+2)^2} = \sqrt{25}$
$z + 2 = \pm\sqrt{25} = \pm 5$
$z + 2 = 5 \quad z + 2 = -5$
$z = 3 \quad z = -7$
The solutions are 3 and –7.

99. $\left(v - \frac{1}{2}\right)^2 = \frac{1}{4}$
$\sqrt{\left(v - \frac{1}{2}\right)^2} = \sqrt{\frac{1}{4}}$
$v - \frac{1}{2} = \pm\sqrt{\frac{1}{4}} = \pm\frac{1}{2}$
$v - \frac{1}{2} = \frac{1}{2} \quad v - \frac{1}{2} = -\frac{1}{2}$
$v = 1 \quad v = 0$
The solutions are 1 and 0.

101. $(x+5)^2 - 6 = 0$
$(x+5)^2 = 6$
$\sqrt{(x+5)^2} = \sqrt{6}$
$x + 5 = \pm\sqrt{6}$
$x + 5 = \sqrt{6} \quad x + 5 = -\sqrt{6}$
$x = -5 + \sqrt{6} \quad x = -5 - \sqrt{6}$
The solutions are $-5 + \sqrt{6}$ and $-5 - \sqrt{6}$.

103. $(v-3)^2 + 45 = 0$
$(v-3)^2 = -45$
$\sqrt{(v-3)^2} = \sqrt{-45}$
$v - 3 = \pm\sqrt{-45} = \pm 3i\sqrt{5}$
$v - 3 = 3i\sqrt{5} \quad v - 3 = -3i\sqrt{5}$
$v = 3 + 3i\sqrt{5} \quad v = 3 - 3i\sqrt{5}$
The solutions are $3 + 3i\sqrt{5}$ and $3 - 3i\sqrt{5}$.

105.
$$\left(u+\frac{2}{3}\right)^2-18=0$$
$$\left(u+\frac{2}{3}\right)^2=18$$
$$\sqrt{\left(u+\frac{2}{3}\right)^2}=\sqrt{18}$$
$$u+\frac{2}{3}=\pm\sqrt{18}=\pm3\sqrt{2}$$

$$u+\frac{2}{3}=3\sqrt{2} \qquad u+\frac{2}{3}=-3\sqrt{2}$$
$$u=-\frac{2}{3}+3\sqrt{2} \qquad u=-\frac{2}{3}-3\sqrt{2}$$
$$u=-\frac{2-9\sqrt{2}}{3} \qquad u=-\frac{2+9\sqrt{2}}{3}$$

The solutions are $-\frac{2-9\sqrt{2}}{3}$ and $-\frac{2+9\sqrt{2}}{3}$.

Applying the Concepts

107.
$$(x-r_1)(x-r_2)=0$$
$$(x-\sqrt{2})[x-(-\sqrt{2})]=0$$
$$(x-\sqrt{2})(x+\sqrt{2})=0$$
$$x^2-2=0$$

109.
$$(x-r_1)(x-r_2)=0$$
$$(x-i)[x-(-i)]=0$$
$$(x-i)(x+i)=0$$
$$x^2+1=0$$

111.
$$(x-r_1)(x-r_2)=0$$
$$(x-2\sqrt{2})[x-(-2\sqrt{2})]=0$$
$$(x-2\sqrt{2})(x+2\sqrt{2})=0$$
$$x^2-8=0$$

113.
$$(x-r_1)(x-r_2)=0$$
$$(x-i\sqrt{2})[x-(-i\sqrt{2})]=0$$
$$(x-i\sqrt{2})(x+i\sqrt{2})=0$$
$$x^2+2=0$$

115.
$$4a^2x^2=36b^2$$
$$x^2=\frac{36b^2}{4a^2}$$
$$x^2=\frac{9b^2}{a^2}$$
$$\sqrt{x^2}=\sqrt{\frac{9b^2}{a^2}}$$
$$x=\pm\sqrt{\frac{9b^2}{a^2}}=\pm\frac{3b}{a}$$

Since $a>0$ and $b>0$, the solutions are $\frac{3b}{a}$ and $-\frac{3b}{a}$.

117.
$$(x+a)^2-4=0$$
$$(x+a)^2=4$$
$$\sqrt{(x+a)^2}=\sqrt{4}$$
$$x+a=\pm\sqrt{4}=\pm2$$
$$x+a=2 \qquad x+a=-2$$
$$x=-a+2 \qquad x=-a-2$$

The solutions are $-a+2$ and $-a-2$.

119.
$$(2x-1)^2=(2x+3)^2$$
$$\sqrt{(2x-1)^2}=\sqrt{(2x+3)^2}$$
$$2x-1=\pm\sqrt{(2x+3)^2}=\pm(2x+3)$$
$$2x-1=2x+3 \qquad 2x-1=-(2x+3)$$
$$-1=3 \qquad 4x=-2$$
$$x=-\frac{1}{2}$$

The solution is $-\frac{1}{2}$.

121.
$$(x-r_1)(x-r_2)=0$$
$$(x-0)\left[x-\left(-\frac{b}{a}\right)\right]=0$$
$$x\left(x+\frac{b}{a}\right)=0$$
$$a\left(x^2+\frac{b}{a}x\right)=a\cdot 0$$
$$ax^2+bx=0$$

123. If $a=0$, the second-degree term drops out of the equation and it is no longer a quadratic equation.

SECTION 8.2

Objective A Exercises

1.
$$x^2-4x-5=0$$
$$x^2-4x=5$$
Complete the square.
$$x^2-4x+4=5+4$$
$$(x-2)^2=9$$
$$\sqrt{(x-2)^2}=\sqrt{9}$$
$$x-2=\pm\sqrt{9}=\pm3$$
$$x-2=3 \qquad x-2=-3$$
$$x=5 \qquad x=-1$$

The solutions are 5 and -1.

3. $v^2+8v-9=0$

$v^2+8v=9$

Complete the square.

$v^2+8v+16=9+16$

$(v+4)^2=25$

$\sqrt{(v+4)^2}=\sqrt{25}$

$v+4=\pm\sqrt{25}=\pm 5$

$v+4=5 \quad v+4=-5$

$v=1 \quad v=-9$

The solutions are 1 and –9.

5. $z^2-6z+9=0$

$z^2-6z=-9$

Complete the square.

$z^2-6z+9=-9+9$

$(z-3)^2=0$

$\sqrt{(z-3)^2}=\sqrt{0}$

$z-3=0$

$z=3$

The solution is 3.

7. $r^2+4r-7=0$

$r^2+4r=7$

Complete the square.

$r^2+4r+4=7+4$

$(r+2)^2=11$

$\sqrt{(r+2)^2}=\sqrt{11}$

$r+2=\pm\sqrt{11}$

$r+2=\sqrt{11} \quad r+2=-\sqrt{11}$

$r=-2+\sqrt{11} \quad r=-2-\sqrt{11}$

The solutions are $-2+\sqrt{11}$ and $-2-\sqrt{11}$.

9. $x^2-6x+7=0$

$x^2-6x=-7$

Complete the square.

$x^2-6x+9=-7+9$

$(x-3)^2=2$

$\sqrt{(x-3)^2}=\sqrt{2}$

$x-3=\pm\sqrt{2}$

$x-3=\sqrt{2} \quad x-3=-\sqrt{2}$

$x=3+\sqrt{2} \quad x=3-\sqrt{2}$

The solutions are $3+\sqrt{2}$ and $3-\sqrt{2}$.

11. $z^2-2z+2=0$

$z^2-2z=-2$

Complete the square.

$z^2-2z+1=-2+1$

$(z-1)^2=-1$

$\sqrt{(z-1)^2}=\sqrt{-1}$

$z-1=\pm i$

$z-1=i \quad z-1=-i$

$z=1+i \quad z=1-i$

The solutions are $1+i$ and $1-i$.

13. $s^2-5s-24=0$

$s^2-5s=24$

Complete the square.

$s^2-5s+\frac{25}{4}=24+\frac{25}{4}$

$\left(s-\frac{5}{2}\right)^2=\frac{121}{4}$

$\sqrt{\left(s-\frac{5}{2}\right)^2}=\sqrt{\frac{121}{4}}$

$s-\frac{5}{2}=\pm\frac{11}{2}$

$s-\frac{5}{2}=\frac{11}{2} \quad s-\frac{5}{2}=-\frac{11}{2}$

$s=\frac{5}{2}+\frac{11}{2} \quad s=\frac{5}{2}-\frac{11}{2}$

$s=\frac{16}{2}=8 \quad s=-\frac{6}{2}=-3$

The solutions are 8 and –3.

15. $x^2+5x-36=0$

$x^2+5x=36$

Complete the square.

$x^2+5x+\frac{25}{4}=36+\frac{25}{4}$

$\left(x+\frac{5}{2}\right)^2=\frac{169}{4}$

$\sqrt{\left(x+\frac{5}{2}\right)^2}=\sqrt{\frac{169}{4}}$

$x+\frac{5}{2}=\pm\frac{13}{2}$

$x+\frac{5}{2}=\frac{13}{2} \quad x+\frac{5}{2}=-\frac{13}{2}$

$x=-\frac{5}{2}+\frac{13}{2} \quad x=-\frac{5}{2}-\frac{13}{2}$

$x=\frac{8}{2}=4 \quad x=-\frac{18}{2}=-9$

The solutions are 4 and –9.

17. $p^2 - 3p + 1 = 0$

$p^2 - 3p = -1$

Complete the square.

$p^2 - 3p + \frac{9}{4} = -1 + \frac{9}{4}$

$\left(p - \frac{3}{2}\right)^2 = \frac{5}{4}$

$\sqrt{\left(p - \frac{3}{2}\right)^2} = \sqrt{\frac{5}{4}}$

$p - \frac{3}{2} = \pm\frac{\sqrt{5}}{2}$

$p - \frac{3}{2} = \frac{\sqrt{5}}{2}$ $\quad p - \frac{3}{2} = -\frac{\sqrt{5}}{2}$

$p = \frac{3}{2} + \frac{\sqrt{5}}{2}$ $\quad p = \frac{3}{2} - \frac{\sqrt{5}}{2}$

The solutions are $\frac{3+\sqrt{5}}{2}$ and $\frac{3-\sqrt{5}}{2}$.

19. $t^2 - t - 1 = 0$

$t^2 - t = 1$

Complete the square.

$t^2 - t + \frac{1}{4} = 1 + \frac{1}{4}$

$\left(t - \frac{1}{2}\right)^2 = \frac{5}{4}$

$\sqrt{\left(t - \frac{1}{2}\right)^2} = \sqrt{\frac{5}{4}}$

$t - \frac{1}{2} = \pm\frac{\sqrt{5}}{2}$

$t - \frac{1}{2} = \frac{\sqrt{5}}{2}$ $\quad t - \frac{1}{2} = -\frac{\sqrt{5}}{2}$

$t = \frac{1}{2} + \frac{\sqrt{5}}{2}$ $\quad t = \frac{1}{2} - \frac{\sqrt{5}}{2}$

The solutions are $\frac{1+\sqrt{5}}{2}$ and $\frac{1-\sqrt{5}}{2}$.

21. $y^2 - 6y = 4$

Complete the square.

$y^2 - 6y + 9 = 4 + 9$

$(y-3)^2 = 13$

$\sqrt{(y-3)^2} = \sqrt{13}$

$y - 3 = \pm\sqrt{13}$

$y - 3 = \sqrt{13}$ $\quad y - 3 = -\sqrt{13}$

$y = 3 + \sqrt{13}$ $\quad y = 3 - \sqrt{13}$

The solutions are $3+\sqrt{13}$ and $3-\sqrt{13}$.

23. $x^2 = 8x - 15$

$x^2 - 8x = -15$

Complete the square.

$x^2 - 8x + 16 = -15 + 16$

$(x-4)^2 = 1$

$\sqrt{(x-4)^2} = \sqrt{1}$

$x - 4 = \pm 1$

$x - 4 = 1$ $\quad x - 4 = -1$

$x = 5$ $\quad x = 3$

The solutions are 5 and 3.

25. $v^2 = 4v - 13$

$v^2 - 4v = -13$

Complete the square.

$v^2 - 4v + 4 = -13 + 4$

$(v-2)^2 = -9$

$\sqrt{(v-2)^2} = \sqrt{-9}$

$v - 2 = \pm 3i$

$v - 2 = 3i$ $\quad v - 2 = -3i$

$v = 2 + 3i$ $\quad v = 2 - 3i$

The solutions are $2 + 3i$ and $2 - 3i$.

27. $p^2 + 6p = -13$

Complete the square.

$p^2 + 6p + 9 = -13 + 9$

$(p+3)^2 = -4$

$\sqrt{(p+3)^2} = \sqrt{-4}$

$p + 3 = \pm 2i$

$p + 3 = 2i$ $\quad p + 3 = -2i$

$p = -3 + 2i$ $\quad p = -3 - 2i$

The solutions are $-3 + 2i$ and $-3 - 2i$.

29. $y^2 - 2y = 17$

Complete the square.

$y^2 - 2y + 1 = 17 + 1$

$(y-1)^2 = 18$

$\sqrt{(y-1)^2} = \sqrt{18}$

$y - 1 = \pm 3\sqrt{2}$

$y - 1 = 3\sqrt{2}$ $\quad y - 1 = -3\sqrt{2}$

$y = 1 + 3\sqrt{2}$ $\quad y = 1 - 3\sqrt{2}$

The solutions are $1+3\sqrt{2}$ and $1-3\sqrt{2}$.

31. $z^2 = z + 4$

$z^2 - z = 4$

Complete the square.

$z^2 - z + \frac{1}{4} = 4 + \frac{1}{4}$

$\left(z - \frac{1}{2}\right)^2 = \frac{17}{4}$

$\sqrt{\left(z - \frac{1}{2}\right)^2} = \sqrt{\frac{17}{4}}$

$z - \frac{1}{2} = \pm\frac{\sqrt{17}}{2}$

$z - \frac{1}{2} = \frac{\sqrt{17}}{2}$ $\qquad$ $z - \frac{1}{2} = -\frac{\sqrt{17}}{2}$

$z = \frac{1}{2} + \frac{\sqrt{17}}{2}$ $\qquad$ $z = \frac{1}{2} - \frac{\sqrt{17}}{2}$

The solutions are $\frac{1+\sqrt{17}}{2}$ and $\frac{1-\sqrt{17}}{2}$.

33. $x^2 + 13 = 2x$

$x^2 - 2x = -13$

Complete the square.

$x^2 - 2x + 1 = -13 + 1$

$(x-1)^2 = -12$

$\sqrt{(x-1)^2} = \sqrt{-12}$

$x - 1 = \pm 2i\sqrt{3}$

$x - 1 = 2i\sqrt{3}$ $\qquad$ $x - 1 = -2i\sqrt{3}$

$x = 1 + 2i\sqrt{3}$ $\qquad$ $x = 1 - 2i\sqrt{3}$

The solutions are $1 + 2i\sqrt{3}$ and $1 - 2i\sqrt{3}$.

35. $4x^2 - 4x + 5 = 0$

$4x^2 - 4x = -5$

$\frac{1}{4}(4x^2 - 4x) = \frac{1}{4}(-5)$

$x^2 - x = -\frac{5}{4}$

Complete the square.

$x^2 - x + \frac{1}{4} = -\frac{5}{4} + \frac{1}{4}$

$\left(x - \frac{1}{2}\right)^2 = -1$

$\sqrt{\left(x - \frac{1}{2}\right)^2} = \sqrt{-1}$

$x - \frac{1}{2} = \pm i$

$x - \frac{1}{2} = i$ $\qquad$ $x - \frac{1}{2} = -i$

$x = \frac{1}{2} + i$ $\qquad$ $x = \frac{1}{2} - i$

The solutions are $\frac{1}{2} + i$ and $\frac{1}{2} - i$.

37. $9x^2 - 6x + 2 = 0$

$9x^2 - 6x = -2$

$\frac{1}{9}(9x^2 - 6x) = \frac{1}{9}(-2)$

$x^2 - \frac{2}{3}x = -\frac{2}{9}$

Complete the square.

$x^2 - \frac{2}{3}x + \frac{1}{9} = -\frac{2}{9} + \frac{1}{9}$

$\left(x - \frac{1}{3}\right)^2 = -\frac{1}{9}$

$\sqrt{\left(x - \frac{1}{3}\right)^2} = \sqrt{-\frac{1}{9}}$

$x - \frac{1}{3} = \pm\frac{1}{3}i$

$x - \frac{1}{3} = \frac{1}{3}i$ $\qquad$ $x - \frac{1}{3} = -\frac{1}{3}i$

$x = \frac{1}{3} + \frac{1}{3}i$ $\qquad$ $x = \frac{1}{3} - \frac{1}{3}i$

The solutions are $\frac{1}{3} + \frac{1}{3}i$ and $\frac{1}{3} - \frac{1}{3}i$.

39. $2s^2 = 4s + 5$

$2s^2 - 4s = 5$

$\frac{1}{2}(2s^2 - 4s) = \frac{1}{2}(5)$

$s^2 - 2s = \frac{5}{2}$

Complete the square.

$s^2 - 2s + 1 = \frac{5}{2} + 1$

$(s-1)^2 = \frac{7}{2}$

$\sqrt{(s-1)^2} = \sqrt{\frac{7}{2}}$

$s - 1 = \pm\sqrt{\frac{7}{2}} = \pm\frac{\sqrt{14}}{2}$

$s - 1 = \frac{\sqrt{14}}{2}$ $\qquad$ $s - 1 = -\frac{\sqrt{14}}{2}$

$s = \frac{2}{2} + \frac{\sqrt{14}}{2}$ $\qquad$ $s = \frac{2}{2} - \frac{\sqrt{14}}{2}$

The solutions are $\frac{2+\sqrt{14}}{2}$ and $\frac{2-\sqrt{14}}{2}$.

41.
$$2r^2 = 3 - r$$
$$2r^2 + r = 3$$
$$\frac{1}{2}(2r^2 + r) = \frac{1}{2}(3)$$
$$r^2 + \frac{1}{2}r = \frac{3}{2}$$
Complete the square.
$$r^2 + \frac{1}{2}r + \frac{1}{16} = \frac{3}{2} + \frac{1}{16}$$
$$\left(r + \frac{1}{4}\right)^2 = \frac{25}{16}$$
$$\sqrt{\left(r + \frac{1}{4}\right)^2} = \sqrt{\frac{25}{16}}$$
$$r + \frac{1}{4} = \pm\frac{5}{4}$$
$$r + \frac{1}{4} = \frac{5}{4} \qquad r + \frac{1}{4} = -\frac{5}{4}$$
$$r = \frac{4}{4} = 1 \qquad r = -\frac{6}{4} = -\frac{3}{2}$$
The solutions are 1 and $-\frac{3}{2}$.

43.
$$y - 2 = (y - 3)(y + 2)$$
$$y - 2 = y^2 - y - 6$$
$$y^2 - 2y = 4$$
Complete the square.
$$y^2 - 2y + 1 = 4 + 1$$
$$(y - 1)^2 = 5$$
$$\sqrt{(y - 1)^2} = \sqrt{5}$$
$$y - 1 = \pm\sqrt{5}$$
$$y - 1 = \sqrt{5} \qquad y - 1 = -\sqrt{5}$$
$$y = 1 + \sqrt{5} \qquad y = 1 - \sqrt{5}$$
The solutions are $1 + \sqrt{5}$ and $1 - \sqrt{5}$.

45.
$$6t - 2 = (2t - 3)(t - 1)$$
$$6t - 2 = 2t^2 - 5t + 3$$
$$2t^2 - 11t = -5$$
$$\frac{1}{2}(2t^2 - 11t) = \frac{1}{2}(-5)$$
$$t^2 - \frac{11}{2}t = -\frac{5}{2}$$
Complete the square.
$$t^2 - \frac{11}{2}t + \frac{121}{16} = -\frac{5}{2} + \frac{121}{16}$$
$$\left(t - \frac{11}{4}\right)^2 = \frac{81}{16}$$
$$\sqrt{\left(t - \frac{11}{4}\right)^2} = \sqrt{\frac{81}{16}}$$
$$t - \frac{11}{4} = \pm\frac{9}{4}$$
$$t - \frac{11}{4} = \frac{9}{4} \qquad t - \frac{11}{4} = -\frac{9}{4}$$
$$t = \frac{20}{4} = 5 \qquad t = \frac{2}{4} = \frac{1}{2}$$
The solutions are 5 and $\frac{1}{2}$.

47.
$$(x - 4)(x + 1) = x - 3$$
$$x^2 - 3x - 4 = x - 3$$
$$x^2 - 4x = 1$$
Complete the square.
$$x^2 - 4x + 4 = 1 + 4$$
$$(x - 2)^2 = 5$$
$$\sqrt{(x - 2)^2} = \sqrt{5}$$
$$x - 2 = \pm\sqrt{5}$$
$$x - 2 = \sqrt{5} \qquad x - 2 = -\sqrt{5}$$
$$x = 2 + \sqrt{5} \qquad x = 2 - \sqrt{5}$$
The solutions are $2 + \sqrt{5}$ and $2 - \sqrt{5}$.

Applying the Concepts

49. To "complete the square" is to add to a binomial a constant that turns the binomial into a perfect square trinomial.

51. Write the equation so that the quadratic and first-degree terms are on one side and the constant term is on the other side.
Divide each term of the equation by the coefficient of x^2.
Find the constant term to complete the square; it is equal to the square of half the coefficient of x squared.
Complete the square by adding the constant term to both sides of the equation.
Factor the trinomial.
Take the square root of each side of the equation.
Solve for x.

53. $t^2 - 4t = 7$

Complete the square.

$$t^2 - 4t + 4 = 7 + 4$$
$$(t-2)^2 = 11$$
$$\sqrt{(t-2)^2} = \sqrt{11}$$
$$t - 2 = \pm\sqrt{11}$$
$$t - 2 = \sqrt{11} \qquad t - 2 = -\sqrt{11}$$
$$t = \sqrt{11} + 2 \qquad t = -\sqrt{11} + 2$$
$$t = 5.317 \qquad t = -1.317$$

The solutions are 5.317 and −1.317.

55. $x^2 - ax - 2a^2 = 0$

$$x^2 - ax = 2a^2$$

Complete the square.

$$x^2 - ax + \frac{1}{4}a^2 = 2a^2 + \frac{1}{4}a^2$$
$$\left(x - \frac{1}{2}a\right)^2 = \frac{9}{4}a^2$$
$$\sqrt{\left(x - \frac{1}{2}a\right)^2} = \sqrt{\frac{9}{4}a^2}$$
$$x - \frac{1}{2}a = \pm\sqrt{\frac{9}{4}a^2} = \pm\frac{3}{2}a$$
$$x - \frac{1}{2}a = \frac{3}{2}a \qquad x - \frac{1}{2}a = -\frac{3}{2}a$$
$$x = 2a \qquad x = -a$$

The solutions are $2a$ and $-a$.

57. $x^2 + 3ax - 10a^2 = 0$

$$x^2 + 3ax = 10a^2$$

Complete the square.

$$x^2 + 3ax + \frac{9}{4}a^2 = 10a^2 + \frac{9}{4}a^2$$
$$\left(x + \frac{3}{2}a\right)^2 = \frac{49}{4}a^2$$
$$\sqrt{\left(x + \frac{3}{2}a\right)^2} = \sqrt{\frac{49}{4}a^2}$$
$$x + \frac{3}{2}a = \pm\frac{7}{2}a$$
$$x + \frac{3}{2}a = \frac{7}{2}a \qquad x + \frac{3}{2}a = -\frac{7}{2}a$$
$$x = 2a \qquad x = -5a$$

The solutions are $2a$ and $-5a$

59. Strategy First find the time it takes for the ball to hit the ground using $y = -16t^2 + 70t + 4$ (the answer is found in Exercise 58). Use this time to find the horizontal distance the ball travels.

Solution $t = 4.431$ seconds, the length of time the ball is in the air

$$s = 44.5t$$
$$s \approx 44.5(4.431)$$
$$s = 197.2 \text{ feet}$$

The ball will not clear the fence.

SECTION 8.3

Objective A Exercises

1. $x^2 - 3x - 10 = 0$

$a = 1,\ b = -3,\ c = -10$

$$x = \frac{-b \pm \sqrt{b^2 - 4ac}}{2a}$$
$$= \frac{-(-3) \pm \sqrt{(-3)^2 - 4(1)(-10)}}{2(1)}$$
$$= \frac{3 \pm \sqrt{9 + 40}}{2} = \frac{3 \pm \sqrt{49}}{2}$$
$$= \frac{3 \pm 7}{2}$$
$$x = \frac{3+7}{2} \qquad x = \frac{3-7}{2}$$
$$= \frac{10}{2} = 5 \qquad = -\frac{4}{2} = -2$$

The solutions are 5 and −2.

3. $y^2 + 5y - 36 = 0$

$a = 1,\ b = 5,\ c = -36$

$$y = \frac{-b \pm \sqrt{b^2 - 4ac}}{2a}$$
$$= \frac{-5 \pm \sqrt{(5)^2 - 4(1)(-36)}}{2(1)}$$
$$= \frac{-5 \pm \sqrt{25 + 144}}{2} = \frac{-5 \pm \sqrt{169}}{2}$$
$$= \frac{-5 \pm 13}{2}$$
$$y = \frac{-5+13}{2} \qquad y = \frac{-5-13}{2}$$
$$= \frac{8}{2} = 4 \qquad = \frac{-18}{2} = -9$$

The solutions are 4 and −9.

5. $w^2 = 8w + 72$

$w^2 - 8w - 72 = 0$

$a = 1,\ b = -8,\ c = -72$

$$w = \frac{-b \pm \sqrt{b^2 - 4ac}}{2a}$$

$$= \frac{-(-8) \pm \sqrt{(-8)^2 - 4(1)(-72)}}{2(1)}$$

$$= \frac{8 \pm \sqrt{64 + 288}}{2} = \frac{8 \pm \sqrt{352}}{2}$$

$$= \frac{8 \pm 4\sqrt{22}}{2}$$

$$= 4 \pm 2\sqrt{22}$$

The solutions are $4 + 2\sqrt{22}$ and $4 - 2\sqrt{22}$.

7. $v^2 = 24 - 5v$

$v^2 + 5v - 24 = 0$

$a = 1,\ b = 5,\ c = -24$

$$v = \frac{-b \pm \sqrt{b^2 - 4ac}}{2a}$$

$$= \frac{-5 \pm \sqrt{(5)^2 - 4(1)(-24)}}{2(1)}$$

$$= \frac{-5 \pm \sqrt{25 + 96}}{2} = \frac{-5 \pm \sqrt{121}}{2} = \frac{-5 \pm 11}{2}$$

$$v = \frac{-5 + 11}{2} \qquad v = \frac{-5 - 11}{2}$$

$$= \frac{6}{2} = 3 \qquad = \frac{-16}{2} = -8$$

The solutions are 3 and –8.

9. $2y^2 + 5y - 3 = 0$

$a = 2,\ b = 5,\ c = -3$

$$y = \frac{-b \pm \sqrt{b^2 - 4ac}}{2a}$$

$$= \frac{-5 \pm \sqrt{(5)^2 - 4(2)(-3)}}{2(2)}$$

$$= \frac{-5 \pm \sqrt{25 + 24}}{4} = \frac{-5 \pm \sqrt{49}}{4} = \frac{-5 \pm 7}{4}$$

$$y = \frac{-5 + 7}{4} \qquad y = \frac{-5 - 7}{4}$$

$$= \frac{2}{4} = \frac{1}{2} \qquad = \frac{-12}{4} = -3$$

The solutions are $\frac{1}{2}$ and –3.

11. $8s^2 = 10s + 3$

$8s^2 - 10s - 3 = 0$

$a = 8,\ b = -10,\ c = -3$

$$s = \frac{-b \pm \sqrt{b^2 - 4ac}}{2a}$$

$$= \frac{-(-10) \pm \sqrt{(-10)^2 - 4(8)(-3)}}{2(8)}$$

$$= \frac{10 \pm \sqrt{100 + 96}}{16} = \frac{10 \pm \sqrt{196}}{16}$$

$$= \frac{10 \pm 14}{16}$$

$$s = \frac{10 + 14}{16} \qquad s = \frac{10 - 14}{16}$$

$$= \frac{24}{16} = \frac{3}{2} \qquad = \frac{-4}{16} = -\frac{1}{4}$$

The solutions are $\frac{3}{2}$ and $-\frac{1}{4}$.

13. $x^2 = 14x - 24$

$x^2 - 14x + 24 = 0$

$a = 1,\ b = -14,\ c = 24$

$$x = \frac{-b \pm \sqrt{b^2 - 4ac}}{2a}$$

$$= \frac{-(-14) \pm \sqrt{(-14)^2 - 4(1)(24)}}{2(1)}$$

$$= \frac{14 \pm \sqrt{196 - 96}}{2} = \frac{14 \pm \sqrt{100}}{2}$$

$$= \frac{14 \pm 10}{2}$$

$$x = \frac{14 + 10}{2} \qquad x = \frac{14 - 10}{2}$$

$$= \frac{24}{2} = 12 \qquad = \frac{4}{2} = 2$$

The solutions are 12 and 2.

15. $2z^2 - 2z - 1 = 0$

$a = 2,\ b = -2,\ c = -1$

$$z = \frac{-b \pm \sqrt{b^2 - 4ac}}{2a}$$

$$= \frac{-(-2) \pm \sqrt{(-2)^2 - 4(2)(-1)}}{2(2)}$$

$$= \frac{2 \pm \sqrt{4 + 8}}{4} = \frac{2 \pm \sqrt{12}}{4}$$

$$= \frac{2 \pm 2\sqrt{3}}{4} = \frac{1 \pm \sqrt{3}}{2}$$

The solutions are $\frac{1 + \sqrt{3}}{2}$ and $\frac{1 - \sqrt{3}}{2}$.

17. $z^2+2z+2=0$

$a=1,\ b=2,\ c=2$

$$z=\frac{-b\pm\sqrt{b^2-4ac}}{2a}$$
$$=\frac{-2\pm\sqrt{(2)^2-4(1)(2)}}{2(1)}$$
$$=\frac{-2\pm\sqrt{4-8}}{2}=\frac{-2\pm\sqrt{-4}}{2}$$
$$=\frac{-2\pm 2i}{2}=-1\pm i$$

The solutions are $-1+i$ and $-1-i$.

19. $y^2-2y+5=0$

$a=1,\ b=-2,\ c=5$

$$y=\frac{-b\pm\sqrt{b^2-4ac}}{2a}$$
$$=\frac{-(-2)\pm\sqrt{(-2)^2-4(1)(5)}}{2(1)}$$
$$=\frac{2\pm\sqrt{4-20}}{2}=\frac{2\pm\sqrt{-16}}{2}$$
$$=\frac{2\pm 4i}{2}=1\pm 2i$$

The solutions are $1+2i$ and $1-2i$.

21. $s^2-4s+13=0$

$a=1,\ b=-4,\ c=13$

$$s=\frac{-b\pm\sqrt{b^2-4ac}}{2a}$$
$$=\frac{-(-4)\pm\sqrt{(-4)^2-4(1)(13)}}{2(1)}$$
$$=\frac{4\pm\sqrt{16-52}}{2}=\frac{4\pm\sqrt{-36}}{2}$$
$$=\frac{4\pm 6i}{2}=2\pm 3i$$

The solutions are $2+3i$ and $2-3i$.

23. $2w^2-2w+5=0$

$a=2,\ b=-2,\ c=5$

$$w=\frac{-b\pm\sqrt{b^2-4ac}}{2a}$$
$$=\frac{-(-2)\pm\sqrt{(-2)^2-4(2)(5)}}{2(2)}$$
$$=\frac{2\pm\sqrt{4-40}}{4}=\frac{2\pm\sqrt{-36}}{4}$$
$$=\frac{2\pm 6i}{4}=\frac{1\pm 3i}{2}$$

The solutions are $\frac{1}{2}+\frac{3}{2}i$ and $\frac{1}{2}-\frac{3}{2}i$.

25. $2x^2+6x+5=0$

$a=2,\ b=6,\ c=5$

$$x=\frac{-b\pm\sqrt{b^2-4ac}}{2a}$$
$$=\frac{-6\pm\sqrt{(6)^2-4(2)(5)}}{2(2)}$$
$$=\frac{-6\pm\sqrt{36-40}}{4}=\frac{-6\pm\sqrt{-4}}{4}$$
$$=\frac{-6\pm 2i}{4}=\frac{-3\pm i}{2}$$

The solutions are $-\frac{3}{2}+\frac{1}{2}i$ and $-\frac{3}{2}-\frac{1}{2}i$.

27. $4t^2-6t+9=0$

$a=4,\ b=-6,\ c=9$

$$t=\frac{-b\pm\sqrt{b^2-4ac}}{2a}$$
$$=\frac{-(-6)\pm\sqrt{(-6)^2-4(4)(9)}}{2(4)}$$
$$=\frac{6\pm\sqrt{36-144}}{8}=\frac{6\pm\sqrt{-108}}{8}$$
$$=\frac{6\pm 6i\sqrt{3}}{8}=\frac{3\pm 3i\sqrt{3}}{4}$$

The solutions are $\frac{3}{4}+\frac{3\sqrt{3}}{4}i$ and $\frac{3}{4}-\frac{3\sqrt{3}}{4}i$.

29. $3y^2+y+1=0$

$a=3,\ b=1,\ c=1$

$$b^2-4ac=1^2-4(3)(1)$$
$$=1-12=-11$$

$-11<0$

Since the discriminant is less than zero, the equation has two complex number solutions.

31. $4x^2+20x+25=0$

$a=4,\ b=20,\ c=25$

$$b^2-4ac=20^2-4(4)(25)$$
$$=400-400=0$$

Since the discriminant is equal to zero, the equation has one real number solution, a double root.

33. $3w^2+3w-2=0$

$a=3,\ b=3,\ c=-2$

$$b^2-4ac=3^2-4(3)(-2)$$
$$=9+24=33$$

$33>0$

Since the discriminant is greater than zero, the equation has two real number solutions that are not equal.

Applying the Concepts

35. $x^2 - 6x + p = 0$

$x^2 - 6x = -p$

Complete the square.

$x^2 - 6x + 9 = -p + 9$

$(x-3)^2 = -p + 9$

$\sqrt{(x-3)^2} = \sqrt{9-p}$

$x - 3 = \pm\sqrt{9-p}$

$x = 3 \pm \sqrt{9-p}$

x will be real, and there will be two nonequal solutions if $9 - p > 0$.

Solving the inequality gives $p < 9$.

The values of p are $\{p|p<9\}$.

37. $x^2 - 2x + p = 0$

$a = 1,\ b = -2,\ c = p$

$$x = \frac{-b \pm \sqrt{b^2 - 4ac}}{2a}$$

$$x = \frac{-(-2) \pm \sqrt{(-2)^2 - 4(p)(1)}}{2(1)} = \frac{2 \pm \sqrt{4-4p}}{2}$$

$x = 1 \pm \sqrt{1-p}$

x will be complex, and there will be two solutions if $1 - p < 0$.

Solving the inequality gives $p > 1$. The value of p are $\{p|p>1\}$.

39. $x^2 + bx - 1 = 0$

$a = 1,\ b = b, c = -1$

$$x = \frac{-b \pm \sqrt{b^2 - 4ac}}{2a}$$

$$= \frac{-b \pm \sqrt{b^2 - 4(1)(-1)}}{2(1)}$$

$$= \frac{-b \pm \sqrt{b^2 + 4}}{2}$$

$$x = -\frac{b}{2} \pm \frac{1}{2}\sqrt{b^2 + 4}$$

If b is real, the quantity $\sqrt{b^2 + 4}$ can never be less than zero and the quadratic will always have real number solutions.

41. Yes, the quadratic formula can always be used to solve a quadratic equation, because the equation can always be written so that the $a, b,$ and c used in the formula are available.

43a. Strategy Plug the values given for the U.S. Forest Service into the quadratic equation, and find the larger root of the solution for x.

Solution

$x^2 - s_a x - s_j s_s f = 0$

$x^2 - 0.97x - (0.34)(0.97)(0.24) = 0$

$x^2 - 0.97x - 0.079 = 0$

$a = 1,\ b = -0.97, c = -0.079$

$$x = \frac{-b \pm \sqrt{b^2 - 4ac}}{2a}$$

$$= \frac{-(-0.97) \pm \sqrt{(-0.97)^2 - 4(1)(-0.079)}}{2(1)}$$

$$\approx 0.485 \pm \frac{1}{2}\sqrt{1.26}$$

$x \approx 1.05, -0.08$

The larger root is 1.05; it predicts that the population will increase.

43b. Strategy Plug the values given by Lande into the quadratic equation, and find the larger root of the solution for x.

Solution

$x^2 - s_a x - s_j s_s f = 0$

$x^2 - 0.94x - (0.11)(0.71)(0.24) = 0$

$x^2 - 0.94x - 0.019 = 0$

$a = 1,\ b = -0.94, c = -0.019$

$$x = \frac{-b \pm \sqrt{b^2 - 4ac}}{2a}$$

$$= \frac{(-0.94) \pm \sqrt{(-0.94)^2 - 4(1)(-0.019)}}{2(1)}$$

$x \approx 0.47 \pm \frac{1}{2}\sqrt{0.96}$

$x \approx 0.96,\ -0.02$

The larger root is 0.96; it predicts that the population will decrease.

SECTION 8.4

Objective A Exercises

1.
$$x^4 - 13x^2 + 36 = 0$$
$$(x^2)^2 - 13(x^2) + 36 = 0$$
$$u^2 - 13u + 36 = 0$$
$$(u-4)(u-9) = 0$$
$$u-4=0 \quad u-9=0$$
$$u=4 \quad u=9$$
Replace u by x^2.
$$x^2 = 4 \quad x^2 = 9$$
$$\sqrt{x^2} = \sqrt{4} \quad \sqrt{x^2} = \sqrt{9}$$
$$x = \pm 2 \quad x = \pm 3$$
The solutions are 2, –2, 3, and –3.

3.
$$z^4 - 6z^2 + 8 = 0$$
$$(z^2)^2 - 6(z^2) + 8 = 0$$
$$u^2 - 6u + 8 = 0$$
$$(u-4)(u-2) = 0$$
$$u-4=0 \quad u-2=0$$
$$u=4 \quad u=2$$
Replace u by z^2.
$$z^2 = 4 \quad z^2 = 2$$
$$\sqrt{z^2} = \sqrt{4} \quad \sqrt{z^2} = \sqrt{2}$$
$$z = \pm 2 \quad z = \pm\sqrt{2}$$
The solutions are 2, –2, $\sqrt{2}$, and $-\sqrt{2}$.

5.
$$p - 3p^{1/2} + 2 = 0$$
$$(p^{1/2})^2 - 3(p^{1/2}) + 2 = 0$$
$$u^2 - 3u + 2 = 0$$
$$(u-1)(u-2) = 0$$
$$u-1=0 \quad u-2=0$$
$$u=1 \quad u=2$$
Replace u by $p^{1/2}$.
$$p^{1/2} = 1 \quad p^{1/2} = 2$$
$$(p^{1/2})^2 = 1^2 \quad (p^{1/2})^2 = 2^2$$
$$p = 1 \quad p = 4$$
The solutions are 1 and 4.

7.
$$x - x^{1/2} - 12 = 0$$
$$(x^{1/2})^2 - (x^{1/2}) - 12 = 0$$
$$u^2 - u - 12 = 0$$
$$(u+3)(u-4) = 0$$
$$u+3=0 \quad u-4=0$$
$$u=-3 \quad u=4$$
Replace u by $x^{1/2}$.
$$x^{1/2} = -3 \quad x^{1/2} = 4$$
$$(x^{1/2})^2 = (-3)^2 \quad (x^{1/2})^2 = 4^2$$
$$x = 9 \quad x = 16$$
16 checks as a solution.
9 does not check as a solution.
The solution is 16.

9.
$$z^4 + 3z^2 - 4 = 0$$
$$(z^2)^2 + 3(z^2) - 4 = 0$$
$$u^2 + 3u - 4 = 0$$
$$(u+4)(u-1) = 0$$
$$u+4=0 \quad u-1=0$$
$$u=-4 \quad u=1$$
Replace u by z^2.
$$z^2 = -4 \quad z^2 = 1$$
$$\sqrt{z^2} = \sqrt{-4} \quad \sqrt{z^2} = \sqrt{1}$$
$$z = \pm 2i \quad z = \pm 1$$
The solutions are $2i$, $-2i$, 1, and –1.

11.
$$x^4 + 12x^2 - 64 = 0$$
$$(x^2)^2 + 12(x^2) - 64 = 0$$
$$u^2 + 12u - 64 = 0$$
$$(u+16)(u-4) = 0$$
$$u+16=0 \quad u-4=0$$
$$u=-16 \quad u=4$$
Replace u by x^2.
$$x^2 = -16 \quad x^2 = 4$$
$$\sqrt{x^2} = \sqrt{-16} \quad \sqrt{x^2} = \sqrt{4}$$
$$x = \pm 4i \quad x = \pm 2$$
The solutions are $4i$, $-4i$, 2, and –2.

13.
$$p+2p^{1/2}-24=0$$
$$(p^{1/2})^2+2(p^{1/2})-24=0$$
$$u^2+2u-24=0$$
$$(u+6)(u-4)=0$$
$$u+6=0 \quad u-4=0$$
$$u=-6 \quad u=4$$
Replace u by $p^{1/2}$.
$$p^{1/2}=-6 \quad p^{1/2}=4$$
$$(p^{1/2})^2=(-6)^2 \quad (p^{1/2})^2=4^2$$
$$p=36 \quad p=16$$
16 checks as a solution.
36 does not check as a solution.
The solution is 16.

15.
$$y^{2/3}-9y^{1/3}+8=0$$
$$(y^{1/3})^2-9(y^{1/3})+8=0$$
$$u^2-9u+8=0$$
$$(u-1)(u-8)=0$$
$$u-1=0 \quad u-8=0$$
$$u=1 \quad u=8$$
Replace u by $y^{1/3}$.
$$y^{1/3}=1 \quad y^{1/3}=8$$
$$(y^{1/3})^3=1^3 \quad (y^{1/3})^3=8^3$$
$$y=1 \quad y=512$$
The solutions are 1 and 512.

17.
$$9w^4-13w^2+4=0$$
$$9(w^2)^2-13(w^2)+4=0$$
$$9u^2-13u+4=0$$
$$(9u-4)(u-1)=0$$
$$9u-4=0 \quad u-1=0$$
$$9u=4 \quad u=1$$
$$u=\frac{4}{9}$$
Replace u by w^2.
$$w^2=\frac{4}{9} \quad w^2=1$$
$$\sqrt{w^2}=\sqrt{\frac{4}{9}} \quad \sqrt{w^2}=\sqrt{1}$$
$$w=\pm\frac{2}{3} \quad w=\pm1$$
The solutions are $\frac{2}{3}$, $-\frac{2}{3}$, 1, and -1.

Objective B Exercises

19.
$$\sqrt{x+1}+x=5$$
$$\sqrt{x+1}=5-x$$
$$\left(\sqrt{x+1}\right)^2=(5-x)^2$$
$$x+1=25-10x+x^2$$
$$0=24-11x+x^2$$
$$0=(3-x)(8-x)$$
$$3-x=0 \quad 8-x=0$$
$$3=x \quad 8=x$$
3 checks as a solution.
8 does not check as a solution.
The solution is 3.

21.
$$x=\sqrt{x}+6$$
$$x-6=\sqrt{x}$$
$$(x-6)^2=\left(\sqrt{x}\right)^2$$
$$x^2-12x+36=x$$
$$x^2-13x+36=0$$
$$(x-4)(x-9)=0$$
$$x-4=0 \quad x-9=0$$
$$x=4 \quad x=9$$
9 checks as a solution.
4 does not check as a solution.
The solution is 9.

23.
$$\sqrt{3w+3}=w+1$$
$$\left(\sqrt{3w+3}\right)^2=(w+1)^2$$
$$3w+3=w^2+2w+1$$
$$0=w^2-w-2$$
$$0=(w-2)(w+1)$$
$$w-2=0 \quad w+1=0$$
$$w=2 \quad w=-1$$
2 and –1 check as solutions.
The solutions are 2 and –1.

25.
$$\sqrt{4y+1}-y=1$$
$$\sqrt{4y+1}=y+1$$
$$\left(\sqrt{4y+1}\right)^2=(y+1)^2$$
$$4y+1=y^2+2y+1$$
$$0=y^2-2y$$
$$0=y(y-2)$$
$$y=0 \quad y-2=0$$
$$y=2$$
0 and 2 check as solutions.
The solutions are 0 and 2.

27.
$$\sqrt{10x+5}-2x=1$$
$$\sqrt{10x+5}=2x+1$$
$$\left(\sqrt{10x+5}\right)^2=(2x+1)^2$$
$$10x+5=4x^2+4x+1$$
$$0=4x^2-6x-4$$
$$0=2(2x^2-3x-2)$$
$$0=2(2x+1)(x-2)$$

$2x+1=0 \quad x-2=0$

$2x=-1 \quad x=2$

$x=-\frac{1}{2}$

$-\frac{1}{2}$ and 2 check as solutions.

The solutions are $-\frac{1}{2}$ and 2.

29.
$$\sqrt{p+11}=1-p$$
$$\left(\sqrt{p+11}\right)^2=(1-p)^2$$
$$p+11=1-2p+p^2$$
$$0=-10-3p+p^2$$
$$0=p^2-3p-10$$
$$0=(p-5)(p+2)$$

$p-5=0 \quad p+2=0$

$p=5 \quad p=-2$

–2 checks as a solution.

5 does not check as a solution.

The solution is –2.

31.
$$\sqrt{x-1}-\sqrt{x}=-1$$
$$\sqrt{x-1}=\sqrt{x}-1$$
$$\left(\sqrt{x-1}\right)^2=\left(\sqrt{x}-1\right)^2$$
$$x-1=x-2\sqrt{x}+1$$
$$2\sqrt{x}=2$$
$$\sqrt{x}=1$$
$$\left(\sqrt{x}\right)^2=1^2$$
$$x=1$$

1 checks as a solution.

The solution is 1.

33.
$$\sqrt{2x-1}=1-\sqrt{x-1}$$
$$\left(\sqrt{2x-1}\right)^2=\left(1-\sqrt{x-1}\right)^2$$
$$2x-1=1-2\sqrt{x-1}+x-1$$
$$2\sqrt{x-1}=-x+1$$
$$\left(2\sqrt{x-1}\right)^2=(-x+1)^2$$
$$4(x-1)=x^2-2x+1$$
$$4x-4=x^2-2x+1$$
$$0=x^2-6x+5$$
$$0=(x-5)(x-1)$$

$x-5=0 \quad x-1=0$

$x=5 \quad x=1$

1 checks as a solution.

5 does not check as a solution.

The solution is 1.

35.
$$\sqrt{t+3}+\sqrt{2t+7}=1$$
$$\sqrt{2t+7}=1-\sqrt{t+3}$$
$$\left(\sqrt{2t+7}\right)^2=\left(1-\sqrt{t+3}\right)^2$$
$$2t+7=1-2\sqrt{t+3}+t+3$$
$$t+3=-2\sqrt{t+3}$$
$$(t+3)^2=\left(-2\sqrt{t+3}\right)^2$$
$$t^2+6t+9=4(t+3)$$
$$t^2+6t+9=4t+12$$
$$t^2+2t-3=0$$
$$(t+3)(t-1)=0$$

$t+3=0 \quad t-1=0$

$t=-3 \quad t=1$

–3 checks as a solution.

1 does not check as a solution.

The solution is –3.

Objective C Exercises

37.
$$x=\frac{10}{x-9}$$
$$(x-9)x=(x-9)\frac{10}{x-9}$$
$$x^2-9x=10$$
$$x^2-9x-10=0$$
$$(x-10)(x+1)=0$$

$x-10=0 \quad x+1=0$

$x=10 \quad x=-1$

The solutions are 10 and –1.

39.

$$\frac{t}{t+1} = \frac{-2}{t-1}$$
$$(t-1)(t+1)\frac{t}{t+1} = (t-1)(t+1)\frac{-2}{t-1}$$
$$(t-1)t = (t+1)(-2)$$
$$t^2 - t = -2t - 2$$
$$t^2 + t + 2 = 0$$

$$t = \frac{-b \pm \sqrt{b^2 - 4ac}}{2a}$$
$$= \frac{-1 \pm \sqrt{1^2 - 4(1)(2)}}{2(1)}$$
$$= \frac{-1 \pm \sqrt{1-8}}{2} = \frac{-1 \pm \sqrt{-7}}{2} = \frac{-1 \pm i\sqrt{7}}{2}$$

The solutions are $-\frac{1}{2} + \frac{\sqrt{7}}{2}i$ and $-\frac{1}{2} - \frac{\sqrt{7}}{2}i$.

41.

$$\frac{y-1}{y+2} + y = 1$$
$$(y+2)\left(\frac{y-1}{y+2} + y\right) = (y+2)1$$
$$(y+2)\left(\frac{y-1}{y+2}\right) + (y+2)y = y+2$$
$$y - 1 + y^2 + 2y = y + 2$$
$$y^2 + 3y - 1 = y + 2$$
$$y^2 + 2y - 3 = 0$$
$$(y+3)(y-1) = 0$$

$y + 3 = 0 \quad y - 1 = 0$

$y = -3 \quad y = 1$

The solutions are –3 and 1.

43.

$$\frac{3r+2}{r+2} - 2r = 1$$
$$(r+2)\left(\frac{3r+2}{r+2} - 2r\right) = (r+2)1$$
$$(r+2)\frac{3r+2}{r+2} - (r+2)2r = r+2$$
$$3r + 2 - 2r^2 - 4r = r + 2$$
$$-2r^2 - r + 2 = r + 2$$
$$-2r^2 - 2r = 0$$
$$-2r(r+1) = 0$$

$-2r = 0 \quad r + 1 = 0$

$r = 0 \quad r = -1$

The solutions are 0 and –1.

45.

$$\frac{2}{2x+1} + \frac{1}{x} = 3$$
$$x(2x+1)\left(\frac{2}{2x+1} + \frac{1}{x}\right) = x(2x+1)3$$
$$x(2x+1)\frac{2}{2x+1} + x(2x+1)\frac{1}{x} = 3x(2x+1)$$
$$2x + 2x + 1 = 6x^2 + 3x$$
$$4x + 1 = 6x^2 + 3x$$
$$0 = 6x^2 - x - 1$$
$$0 = (2x-1)(3x+1)$$

$2x - 1 = 0 \quad 3x + 1 = 0$

$2x = 1 \quad 3x = -1$

$x = \frac{1}{2} \quad x = -\frac{1}{3}$

The solutions are $\frac{1}{2}$ and $-\frac{1}{3}$.

47.

$$\frac{16}{z-2} + \frac{16}{z+2} = 6$$
$$(z-2)(z+2)\left(\frac{16}{z-2} + \frac{16}{z+2}\right) = (z-2)(z+2)6$$
$$(z-2)(z+2)\frac{16}{z-2} + (z-2)(z+2)\frac{16}{z+2} = (z^2 - 4)6$$
$$(z+2)16 + (z-2)16 = 6z^2 - 24$$
$$16z + 32 + 16z - 32 = 6z^2 - 24$$
$$32z = 6z^2 - 24$$
$$0 = 6z^2 - 32z - 24$$
$$0 = 2(3z^2 - 16z - 12)$$
$$0 = 2(3z+2)(z-6)$$

$3z + 2 = 0 \quad z - 6 = 0$

$3z = -2 \quad z = 6$

$z = -\frac{2}{3}$

The solutions are $-\frac{2}{3}$ and 6.

49.
$$\frac{t}{t-2}+\frac{2}{t-1}=4$$
$$(t-2)(t-1)\left(\frac{t}{t-2}+\frac{2}{t-1}\right)=(t-2)(t-1)4$$
$$(t-2)(t-1)\frac{t}{t-2}+(t-2)(t-1)\frac{2}{t-1}=(t^2-3t+2)4$$
$$(t-1)t+(t-2)2=4t^2-12t+8$$
$$t^2-t+2t-4=4t^2-12t+8$$
$$t^2+t-4=4t^2-12t+8$$
$$0=3t^2-13t+12$$
$$0=(3t-4)(t-3)$$

$3t-4=0 \quad t-3=0$

$3t=4 \quad t=3$

$t=\frac{4}{3}$

The solutions are $\frac{4}{3}$ and 3.

51.
$$\frac{5}{2p-1}+\frac{4}{p+1}=2$$
$$(2p-1)(p+1)\left(\frac{5}{2p-1}+\frac{4}{p+1}\right)=(2p-1)(p+1)2$$
$$(2p-1)(p+1)\frac{5}{2p-1}+(2p-1)(p+1)\frac{4}{p+1}=(2p^2+p-1)2$$
$$(p+1)5+(2p-1)4=4p^2+2p-2$$
$$5p+5+8p-4=4p^2+2p-2$$
$$13p+1=4p^2+2p-2$$
$$0=4p^2-11p-3$$
$$0=(4p+1)(p-3)$$

$4p+1=0 \quad p-3=0$

$4p=-1 \quad p=3$

$p=-\frac{1}{4}$

The solutions are $-\frac{1}{4}$ and 3.

Applying the Concepts

53. $\left(\sqrt{x}-1\right)^2-4\sqrt{x}-1=0$

Let $u=\sqrt{x}-1$.

$u^2-4(u+1)-1=0$

$u^2-4u-4-1=0$

$u^2-4u-5=0$

$(u-5)(u+1)=0$

$u-5=0 \quad u+1=0$

$u=5 \quad u=-1$

Replace u by $\sqrt{x}-1$.

$\sqrt{x}-1=5 \quad \sqrt{x}-1=-1$

$\sqrt{x}=6 \quad \sqrt{x}=0$

$\left(\sqrt{x}\right)^2=(6)^2 \quad \left(\sqrt{x}\right)^2=(0)^2$

$x=36 \quad x=0$

The solutions are 36 and 0.

SECTION 8.5

Objective A Exercises

1. $(x-4)(x+2)>0$

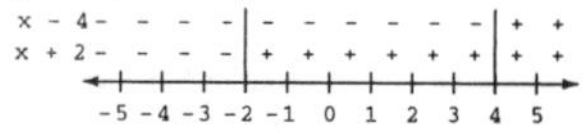

$\{x|x<-2 \text{ or } x>4\}$

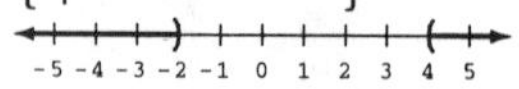

3. $x^2-3x+2\ge 0$
$(x-1)(x-2)\ge 0$

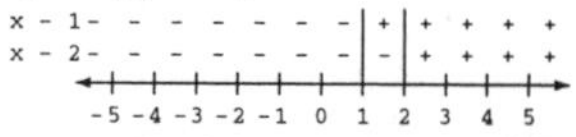

$\{x|x\le 1 \text{ or } x\ge 2\}$

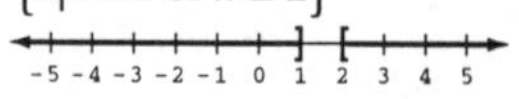

5. $x^2-x-12<0$
$(x+3)(x-4)<0$

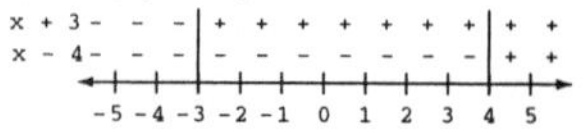

$\{x|-3<x<4\}$

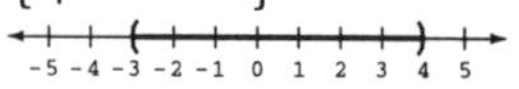

7. $(x-1)(x+2)(x-3)<0$

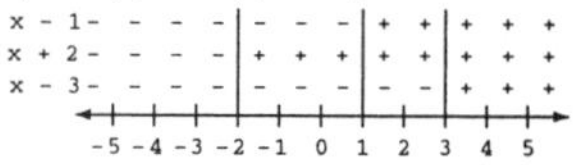

$\{x|x<-2 \text{ or } 1<x<3\}$

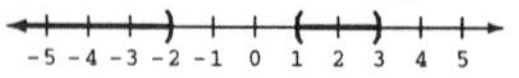

9. $(x+4)(x-2)(x-1)\ge 0$

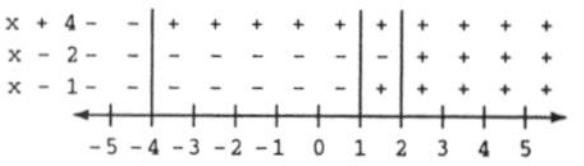

$\{x|-4\le x\le 1 \text{ or } x\ge 2\}$

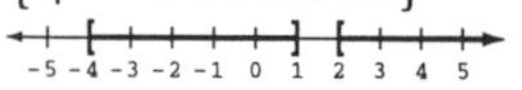

11. $\dfrac{x-4}{x+2}>0$

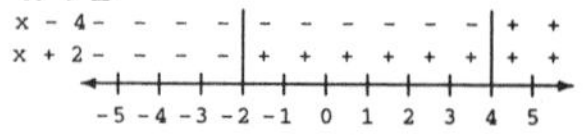

$\{x|x<-2 \text{ or } x>4\}$

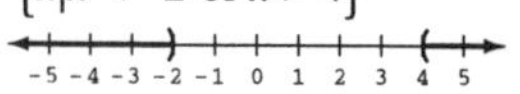

13. $\dfrac{x-3}{x+1}\le 0$

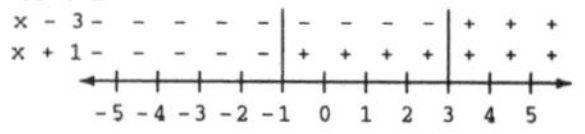

$\{x|-1<x\le 3\}$

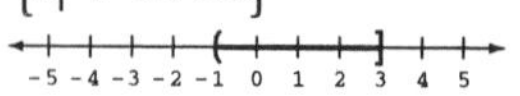

15. $\dfrac{(x-1)(x+2)}{x-3}\le 0$

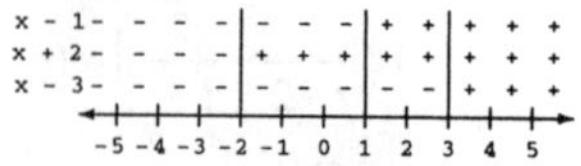

$\{x|x\le -2 \text{ or } 1\le x<3\}$

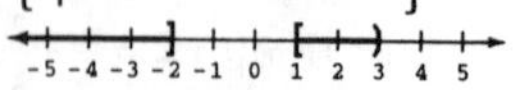

17. $x^2-16>0$
$(x-4)(x+4)>0$

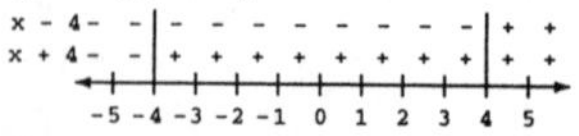

$\{x|x>4 \text{ or } x<-4\}$

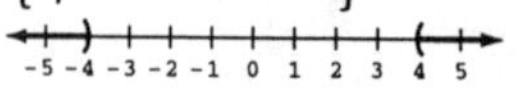

19. $x^2-9x\le 36$
$x^2-9x-36\le 0$
$(x+3)(x-12)\le 0$

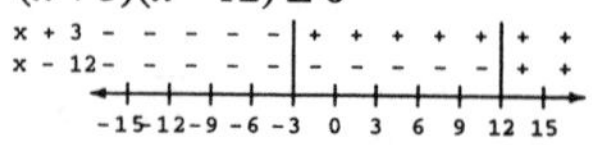

$\{x|-3\le x\le 12\}$

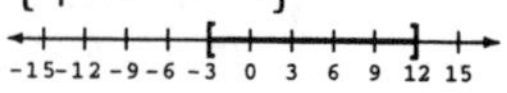

21. $4x^2-8x+3<0$
$(2x-1)(2x-3)<0$

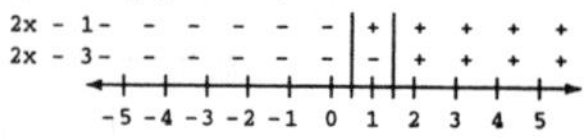

$\left\{x\left|\dfrac{1}{2}<x<\dfrac{3}{2}\right.\right\}$

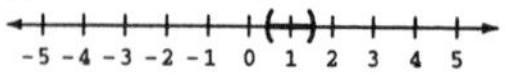

23. $\dfrac{3}{x-1}<2$

$\dfrac{3}{x-1}-2<0$

$\dfrac{3}{x-1}-\dfrac{2x-2}{x-1}<0$

$\dfrac{-2x+5}{x-1}<0$

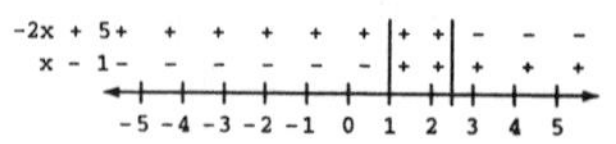

$\left\{x\left|x<1 \text{ or } x>\dfrac{5}{2}\right.\right\}$

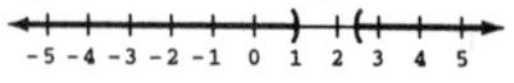

25. $\dfrac{x-2}{(x+1)(x-1)}\le 0$

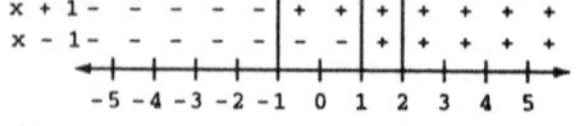

$\{x|x<-1 \text{ or } 1<x\le 2\}$

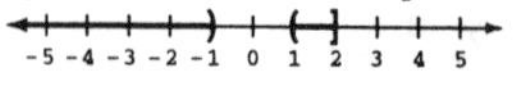

27. $$\frac{x}{2x-1} \ge 1$$
$$\frac{x}{2x-1} - 1 \ge 0$$
$$\frac{x}{2x-1} - \frac{2x-1}{2x-1} \ge 0$$
$$\frac{-x+1}{2x-1} \ge 0$$

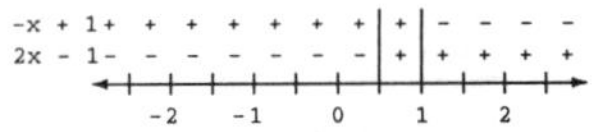

$$\left\{x \middle| \frac{1}{2} < x \le 1\right\}$$

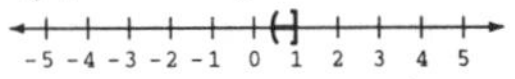

29. $$\frac{x}{2-x} \le -3$$
$$\frac{x}{2-x} + 3 \le 0$$
$$\frac{x}{2-x} + \frac{3(2-x)}{2-x} \le 0$$
$$\frac{x+3(2-x)}{2-x} \le 0$$
$$\frac{x+6-3x}{2-x} \le 0$$
$$\frac{6-2x}{2-x} \le 0$$

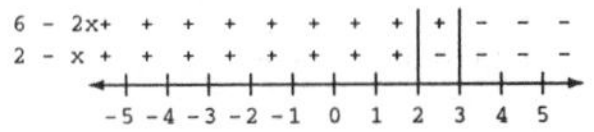

$$\{x | 2 < x \le 3\}$$

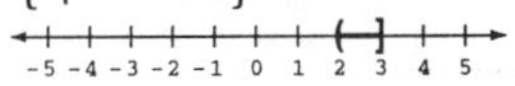

31. $$\frac{3}{x-5} > \frac{1}{x+1}$$
$$\frac{3}{x-5} - \frac{1}{x+1} > 0$$
$$\frac{3(x+1)}{(x-5)(x+1)} - \frac{1(x-5)}{(x-5)(x+1)} > 0$$
$$\frac{3(x+1)-1(x-5)}{(x-5)(x+1)} > 0$$
$$\frac{3x+3-x+5}{(x-5)(x+1)} > 0$$
$$\frac{2x+8}{(x-5)(x+1)} > 0$$
$$\frac{2(x+4)}{(x-5)(x+1)} > 0$$

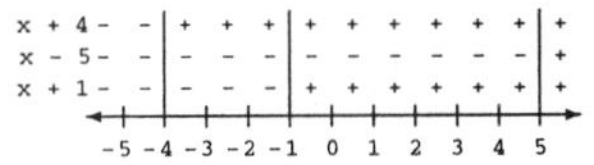

$$\{x | x > 5 \text{ or } -4 < x < -1\}$$

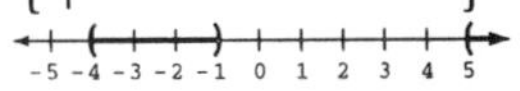

Applying the Concepts

33. $(x-1)(x+3)(x-2)(x-4) \ge 0$

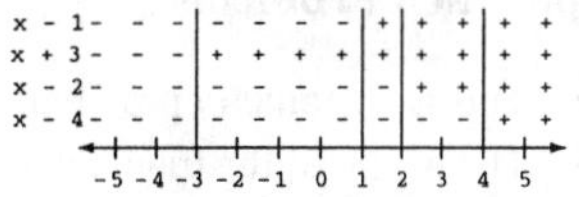

$$\{x | x \le -3 \text{ or } 1 \le x \le 2 \text{ or } x \ge 4\}$$

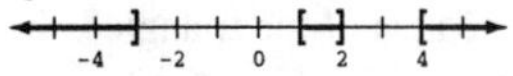

35. $(x^2+2x-3)(x^2+3x+2) \ge 0$
$(x+3)(x-1)(x+2)(x+1) \ge 0$

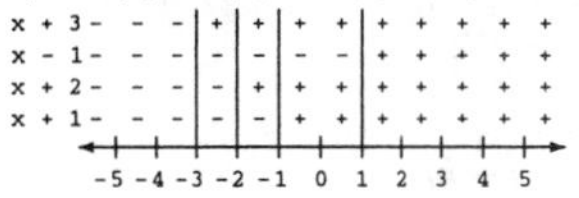

$$\{x | x \le -3 \text{ or } -2 \le x \le -1 \text{ or } x \ge 1\}$$

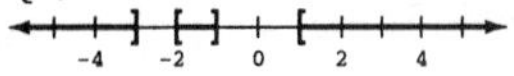

37. $$\frac{x^2(3-x)(2x+1)}{(x+4)(x+2)} \ge 0$$

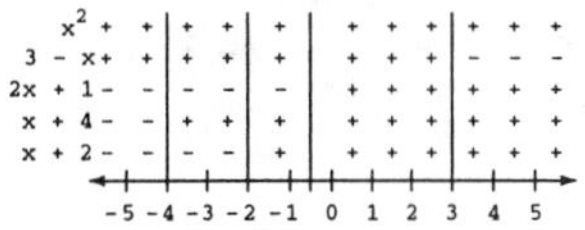

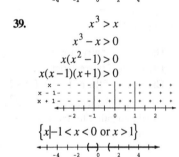

$$\left\{x \middle| -4 < x < -2 \text{ or } -\frac{1}{2} \le x \le 3\right\}$$

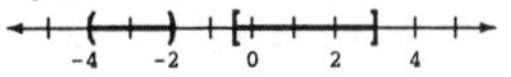

39. $$x^3 > x$$
$$x^3 - x > 0$$
$$x(x^2-1) > 0$$
$$x(x-1)(x+1) > 0$$

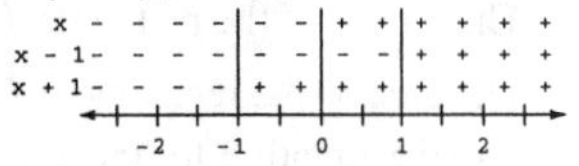

$$\{x | -1 < x < 0 \text{ or } x > 1\}$$

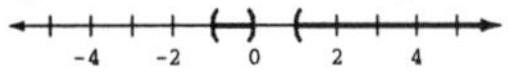

SECTION 8.6

Objective A Application Problems

1. Strategy
   - This is a geometry problem.
   - The height of the triangle: x
     The base of the triangle: $5x - 1$
   - The area of the triangle is 21 cm^2. Use the equation for the area of a triangle. $\left(A = \frac{1}{2}bh\right)$

   Solution
   $$A = \frac{1}{2}bh$$
   $$21 = \frac{1}{2}(5x-1)x$$
   $$42 = 5x^2 - x$$
   $$0 = 5x^2 - x - 42$$
   $$0 = (5x+14)(x-3)$$
   $$5x+14=0 \qquad x-3=0$$
   $$x = -\frac{14}{5} \qquad x=3$$
   Since the height cannot be negative, $-\frac{14}{5}$ cannot be a solution.
   $5x - 1 = 5(3) - 1 = 15 - 1 = 14$
   The height is 3 cm.
   The base is 14 cm.

3. Strategy
   - This is a geometry problem.
   - The width of the rectangle: x
     The length of the rectangle: $3x - 2$
   - The area of the rectangle is 65 ft^2. Use the equation for the area of a rectangle. ($A = L \cdot W$)

   Solution
   $$A = L \cdot W$$
   $$65 = (3x-2)x$$
   $$65 = 3x^2 - 2x$$
   $$0 = 3x^2 - 2x - 65$$
   $$0 = (3x+13)(x-5)$$
   $$3x+13=0 \qquad x-5=0$$
   $$x = -\frac{13}{3} \qquad x=5$$
   Since the width cannot be negative, $-\frac{13}{3}$ cannot be a solution.
   $3x - 2 = 3(5) - 2 = 13$
   The length is 13 ft.
   The width is 5 ft.

5. Strategy
   - This is a geometry problem.
   - The width of the rectangle: x
     The length of the rectangle: $x + 111$
   - The area of the rectangle is 104,000 sq. mi. Use the equation for the area of a rectangle. ($A = L \cdot W$)

   Solution $A = L \cdot W$
   $$104{,}000 = (x+111)x$$
   $$104{,}000 = x^2 + 111x$$
   $$0 = x^2 + 111x - 104{,}000$$
   $$x = \frac{-b \pm \sqrt{b^2 - 4ac}}{2a}$$
   $$x = \frac{-111 \pm \sqrt{111^2 - 4(1)(-104{,}000)}}{2(1)}$$
   $$x = \frac{-111 \pm \sqrt{428{,}321}}{2}$$
   $$x \approx 272 \text{ or } -383$$
   Since distance cannot be a negative number, –383 cannot be a solution.
   $x + 111 = 272 + 111 = 383$
   The dimensions of Colorado are 272 mi by 383 mi.

7. Strategy
   - This is a geometry problem.
   - The base of the box is a square with side x.
   - The volume of the box is 49,000 cm^2. Use the equation for a rectangular solid. ($V = LWH$)

   Solution
   $$V = LWH$$
   $$49{,}000 = (x)(x)(10)$$
   $$49{,}000 = 10x^2$$
   $$4900 = x^2$$
   $$70 = x$$
   The side of the original square is 20 cm more than side x.
   $x + 20 = 70 + 20 = 90$
   The dimension of the original square is 90 cm by 90 cm.

9. Strategy To find the time for a projectile to reach a height of 64 ft, substitute for height ($s = 64$) and initial velocity ($v_0 = 128$ ft / s) and solve for t.

Solution

$$s = v_0 t - 16t^2$$
$$64 = 128t - 16t^2$$

$$16t^2 - 128t + 64 = 0$$
$$16(t^2 - 8t + 4) = 0$$
$$t^2 - 8t + 4 = 0$$

$$t = \frac{-b \pm \sqrt{b^2 - 4ac}}{2a}$$
$$= \frac{8 \pm \sqrt{64 - 4(1)(4)}}{2(1)}$$
$$= \frac{8 \pm \sqrt{48}}{2}$$
$$= 7.46 \text{ or } 0.54$$

The projectile reaches the height of 64 ft at 7.46 s after it is fired and 0.54 s after it is fired.

11. Strategy

- This is a work problem.
- Time for the smaller pipe to fill the tank: t.
- Time for the larger pipe to fill the tank: $t - 6$.

	Rate	Time	Part
Smaller Pipe	$\frac{1}{t}$	4	$\frac{4}{t}$
Larger pipe	$\frac{1}{t-6}$	4	$\frac{4}{t-6}$

- The sum of the parts of the task completed must equal 1.

$$\frac{4}{t} + \frac{4}{t-6} = 1$$

Solution

$$\frac{4}{t} + \frac{4}{t-6} = 1$$
$$t(t-6)\left(\frac{4}{t} + \frac{4}{t-6}\right) = t(t-6)1$$
$$(t-6)4 + 4t = t^2 - 6t$$
$$4t - 24 + 4t = t^2 - 6t$$
$$8t - 24 = t^2 - 6t$$
$$0 = t^2 - 14t + 24$$
$$0 = (t-12)(t-2)$$

$$t - 12 = 0 \qquad t - 2 = 0$$
$$t = 12 \qquad t = 2$$
$$t - 6 = 12 - 6 = 6$$
$$t - 6 = 2 - 6 = -4$$

The solution –4 is not possible, since time cannot be a negative number. It would take the larger pipe 6 min to fill the tank. It would take the smaller pipe 12 min to fill the tank.

13. Strategy
- This is a uniform motion problem.
- Rate of the wind: w.

	Distance	Rate	Time
With wind	4000	$1320+w$	$\frac{4000}{1320+w}$
Against wind	4000	$1320-w$	$\frac{4000}{1320-w}$

- It took 0.5 h less time to make the return trip.

Solution

$$\frac{4000}{1320-w}-\frac{4000}{1320+w}=0.5$$
$$(1320-w)(1320+w)\left(\frac{4000}{1320-w}-\frac{4000}{1320+w}\right)=(1320-w)(1320+w)0.5$$
$$(1320+w)4000-(1320-w)4000=0.5(1,742,400-w^2)$$
$$5,280,000+4000w-5,280,000+4000w=871,200-0.5w^2$$
$$8000w=871,200-0.5w^2$$
$$0.5w^2+8000w-871,200=0$$

$$w=\frac{-b\pm\sqrt{b^2-4ac}}{2a}$$
$$w=\frac{-8000\pm\sqrt{(8000)^2-4(0.5)(-871,200)}}{2(0.5)}$$
$$w=\frac{-8000\pm\sqrt{65,742,400}}{1}$$
$$w\approx-8000\pm8108$$
$$w=108 \text{ or } -16,108$$

The rate cannot be a negative number.
The rate of the wind is approximately 108 mph.

15. Strategy
- This is a uniform motion problem.
- The rate of the boat in calm water: r.

	Distance	Rate	Time
With current	5	$r+4$	$\frac{5}{r+4}$
Against current	5	$r-4$	$\frac{5}{r-4}$

- The total time for the trip is 3 h.

Solution

$$\frac{5}{r+4}+\frac{5}{r-4}=3$$
$$(r+4)(r-4)\left(\frac{5}{r+4}+\frac{5}{r-4}\right)=(r+4)(r-4)3$$
$$(r-4)5+(r+4)5=(r^2-16)3$$
$$5r-20+5r+20=3r^2-48$$
$$10r=3r^2-48$$
$$0=3r^2-10r-48$$
$$0=(3r+8)(r-6)$$

$$3r+8=0 \qquad r-6=0$$
$$r=-\frac{8}{3} \qquad r=6$$

The rate cannot be a negative number.
The rowing rate of the guide is 6 mph.

17. Strategy Substitute \$200 billion for $R(t)$ in the given equation and solve for t.

Solution
$$R(t) = 15.8t^2 - 17.2t + 10.2$$
$$200 = 15.8t^2 - 17.2t + 10.2$$
$$0 = 15.8t^2 - 17.2t - 189.8$$
$$t = \frac{-b \pm \sqrt{b^2 - 4ac}}{2a}$$
$$t = \frac{-(-17.2) \pm \sqrt{17.2^2 - 4(15.8)(-189.8)}}{2(15.8)}$$
$$t = \frac{17.2 \pm \sqrt{12{,}291.2}}{31.6}$$
$$t = 4 \text{ or } -3$$

The positive t corresponds to 4 years beyond 1997, which is 2001.
The negative t corresponds to a year before 1997, which is not between 1997 and 2002.

CHAPTER REVIEW

1.
$$2x^2 - 3x = 0$$
$$x(2x - 3) = 0$$
$$x = 0 \quad 2x - 3 = 0$$
$$2x = 3$$
$$x = \frac{3}{2}$$

The solutions are 0 and $\frac{3}{2}$.

2.
$$6x^2 + 9cx = 6c^2$$
$$6x^2 + 9cx - 6c^2 = 0$$
$$3(2x^2 + 3cx - 2c^2) = 0$$
$$3(2x - c)(x + 2c) = 0$$
$$2x - c = 0 \quad x + 2c = 0$$
$$2x = c \quad x = -2c$$
$$x = \frac{c}{2}$$

The solutions are $\frac{c}{2}$ and $-2c$.

3.
$$x^2 = 48$$
$$\sqrt{x^2} = \sqrt{48}$$
$$x = \pm\sqrt{48} = \pm 4\sqrt{3}$$

The solutions are $4\sqrt{3}$ and $-4\sqrt{3}$.

4.
$$\left(x + \frac{1}{2}\right)^2 + 4 = 0$$
$$\left(x + \frac{1}{2}\right)^2 = -4$$
$$\sqrt{\left(x + \frac{1}{2}\right)^2} = \sqrt{-4}$$
$$x + \frac{1}{2} = \pm\sqrt{-4} = \pm 2i$$

$$x + \frac{1}{2} = 2i \qquad x + \frac{1}{2} = -2i$$
$$x = -\frac{1}{2} + 2i \qquad x = -\frac{1}{2} - 2i$$

The solutions are $-\frac{1}{2} + 2i$ and $-\frac{1}{2} - 2i$.

5.
$$x^2 + 4x + 3 = 0$$
$$x^2 + 4x = -3$$

Complete the square.
$$x^2 + 4x + 4 = -3 + 4$$
$$(x + 2)^2 = 1$$
$$\sqrt{(x + 2)^2} = \sqrt{1}$$
$$x + 2 = \pm\sqrt{1} = \pm 1$$
$$x + 2 = 1 \quad x + 2 = -1$$
$$x = -1 \quad x = -3$$

The solutions are -1 and -3.

6. $7x^2 - 14x + 3 = 0$

$$7x^2 - 14x = -3$$
$$\frac{1}{7}(7x^2 - 14x) = \frac{1}{7}(-3)$$
$$x^2 - 2x = -\frac{3}{7}$$

Complete the square.

$$x^2 - 2x + 1 = -\frac{3}{7} + 1$$
$$(x-1)^2 = \frac{4}{7}$$
$$\sqrt{(x-1)^2} = \sqrt{\frac{4}{7}}$$
$$x - 1 = \pm\sqrt{\frac{4}{7}} = \pm\frac{2\sqrt{7}}{7}$$

$$x - 1 = \frac{2\sqrt{7}}{7} \qquad x - 1 = -\frac{2\sqrt{7}}{7}$$
$$x = 1 + \frac{2\sqrt{7}}{7} \qquad x = 1 - \frac{2\sqrt{7}}{7}$$
$$= \frac{7 + 2\sqrt{7}}{7} \qquad = \frac{7 - 2\sqrt{7}}{7}$$

The solutions are $\frac{7+2\sqrt{7}}{7}$ and $\frac{7-2\sqrt{7}}{7}$.

7. $12x^2 - 25x + 12 = 0$

$a = 12,\ b = -25,\ c = 12$

$$x = \frac{-b \pm \sqrt{b^2 - 4ac}}{2a}$$
$$= \frac{-(-25) \pm \sqrt{(-25)^2 - 4(12)(12)}}{2(12)}$$
$$= \frac{25 \pm \sqrt{625 - 576}}{24}$$
$$= \frac{25 \pm \sqrt{49}}{24} = \frac{25 \pm 7}{24}$$
$$x = \frac{25+7}{24} \qquad x = \frac{25-7}{24}$$
$$= \frac{32}{24} \qquad = \frac{18}{24}$$
$$= \frac{4}{3} \qquad = \frac{3}{4}$$

The solutions are $\frac{4}{3}$ and $\frac{3}{4}$.

8. $x^2 - x + 8 = 0$

$a = 1,\ b = -1,\ c = 8$

$$x = \frac{-b \pm \sqrt{b^2 - 4ac}}{2a}$$
$$= \frac{-(-1) \pm \sqrt{(-1)^2 - 4(1)(8)}}{2(1)}$$
$$= \frac{1 \pm \sqrt{1 - 32}}{2}$$
$$= \frac{1 \pm \sqrt{-31}}{2} = \frac{1 \pm i\sqrt{31}}{2}$$
$$= \frac{1}{2} \pm \frac{\sqrt{31}}{2}i$$

The solutions are $\frac{1}{2} + \frac{\sqrt{31}}{2}i$ and $\frac{1}{2} - \frac{\sqrt{31}}{2}i$.

9. $(x - r_1)(x - r_2) = 0$

$$(x - 0)[x - (-3)] = 0$$
$$x(x + 3) = 0$$
$$x^2 + 3x = 0$$

10. $(x - r_1)(x - r_2) = 0$

$$\left(x - \frac{3}{4}\right)\left[x - \left(-\frac{2}{3}\right)\right] = 0$$
$$\left(x - \frac{3}{4}\right)\left(x + \frac{2}{3}\right) = 0$$
$$x^2 - \frac{1}{12}x - \frac{1}{2} = 0$$
$$12\left(x^2 - \frac{1}{12}x - \frac{1}{2}\right) = 12 \cdot 0$$
$$12x^2 - x - 6 = 0$$

11. $x^2 - 2x + 8 = 0$

$$x^2 - 2x = -8$$

Complete the square.

$$x^2 - 2x + 1 = -8 + 1$$
$$(x-1)^2 = -7$$
$$\sqrt{(x-1)^2} = \sqrt{-7}$$
$$(x - 1) = \pm\sqrt{-7} = \pm i\sqrt{7}$$
$$x - 1 = i\sqrt{7} \qquad x - 1 = -i\sqrt{7}$$
$$x = 1 + i\sqrt{7} \qquad x = 1 - i\sqrt{7}$$

The solutions are $1 + i\sqrt{7}$ and $1 - i\sqrt{7}$.

12. $(x - 2)(x + 3) = x - 10$

$$x^2 + x - 6 = x - 10$$
$$x^2 = -4$$

Complete the square.

$$x^2 + 0 = -4 + 0$$
$$x^2 = -4$$
$$\sqrt{x^2} = \sqrt{-4}$$
$$x = \pm\sqrt{-4}$$
$$x = \pm 2i$$

The solutions are $2i$ and $-2i$.

13.

$$3x(x-3) = 2x-4$$
$$3x^2 - 9x = 2x - 4$$
$$3x^2 - 11x + 4 = 0$$
$$a=3,\ b=-11,\ c=4$$
$$x = \frac{-b \pm \sqrt{b^2-4ac}}{2a}$$
$$= \frac{-(-11) \pm \sqrt{(-11)^2 - 4(3)(4)}}{2(3)}$$
$$= \frac{11 \pm \sqrt{121-48}}{6}$$
$$= \frac{11 \pm \sqrt{73}}{6}$$

The solutions are $\frac{11+\sqrt{73}}{6}$ and $\frac{11-\sqrt{73}}{6}$.

14. $3x^2 - 5x + 1 = 0$

$$a=3,\ b=-5,\ c=1$$
$$b^2 - 4ac = (-5)^2 - 4(3)(1)$$
$$25 - 12 = 13$$
$$13 > 0$$

Since the discriminant is greater than zero, the equation has two real number solutions.

15. $(x+3)(2x-5) < 0$

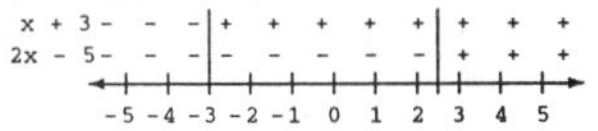

$$\left\{x \mid -3 < x < \frac{5}{2}\right\}$$

16. $(x-2)(x+4)(2x+3) \le 0$

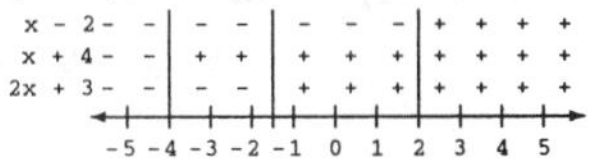

$$\left\{x \mid x \le -4 \text{ or } -\frac{3}{2} \le x \le 2\right\}$$

17.

$$x^{2/3} + x^{1/3} - 12 = 0$$
$$(x^{1/3})^2 + x^{1/3} - 12 = 0$$
$$u^2 + u - 12 = 0$$
$$(u+4)(u-3) = 0$$
$$u+4=0 \quad u-3=0$$
$$u=-4 \quad u=3$$

Replace u by $x^{1/3}$.

$$x^{1/3} = -4 \qquad x^{1/3} = 3$$
$$(x^{1/3})^3 = (-4)^3 \quad (x^{1/3})^3 = 3^3$$
$$x = -64 \qquad x = 27$$

The solutions are –64 and 27.

18.

$$2(x-1) + 3\sqrt{x-1} - 2 = 0$$
$$2\left(\sqrt{x-1}\right)^2 + 3\sqrt{x-1} - 2 = 0$$
$$2u^2 + 3u - 2 = 0$$
$$(2u-1)(u+2) = 0$$
$$2u-1=0 \quad u+2=0$$
$$2u = 1 \qquad u = -2$$
$$u = \frac{1}{2}$$

Replace u by $\sqrt{x-1}$.

$$\sqrt{x-1} = \frac{1}{2} \qquad \sqrt{x-1} = -2$$
$$\left(\sqrt{x-1}\right)^2 = \left(\frac{1}{2}\right)^2 \quad \left(\sqrt{x-1}\right)^2 = (-2)^2$$
$$x-1 = \frac{1}{4} \qquad x-1 = 4$$
$$x = \frac{5}{4} \qquad x = 5$$

5 does not check as a solution.

The solution is $\frac{5}{4}$.

19.

$$3x = \frac{9}{x-2}$$
$$3x(x-2) = \frac{9}{x-2}(x-2)$$
$$3x^2 - 6x = 9$$
$$3x^2 - 6x - 9 = 0$$
$$3(x^2 - 2x - 3) = 0$$
$$3(x-3)(x+1) = 0$$
$$x-3=0 \quad x+1=0$$
$$x=3 \qquad x=-1$$

The solutions are 3 and –1.

20.

$$\frac{3x+7}{x+2} + x = 3$$
$$(x+2)\left(\frac{3x+7}{x+2} + x\right) = 3(x+2)$$
$$3x + 7 + x(x+2) = 3x + 6$$
$$3x + 7 + x^2 + 2x = 3x + 6$$
$$x^2 + 5x + 7 = 3x + 6$$
$$x^2 + 2x + 1 = 0$$
$$(x+1)^2 = 0$$
$$\sqrt{(x+1)^2} = \sqrt{0}$$
$$x+1 = 0$$
$$x = -1$$

The solution is –1.

21. $\dfrac{x-2}{2x-3} \ge 0$

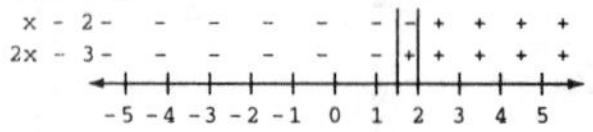

$\left\{x \middle| x < \dfrac{3}{2} \text{ or } x \ge 2\right\}$

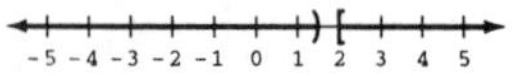

22. $\dfrac{(2x-1)(x+3)}{x-4} \le 0$

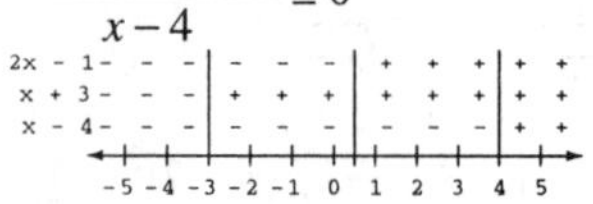

$\left\{x \middle| x \le 3 \text{ or } \dfrac{1}{2} \le x < 4\right\}$

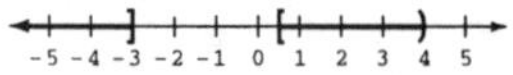

23.

$$x = \sqrt{x} + 2$$
$$x - \sqrt{x} - 2 = 0$$
$$\left(\sqrt{x}\right)^2 - \sqrt{x} - 2 = 0$$
$$u^2 - u - 2 = 0$$
$$(u-2)(u+1) = 0$$
$$u - 2 = 0 \quad u + 1 = 0$$
$$u = 2 \quad u = -1$$

Replace u by $\sqrt{x}$.

$$\sqrt{x} = 2 \quad \sqrt{x} = -1$$
$$\left(\sqrt{x}\right)^2 = 2^2 \quad \left(\sqrt{x}\right)^2 = (-1)^2$$
$$x = 4 \quad x = 1$$

4 checks as a solution.

1 does not check as a solution.

The solution is 4.

24.

$$2x = \sqrt{5x+24} + 3$$
$$2x - 3 = \sqrt{5x+24}$$
$$(2x-3)^2 = \left(\sqrt{5x+24}\right)^2$$
$$4x^2 - 12x + 9 = 5x + 24$$
$$4x^2 - 17x - 15 = 0$$
$$(4x+3)(x-5) = 0$$

$$4x + 3 = 0 \quad x - 5 = 0$$
$$4x = -3 \quad x = 5$$
$$x = -\frac{3}{4}$$

$-\dfrac{3}{4}$ does not check as a solution.

5 checks as a solution.

The solution is 5.

25.

$$\frac{x-2}{2x+3} - \frac{x-4}{x} = 2$$
$$x(2x+3)\left[\frac{x-2}{2x+3} - \frac{x-4}{x}\right] = 2[x(2x+3)]$$
$$x(x-2) - (2x+3)(x-4) = 2x(2x+3)$$
$$x^2 - 2x - (2x^2 - 5x - 12) = 4x^2 + 6x$$
$$x^2 - 2x - 2x^2 + 5x + 12 = 4x^2 + 6x$$
$$-x^2 + 3x + 12 = 4x^2 + 6x$$
$$0 = 5x^2 + 3x - 12$$

$a = 5,\ b = 3,\ c = -12$

$$x = \frac{-b \pm \sqrt{b^2 - 4ac}}{2a}$$
$$= \frac{-3 \pm \sqrt{3^2 - 4(5)(-12)}}{2(5)}$$
$$= \frac{-3 \pm \sqrt{9 + 240}}{10}$$
$$= \frac{-3 \pm \sqrt{249}}{10}$$

The solutions are $\dfrac{-3 + \sqrt{249}}{10}$ and $\dfrac{-3 - \sqrt{249}}{10}$.

26.

$$1 - \frac{x+4}{2-x} = \frac{x-3}{x+2}$$
$$(x+2)(2-x)\left(1 - \frac{x+4}{2-x}\right) = (x+2)(2-x)\frac{x-3}{x+2}$$
$$(x+2)(2-x) - (x+4)(x+2) = (x-3)(2-x)$$
$$4 - x^2 - (x^2 + 6x + 8) = -x^2 + 5x - 6$$
$$4 - x^2 - x^2 - 6x - 8 = -x^2 + 5x - 6$$
$$-2x^2 - 6x - 4 = -x^2 + 5x - 6$$
$$0 = x^2 + 11x - 2$$

$a = 1,\ b = 11,\ c = -2$

$$x = \frac{-b \pm \sqrt{b^2 - 4ac}}{2a}$$
$$= \frac{-11 \pm \sqrt{11^2 - 4(1)(-2)}}{2(1)}$$
$$= \frac{-11 \pm \sqrt{121 + 8}}{2} = \frac{-11 \pm \sqrt{129}}{2}$$

The solutions are $\dfrac{-11 + \sqrt{129}}{2}$ and $\dfrac{-11 - \sqrt{129}}{2}$.

27. Strategy

- This is a geometry problem.
- The width of the rectangle: x.
  The length of the rectangle: $2x + 2$.
- The area of the rectangle is 60 cm^2.
  Use the equation for the area of the rectangle ($A = L \cdot W$).

Solution

$$A = L \cdot W$$
$$60 = x(2x+2)$$
$$60 = 2x^2 + 2x$$
$$0 = 2x^2 + 2x - 60$$
$$0 = 2(x^2 + x - 30)$$
$$0 = 2(x+6)(x-5)$$
$$x+6=0 \qquad x-5=0$$
$$x=-6 \qquad x=5$$

Since the width of the rectangle cannot be negative, –6 cannot be a solution.

$2x + 2 = 2(5) + 2 = 10 + 2 = 12$

The width of the rectangle is 5 cm.
The length of the rectangle is 12 cm.

28. Strategy

- This is an integer problem.
- The first integer: x.
  The second consecutive even integer: $x + 2$.
- The third consecutive even integer: $x + 4$.
- The sum of the squares of the three consecutive even integers is 56.

$$x^2 + (x+2)^2 + (x+4)^2 = 56$$

Solution

$$x^2 + (x+2)^2 + (x+4)^2 = 56$$
$$x^2 + x^2 + 4x + 4 + x^2 + 8x + 16 = 56$$
$$3x^2 + 12x - 36 = 0$$
$$3(x^2 + 4x - 12) = 0$$
$$3(x+6)(x-2) = 0$$
$$x+6=0 \qquad x-2=0$$
$$x=-6 \qquad x=2$$

$x = 2,\ x + 2 = 4,\ x + 4 = 6$

$x = -6,\ x + 2 = -4,\ x + 4 = -2$

The integers are 2, 4, and 6 or –6, –4, and –2.

29. Strategy

- This is a work problem.
  Time for new computer to print payroll: x
  Time for older computer to print payroll: $x + 12$

	Rate	Time	Part
New Computer	$\frac{1}{x}$	8	$\frac{8}{x}$
Older Computer	$\frac{1}{x+12}$	8	$\frac{8}{x+12}$

- The sum of the parts of the task completed must be 1.

$$\frac{8}{x} + \frac{8}{x+12} = 1$$

Solution

$$\frac{8}{x} + \frac{8}{x+12} = 1$$
$$x(x+12)\left(\frac{8}{x} + \frac{8}{x+12}\right) = x(x+12)(1)$$
$$8(x+12) + 8x = x(x+12)$$
$$8x + 96 + 8x = x^2 + 12x$$
$$16x + 96 = x^2 + 12x$$
$$0 = x^2 - 4x - 96$$
$$0 = (x-12)(x+8)$$
$$x-12=0 \qquad x+8=0$$
$$x=12 \qquad x=-8$$

The solution –8 is not possible, since time cannot be a negative number.

Working alone, the new computer can print the payroll in 12 min.

30. Strategy
- This is a distance-rate problem.
- Rate of the first car: r
  Rate of the second car: $r + 10$

	Distance	Rate	Time
1st car	200	r	$\frac{200}{r}$
2nd car	200	$r+10$	$\frac{200}{r+10}$

- The second car's time is one hour less than the time of the first car.

$$\frac{200}{r+10} = \frac{200}{r} - 1$$

Solution

$$\frac{200}{r+10} = \frac{200}{r} - 1$$
$$r(r+10)\left(\frac{200}{r+10}\right) = \left(\frac{200}{r} - 1\right)r(r+10)$$
$$200r = 200(r+10) - r(r+10)$$
$$200r = 200r + 2000 - r^2 - 10r$$
$$r^2 + 10r - 2000 = 0$$
$$(r+50)(r-40) = 0$$

$r + 50 = 0 \qquad r - 40 = 0$

$r = -50 \qquad r = 40$

The solution –50 is not possible, since rate cannot be a negative number.

$r + 10 = 40 + 10 = 50$

The rate of the first car is 40 mph.

The rate of the second car is 50 mph.

CHAPTER TEST

1.
$$3x^2 + 10x = 8$$
$$3x^2 + 10x - 8 = 0$$
$$(3x-2)(x+4) = 0$$

$3x - 2 = 0 \qquad x + 4 = 0$

$3x = 2 \qquad x = -4$

$x = \frac{2}{3}$

The solutions are $\frac{2}{3}$ and –4.

2.
$$6x^2 - 5x - 6 = 0$$
$$(2x-3)(3x+2) = 0$$

$2x - 3 = 0 \qquad 3x + 2 = 0$

$2x = 3 \qquad 3x = -2$

$x = \frac{3}{2} \qquad x = -\frac{2}{3}$

The solutions are $\frac{3}{2}$ and $-\frac{2}{3}$.

3.
$$(x - r_1)(x - r_2) = 0$$
$$(x-3)[x-(-3)] = 0$$
$$(x-3)(x+3) = 0$$
$$x^2 - 9 = 0$$

4.
$$(x - r_1)(x - r_2) = 0$$
$$\left(x - \frac{1}{2}\right)[x - (-4)] = 0$$
$$\left(x - \frac{1}{2}\right)(x+4) = 0$$
$$x^2 + \frac{7}{2}x - 2 = 0$$
$$2\left(x^2 + \frac{7}{2}x - 2\right) = 2 \cdot 0$$
$$2x^2 + 7x - 4 = 0$$

5.
$$3(x-2)^2 - 24 = 0$$
$$3(x-2)^2 = 24$$
$$(x-2)^2 = 8$$
$$\sqrt{(x-2)^2} = \sqrt{8}$$
$$x - 2 = \pm 2\sqrt{2}$$

$x - 2 = 2\sqrt{2} \qquad x - 2 = -2\sqrt{2}$

$x = 2 + 2\sqrt{2} \qquad x = 2 - 2\sqrt{2}$

The solutions are $2 + 2\sqrt{2}$ and $2 - 2\sqrt{2}$.

6.
$$x^2 - 6x - 2 = 0$$
$$x^2 - 6x = 2$$

Complete the square.

$$x^2 - 6x + 9 = 2 + 9$$
$$(x-3)^2 = 11$$
$$\sqrt{(x-3)^2} = \sqrt{11}$$
$$x - 3 = \pm\sqrt{11}$$

$x - 3 = \sqrt{11} \qquad x - 3 = -\sqrt{11}$

$x = 3 + \sqrt{11} \qquad x = 3 - \sqrt{11}$

The solutions are $3 + \sqrt{11}$ and $3 - \sqrt{11}$.

7.
$$3x^2 - 6x = 2$$
$$\frac{1}{3}(3x^2 - 6x) = \frac{1}{3}(2)$$
$$x^2 - 2x = \frac{2}{3}$$

Complete the square.

$$x^2 - 2x + 1 = \frac{2}{3} + 1$$
$$(x-1)^2 = \frac{5}{3}$$
$$\sqrt{(x-1)^2} = \sqrt{\frac{5}{3}}$$
$$x - 1 = \pm\frac{\sqrt{15}}{3}$$

$x - 1 = \frac{\sqrt{15}}{3} \qquad x - 1 = -\frac{\sqrt{15}}{3}$

$x = 1 + \frac{\sqrt{15}}{3} \qquad x = 1 - \frac{\sqrt{15}}{3}$

$= \frac{3+\sqrt{15}}{3} \qquad = \frac{3-\sqrt{15}}{3}$

The solutions are $\frac{3+\sqrt{15}}{3}$ and $\frac{3-\sqrt{15}}{3}$.

8.
$$2x^2 - 2x = 1$$
$$2x^2 - 2x - 1 = 0$$
$$a = 2,\ b = -2,\ c = -1$$
$$x = \frac{-b \pm \sqrt{b^2 - 4ac}}{2a}$$
$$= \frac{-(-2) \pm \sqrt{(-2)^2 - 4(2)(-1)}}{2(2)}$$
$$= \frac{2 \pm \sqrt{4+8}}{4}$$
$$= \frac{2 \pm \sqrt{12}}{4}$$
$$= \frac{2 \pm 2\sqrt{3}}{4}$$
$$= \frac{1 \pm \sqrt{3}}{2}$$

The solutions are $\frac{1+\sqrt{3}}{2}$ and $\frac{1-\sqrt{3}}{2}$.

9.
$$x^2 + 4x + 12 = 0$$
$$a = 1,\ b = 4,\ c = 12$$
$$x = \frac{-b \pm \sqrt{b^2 - 4ac}}{2a}$$
$$= \frac{-4 \pm \sqrt{(4)^2 - 4(1)(12)}}{2(1)}$$
$$= \frac{-4 \pm \sqrt{16-48}}{2}$$
$$= \frac{-4 \pm \sqrt{-32}}{2}$$
$$= \frac{-4 \pm 4i\sqrt{2}}{2}$$
$$= -2 \pm 2i\sqrt{2}$$

The solutions are $-2 + 2i\sqrt{2}$ and $-2 - 2i\sqrt{2}$.

10.
$$3x^2 - 4x = 1$$
$$3x^2 - 4x - 1 = 0$$
$$a = 3,\ b = -4,\ c = -1$$
$$b^2 - 4ac = (-4)^2 - 4(3)(-1)$$
$$= 16 + 12 = 28$$
$$28 > 0$$

Since the discriminant is greater than zero, the equation has two real number solutions.

11.
$$x^2 - 6x = -15$$
$$x^2 - 6x + 15 = 0$$
$$a = 1,\ b = -6,\ c = 15$$
$$b^2 - 4ac = (-6)^2 - 4(1)(15)$$
$$= 36 - 60 = -24$$
$$-24 < 0$$

Since the discriminant is less than zero, the equation has two complex number solutions.

12.
$$2x + 7x^{1/2} - 4 = 0$$
$$2(x^{1/2})^2 + 7x^{1/2} - 4 = 0$$
$$2u^2 + 7u - 4 = 0$$
$$(2u-1)(u+4) = 0$$
$$2u - 1 = 0 \quad u + 4 = 0$$
$$2u = 1 \quad u = -4$$
$$u = \frac{1}{2}$$

Replace u by $x^{1/2}$.
$$x^{1/2} = \frac{1}{2} \quad x^{1/2} = -4$$
$$(x^{1/2})^2 = \left(\frac{1}{2}\right)^2 \quad (x^{1/2})^2 = (-4)^2$$
$$x = \frac{1}{4} \quad x = 16$$

16 does not check as a solution.

$\frac{1}{4}$ does check as a solution.

The solution is $\frac{1}{4}$.

13.
$$x^4 - 4x^2 + 3 = 0$$
$$(x^2)^2 - 4(x^2) + 3 = 0$$
$$u^2 - 4u + 3 = 0$$
$$(u-3)(u-1) = 0$$
$$u - 3 = 0 \quad u - 1 = 0$$
$$u = 3 \quad u = 1$$

Replace u by x^2.
$$x^2 = 3 \quad x^2 = 1$$
$$\sqrt{x^2} = \sqrt{3} \quad \sqrt{x^2} = \sqrt{1}$$
$$x = \pm\sqrt{3} \quad x = \pm 1$$

The solutions are $\sqrt{3}$, $-\sqrt{3}$, 1, and -1.

14.
$$\sqrt{2x+1} + 5 = 2x$$
$$\sqrt{2x+1} = 2x - 5$$
$$\left(\sqrt{2x+1}\right)^2 = (2x-5)^2$$
$$2x + 1 = 4x^2 - 20x + 25$$
$$0 = 4x^2 - 22x + 24$$
$$0 = 2(2x^2 - 11x + 12)$$
$$0 = 2(2x-3)(x-4)$$
$$2x - 3 = 0 \quad x - 4 = 0$$
$$2x = 3 \quad x = 4$$
$$x = \frac{3}{2}$$

$\frac{3}{2}$ does not check as a solution.

4 does check as a solution.

The solution is 4.

15.

$$\sqrt{x-2} = \sqrt{x} - 2$$
$$\left(\sqrt{x-2}\right)^2 = \left(\sqrt{x} - 2\right)^2$$
$$x - 2 = x - 4\sqrt{x} + 4$$
$$-6 = -4\sqrt{x}$$
$$-\frac{1}{4}(-6) = \left(-4\sqrt{x}\right)\left(-\frac{1}{4}\right)$$
$$\frac{3}{2} = \sqrt{x}$$
$$\frac{9}{4} = x$$

$\frac{9}{4}$ does not check as a solution.

The equation has no solution.

16.

$$\frac{2x}{x-3} + \frac{5}{x-1} = 1$$
$$(x-3)(x-1)\left(\frac{2x}{x-3} + \frac{5}{x-1}\right) = (x-3)(x-1)1$$
$$2x(x-1) + 5(x-3) = (x-3)(x-1)$$
$$2x^2 - 2x + 5x - 15 = x^2 - 4x + 3$$
$$2x^2 + 3x - 15 = x^2 - 4x + 3$$
$$x^2 + 7x - 18 = 0$$
$$(x+9)(x-2) = 0$$

$x + 9 = 0 \qquad x - 2 = 0$

$x = -9 \qquad x = 2$

The solutions are –9 and 2.

17. $(x-2)(x+4)(x-4) < 0$

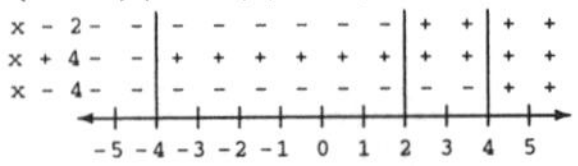

$\{x \mid x < -4 \text{ or } 2 < x < 4\}$

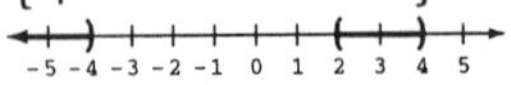

18. $\frac{2x-3}{x+4} \le 0$

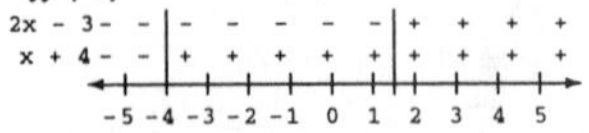

$\left\{x \,\middle|\, -4 < x \le \frac{3}{2}\right\}$

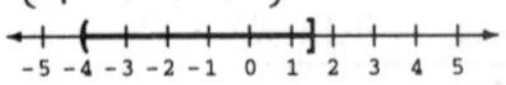

19. Strategy

- This is a geometry problem.
- The height of the triangle: x.
  The base of the triangle: $3x + 3$.
- The area of the triangle is 30 ft^2.
  Use the formula for the area of the triangle $\left(A = \frac{1}{2}bh\right)$.

Solution

$$A = \frac{1}{2}bh$$
$$30 = \frac{1}{2}(3x+3)x$$
$$60 = 3x^2 + 3x$$
$$0 = 3x^2 + 3x - 60$$
$$0 = 3(x^2 + x - 20)$$
$$0 = 3(x+5)(x-4)$$

$x + 5 = 0 \qquad x - 4 = 0$

$x = -5 \qquad x = 4$

The solution –5 is not possible, since height cannot be a negative number.

$3x + 3 = 3(4) + 3 = 15$

The height of the triangle is 4 ft.

The base of the triangle is 15 ft.

20. Strategy
- This is a distance-rate problem.
- The rate of the canoe in calm water: x.

	Distance	Rate	Time
With current	6	$x+2$	$\frac{6}{x+2}$
Against current	6	$x-2$	$\frac{6}{x-2}$

- The total traveling time is 4 h.

$$\frac{6}{x+2}+\frac{6}{x-2}=4$$

Solution

$$\begin{aligned}\frac{6}{x+2}+\frac{6}{x-2}&=4\\(x+2)(x-2)\left(\frac{6}{x+2}+\frac{6}{x-2}\right)&=(4)(x+2)(x-2)\\6(x-2)+6(x+2)&=4(x^2-4)\\6x-12+6x+12&=4x^2-16\\12x&=4x^2-16\\0&=4x^2-12x-16\\0&=4(x^2-3x-4)\\0&=4(x-4)(x+1)\end{aligned}$$

$$x-4=0 \quad x+1=0$$
$$x=4 \qquad x=-1$$

The solution -1 is not possible, since rate cannot be a negative number. The rate of the canoe in calm water is 4 mph.

CUMULATIVE REVIEW

1. $$\begin{aligned}2a^2-b^2\div c&=2(3)^2-(-4)^2\div(-2)^2\\&=2(9)-16\div 4\\&=18-16\div 4\\&=18-4\\&=14\end{aligned}$$

2. $$\begin{aligned}\frac{2x-3}{4}-\frac{x+4}{6}&=\frac{3x-2}{8}\\24\left(\frac{2x-3}{4}-\frac{x+4}{6}\right)&=24\left(\frac{3x-2}{8}\right)\\6(2x-3)-4(x+4)&=3(3x-2)\\12x-18-4x-16&=9x-6\\8x-34&=9x-6\\-x-34&=-6\\-x&=28\\x&=-28\end{aligned}$$

The solution is -28.

3. $P_1(3,-4),\ P_2(-1,2)$

$$m=\frac{y_2-y_1}{x_2-x_1}=\frac{2-(-4)}{-1-3}=\frac{2+4}{-4}=\frac{6}{-4}=-\frac{3}{2}$$

4. $$\begin{aligned}x-y&=1\\y&=x-1\end{aligned}$$

$m=1,\ (x_1,y_1)=(1,2)$

$$\begin{aligned}y-y_1&=m(x-x_1)\\y-2&=1(x-1)\\y-2&=x-1\\y&=x+1\end{aligned}$$

5. $-3x^3y+6x^2y^2-9xy^3=-3xy(x^2-2xy+3y^2)$

6. $6x^2-7x-20=(2x-5)(3x+4)$

7. $$\begin{aligned}a^nx+a^ny-2x-2y&=a^n(x+y)-2(x+y)\\&=(x+y)(a^n-2)\end{aligned}$$

8. $$\begin{array}{r}x^2-3x-4\\3x-4\overline{)3x^3-13x^2+0x+10}\\\underline{3x^3-4x^2}\\-9x^2+0x\\\underline{-9x^2+12x}\\-12x+10\\\underline{-12x+16}\\-6\end{array}$$

$$\begin{aligned}&(3x^3-13x^2+10)\div(3x-4)\\&=x^2-3x-4-\frac{6}{3x-4}\end{aligned}$$

9. $$\frac{x^2+2x+1}{8x^2+8x}\cdot\frac{4x^3-4x^2}{x^2-1} = \frac{(x+1)(x+1)}{8x(x+1)}\cdot\frac{4x^2(x-1)}{(x+1)(x-1)} = \frac{(x+1)(x+1)4x^2(x-1)}{8x(x+1)(x+1)(x-1)} = \frac{x}{2}$$

10. Distance between points is $\sqrt{(x_2-x_1)^2+(y_2-y_1)^2}$.

$$\text{Distance} = \sqrt{[2-(-2)]^2+(5-3)^2} = \sqrt{4^2+2^2} = \sqrt{20} = \sqrt{4\cdot 5} = 2\sqrt{5}$$

The distance between the points is $2\sqrt{5}$.

11.
$$\begin{aligned} S &= \frac{n}{2}(a+b) \\ 2S &= n(a+b) \\ 2S &= an+bn \\ 2S-an &= bn \\ \frac{2S-an}{n} &= b \\ b &= \frac{2S-an}{n} \end{aligned}$$

12. $$-2i(7-4i) = -14i+8i^2 = -8-14i$$

13. $$a^{-1/2}(a^{1/2}-a^{3/2}) = a^0-a^1 = 1-a$$

14. $$\frac{\sqrt[3]{8x^4y^5}}{\sqrt[3]{16xy^6}} = \sqrt[3]{\frac{8x^4y^5}{16xy^6}} = \sqrt[3]{\frac{x^3}{2y}} = \frac{\sqrt[3]{x^3}}{\sqrt[3]{2y}} = \frac{x}{\sqrt[3]{2y}}\cdot\frac{\sqrt[3]{4y^2}}{\sqrt[3]{4y^2}} = \frac{x\sqrt[3]{4y^2}}{\sqrt[3]{8y^3}} = \frac{x\sqrt[3]{4y^2}}{2y}$$

15.
$$\begin{aligned} \frac{x}{x+2}-\frac{4x}{x+3} &= 1 \\ (x+2)(x+3)\left[\frac{x}{x+2}-\frac{4x}{x+3}\right] &= (x+2)(x+3)1 \\ x(x+3)-4x(x+2) &= (x+2)(x+3) \\ x^2+3x-4x^2-8x &= x^2+5x+6 \\ -3x^2-5x &= x^2+5x+6 \\ 0 &= 4x^2+10x+6 \\ 0 &= 2(2x^2+5x+3) \\ 0 &= 2(2x+3)(x+1) \end{aligned}$$

$$2x+3=0 \qquad x+1=0$$
$$2x=-3 \qquad x=-1$$
$$x=-\frac{3}{2}$$

The solutions are $-\frac{3}{2}$ and -1.

16.
$$\begin{aligned} \frac{x}{2x+3}-\frac{3}{4x^2-9} &= \frac{x}{2x-3} \\ \frac{x}{2x+3}-\frac{3}{(2x+3)(2x-3)} &= \frac{x}{2x-3} \\ (2x+3)(2x-3)\left[\frac{x}{2x+3}-\frac{3}{(2x+3)(2x-3)}\right] &= \frac{x}{2x-3}(2x+3)(2x-3) \\ (2x-3)x-3 &= (2x+3)x \\ 2x^2-3x-3 &= 2x^2+3x \\ -3 &= 6x \\ x &= -\frac{1}{2} \end{aligned}$$

Check:
$$\begin{aligned} \frac{-\frac{1}{2}}{2\left(-\frac{1}{2}\right)+3}-\frac{3}{4\left(-\frac{1}{2}\right)^2-9} &= \frac{-\frac{1}{2}}{2\left(-\frac{1}{2}\right)-3} \\ \frac{-\frac{1}{2}}{2}-\frac{3}{-8} &= \frac{-\frac{1}{2}}{-4} \\ \frac{1}{8} &= \frac{1}{8} \end{aligned}$$

The solution is $-\frac{1}{2}$.

17.
$$x^4-6x^2+8=0$$
$$(x^2)^2-6(x^2)+8=0$$
$$u^2-6y+8=0$$
$$(u-4)(u-2)=0$$
$$u-4=0 \quad u-2=0$$
$$u=4 \qquad u=2$$
Replace u by x^2.
$$x^2=4 \qquad x^2=2$$
$$\sqrt{x^2}=\sqrt{4} \quad \sqrt{x^2}=\sqrt{2}$$
$$x=\pm 2 \qquad x=\pm\sqrt{2}$$
The solutions are 2, –2, $\sqrt{2}$, and $-\sqrt{2}$.

18.
$$\sqrt{3x+1}-1=x$$
$$\sqrt{3x+1}=x+1$$
$$\left(\sqrt{3x+1}\right)^2=(x+1)^2$$
$$3x+1=x^2+2x+1$$
$$0=x^2-x$$
$$0=x(x-1)$$
$$x=0 \quad x-1=0$$
$$x=1$$
0 and 1 both check as solutions.
The solutions are 0 and 1.

19.
$$|3x-2|<8$$
$$-8<3x-2<8$$
$$-8+2<3x-2+2<8+2$$
$$-6<3x<10$$
$$\frac{1}{3}\cdot(-6)<\frac{1}{3}\cdot(3x)<\frac{1}{3}\cdot 10$$
$$\left\{x \middle| -2<x<\frac{10}{3}\right\}$$

20.
$$6x-5y=15$$
$$6x-5(0)=15$$
$$6x=15$$
$$x=\frac{15}{6}=\frac{5}{2}$$
The x-intercept is $\left(\frac{5}{2}, 0\right)$.
$$6(0)-5y=15$$
$$-5y=15$$
$$y=-3$$
The y-intercept is (0, –3).

21. Solve each inequality.
$$x+y\le 3 \qquad 2x-y<4$$
$$y\le 3-x \qquad -y<4-2x$$
$$y>-4+2x$$

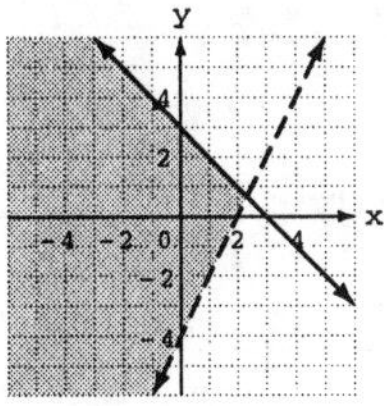

22.
$$x+y+z=2$$
$$-x+2y-3z=-9$$
$$x-2y-2z=-1$$
$$D=\begin{vmatrix}1&1&1\\-1&2&-3\\1&-2&-2\end{vmatrix}$$
$$=\begin{vmatrix}2&-3\\-2&-2\end{vmatrix}-\begin{vmatrix}-1&-3\\1&-2\end{vmatrix}+\begin{vmatrix}-1&2\\1&-2\end{vmatrix}=-15$$
$$D_x=\begin{vmatrix}2&1&1\\-9&2&-3\\-1&-2&-2\end{vmatrix}$$
$$=2\begin{vmatrix}2&-3\\-2&-2\end{vmatrix}-\begin{vmatrix}-9&-3\\-1&-2\end{vmatrix}+\begin{vmatrix}-9&2\\-1&-2\end{vmatrix}=-15$$
$$D_y=\begin{vmatrix}1&2&1\\-1&-9&-3\\1&-1&-2\end{vmatrix}$$
$$=\begin{vmatrix}-9&-3\\-1&-2\end{vmatrix}-2\begin{vmatrix}-1&-3\\1&-2\end{vmatrix}+\begin{vmatrix}-1&-9\\1&-1\end{vmatrix}=15$$
$$D_z=\begin{vmatrix}1&1&2\\-1&2&-9\\1&-2&-1\end{vmatrix}$$
$$=\begin{vmatrix}2&-9\\-2&-1\end{vmatrix}-\begin{vmatrix}-1&-9\\1&-1\end{vmatrix}+2\begin{vmatrix}-1&2\\1&-2\end{vmatrix}=-30$$
$$x=\frac{D_x}{D}=\frac{-15}{-15}=1$$
$$y=\frac{D_y}{D}=\frac{15}{-15}=-1$$
$$z=\frac{D_z}{D}=\frac{-30}{-15}=2$$
The solution is (1, –1, 2).

23. $f(-2)=\dfrac{2(-2)-3}{(-2)^2-1}=\dfrac{-4-3}{4-1}=\dfrac{-7}{3}=-\dfrac{7}{3}$

24.
$$f(x)=\frac{x-2}{x^2-2x-15}$$
$$f(x)=\frac{x-2}{(x-5)(x+3)}$$
The domain of $f(x)$ is all real numbers except $x=5$ and $x=-3$, where the function is undefined.

25. $x^3 + x^2 - 6x < 0$

$x(x^2 + x - 6) < 0$

$x(x + 3)(x - 2) < 0$

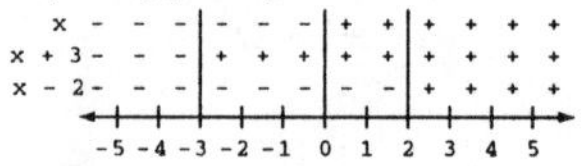

$\{x \mid x < -3 \text{ or } 0 < x < 2\}$

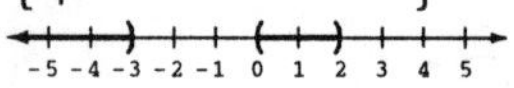

26. $\dfrac{(x-1)(x-5)}{x+3} \ge 0$

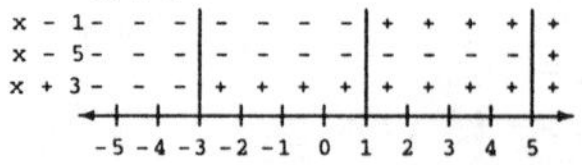

$\{x \mid -3 < x \le 1 \text{ or } x \ge 5\}$

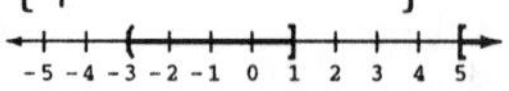

27. Strategy Let p represent the length of the piston rod, T the tolerance, and m the given length. Solve the absolute value inequality $|m - p| \le T$ for m.

Solution

$$|m - p| \le T$$

$$\left|m - 9\frac{3}{8}\right| \le \frac{1}{64}$$

$$-\frac{1}{64} \le m - 9\frac{3}{8} \le \frac{1}{64}$$

$$-\frac{1}{64} + 9\frac{3}{8} \le m \le \frac{1}{64} + 9\frac{3}{8}$$

$$9\frac{23}{64} \le m \le 9\frac{25}{64}$$

The lower limit is $9\frac{23}{64}$ in.

The upper limit is $9\frac{25}{64}$ in.

28.

$$\begin{aligned} A &= \frac{1}{2} b \cdot h \\ &= \frac{1}{2}(x+8)(2x-4) \\ &= \frac{1}{2}(2x^2 + 12x - 32) \\ &= (x^2 + 6x - 16)\ \text{ft}^2 \end{aligned}$$

29. $2x^2 + 4x + 3 = 0$

$a = 2,\ b = 4,\ c = 3$

$$\begin{aligned} b^2 - 4ac &= 4^2 - 4(2)(3) \\ &= 16 - 24 = -8 \end{aligned}$$

$-8 < 0$

Since the discriminant is less than zero, the equation has two complex number solutions.

30.

$$\begin{aligned} m &= \frac{y_2 - y_1}{x_2 - x_1} \\ &= \frac{0 - 250{,}000}{30 - 0} \\ &= \frac{-250{,}000}{30} = -\frac{25{,}000}{3} \end{aligned}$$

The slope represents the amount in dollars that the building depreciates each year. The building depreciates $\dfrac{\$25{,}000}{3}$ or about \$8333 each year.

Chapter 9: Functions and Relations

SECTION 9.1

Objective A Exercises

1. $y = x^2 - 2x - 4$

$-\frac{b}{2a} = -\frac{-2}{2(1)} = 1$

$y = 1^2 - 2(1) - 4 = -5$

Vertex: $(1, -5)$

Axis of symmetry: $x = 1$

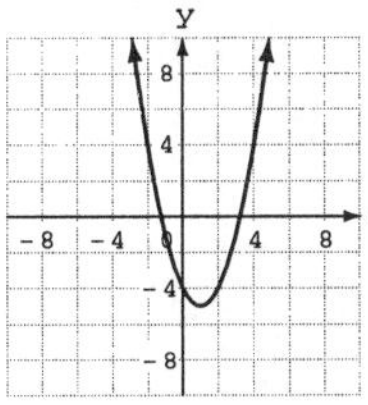

3. $y = -x^2 + 2x - 3$

$-\frac{b}{2a} = -\frac{2}{2(-1)} = 1$

$y = -(1)^2 + 2(1) - 3 = -2$

Vertex: $(1, -2)$

Axis of symmetry: $x = 1$

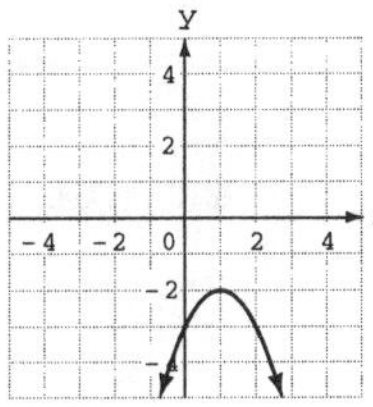

5. $f(x) = x^2 + 6x + 5$

$-\frac{b}{2a} = -\frac{6}{2 \cdot 1} = -3$

$f(x) = (-3)^2 + 6(-3) + 5 = -4$

Vertex: $(-3, -4)$

Axis of symmetry: $x = -3$

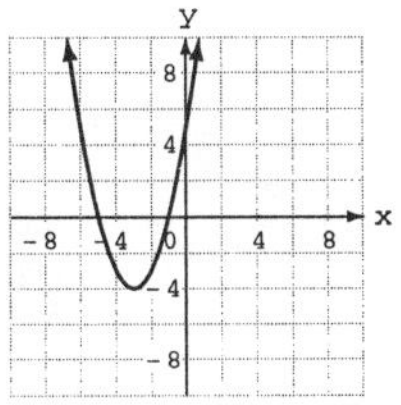

7. $G(x) = x^2 - x - 2$

$-\frac{b}{2a} = -\frac{-1}{2(1)} = \frac{1}{2}$

$G(x) = \left(\frac{1}{2}\right)^2 - \left(\frac{1}{2}\right) - 2 = -\frac{9}{4}$

Vertex: $\left(\frac{1}{2}, -\frac{9}{4}\right)$

Axis of symmetry: $x = \frac{1}{2}$

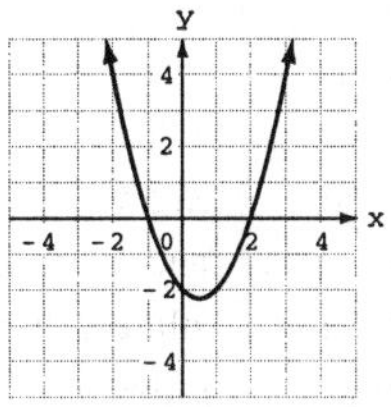

9. $y = 2x^2 - 4x + 1$

$-\frac{b}{2a} = -\frac{-4}{2(2)} = 1$

$y = 2(1)^2 - 4(1) + 1 = -1$

Vertex: $(1, -1)$

Axis of symmetry: $x = 1$

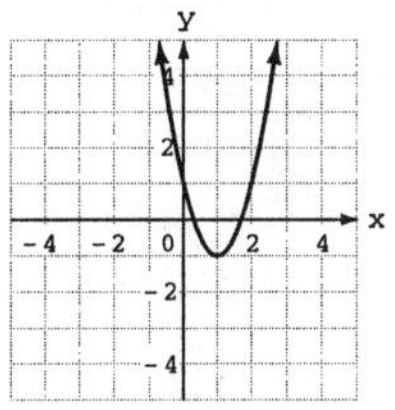

11. $y = x^2 + 4x + 5$

$-\frac{b}{2a} = -\frac{4}{2(1)} = -2$

$y = (-2)^2 + 4(-2) + 5 = 1$

Vertex: $(-2, 1)$

Axis of symmetry: $x = -2$

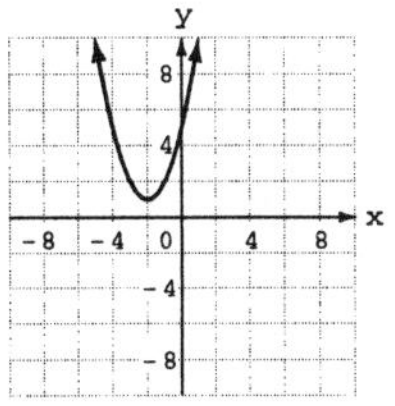

13. $y=\frac{1}{2}x^2+4$

$-\frac{b}{2a}=-\frac{0}{2\left(\frac{1}{2}\right)}=0$

$y=\frac{1}{2}(0)^2+4=4$

Vertex: (0, 4)

Axis of symmetry: $x=0$

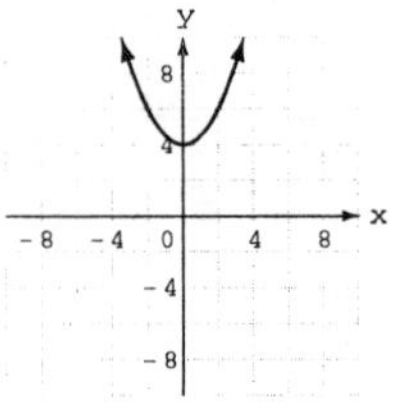

15. $h(x)=\frac{1}{2}x^2-x+1$

$-\frac{b}{2a}=-\frac{-1}{2\left(\frac{1}{2}\right)}=1$

$h(x)=\frac{1}{2}(1)^2-1+1=\frac{1}{2}$

Vertex: $\left(1,\frac{1}{2}\right)$

Axis of symmetry: $x=1$

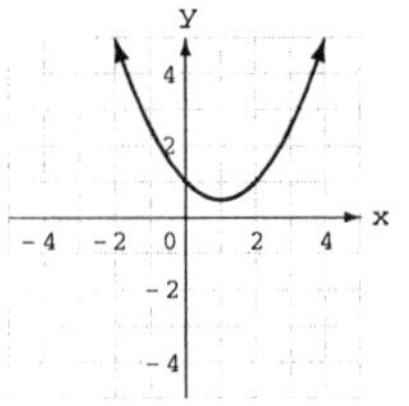

17. $y=\frac{1}{2}x^2+2x-6$

$-\frac{b}{2a}=-\frac{2}{2\left(\frac{1}{2}\right)}=-2$

$y=\frac{1}{2}(-2)^2+2(-2)-6=-8$

Vertex: (–2, –8)

Axis of symmetry: $x=-2$

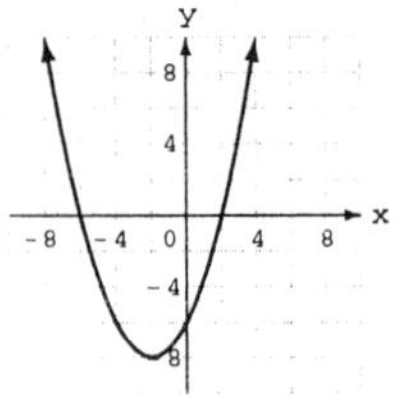

Objective B Exercises

19. $y=x^2-4$

$0=x^2-4$

$0=(x-2)(x+2)$

$x-2=0 \quad x+2=0$

$x=2 \qquad x=-2$

The x-intercepts are (2, 0) and (–2, 0)

21. $y=2x^2-4x$

$0=2x^2-4x$

$0=2x(x-2)$

$2x=0 \quad x-2=0$

$x=0 \qquad x=2$

The x-intercepts are (0, 0) and (2, 0).

23. $y=x^2-x-2$

$0=x^2-x-2$

$0=(x-2)(x+1)$

$x-2=0 \quad x+1=0$

$x=2 \qquad x=-1$

The x-intercepts are (2, 0) and (–1, 0).

25. $y=2x^2-x-1$

$0=2x^2-x-1$

$0=(2x+1)(x-1)$

$2x+1=0 \qquad x-1=0$

$2x=-1 \qquad x=1$

$x=-\frac{1}{2}$

The x-intercepts are $\left(-\frac{1}{2},\ 0\right)$ and (1, 0).

27. $y=x^2+2x-1$

$0=x^2+2x-1$

$a=1,\ b=2,\ c=-1$

$$x=\frac{-b\pm\sqrt{b^2-4ac}}{2a}$$

$$=\frac{-2\pm\sqrt{(2)^2-4(1)(-1)}}{2(1)}$$

$$=\frac{-2\pm\sqrt{4+4}}{2}$$

$$=\frac{-2\pm\sqrt{8}}{2}=\frac{-2\pm2\sqrt{2}}{2}$$

$$=-1\pm\sqrt{2}$$

The x-intercepts are

$(-1+\sqrt{2},\ 0)$ and $(-1-\sqrt{2},\ 0)$.

29. $y = x^2 + 6x + 10$

$0 = x^2 + 6x + 10$

$a = 1,\ b = 6,\ c = 10$

$$x = \frac{-b \pm \sqrt{b^2 - 4ac}}{2a}$$

$$= \frac{-6 \pm \sqrt{(6)^2 - 4(1)(10)}}{2(1)}$$

$$= \frac{-6 \pm \sqrt{36 - 40}}{2} = \frac{-6 \pm \sqrt{-4}}{2}$$

$$= \frac{-6 + 2i}{2} = -3 \pm i$$

The equation has no real solutions.
The parabola has no x-intercepts.

31. $y = x^2 - 2x - 2$

$0 = x^2 - 2x - 2$

$a = 1,\ b = -2,\ c = -2$

$$x = \frac{-b \pm \sqrt{b^2 - 4ac}}{2a}$$

$$= \frac{-(-2) \pm \sqrt{(-2)^2 - 4(1)(-2)}}{2(1)}$$

$$= \frac{2 \pm \sqrt{4 + 8}}{2} = \frac{2 \pm \sqrt{12}}{2}$$

$$= \frac{2 \pm 2\sqrt{3}}{2} = 1 \pm \sqrt{3}$$

The x-intercepts are $(1 + \sqrt{3},\ 0)$ and $(1 - \sqrt{3},\ 0)$.

33. $y = -x^2 + 4x + 1$

$0 = -x^2 + 4x + 1$

$0 = x^2 - 4x - 1$

$a = 1,\ b = -4,\ c = -1$

$$x = \frac{-b \pm \sqrt{b^2 - 4ac}}{2a}$$

$$= \frac{-(-4) \pm \sqrt{(-4)^2 - 4(1)(-1)}}{2(1)}$$

$$= \frac{4 \pm \sqrt{16 + 4}}{2} = \frac{4 \pm \sqrt{20}}{2}$$

$$= \frac{4 \pm 2\sqrt{5}}{2} = 2 \pm \sqrt{5}$$

The x-intercepts are $(2 + \sqrt{5},\ 0)$ and $(2 - \sqrt{5},\ 0)$.

35. $f(x) = x^2 - 6x + 9$

$x^2 - 6x + 9 = 0$

$(x - 3)(x - 3) = 0$

$x - 3 = 0 \quad x - 3 = 0$

$x = 3 \quad\quad x = 3$

The zero is 3.

37. $f(x) = -x^2 + 3x + 8$

$-x^2 + 3x + 8 = 0$

$$x = \frac{-b \pm \sqrt{b^2 - 4ac}}{2a}$$

$$x = \frac{-3 \pm \sqrt{3^2 - 4(-1)(8)}}{2(-1)} = \frac{-3 \pm \sqrt{41}}{-2}$$

$$x = \frac{3}{2} \pm \frac{\sqrt{41}}{2}$$

The zeros are $\frac{3 + \sqrt{41}}{2}$ and $\frac{3 - \sqrt{41}}{2}$.

39. $f(x) = -3x^2 + 4x$

$-3x^2 + 4x = 0$

$x(-3x + 4) = 0$

$x = 0 \quad -3x + 4 = 0$

$-3x = -4$

$x = \frac{4}{3}$

The zeros are 0 and $\frac{4}{3}$.

41. $f(x) = 3x^2 + 6$

$3x^2 + 6 = 0$

$3(x^2 + 2) = 0$

$x^2 + 2 = 0$

$x^2 = -2$

$x = \pm\sqrt{-2} = \pm i\sqrt{2}$

The zeros are $i\sqrt{2}$ and $-i\sqrt{2}$.

43. $f(x) = 3x^2 - x + 4$

$3x^2 - x + 4 = 0$

$$x = \frac{-b \pm \sqrt{b^2 - 4ac}}{2a}$$

$$x = \frac{-(-1) \pm \sqrt{(-1)^2 - 4(3)(4)}}{2(3)} = \frac{1 \pm \sqrt{-47}}{6}$$

$$x = \frac{1 \pm \sqrt{47}i}{6} = \frac{1}{6} \pm \frac{\sqrt{47}}{6}i$$

The zeros are $\frac{1}{6} + \frac{\sqrt{47}}{6}i$ and $\frac{1}{6} - \frac{\sqrt{47}}{6}i$.

45. $f(x) = -2x^2 + x + 5$

$-2x^2 + x + 5 = 0$

$$x = \frac{-b \pm \sqrt{b^2 - 4ac}}{2a}$$

$$x = \frac{-1 \pm \sqrt{1^2 - 4(-2)(5)}}{2(-2)} = \frac{-1 \pm \sqrt{41}}{-4}$$

$$x = \frac{1}{4} \pm \frac{\sqrt{41}}{4}$$

The zeros are $\frac{1 + \sqrt{41}}{4}$ and $\frac{1 - \sqrt{41}}{4}$.

47. $y = 2x^2 + 2x - 1$
$a = 2,\ b = 2,\ c = -1$
$b^2 - 4ac$
$(2)^2 - 4(2)(-1) = 4 + 8 = 12$
$12 > 0$
Since the discriminant is greater than zero, the parabola has two x-intercepts.

49. $y = -2x^2 + x + 1$
$a = -2,\ b = 1,\ c = 1$
$b^2 - 4ac$
$(1)^2 - 4(-2)(1) = 1 + 8 = 9$
$9 > 0$
Since the discriminant is greater than zero, the parabola has two x-intercepts.

51. $y = x^2 - 10x + 25$
$a = 1,\ b = -10,\ c = 25$
$b^2 - 4ac$
$(-10)^2 - 4(1)(25) = 100 - 100 = 0$
Since the discriminant is equal to zero, the parabola has one x-intercept.

53. $y = -2x^2 + x - 1$
$a = -2,\ b = 1,\ c = -1$
$b^2 - 4ac$
$(1)^2 - 4(-2)(-1) = 1 - 8 = -7$
$-7 < 0$
Since the discriminant is less than zero, the parabola has no x-intercepts.

55. $y = 2x^2 + x + 4$
$a = 2,\ b = 1,\ c = 4$
$b^2 - 4ac$
$(1)^2 - 4(2)(4) = 1 - 32 = -31$
$-31 < 0$
Since the discriminant is less than zero, the parabola has no x-intercepts.

57. $y = -3x^2 + 4x - 5$
$a = -3,\ b = 4,\ c = -5$
$b^2 - 4ac$
$(4)^2 - 4(-3)(-5) = 16 - 60 = -44$
$-44 < 0$
Since the discriminant is less than zero, the parabola has no x-intercepts.

59. $y = -3x^2 + 2x - 8$
$a = -3,\ b = 2,\ c = -8$
$b^2 - 4ac$
$(2)^2 - 4(-3)(-8) = 4 - 96 = -92$
$-92 > 0$
Since the discriminant is less than zero, the parabola has no x-intercepts.

Objective C Exercises

61. $f(x) = x^2 - 2x + 3$
$$x = -\frac{b}{2a} = -\frac{-2}{2(1)} = 1$$
$f(x) = x^2 - 2x + 3$
$f(1) = 1^2 - 2(1) + 3$
$= 1 - 2 + 3 = 2$
Since a is positive, the function has a minimum value. The minimum value of the function is 2.

63. $f(x) = -2x^2 + 4x - 3$
$$x = -\frac{b}{2a} = -\frac{4}{2(-2)} = 1$$
$f(x) = -2x^2 + 4x - 3$
$f(1) = -2(1)^2 + 4(1) - 3$
$= -2 + 4 - 3 = -1$
Since a is negative, the function has a maximum value. The maximum value of the function is -1.

65. $f(x) = 2x^2 + 4x$
$$x = -\frac{b}{2a} = -\frac{4}{2(2)} = -1$$
$f(1) = 2(-1)^2 + 4(-1) = 2 - 4 = -2$
Since a is positive, the function has a minimum value. The minimum value of the function is -2.

67. $f(x) = -2x^2 + 4x - 5$
$$x = -\frac{b}{2a} = -\frac{4}{2(-2)} = 1$$
$f(1) = -2(1)^2 + 4(1) - 5 = -3$
Since a is negative, the function has a maximum value. The maximum value of the function is -3.

69. $f(x) = 2x^2 + 3x - 8$
$$x = -\frac{b}{2a} = -\frac{3}{2(2)} = -\frac{3}{4}$$
$$f\left(-\frac{3}{4}\right) = 2\left(-\frac{3}{4}\right)^2 + 3\left(-\frac{3}{4}\right) - 8 = -\frac{73}{8}$$
Since a is positive, the function has a minimum value. The minimum value of the function is $-\frac{73}{8}$.

71. $f(x) = 3x^2 + 3x - 2$

$$x = -\frac{b}{2a} = -\frac{3}{2(3)} = -\frac{1}{2}$$

$$f(x) = 3x^2 + 3x - 2$$

$$f\left(-\frac{1}{2}\right) = 3\left(-\frac{1}{2}\right)^2 + 3\left(-\frac{1}{2}\right) - 2$$

$$= \frac{3}{4} - \frac{3}{2} - 2 = -\frac{11}{4}$$

Since a is positive, the function has a minimum value. The minimum value of the function is $-\frac{11}{4}$.

73. $f(x) = -3x^2 + 4x - 2$

$$x = -\frac{b}{2a} = -\frac{4}{2(-3)} = \frac{2}{3}$$

$$f(x) = -3x^2 + 4x - 2$$

$$f\left(\frac{2}{3}\right) = -3\left(\frac{2}{3}\right)^2 + 4\left(\frac{2}{3}\right) - 2$$

$$= -\frac{4}{3} + \frac{8}{3} - 2 = -\frac{2}{3}$$

Since a is negative, the function has a maximum value. The maximum value of the function is $-\frac{2}{3}$.

75. $f(x) = 3x^2 + 5x + 2$

$$x = -\frac{b}{2a} = -\frac{5}{2(3)} = -\frac{5}{6}$$

$$f(x) = 3x^2 + 5x + 2$$

$$f\left(-\frac{5}{6}\right) = 3\left(-\frac{5}{6}\right)^2 + 5\left(-\frac{5}{6}\right) + 2$$

$$= 3\left(\frac{25}{36}\right) + \left(\frac{-25}{6}\right) + 2$$

$$= \frac{25}{12} - \frac{25}{6} + 2 = -\frac{1}{12}$$

Since a is positive, the function has a minimum value. The minimum value of the function is $-\frac{1}{12}$.

Objective D Application Problems

77. Strategy

- To find the time it takes for the diver to reach the maximum height, find the t-coordinate of the vertex.
- To find the maximum height, evaluate the function at the t- coordinate of the vertex.

Solution $t = -\frac{b}{2a} = -\frac{7.8}{2(-4.9)} = \frac{78}{98}$

The diver reaches the maximum height in $\frac{78}{98}$ s.

$$s(t) = -4.9t^2 + 7.8t + 10$$

$$s\left(\frac{78}{98}\right) = -4.9\left(\frac{78}{98}\right)^2 + 7.8\left(\frac{78}{98}\right) + 10$$

$$\approx -3.104 + 6.2082 + 10$$

$$\approx 13.1$$

The diver reaches a height of 13.1 m above the water.

79. Strategy

- To find the distance from one end of the bridge where the cable is at its minimum height, find the x-coordinate of the vertex.
- To find the minimum height, evaluate the function at the x-coordinate of the vertex.

Solution $t = -\frac{b}{2a} = -\frac{-0.8}{2(0.25)} = 1.6$

The cable is at its minimum height 1.6 ft from one end of the bridge.

$$h(x) = 0.25x^2 - 0.8x + 25$$

$$h(1.6) = 0.25(1.6)^2 - 0.8(1.6) + 25$$

$$= 0.64 - 1.28 + 25 = 24.36$$

The minimum height is 24.36 ft.

81. Strategy

- To find the distance from the edge for minimum thickness, find the x-coordinate of the vertex.
- To find the minimum thickness, evaluate the function at the x-coordinate of the vertex.

Solution $x = -\frac{b}{a} = -\frac{-0.0758}{2(0.000379)} = 100$

The mirror reaches minimum thickness at $x = 100$.

$$h(x) = 0.000379x^2 - 0.0758x + 24$$

$$h(100) = 0.000379(100^2) - 0.0758(100) + 24$$

$$h(100) = 3.79 - 7.58 + 24$$

$$h(100) = 20.21$$

83. Strategy • To determine if the ball will clear the fence, evaluate the function at $d = 340$.

Solution
$$h(d) = -0.0015d^2 + 0.52d + 5$$
$$h(340) = -0.0015(340)^2 + 0.52(340) + 5$$
$$h(340) = -173.4 + 176.8 + 5$$
$$h(340) = 8.4$$

Yes, the ball will clear a fence 340 ft from the batter.

85. Strategy • The perimeter is 14 ft.
$$14 = 4x + 3y$$
$$\frac{14}{3} - \frac{4}{3}x = y$$
The area is $2xy$.
$$A = 2x\left(\frac{14}{3} - \frac{4}{3}x\right)$$
$$A = \frac{28}{3}x - \frac{8}{3}x^2$$

Solution To find the x-dimension for the largest area, find the x-coordinate of the vertex.
$$x = -\frac{b}{2a} = -\frac{\frac{28}{3}}{2\left(-\frac{8}{3}\right)} = \frac{7}{4} = 1\frac{3}{4}$$
Substitute $\frac{7}{4}$ for x and solve for y.
$$y = \frac{14}{3} - \frac{4}{3}\left(\frac{7}{4}\right) = \frac{7}{3} = 2\frac{1}{3}$$
For maximum area, $x = 1\frac{3}{4}$ ft. and $y = 2\frac{1}{3}$ ft.

87.
$$S = (2-x)^2 + (5-x)^2 + (4-x)^2 + (7-x)^2$$
$$S = 4 - 4x + x^2 + 25 - 10x + x^2 + 16 - 8x + x^2 + 49 - 14x + x^2$$
$$S = 4x^2 - 36x + 94$$
$$-\frac{b}{2a} = -\frac{-36}{2(4)} = \frac{9}{2} = 4.5$$
The minimum value of the function occurs when $x = 4.5$
$$\frac{2+5+4+7}{4} = \frac{9}{2} = 4.5$$
The average of the four numbers 2, 5, 4, and 7 is 4.5.

89.

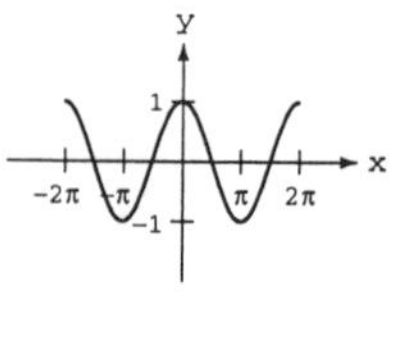

91.

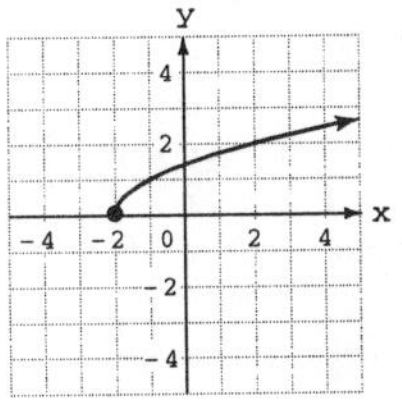

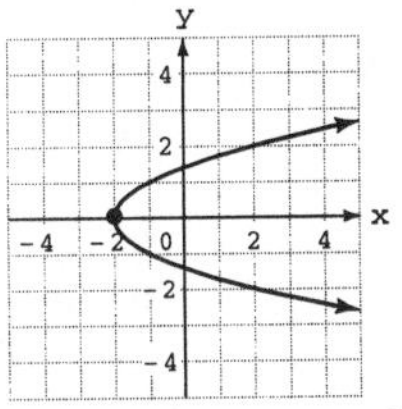

The graphs are exactly the same for $x \geq -2$, but $y = \sqrt{x+2}$ is not real for $x < -2$, so it is not plotted for $x < -2$.

93. a. $y = x^2 - 4x + 7$
$y = (x-2)^2 - 4 + 7$
$y = (x-2)^2 + 3$
Vertex: (2, 3)

b. $y = x^2 - 2x - 2$
$= (x-1)^2 - 1 - 2$
$y = (x-1)^2 - 3$
Vertex: (1, –3)

c. $y = x^2 - 6x + 3$
$= (x-3)^2 - 9 + 3$
$y = (x-3)^2 - 6$
Vertex: (3, –6)

d. $y = x^2 + 4x - 1$
$= (x+2)^2 - 4 - 1$
$y = (x+2)^2 - 5$
Vertex: (–2, –5)

e. $y = x^2 + x + 2$
$= \left(x + \frac{1}{2}\right)^2 - \frac{1}{4} + 2$
$y = \left(x + \frac{1}{2}\right)^2 + \frac{7}{4}$
Vertex: $\left(-\frac{1}{2}, \frac{7}{4}\right)$

f. $y = x^2 - x - 3$
$y = \left(x - \frac{1}{2}\right)^2 - \frac{1}{4} - 3$
$y = \left(x - \frac{1}{2}\right)^2 - \frac{13}{4}$
Vertex: $\left(\frac{1}{2}, -\frac{13}{4}\right)$

SECTION 9.2

Objective A Exercises

1. A vertical line intersects the function no more than once. The graph is a function.

3. A vertical line intersects the relation more than once. The graph is not a function.

5. A vertical line intersects the function no more than once. The graph is a function.

7. $f(x) = 3|x-2|$
The domain is all real numbers.
The range is all positive real numbers $y \geq 0$.

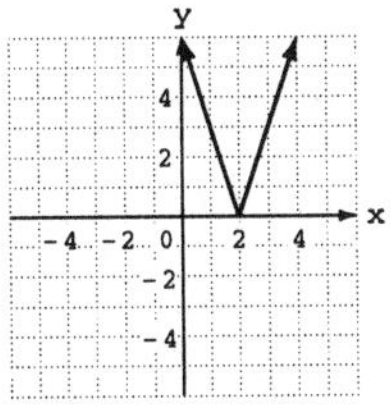

9. $f(x) = 1 - x^3$
The domain is all real numbers.
The range is all real numbers.

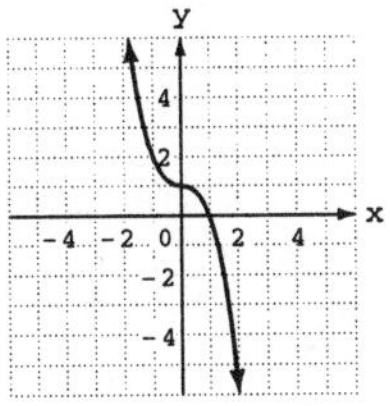

11. $f(x) = \sqrt{4-x}$
The domain is all real numbers $x \leq 4$. The range is all positive real numbers $y \geq 0$.

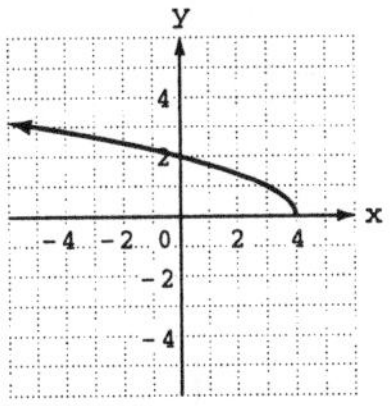

13. $f(x) = x^3 + 4x^2 + 4x$
The domain is all real numbers.
The range is all real numbers.

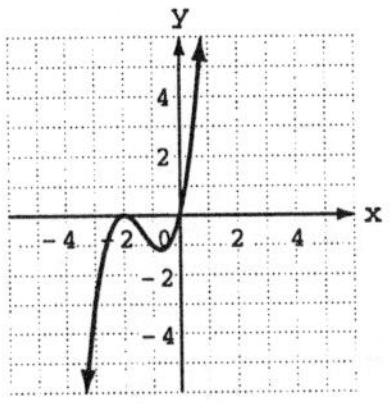

15. $f(x) = -\sqrt{x+2}$
The domain is all real numbers $x \geq -2$. The range is all negative real numbers $y \leq 0$.

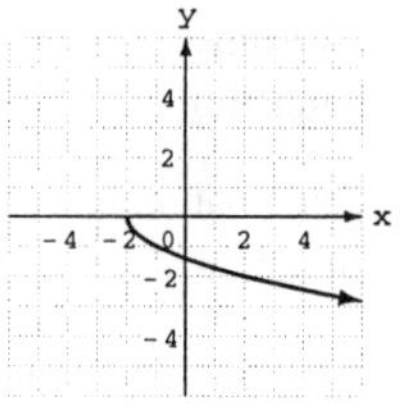

17. $f(x) = |2x+2|$
The domain is all real numbers.
The range is all positive real numbers $y \geq 0$.

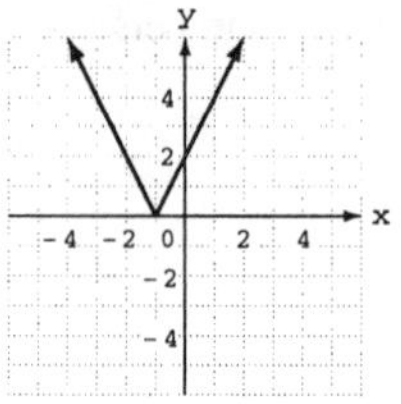

Applying the Concepts

19. $f(x) = \sqrt{x-2}$
$f(a) = 4 = \sqrt{a-2}$
$4^2 = \left(\sqrt{a-2}\right)^2$
$16 = a - 2$
$18 = a$

21. $f(a, b) = a + b$
$g(a, b) = a \cdot b$
$f(2, 5) = 2 + 5 = 7$
$g(2, 5) = 2 \cdot 5 = 10$
$f(2, 5) + g(2, 5) = 7 + 10 = 17$

23. $f(14) = 8$

25. 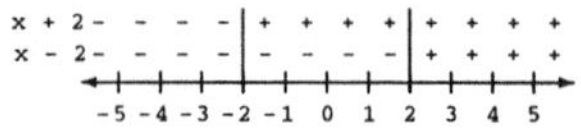

$\{x | -2 < x < 2\}$

27. $f(x) = |2x-2|$
$f(x)$ is smallest when $2x - 2 = 0$
$2x = 2$
$x = 1$

SECTION 9.3

Objective A Exercises

1. $D(x) = f(x) - g(x)$
$= 2x^2 - 3 - (-2x + 4)$
$= 2x^2 + 2x - 7$
$D(2) = 2(2)^2 + 2(2) - 7 = 5$
$f(2) - g(2) = 5$

3. $S(x) = f(x) + g(x)$
$= 2x^2 - 3 + (-2x + 4)$
$= 2x^2 - 2x + 1$
$S(0) = 2(0)^2 - 2(0) + 1 = 1$
$f(0) + g(0) = 1$

5. $P(x) = (f \cdot g)(x) = f(x) \cdot g(x)$
$= (2x^2 - 3)(-2x + 4)$
$= -4x^3 + 8x^2 + 6x - 12$
$P(2) = -4(2)^3 + 8(2)^2 + 6(2) - 12 = 0$
$(f \cdot g)(2) = 0$

7. $\left(\dfrac{f}{g}\right)(x) = \dfrac{2x^2 - 3}{-2x + 4}$
$\left(\dfrac{f}{g}\right)(4) = \dfrac{2(4)^2 - 3}{-2(4) + 4} = \dfrac{32 - 3}{-8 + 4} = -\dfrac{29}{4}$
$\left(\dfrac{f}{g}\right)(4) = -\dfrac{29}{4}$

9. $\left(\dfrac{g}{f}\right)(x) = \dfrac{-2x + 4}{2x^2 - 3}$
$\left(\dfrac{g}{f}\right)(-3) = \dfrac{-2(-3) + 4}{2(-3)^2 - 3} = \dfrac{6 + 4}{18 - 3} = \dfrac{10}{15}$
$\left(\dfrac{g}{f}\right)(-3) = \dfrac{2}{3}$

11. $S(x) = 2x^2 + 5x - 5$
$S(1) = 2(1)^2 + 5(1) - 5 = 2$
$f(1) + g(1) = 2$

13. $D(x) = 2x^2 + x + 3$
$D(4) = 2(4)^2 + 4 + 3 = 39$
$f(4) - g(4) = 39$

15. $P(x) = 4x^3 - 2x^2 - 14x + 4$
$P(1) = 4(1)^3 - 2(1)^2 - 14(1) + 4$
$= 4 - 2 - 14 + 4 = -8$
$P(1) = -8 = (f \cdot g)(1)$

17. $\left(\dfrac{f}{g}\right)(x) = \dfrac{2x^2 + 3x - 1}{2x - 4}$
$\left(\dfrac{f}{g}\right)(-3) = \dfrac{2(-3)^2 + 3(-3) - 1}{2(-3) - 4}$
$= \dfrac{18 - 9 - 1}{-10} = -\dfrac{8}{10} = -\dfrac{4}{5}$

19. $D(x) = f(x) - g(x)$
$= (x^2 + 3x - 5) - (x^3 - 2x + 3)$
$D(x) = -x^3 + x^2 + 5x - 8$
$D(2) = -(2)^3 + (2)^2 + 5(2) - 8$
$= -8 + 4 + 10 - 8 = -2$
$D(2) = -2 = f(2) - g(2)$

21. $\left(\frac{f}{g}\right)(x) = \frac{x^2+3x-5}{x^3-2x+3}$

$\left(\frac{f}{g}\right)(-2) = \frac{(-2)^2+3(-2)-5}{(-2)^3-2(-2)+3} = \frac{4-6-5}{-8+4+3}$

$= \frac{-7}{-1} = 7$

Objective B Exercises

23. $f(x) = 2x-3$
$f(0) = 2(0)-3$
$= 0-3 = -3$
$g(x) = 4x-1$
$g(-3) = 4(-3)-1$
$= -12-1 = -13$
$g[f(0)] = -13$

25. $f(x) = 2x-3$
$f(-2) = 2(-2)-3$
$= -4-3 = -7$
$g(x) = 4x-1$
$g(-7) = 4(-7)-1$
$= -28-1 = -29$
$f[g(-2)] = -29$

27. $f(x) = 2x-3$
$g(x) = 4x-1$
$g(2x-3) = 4(2x-3)-1$
$= 8x-12-1$
$= 8x-13$
$g[f(x)] = 8x-13$

29. $h(x) = 2x+4$
$h(0) = 2(0)+4$
$= 0+4 = 4$
$f(x) = \frac{1}{2}x+2$
$f(4) = \frac{1}{2}(4)+2$
$= 2+2 = 4$
$f[h(0)] = 4$

31. $h(x) = 2x+4$
$h(-1) = 2(-1)+4$
$= -2+4 = 2$
$f(x) = \frac{1}{2}x+2$
$f(2) = \frac{1}{2}(2)+2$
$f(2) = \frac{1}{2}(2)+2$
$= 1+2 = 3$
$f[h(-1)] = 3$

33. $h(x) = 2x+4$
$f(x) = \frac{1}{2}x+2$
$f(2x+4) = \frac{1}{2}(2x+4)+2$
$= x+2+2$
$= x+4$
$f[h(x)] = x+4$

35. $g(x) = x^2+3$
$g(0) = 0^2+3 = 3$
$h(x) = x-2$
$h(3) = 3-2 = 1$
$h[g(0)] = 1$

37. $g(x) = x^2+3$
$g(-2) = (-2)^2+3$
$= 4+3 = 7$
$h(x) = x-2$
$h(7) = 7-2 = 5$
$h[g(-2)] = 5$

39. $g(x) = x^2+3$
$h(x) = x-2$
$h(x^2+3) = x^2+3-2$
$= x^2+1$
$h[g(x)] = x^2+1$

41. $f(x) = x^2+x+1$
$f(0) = 0^2+0+1$
$= 0+0+1 = 1$
$h(x) = 3x+2$
$h(1) = 3(1)+2$
$= 3+2 = 5$
$h[f(0)] = 5$

43. $f(x) = x^2+x+1$
$f(-2) = (-2)^2-2+1$
$= 4-2+1 = 3$
$h(x) = 3x+2$
$h(3) = 3(3)+2$
$= 9+2 = 11$
$h[f(-2)] = 11$

45. $f(x) = x^2+x+1$
$h(x) = 3x+2$
$h(x^2+x+1) = 3(x^2+x+1)+2$
$= 3x^2+3x+3+2$
$= 3x^2+3x+5$
$h[f(x)] = 3x^2+3x+5$

47. $g(x) = x^3$
$g(-1) = (-1)^3 = -1$
$f(x) = x-2$
$f(-1) = -1-2 = -3$
$f[g(-1)] = -3$

49. $f(x) = x - 2$
$f(-1) = -1 - 2 = -3$
$g(x) = x^3$
$g(-3) = (-3)^3 = -27$
$g[f(2)] = -27$

51. $f(x) = x - 2$
$g(x - 2) = (x - 2)^3$
$g[f(x)] = x^3 - 6x^2 + 12x - 8$

Applying the Concepts

53. $g(3 + h) - g(3) = (3 + h)^2 - 1 - ((3)^2 - 1)$
$= 9 + 6h + h^2 - 1 - 8$
$g(3 + h) - g(3) = h^2 + 6h$

55. $\frac{g(1+h) - g(1)}{h} = \frac{[(1+h)^2 - 1] - [(1)^2 - 1]}{h}$
$= \frac{1 + 2h + h^2 - 1 - 0}{h}$
$= \frac{2h + h^2}{h}$
$\frac{g(1-h) - g(1)}{h} = 2 + h$

57. $\frac{g(a+h) - g(a)}{h} = \frac{[(a+h)^2 - 1] - (a^2 - 1)}{h}$
$= \frac{a^2 + 2ah + h^2 - 1 - a^2 + 1}{h}$
$= \frac{2ah + h^2}{h}$
$\frac{g(a+h) - g(a)}{h} = 2a + h$

59. $f(x) = 2x$
$f(1) = 2 \cdot 1 = 2$
$h(x) = x - 2$
$h(2) = 2 - 2 = 0$
$g(x) = 3x - 1$
$g(0) = 3 \cdot 0 - 1 = -1$
$g\{h[f(1)]\} = -1$

61. $g(x) = 3x - 1$
$g(0) = 3 \cdot 0 - 1 = -1$
$h(x) = x - 2$
$h(-1) = -1 - 2 = -3$
$f(x) = 2x$
$f(-3) = 2(-3) = -6$
$f\{h[f(0)]\} = -6$

63. $h(x) = x - 2$
$f(x - 2) = 2(x - 2) = 2x - 4$
$g(2x - 4) = 3(2x - 4) - 1 = 6x - 12 - 1 = 6x - 13$
$g\{f[h(x)]\} = 6x - 13$

SECTION 9.4

Objective A Exercises

1. The graph represents a 1-1 function.

3. The graph is not a 1-1 function. It fails the horizontal-line test.

5. The graph is a 1-1 function.

7. The graph is not a 1-1 function. It fails the horizontal- and vertical-line tests.

9. The graph is not a 1-1 function. It fails the horizontal line test.

11. The graph is not a 1-1 function. It fails the horizontal-line test.

Objective B Exercises

13. The inverse of {(1, 0), (2, 3), (3, 8), (4, 15)} is {(0, 1), (3, 2), (8, 3), (15, 4)}.

15. {(3, 5), (–3, –5), (2, 5), (–2, –5)} has no inverse because the numbers 5 and –5 would be paired with different members of the range.

17. The inverse of {(0, –2), (–1, 5), (3, 3), (–4, 6)} is {(–2, 0), (5, –1), (3, 3), (6, –4)}.

19. No inverse.

21. $f(x) = 4x - 8$
$y = 4x - 8$
$x = 4y - 8$
$x + 8 = 4y$
$\frac{1}{4}x + 2 = y$

The inverse function is $f^{-1}(x) = \frac{1}{4}x + 2$.

23. $f(x) = 2x + 4$
$y = 2x + 4$
$x = 2y + 4$
$x - 4 = 2y$
$\frac{1}{2}x - 2 = y$

The inverse function is $f^{-1}(x) = \frac{1}{2}x - 2$.

25. $f(x) = \frac{1}{2}x - 1$
$y = \frac{1}{2}x - 1$
$x = \frac{1}{2}y - 1$
$x + 1 = \frac{1}{2}y$
$2x + 2 = y$

The inverse function is $f^{-1}(x) = 2x + 2$.

27. $f(x)=-2x+2$
$$y=-2x+2$$
$$x=-2y+2$$
$$2y=-x+2$$
$$y=-\frac{1}{2}x+1$$
The inverse function is $f^{-1}(x)=-\frac{1}{2}x+1$.

29. $f(x)=\frac{2}{3}x+4$
$$y=\frac{2}{3}x+4$$
$$x=\frac{2}{3}y+4$$
$$x-4=\frac{2}{3}y$$
$$\frac{3}{2}(x-4)=y$$
$$\frac{3}{2}x-6=y$$
The inverse function is $f^{-1}(x)=\frac{3}{2}x-6$.

31. $f(x)=-\frac{1}{3}x+1$
$$y=-\frac{1}{3}x+1$$
$$x=-\frac{1}{3}y+1$$
$$x-1=-\frac{1}{3}y$$
$$-3(x-1)=y$$
$$-3x+3=y$$
The inverse function is $f^{-1}(x)=-3x+3$.

33. $f(x)=2x-5$
$$y=2x-5$$
$$x=2y-5$$
$$x+5=2y$$
$$\frac{1}{2}x+\frac{5}{2}=y$$
The inverse function is $f^{-1}(x)=\frac{1}{2}x+\frac{5}{2}$.

35. $f(x)=5x-2$
$$y=5x-2$$
$$x=5y-2$$
$$x+2=5y$$
$$\frac{1}{5}x+\frac{2}{5}=y$$
The inverse function is $f^{-1}(x)=\frac{1}{5}x+\frac{2}{5}$.

37. $f(x)=6x-3$
$$y=6x-3$$
$$x=6y-3$$
$$x+3=6y$$
$$\frac{1}{6}x+\frac{1}{2}=y$$
The inverse function is $f^{-1}(x)=\frac{1}{6}x+\frac{1}{2}$.

39. $f(x)=-6x+2$
$$y=-6x+2$$
$$x=-6y+2$$
$$x-2=-6y$$
$$-\frac{1}{6}x+\frac{1}{3}=y$$
The inverse function is $f^{-1}(x)=-\frac{1}{6}x+\frac{1}{3}$.

41. $f(x)=3x-4$
$$y=3x-4$$
$$x=3y-4$$
$$x+4=3y$$
$$\frac{1}{3}x+\frac{4}{3}=y$$
The inverse function is $f^{-1}(x)=\frac{1}{3}x+\frac{4}{3}$.

43. $f(x)=-\frac{2}{3}x+4$
$$y=-\frac{2}{3}x+4$$
$$x=-\frac{2}{3}y+4$$
$$x-4=-\frac{2}{3}y$$
$$-\frac{3}{2}x+6=y$$
The inverse function is $f^{-1}(x)=-\frac{3}{2}x+6$.

45. $f(x)=3x-2$
$$y=3x-2$$
$$x=3y-2$$
$$x+2=3y$$
$$\frac{1}{3}x+\frac{2}{3}=y$$
The inverse function is $f^{-1}(x)=\frac{1}{3}x+\frac{2}{3}$.

47.
$$f(x) = -\frac{3}{4}x - 2$$
$$y = -\frac{3}{4}x - 2$$
$$x = -\frac{3}{4}y - 2$$
$$x + 2 = -\frac{3}{4}y$$
$$-\frac{4}{3}x - \frac{8}{3} = y$$

The inverse function is $f^{-1}(x) = -\frac{4}{3}x - \frac{8}{3}$.

49.
$$\begin{aligned} g(h(x)) &= g(x-5) \\ &= x - 5 + 5 \\ &= x \\ h(g(x)) &= h(x+5) \\ &= x + 5 - 5 \\ &= x \end{aligned}$$

The functions are inverses of each other.

51.
$$\begin{aligned} h(g(x)) &= h(2-x) \\ &= 2 - x + 2 \\ &= 4 - x \\ g(h(x)) &= g(x+2) \\ &= 2 - (x+2) \\ &= -x \end{aligned}$$

The functions are not inverses of each other.

53.
$$\begin{aligned} h(f(x)) &= h\left(\frac{1}{4}x + \frac{1}{4}\right) \\ &= 4\left(\frac{1}{4}x + \frac{1}{4}\right) - 1 \\ &= x + 1 - 1 = x \\ f(h(x)) &= f(4x-1) \\ &= \frac{1}{4}(4x-1) + \frac{1}{4} \\ &= x - \frac{1}{4} + \frac{1}{4} = x \end{aligned}$$

The functions are inverses of each other.

55.
$$\begin{aligned} g(h(x)) &= g(-2x+1) \\ &= -\frac{1}{2}(-2x+1) - \frac{1}{2} \\ &= x - \frac{1}{2} - \frac{1}{2} = x - 1 \\ h(g(x)) &= h\left(-\frac{1}{2}x - \frac{1}{2}\right) \\ &= -2\left(-\frac{1}{2}x - \frac{1}{2}\right) + 1 \\ &= x + 1 + 1 = x + 2 \end{aligned}$$

The functions are not inverses of each other.

57.
$$\begin{aligned} f[g(x)] &= f(2-3x) \\ &= 3(2-3x) - 2 \\ &= 6 - 9x - 2 \\ &= 4 - 9x \\ g[f(x)] &= g(3x-2) \\ &= 2 - 3(3x-2) \\ &= 2 - 9x + 6 \\ &= 8 - 9x \end{aligned}$$

The functions are not inverses of each other.

59.
$$\begin{aligned} g[f(x)] &= g(-2x-4) \\ &= -\frac{1}{2}(-2x-4) - 2 \\ &= x + 2 - 2 \\ &= x \\ f[g(x)] &= f\left(-\frac{1}{2}x - 2\right) \\ &= -2\left(-\frac{1}{2}x - 2\right) - 4 \\ &= x + 4 - 4 = x \end{aligned}$$

The functions are inverses of each other.

61.
$$\begin{aligned} f[h(x)] &= f(-2x+3) \\ &= -\frac{1}{2}(-2x+3) + \frac{3}{2} \\ &= x - \frac{3}{2} + \frac{3}{2} \\ &= x \\ h[f(x)] &= h\left(-\frac{1}{2}x + \frac{3}{2}\right) \\ &= -2\left(-\frac{1}{2}x + \frac{3}{2}\right) + 3 \\ &= x - 3 + 3 \\ &= x \end{aligned}$$

The functions are inverses of each other.

Applying the Concepts

63.

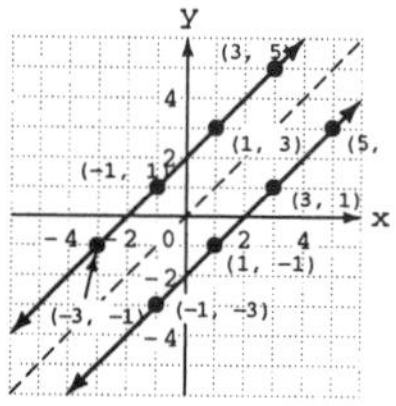

65.

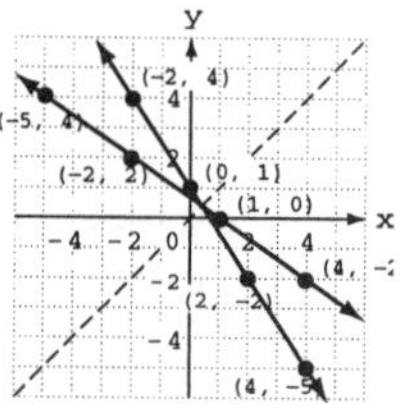

67. 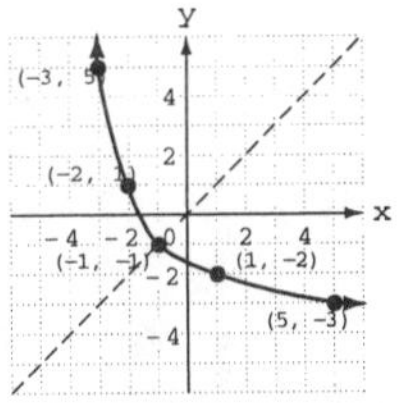

69. Inverse of the Function

Cost	Weight
\$.32	$0< w<1$
\$.55	$1< w\le 2$
\$.78	$2< w\le 3$
\$1.01	$3< w\le 4$

The inverse of the function is not a function because each cost has more than one weight assigned to it.

71. $-1=f(3)$
$f^{-1}[f(3)]=3$

73. $3=f(-3)$
$f^{-1}[f(-3)]=-3$

75. $8=f(0)$
$f^{-1}[f(0)]=0$

77. Yes, all functions $f(x)=mx+b$ are 1-1 functions. All the functions pass the horizontal-line test.

CHAPTER REVIEW

1. Yes, the graph is that of a function. It passes the vertical-line test.

2. The graph is a 1-1 function. It passes the horizontal- and vertical-line tests.

3. $f(x)=3x^3-2$
Domain: $(-\infty, \infty)$
Range: $(-\infty, \infty)$

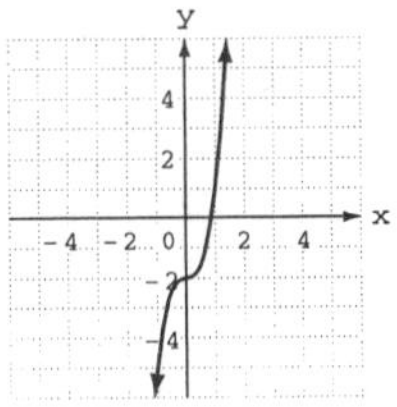

4. $f(x)=\sqrt{x+4}$
Domain: $\{x|x\ge -4\}$
Range: $\{y|y\ge 0\}$

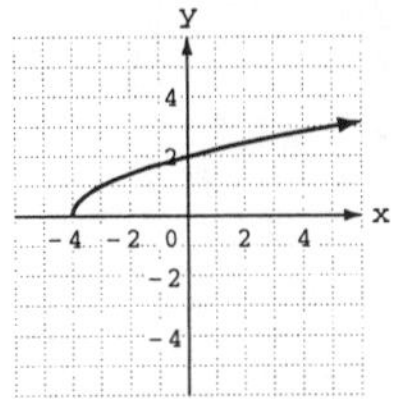

5. $y=-3x^2+4x+6$
$a=-3,\ b=4,\ c=6$
b^2-4ac
$(4)^2-4(-3)(6)=16+72=88$
$88>0$
Since the discriminant is greater than zero, the function has two x-intercepts.

6. $y=3x^2+9x$
$0=3x^2+9x$
$0=3x(x+3)$
$3x=0 \quad x+3=0$
$x=0 \qquad x=-3$
The x-intercepts are (0, 0) and (–3, 0).

7. $f(x)=3x^2+2x+2$
$0=3x^2+2x+2$
$x=\dfrac{-b\pm\sqrt{b^2-4ac}}{2a}$
$x=\dfrac{-2\pm\sqrt{2^2-4(3)(2)}}{2\cdot 3}=\dfrac{-2\pm\sqrt{-20}}{6}$
$x=-\dfrac{1}{3}\pm\dfrac{2i\sqrt{5}}{6}=-\dfrac{1}{3}\pm\dfrac{i\sqrt{5}}{3}$
The zeros are $-\dfrac{1}{3}+\dfrac{\sqrt{5}}{3}i$ and $-\dfrac{1}{3}-\dfrac{\sqrt{5}}{3}i$.

8. $f(x)=-2x^2+4x+1$
$x=\dfrac{-b}{2a}=\dfrac{-4}{2\cdot(-2)}=1$
$f(1)=-2(1)^2+4(1)+1$
$=-2+4+1$
$=3$
The maximum value of the function is 3.

9. $f(x) = x^2 - 7x + 8$

$$x = \frac{-b}{2a} = \frac{-(-7)}{2 \cdot 1} = \frac{7}{2}$$

$$f\left(\frac{7}{2}\right) = \left(\frac{7}{2}\right)^2 - 7\left(\frac{7}{2}\right) + 8$$
$$= \frac{49}{4} - \frac{49}{2} + 8$$
$$= -\frac{17}{4}$$

The minimum value of the function is $-\frac{17}{4}$.

10. $f(x) = x^2 + 4,\ g(x) = 4x - 1$
$g(0) = 4(0) - 1 = 0 - 1 = -1$
$f(-1) = (-1)^2 + 4 = 1 + 4 = 5$
$f[g(0)] = 5$

11. $f(x) = 6x + 8,\ g(x) = 4x + 2$
$f(-1) = 6(-1) + 8 = -6 + 8 = 2$
$g(2) = 4(2) + 2 = 8 + 2 = 10$
$g[f(-1)] = 10$

12. $f(x) = 3x^2 - 4,\ g(x) = 2x + 1$

$$f[g(x)] = f(2x+1)$$
$$= 3(2x+1)^2 - 4$$
$$= 3(4x^2 + 4x + 1) - 4$$
$$= 12x^2 + 12x + 3 - 4$$
$$f[g(x)] = 12x^2 + 12x - 1$$

13. $f(g(x)) = f(-4x + 5)$

$$= -\frac{1}{4}(-4x+5) + \frac{5}{4}$$
$$= x - \frac{5}{4} + \frac{5}{4} = x$$
$$g(f(x)) = g\left(-\frac{1}{4}x + \frac{5}{4}\right)$$
$$= -4\left(-\frac{1}{4}x + \frac{5}{4}\right) + 5$$
$$= x - 5 + 5 = x$$

The functions are inverses of each other.

14. $f(x) = x^2 + 2x - 4$
The domain is all real numbers.
The range is $\{y \mid y \geq -5\}$.

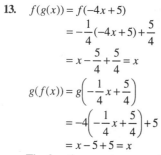

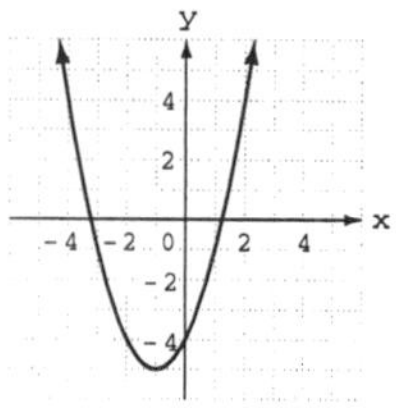

15. $y = x^2 - 2x + 3$

$$y = (x-1)^2 - 1 + 3$$
$$y = (x-1)^2 + 2$$

Vertex: (1, 2)
Axis of symmetry: $x = 1$

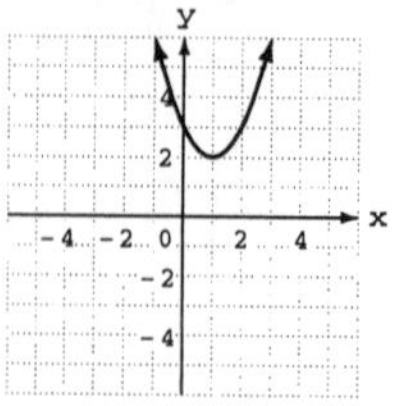

16. $f(x) = |x| - 3$
Domain: $(-\infty, \infty)$
Range: $\{y \mid y \geq -3\}$

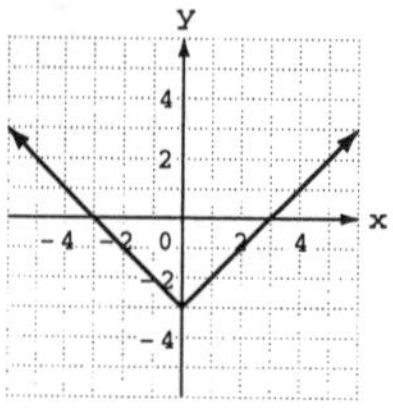

17. The graph is not a 1-1 function. It fails the horizontal-line test.

18. $S(x) = f(x) + g(x)$

$$= x^2 + 2x - 3 + (x^2 - 2)$$
$$S(x) = 2x^2 + 2x - 5$$
$$S(2) = 2(2)^2 + 2(2) - 5$$
$$= 8 + 4 - 5$$
$$S(2) = 7 = (f+g)(2)$$

19. $D(x) = f(x) - g(x)$

$$= x^2 + 2x - 3 - (x^2 - 2)$$
$$D(x) = 2x - 1$$
$$D(-4) = 2(-4) - 1$$
$$D(-4) = -9 = (f-g)(-4)$$

20. $P(x) = (f \cdot g)(x)$

$$= (x^2 + 2x - 3)(x^2 - 2)$$
$$= x^4 - 2x^2 + 2x^3 - 4x - 3x^2 + 6$$
$$P(x) = x^4 + 2x^3 - 5x^2 - 4x + 6$$
$$P(-4) = (-4)^4 + 2(-4)^3 - 5(-4)^2 - 4(-4) + 6$$
$$= 256 - 128 - 80 + 16 + 6$$
$$P(-4) = 70 = (f \cdot g)(-4)$$

21. $\left(\frac{f}{g}\right)(x) = \frac{x^2 + 2x - 3}{x^2 - 2}$

$$\left(\frac{f}{g}\right)(3) = \frac{(3)^2 + 2(3) - 3}{(3)^2 - 2} = \frac{9 + 6 - 3}{9 - 2} = \frac{12}{7}$$
$$\left(\frac{f}{g}\right)(3) = \frac{12}{7}$$

22. $f(x) = 2x^2 + x - 5,\ g(x) = 3x - 1$

$$\begin{aligned} g[f(x)] &= g(2x^2 + x - 5) \\ &= 3(2x^2 + x - 5) - 1 \\ &= 6x^2 + 3x - 15 - 1 \\ g[f(x)] &= 6x^2 + 3x - 16 \end{aligned}$$

23.

$$\begin{aligned} f(x) &= -6x + 4 \\ y &= -6x + 4 \\ x &= -6y + 4 \\ x - 4 &= -6y \\ -\frac{1}{6}x + \frac{2}{3} &= y \end{aligned}$$

The inverse function is $f^{-1}(x) = -\frac{1}{6}x + \frac{2}{3}$.

24.

$$\begin{aligned} f(x) &= \frac{2}{3}x - 12 \\ y &= \frac{2}{3}x - 12 \\ x &= \frac{2}{3}y - 12 \\ x + 12 &= \frac{2}{3}y \\ \frac{3}{2}(x + 12) &= y \\ \frac{3}{2}x + 18 &= y \end{aligned}$$

The inverse function is $f^{-1}(x) = \frac{3}{2}x + 18$.

25.

$$\begin{aligned} f(x) &= \frac{1}{2}x + 8 \\ y &= \frac{1}{2}x + 8 \\ x &= \frac{1}{2}y + 8 \\ x - 8 &= \frac{1}{2}y \\ 2(x - 8) &= 2 \cdot \frac{1}{2}y \\ 2x - 16 &= y \end{aligned}$$

The inverse function is $f^{-1}(x) = 2x - 16$.

26. Strategy The perimeter is 28 ft.

$$\begin{aligned} 28 &= 2L + 2W \\ 14 &= L + W \\ 14 - L &= W \end{aligned}$$

The area is

$$\begin{aligned} L \cdot W &= L \cdot (14 - L) \\ &= 14L - L^2 \end{aligned}$$

- To find the length, find the L-coordinate of the vertex of the function $f(L) = -L^2 + 14L$.
- To find the width, replace L in $14 - L$ by the L-coordinate of the vertex and evaluate.
- To find the maximum area, multiply the length by the width.

Solution $L = \frac{-b}{2a} = \frac{-14}{2 \cdot (-1)} = 7$

The length is 7 ft.

$14 - L = 14 - 7 = 7$

The width is 7 ft.

$L \cdot W = 7 \cdot 7 = 49$

The dimensions are 7 ft by 7 ft.

The maximum area is 49 ft^2.

CHAPTER TEST

1.

$$\begin{aligned} y &= 2x^2 - 3x + 4 \\ 0 &= 2x^2 - 3x + 4 \\ x &= \frac{-b \pm \sqrt{b^2 - 4ac}}{2a} \\ x &= \frac{-(-3) \pm \sqrt{(-3)^2 - 4(2)(4)}}{2(2)} \\ &= \frac{3 \pm \sqrt{-23}}{4} \\ x &= \frac{3}{4} \pm \frac{i\sqrt{23}}{4} \end{aligned}$$

The x-intercepts are $\frac{3}{4} + \frac{\sqrt{23}}{4}i$ and $\frac{3}{4} - \frac{i\sqrt{23}}{4}$.

2.

$$\begin{aligned} g(x) &= x^2 + 3x - 8 \\ 0 &= x^2 + 3x - 8 \\ x &= \frac{-b \pm \sqrt{b^2 - 4ac}}{2a} \\ x &= \frac{-3 \pm \sqrt{3^2 - 4(1)(-8)}}{2 \cdot 1} \\ &= \frac{-3 \pm \sqrt{41}}{2} \end{aligned}$$

The zeros of the function are

$\frac{-3 + \sqrt{41}}{2}$ and $\frac{-3 - \sqrt{41}}{2}$.

3. $y = 3x^2 + 2x - 4$

$a = 3,\ b = 2,\ c = -4$

$b^2 - 4ac$

$2^2 - 4(3)(-4) = 4 + 48 = 52$

$52 > 0$

Since the discriminant is greater than zero, the parabola has two real zeros.

4. $D(x) = f(x) - g(x)$

$= x^2 + 2x - 3 - (x^3 - 1)$

$D(x) = -x^3 + x^2 + 2x - 2$

$D(2) = -(2)^3 + (2)^2 + 2(2) - 2$

$= -8 + 4 + 4 - 2 = -2$

$D(2) = -2 = (f - g)(2)$

5. $P(x) = f(x) \cdot g(x)$

$= (x^3 + 1) \cdot (2x - 3)$

$P(x) = 2x^4 - 3x^3 + 2x - 3$

$P(-3) = 2(-3)^4 - 3(-3)^3 + 2(-3) - 3$

$= 162 + 81 - 6 - 3 = 234$

$P(-3) = 234 = (f \cdot g)(-3)$

6. $\left(\dfrac{f}{g}\right)(x) = \dfrac{4x - 5}{x^2 + 3x + 4}$

$\left(\dfrac{f}{g}\right)(-2) = \dfrac{4(-2) - 5}{(-2)^2 + 3(-2) + 4}$

$= \dfrac{-13}{4 - 6 + 4} = \dfrac{-13}{2} = -\dfrac{13}{2}$

7. $D(x) = f(x) - g(x)$

$= x^2 + 4 - (2x^2 + 2x + 1)$

$D(x) = -x^2 - 2x + 3$

$D(-4) = -(-4)^2 - 2(-4) + 3$

$= -16 + 8 + 3 = -5$

$D(-4) = -5 = (f - g)(-4)$

8. $g(x) = \dfrac{x}{x + 1}$

$g(3) = \dfrac{3}{3 + 1} = \dfrac{3}{4}$

$f(x) = 4x + 2$

$f\left(\dfrac{3}{4}\right) = 4 \cdot \dfrac{3}{4} + 2 = 5$

$f[g(3)] = 5$

9. $g(x) = x - 1$

$f[g(x)] = 2(x - 1)^2 - 7$

$= 2(x^2 - 2x + 1) - 7$

$= 2x^2 - 4x + 2 - 7$

$f[g(x)] = 2x^2 - 4x - 5$

10. $f(x) = -x^2 + 8x - 7$

$x = -\dfrac{b}{2a} = \dfrac{-8}{2 \cdot (-1)} = 4$

$f(4) = -(4)^2 + 8(4) - 7$

$= -16 + 32 - 7 = 9$

The maximum value of the function is 9.

11. $f(x) = 4x - 2$

$y = 4x - 2$

$x = 4y - 2$

$x + 2 = 4y$

$\dfrac{1}{4}x + \dfrac{1}{2} = y$

The inverse function is $f^{-1}(x) = \dfrac{1}{4}x + \dfrac{1}{2}$.

12. $f(x) = \dfrac{1}{4}x - 4$

$y = \dfrac{1}{4}x - 4$

$x = \dfrac{1}{4}y - 4$

$x + 4 = \dfrac{1}{4}y$

$4x + 16 = y$

The inverse of the function is $f^{-1}(x) = 4x + 16$.

13. The inverse of the function of $\{(2, 6), (3, 5), (4, 4), (5, 3)\}$ is $\{(6, 2), (5, 3), (4, 4), (3, 5)\}$.

14. $f[g(x)] = \dfrac{1}{2}(2x - 4) + 2$

$= x - 2 + 2$

$= x$

$g[f(x)] = 2\left(\dfrac{1}{2}x + 2\right) - 4$

$= x + 4 - 4$

$= x$

The functions are inverses of each other.

15. Strategy

- Let x represent one number. Since the sum of the two numbers is 20, the other number is $20 - x$. Their product is $20x - x^2$.
- To find the first number, find the x-coordinate of the vertex of the function $f(x) = -x^2 + 20x$.
- To find the other number, replace x in $20 - x$ with the x-coordinate of the vertex and evaluate.

Solution

$x = -\dfrac{b}{2a} = \dfrac{-20}{2 \cdot (-1)} = 10$

$20 - x = 20 - 10 = 10$

The numbers are 10 and 10, so their product is 100.

16. $f(x) = -\sqrt{3-x}$

The domain is $\{x|x \le 3\}$

The range is $\{y|y \le 0\}$.

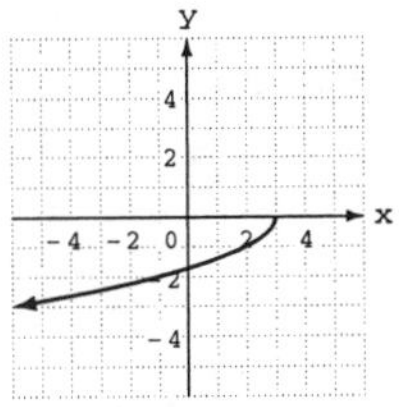

17. $f(x) = \left|\frac{1}{2}x\right| - 2$

The domain is all real numbers.

The range is $\{y|y \ge -2\}$.

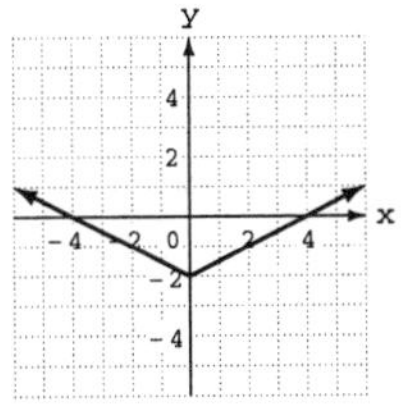

18. $f(x) = x^3 - 3x + 2$

The domain is all real numbers.

The range is all real numbers.

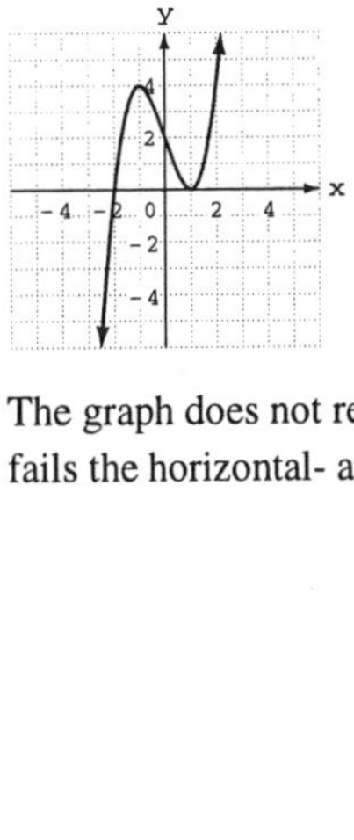

19. The graph does not represent a 1-1 function. It fails the horizontal- and vertical-line tests.

20. Strategy The perimeter is 200 cm.

$$200 = 2L + 2W$$
$$100 = L + W$$
$$100 - L = W$$

The area is $L \cdot W = L(100 - L)$
$$= 100L - L^2$$

- To find the length, find the L-coordinate of the vertex of the function $f(L) = -L^2 + 100L$.
- To find the width, replace L in $100 - L$ by the L-coordinate of the vertex and evaluate.
- To find the maximum area, multiply the length by the width.

Solution $L = -\frac{b}{2a} = -\frac{100}{2(-1)} = 50$

The length is 50 cm.

$100 - L = 100 - 50 = 50$

The width is 50 cm.

$L \cdot W = 50 \cdot 50 = 2500$

The maximum area is 2500 cm^2.

CUMULATIVE REVIEW

1. $$-3a + \left|\frac{3b - ab}{3b - c}\right| = -3(2) + \left|\frac{3(2) - 2(2)}{3(2) - (-2)}\right|$$
$$= -6 + \left|\frac{6-4}{6+2}\right| = -6 + \left|\frac{2}{8}\right|$$
$$= -6 + \left|\frac{1}{4}\right| = -6 + \frac{1}{4} = -\frac{23}{4}$$

2. 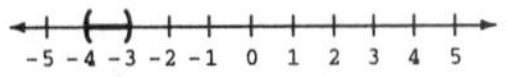

3. $$\frac{3x-1}{6} - \frac{5-x}{4} = \frac{5}{6}$$
$$12\left(\frac{3x-1}{6} - \frac{5-x}{4}\right) = 12\left(\frac{5}{6}\right)$$
$$2(3x-1) - 3(5-x) = 2(5)$$
$$6x - 2 - 15 + 3x = 10$$
$$9x - 17 = 10$$
$$9x = 27$$
$$x = 3$$

The solution is 3.

4. $4x - 2 < -10$ or $3x - 1 > 8$

$4x - 2 < -10 \qquad 3x - 1 > 8$

$4x < -8 \qquad 3x > 9$

$x < -2 \qquad x > 3$

$\{x|x < -2\}$ or $\{x|x > 3\}$

$\{x|x < -2\} \cup \{x|x > 3\} = \{x|x < -2 \text{ or } x > 3\}$

5. $|8-2x| \geq 0$

$8-2x \leq 0 \quad 8-2x \geq 0$

$8 \leq 2x \quad 8 \geq 2x$

$4 \leq x \quad 4 \geq x$

$\{x|x \geq 4\}$ or $\{x|x \leq 4\}$

$\{x|x \geq 4\} \cup \{x|x \leq 4\} = \{x|x \in \text{real numbers}\}$

6. $$\left(\frac{3a^3b}{2a}\right)^2\left(\frac{a^2}{-3b^2}\right)^3 = \left(\frac{3a^2b}{2}\right)^2\left(\frac{a^2}{-3b^2}\right)^3$$
$$= \left(\frac{3^2a^4b^2}{2^2}\right)\left(\frac{a^6}{(-3)^3b^6}\right)$$
$$= \left(\frac{9a^4b^2}{4}\right)\left(\frac{a^6}{-27b^6}\right)$$
$$= \frac{9a^4b^2a^6}{4(-27)b^6}$$
$$= \frac{9a^{10}b^2}{-108b^6}$$
$$= -\frac{a^{10}}{12b^4}$$

7. $(x-4)(2x^2+4x-1)$
$= 2x^2(x-4)+4x(x-4)-1(x-4)$
$= 2x^3-8x^2+4x^2-16x-x+4$
$= 2x^3-4x^2-17x+4$

8. $a^4-2a^2-8 = (a^2)^2-2(a^2)-8$
$= (a^2-4)(a^2+2)$
$= (a+2)(a-2)(a^2+2)$

9. $x^3y+x^2y^2-6xy^3 = xy(x^2+xy-6y^2)$
$= xy(x+3y)(x-2y)$

10. $(b+2)(b-5) = 2b+14$
$b^2-3b-10 = 2b+14$
$b^2-5b-24 = 0$
$(b-8)(b+3) = 0$
$b-8=0 \quad b+3=0$
$b=8 \quad b=-3$

The solutions are 8 and –3.

11. $x^2-2x > 15$
$x^2-2x-15 > 0$
$(x-5)(x+3) > 0$

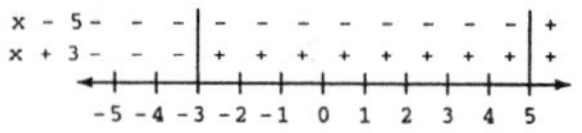

$\{x|x < -3 \text{ or } x > 5\}$

12. $$\frac{x^2+4x-5}{2x^2-3x+1} - \frac{x}{2x-1}$$
$$= \frac{(x+5)(x-1)}{(2x-1)(x-1)} - \frac{x}{2x-1}$$
$$= \frac{x+5}{2x-1} - \frac{x}{2x-1}$$
$$= \frac{x+5-x}{2x-1} = \frac{5}{2x-1}$$

13. $$\frac{5}{x^2+7x+12} = \frac{9}{x+4} - \frac{2}{x+3}$$
$$\frac{5}{(x+4)(x+3)} = \frac{9}{x+4}\cdot\frac{x+3}{x+3} - \frac{2}{x+3}\cdot\frac{x+4}{x+4}$$
$$\frac{5}{(x+4)(x+3)} = \frac{9x+27}{(x+4)(x+3)} - \frac{2x+8}{(x+4)(x+3)}$$
$$5 = (9x+27)-(2x+8)$$
$$5 = 9x+27-2x-8$$
$$5 = 7x+19$$
$$-14 = 7x$$
$$-2 = x$$

The solution is –2.

14. $$\frac{4-6i}{2i} = \frac{4-6i}{2i}\cdot\frac{i}{i}$$
$$= \frac{4i-6i^2}{2i^2}$$
$$= \frac{4i+6}{-2}$$
$$= -3-2i$$

15. Vertex: (0, 0)

Axis of symmetry: $x=0$

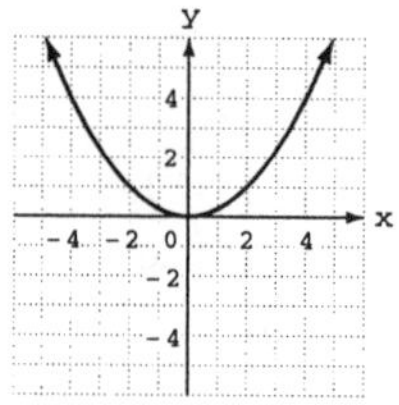

16. $3x-4y \geq 8$
$-4y \geq -3x+8$
$y \leq \frac{3}{4}x-2$

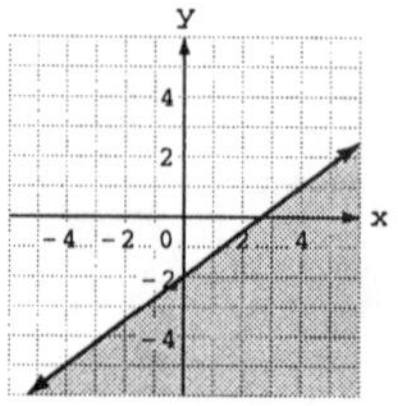

17. $$m = \frac{y_2-y_1}{x_2-x_1} = \frac{-6-4}{2-(-3)} = \frac{-10}{5} = -2$$
$y-y_1 = m(x-x_1)$
$y-4 = -2[x-(-3)]$
$y-4 = -2(x+3)$
$y-4 = -2x-6$
$y = -2x-2$

18. The product of the slopes of perpendicular lines is –1.

$$2x-3y=6 \qquad m_1 \cdot m_2 = -1$$
$$-3y=-2x+6 \qquad \frac{2}{3}\cdot m_2 = -1$$
$$y=\frac{2}{3}x-2 \qquad m_2 = -\frac{3}{2}$$
$$y-y_1=m(x-x_1)$$
$$y-1=-\frac{3}{2}[x-(-3)]$$
$$y-1=-\frac{3}{2}(x+3)$$
$$y-1=-\frac{3}{2}x-\frac{9}{2}$$
$$y=-\frac{3}{2}x-\frac{7}{2}$$

19.
$$3x^2=3x-1$$
$$3x^2-3x+1=0$$
$$a=3,\ b=-3,\ c=1$$
$$x=\frac{-b\pm\sqrt{b^2-4ac}}{2a}$$
$$=\frac{-(-3)\pm\sqrt{(-3)^2-4(3)(1)}}{2(3)}$$
$$=\frac{3\pm\sqrt{9-12}}{6}$$
$$=\frac{3\pm\sqrt{-3}}{6}=\frac{3\pm i\sqrt{-3}}{6}=\frac{1}{2}\pm\frac{\sqrt{3}}{6}i$$

The solutions are $\frac{1}{2}+\frac{\sqrt{3}}{6}i$ and $\frac{1}{2}-\frac{\sqrt{3}}{6}i$.

20.
$$\sqrt{8x+1}=2x-1$$
$$\left(\sqrt{8x+1}\right)^2=(2x-1)^2$$
$$8x+1=4x^2-4x+1$$
$$0=4x^2-12x$$
$$0=4x(x-3)$$
$$4x=0 \qquad x-3=0$$
$$x=0 \qquad x=3$$

Check:

$\sqrt{8x+1}$	$=$ $2x-1$
$\sqrt{8(0)+1}$	$2(0)-1$
$\sqrt{1}$	-1
$1 \neq$	-1

Check:

$\sqrt{8x+1}$	$=$ $2x-1$
$\sqrt{8(3)+1}$	$2(3)-1$
$\sqrt{24+1}$	$6-1$
$\sqrt{25}$	5
$5 =$	5

The solution is 3.

21. $f(x)=2x^2-3$

$a=2,\ b=0,\ c=-3$

$x=\frac{-b}{2a}=\frac{-0}{2\cdot 2}=0$

$f(0)=2(0)^2-3=-3$

The minimum value of the function is –3.

22. $f(x)=|3x-4|$;

domain = {0, 1, 2, 3}

$f(x)=|3x-4|$

$f(0)=|3(0)-4|=|0-4|=|-4|=4$

$f(1)=|3(1)-4|=|3-4|=|-1|=1$

$f(2)=|3(2)-4|=|6-4|=|2|=2$

$f(3)=|3(3)-4|=|9-4|=|5|=5$

The range is {1, 2, 4, 5}.

23. {(–3, 0), (–2, 0), (–1, 1), (0, 1)}

Each member of the domain is paired with only one member of the range. The set of ordered pairs is a function.

24.
$$\sqrt[3]{5x-2}=2$$
$$\left(\sqrt[3]{5x-2}\right)^3=2^3$$
$$5x-2=8$$
$$5x=10$$
$$x=2$$

The solution is 2.

25.
$$h(x) = \frac{1}{2}x + 4$$
$$h(2) = \frac{1}{2}(2) + 4 = 1 + 4 = 5$$
$$g(x) = 3x - 5$$
$$g(5) = 3(5) - 5 = 15 - 5 = 10$$
$$g(h(2)) = g(5) = 10$$

26.
$$f(x) = -3x + 9$$
$$y = -3x + 9$$
$$x = -3y + 9$$
$$3y = -x + 9$$
$$y = -\frac{1}{3}x + 3$$

The inverse function is $f^{-1}(x) = -\frac{1}{3}x + 3$.

27. Strategy

- Cost per pound of the mixture: x

	Amount	Cost	Value
\$4.50 tea	30	4.50	4.50(3)
\$3.60 tea	45	3.60	3.60(45)
Mixture	75	x	$75x$

- The sum of the values before mixing equals the value after mixing.

Solution
$$4.50(30) + 3.60(45) = 75x$$
$$135 + 162 = 75x$$
$$297 = 75x$$
$$3.96 = x$$

The cost per pound of the mixture is \$3.96.

28. Strategy

- Pounds of 80% copper alloy: x

	Amount	Percent	Quantity
80%	x	0.80	$0.80x$
20%	50	0.20	0.20(50)
40%	$50 + x$	0.40	$0.40(50 + x)$

- The sum of the quantities before mixing is equal to the quantity after mixing.

Solution
$$0.80x + 0.20(50) = 0.40(50 + x)$$
$$0.80x + 10 = 20 + 0.40x$$
$$0.40x + 10 = 20$$
$$0.40x = 10$$
$$x = 25$$

25 lb of the 80% copper alloy must be used.

29. Strategy

To find the additional amount of insecticide, write and solve a proportion using x to represent the additional amount of insecticide. Then, $x + 6$ is the total amount of insecticide.

Solution
$$\frac{6}{16} = \frac{x+6}{28}$$
$$\frac{3}{8} = \frac{x+6}{28}$$
$$\frac{3}{8} \cdot 56 = \frac{x+6}{28} \cdot 56$$
$$21 = (x+6)2$$
$$21 = 2x + 12$$
$$9 = 2x$$
$$4.5 = x$$

An additional 4.5 oz of insecticide are required.

30. Strategy

- This is a work problem.
- Time for the smaller pipe to fill the tank: t
  Time for the larger pipe to fill the tank: $t - 8$

	Rate	Time	Part
Smaller pipe	$\frac{1}{t}$	3	$\frac{3}{t}$
Larger pipe	$\frac{1}{t-8}$	3	$\frac{3}{t-8}$

- The sum of the parts of the task completed must equal 1.

Solution
$$\frac{3}{t} + \frac{3}{t-8} = 1$$
$$t(t-8)\left(\frac{3}{t} + \frac{3}{t-8}\right) = t(t-8)$$
$$(t-8)3 + 3t = t^2 - 8t$$
$$3t - 24 + 3t = t^2 - 8t$$
$$6t - 24 = t^2 - 8t$$
$$0 = t^2 - 14t + 24$$
$$= (t-2)(t-12)$$

$t - 2 = 0 \quad t - 12 = 0$

$t = 2 \quad\quad t = 12$

The solution 2 is not possible since the time for the larger pipe would then be a negative number.

$t - 8 = 12 - 8 = 4$

It would take the larger pipe 4 min to fill the tank.

31. Strategy To find the distance:

- Write the basic direct variation equation, replace the variables by the given values, and solve for k.
- Write the direct variation equation, replacing k by its value. Substitute 40 for f and solve for d.

Solution

$$d = kf \qquad d = \frac{3}{5}f$$
$$30 = k(50) \qquad = \frac{3}{5}(40)$$
$$\frac{3}{5} = k \qquad = 24$$

A force of 40 lb will stretch the string 24 in.

32. Strategy To find the frequency:

- Write the basic indirect variation equation, replace the variables by the given values, and solve for k.
- Write the inverse variation equation, replacing k by its value. Substitute 1.5 for L and solve for f.

Solution

$$f = \frac{k}{L} \qquad f = \frac{120}{L}$$
$$60 = \frac{k}{2} \qquad = \frac{120}{1.5}$$
$$120 = k \qquad = 80$$

The frequency is 80 times per minute.

Chapter 10: Exponential and Logarithmic Functions

SECTION 10.1

Objective A Exercises

1. $f(x) = 3^x$

   a. $f(2) = 3^2 = 9$

   b. $f(0) = 3^0 = 1$

   c. $f(-2) = 3^{-2} = \dfrac{1}{3^2} = \dfrac{1}{9}$

3. $g(x) = 2^{x+1}$

   a. $g(3) = 2^{3+1} = 2^4 = 16$

   b. $g(1) = 2^{1+1} = 2^2 = 4$

   c. $g(-3) = 2^{-3+1} = 2^{-2} = \dfrac{1}{2^2} = \dfrac{1}{4}$

5. $P(x) = \left(\dfrac{1}{2}\right)^{2x}$

   a. $P(0) = \left(\dfrac{1}{2}\right)^{2\cdot 0} = \left(\dfrac{1}{2}\right)^0 = 1$

   b. $P\left(\dfrac{3}{2}\right) = \left(\dfrac{1}{2}\right)^{2\cdot\frac{3}{2}} = \left(\dfrac{1}{2}\right)^3 = \dfrac{1}{8}$

   c. $P(-2) = \left(\dfrac{1}{2}\right)^{2\cdot(-2)} = \left(\dfrac{1}{2}\right)^{-4} = 2^4 = 16$

7. $G(x) = e^{x/2}$

   a. $G(4) = e^{4/2} = e^2 = 7.3891$

   b. $G(-2) = e^{-2/2} = e^{-1} = \dfrac{1}{e} = 0.3679$

   c. $G\left(\dfrac{1}{2}\right) = e^{\frac{1}{2}/2} = e^{1/4} = e^{0.25} = 1.2840$

9. $H(r) = e^{-r+3}$

   a. $H(-1) = e^{-(-1)+3} = e^4 = 54.5982$

   b. $H(3) = e^{-3+3} = e^0 = 1$

   c. $H(5) = e^{-5+3} = e^{-2} = \dfrac{1}{e^2} = 0.1353$

11. $F(x) = 2^{x^2}$

   a. $F(2) = 2^{2^2} = 2^4 = 16$

   b. $F(-2) = 2^{(-2)^2} = 2^4 = 16$

   c. $F\left(\dfrac{3}{4}\right) = 2^{\left(\frac{3}{4}\right)^2} = 2^{\frac{9}{16}} = \sqrt[16]{2^9} = \sqrt[16]{512} = 1.4768$

13. $f(x) = e^{-x^2/2}$

   a. $f(-2) = e^{-(-2)^2/2}$
   $= e^{-4/2}$
   $= e^{-2} = \dfrac{1}{e^2} = 0.1353$

   b. $f(2) = e^{-(2)^2/2} = e^{-4/2} = e^{-2} = \dfrac{1}{e^2} = 0.1353$

   c. $f(-3) = e^{-(-3)^2/2} = e^{-9/2} = \dfrac{1}{e^{9/2}} = 0.0111$

Objective B Exercises

15.

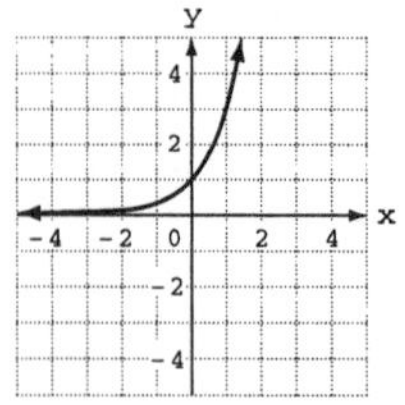

17.

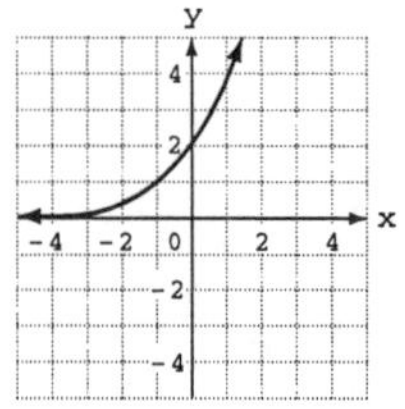

19.

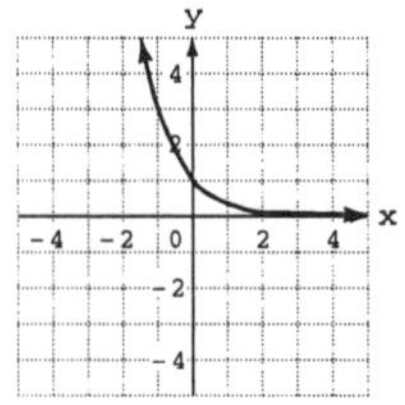

21.

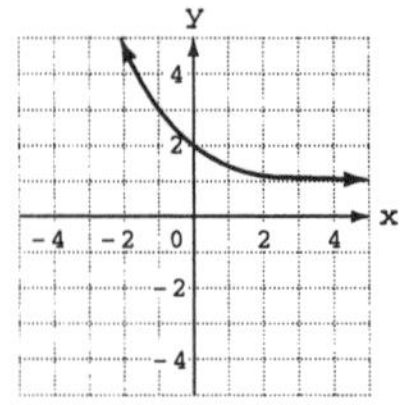

23.

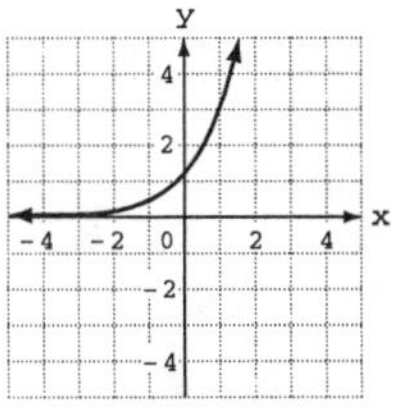

25.

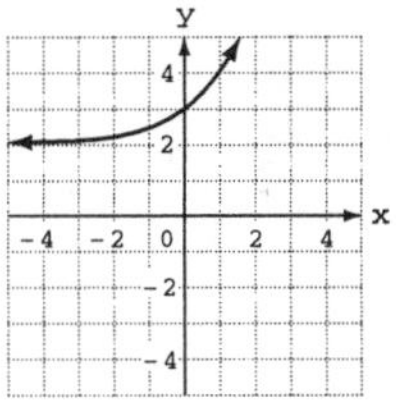

Applying the Concepts

27. $P(x) = \left(\sqrt{3}\right)^x$

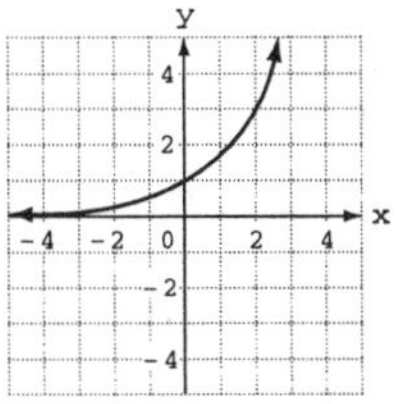

29. $Q(x) = \left(\sqrt{3}\right)^{-x}$

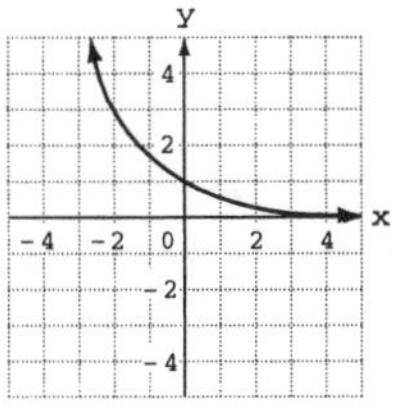

31. $\sinh(x) = \dfrac{e^x - e^{-x}}{2}$

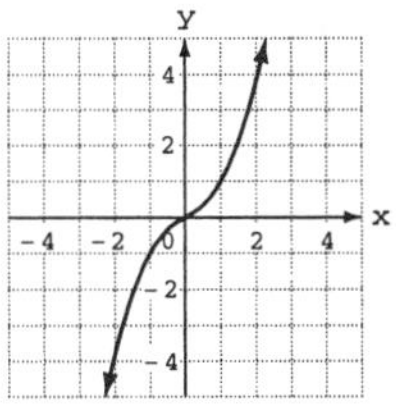

33. $N(x) = e^{-x^2/2}$

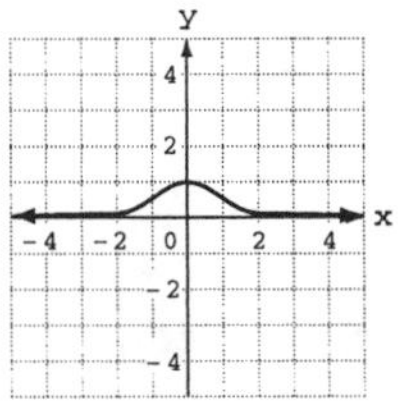

35. $f(x) = 2^x - x^2$

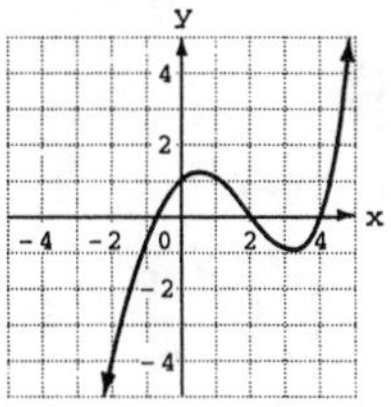

37. $f(x) = \pi^x$

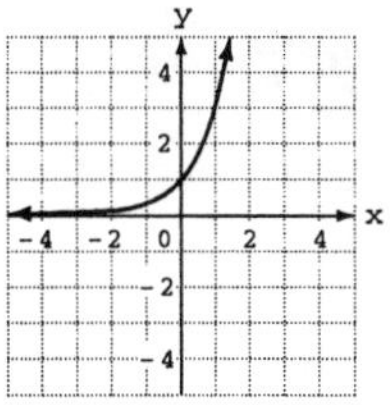

39. a.

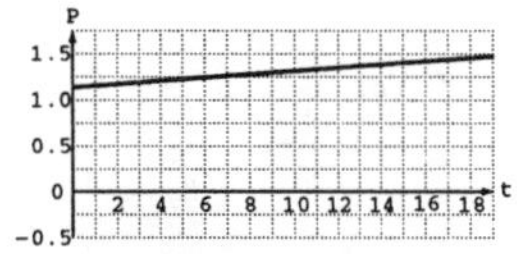

b. In 1998 the population of China will be 1.242 billion people.

41. a.

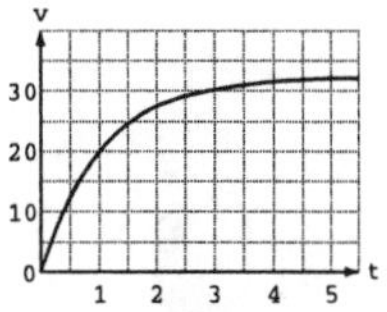

b. At $t = 2$ seconds after the object is dropped, it will be falling at 27.7 feet per second.

43. $f(x) = b^x$

a. Always true.

b. Always true.

45.

x	$(1+x)^{1/x}$
0.1	2.593742
0.01	2.704814
0.001	2.716924
0.00001	2.718268
0.0000001	2.718282

$e = 2.718282$

As $x \to 0$, $(1+x)^{1/x}$ becomes closer to e.

SECTION 10.2

Objective A Exercises

1. $5^2 = 25$ is equivalent to $\log_5 25 = 2$.

3. $4^{-2} = \frac{1}{16}$ is equivalent to $\log_4\left(\frac{1}{16}\right) = -2$.

5. $10^y = x$ is equivalent to $\log_{10}(x) = y$.

7. $a^x = w$ is equivalent to $\log_a(w) = x$.

9. $\log_3 9 = 2$ is equivalent to $3^2 = 9$.

11. $\log 0.01 = -2$ is equivalent to $10^{-2} = 0.01$.

13. $\ln x = y$ is equivalent to $e^y = x$.

15. $\log_b u = v$ is equivalent to $b^v = u$.

17.
$$\log_3 81 = x$$
$$81 = 3^x$$
$$x = 4$$
$$\log_3 81 = 4$$

19.
$$\log_2 128 = x$$
$$2^x = 128$$
$$x = 7$$
$$\log_2 128 = 7$$

21.
$$\log 100 = x$$
$$10^x = 100$$
$$x = 2$$
$$\log 100 = 2$$

23.
$$\ln e^3 = x$$
$$3\ln e = x$$
$$3(1) = x$$
$$x = 3$$
$$\ln e^3 = 3$$

25.
$$\log_8 1 = x$$
$$8^x = 1$$
$$x = 0$$
$$\log_8 1 = 0$$

27.
$$\log_5 625 = x$$
$$5^x = 625$$
$$x = 4$$
$$\log_5 625 = 4$$

29.
$$\log_3 x = 2$$
$$3^2 = x$$
$$9 = x$$

31.
$$\log_4 x = 3$$
$$4^3 = x$$
$$64 = x$$

33.
$$\log_7 x = -1$$
$$7^{-1} = x$$
$$\frac{1}{7} = x$$

35.
$$\log_6 x = 0$$
$$6^0 = x$$
$$1 = x$$

37.
$$\log x = 2.5$$
$$10^{2.5} = x$$
$$316.23 = x$$

39.
$$\log x = -1.75$$
$$10^{-1.75} = x$$
$$0.02 = x$$

41.
$$\ln x = 2$$
$$e^2 = x$$
$$7.39 = x$$

43.
$$\ln x = -\frac{1}{2}$$
$$e^{-1/2} = x$$
$$0.61 = x$$

45. $\log_3 x^3 + \log_3 y^2 = \log_3(x^3y^2)$

47. $\ln x^4 - \ln y^2 = \ln\frac{x^4}{y^2}$

49. $3\log_7 x = \log_7 x^3$

51. $3\ln x + 4\ln y = \ln x^3 + \ln y^4 = \ln(x^3y^4)$

53.
$$2(\log_4 x + \log_4 y) = 2\log_4(xy)$$
$$= \log_4(xy)^2$$
$$= \log_4(x^2y^2)$$

55.
$$2\log_3 x - \log_3 y + 2\log_3 z$$
$$= \log_3 x^2 - \log_3 y + \log_3 z^2$$
$$= \log_3\frac{x^2}{y} + \log_3 z^2$$
$$= \log_3\frac{x^2z^2}{y}$$

57.
$$\ln x - (2\ln y + \ln z) = \ln x - (\ln y^2 + \ln z)$$
$$= \ln x - \ln(y^2 \cdot z)$$
$$= \ln\left(\frac{x}{y^2z}\right)$$

59.
$$\frac{1}{2}(\log_6 x - \log_6 y) = \frac{1}{2}\log_6\frac{x}{y} = \log_6\left(\frac{x}{y}\right)^{1/2}$$
$$= \log_6\sqrt{\frac{x}{y}}$$

61. $2(\log_4 s - 2\log_4 t + \log_4 r)$
$= 2(\log_4 s - \log_4 t^2 + \log_4 r)$
$= 2\left(\log_4 \frac{s}{t^2} + \log_4 r\right)$
$= 2\log_4\left(\frac{sr}{t^2}\right)$
$= \log_4\left(\frac{sr}{t^2}\right)^2$
$= \log_4 \frac{s^2r^2}{t^4}$

63. $\ln x - 2(\ln y + \ln z) = \ln x - 2[\ln(yz)]$
$= \ln x - \ln(yz)^2$
$= \ln x - \ln(y^2z^2) = \ln \frac{x}{y^2z^2}$

65. $3\log_2 t - 2(\log_2 r - \log_2 v)$
$= \log_2 t^3 - 2\log_2\left(\frac{r}{v}\right)$
$= \log_2 t^3 - \log_2\left(\frac{r}{v}\right)^2$
$= \log_2 t^3 - \log_2\left(\frac{r^2}{v^2}\right)$
$= \log_2 \frac{t^3v^2}{r^2}$

67. $\frac{1}{2}(3\log_4 x - 2\log_4 y + \log_4 z)$
$= \frac{1}{2}(\log_4 x^3 - \log_4 y^2 + \log_4 z)$
$= \frac{1}{2}\left(\log_4 \frac{x^3}{y^2} + \log_4 z\right)$
$= \frac{1}{2}\log_4 \frac{x^3z}{y^2}$
$= \log_4\left(\frac{x^3z}{y^2}\right)^{1/2}$
$= \log_4 \sqrt{\frac{x^3z}{y^2}}$

69. $\frac{1}{2}(\ln x - 3\ln y)$
$= \frac{1}{2}(\ln x - \ln y^3)$
$= \frac{1}{2}\left[\ln\left(\frac{x}{y^3}\right)\right]$
$= \ln\left(\frac{x}{y^3}\right)^{1/2}$
$= \ln\left(\sqrt{\frac{x}{y^3}}\right)$

71. $\frac{1}{2}\log_2 x - \frac{2}{3}\log_2 y + \frac{1}{2}\log_2 z$
$= \log_2 x^{1/2} - \log_2 y^{2/3} + \log_2 z^{1/2}$
$= \log_2\left(\frac{x^{1/2}}{y^{2/3}}\right) + \log_2 z^{1/2}$
$= \log_2\left(\frac{x^{1/2}z^{1/2}}{y^{2/3}}\right)$
$= \log_2\left(\frac{\sqrt{xz}}{\sqrt[3]{y^2}}\right)$

Objective B Exercises

73. $\log_8(xz) = \log_8 x + \log_8 z$

75. $\log_3 x^5 = 5\log_3 x$

77. $\log_b\left(\frac{r}{s}\right) = \log_b r - \log_b s$

79. $\log_3(x^2y^6) = \log_3 x^2 + \log_3 y^6$
$= 2\log_3 x + 6\log_3 y$

81. $\log_7 \frac{u^3}{v^4} = \log_7 u^3 - \log_7 v^4$
$= 3\log_7 u - 4\log_7 v$

83. $\log_2(rs)^2 = 2\log_2(rs)$
$= 2(\log_2 r + \log_2 s)$
$= 2\log_2 r + 2\log_2 s$

85. $\ln x^2yz = \ln x^2 + \ln y + \ln z$
$= 2\ln x + \ln y + \ln z$

87. $\log_5\left(\frac{xy^2}{z^4}\right) = \log_5(xy^2) - \log_5 z^4$
$= \log_5 x + \log_5 y^2 - \log_5 z^4$
$= \log_5 x + 2\log_5 y - 4\log_5 z$

89. $\log_8\left(\frac{x^2}{yz^2}\right) = \log_8 x^2 - \log_8(yz^2)$
$= 2\log_8 x - (\log_8 y + \log_8 z^2)$
$= 2\log_8 x - \log_8 y - \log_8 z^2$
$= 2\log_8 x - \log_8 y - 2\log_8 z$

91. $\log_4 \sqrt{x^3y} = \log_4(x^3y)^{1/2}$
$= \frac{1}{2}[\log_4(x^3y)]$
$= \frac{1}{2}(\log_4 x^3 + \log_4 y)$
$= \frac{1}{2}(3\log_4 x + \log_4 y)$
$= \frac{3}{2}\log_4 x + \frac{1}{2}\log_4 y$

93.
$$\log_7\sqrt{\frac{x^3}{y}} = \log_7\left(\frac{x^3}{y}\right)^{1/2}$$
$$= \frac{1}{2}\log_7\left(\frac{x^3}{y}\right)$$
$$= \frac{1}{2}(\log_7 x^3 - \log_7 y)$$
$$= \frac{1}{2}(3\log_7 x - \log_7 y)$$
$$= \frac{3}{2}\log_7 x - \frac{1}{2}\log_7 y$$

95.
$$\ln x\sqrt{\frac{y}{z}} = \ln x\left(\frac{y}{z}\right)^{1/2}$$
$$= \ln x + \ln\left(\frac{y}{z}\right)^{1/2}$$
$$= \ln x + \frac{1}{2}\ln\frac{y}{z}$$
$$= \ln x + \frac{1}{2}(\ln y - \ln z)$$
$$= \ln x + \frac{1}{2}\ln y - \frac{1}{2}\ln z$$

97.
$$\log_3\frac{t}{\sqrt{x}} = \log_3 t - \log_3\sqrt{x}$$
$$= \log_3 t - \log_3 x^{1/2}$$
$$= \log_3 t - \frac{1}{2}\log_3 x$$

99.
$$\log_7\left(\frac{\sqrt{uv}}{x}\right) = \log_7\left(\frac{(uv)^{1/2}}{x}\right)$$
$$= \log_7(uv)^{1/2} - \log_7 x$$
$$= \frac{1}{2}\log_7(uv) - \log_7 x$$
$$= \frac{1}{2}(\log_7 u + \log_7 v) - \log_7 x$$
$$= \frac{1}{2}\log_7 u + \frac{1}{2}\log_7 v - \log_7 x$$

Objective C Exercises

101. $\log_{10} 7 = 0.8451$

103. $\log_{10}\left(\frac{3}{5}\right) = \log_{10} 3 - \log_{10} 5 = -0.2218$

105. $\ln 4 = 1.3863$

107. $\ln\left(\frac{17}{6}\right) = \ln 17 - \ln 6 = 1.0415$

109. $\log_8 6 = \frac{\log_{10} 6}{\log_{10} 8} = 0.8617$

111. $\log_5 30 = \frac{\log_{10} 30}{\log_{10} 5} = 2.1133$

113. $\log_3(0.5) = \frac{\log_{10}(0.5)}{\log_{10} 3} = -0.6309$

115. $\log_7(1.7) = \frac{\log_{10} 1.7}{\log_{10} 7} = 0.2727$

117. $\log_5 15 = \frac{\log_{10} 15}{\log_{10} 5} = 1.6826$

119. $\log_{12} 120 = \frac{\log_{10} 120}{\log_{10} 12} = 1.9266$

121. $\log_4 2.55 = \frac{\log_{10} 2.55}{\log_{10} 4} = 0.6752$

123. $\log_5 67 = \frac{\log_{10} 67}{\log_{10} 5} = 2.6125$

Applying the Concepts

125. **a.** $\log_3(-9) = -2$

$$3^{-2} = \frac{1}{3^2} = \frac{1}{9}$$
$$\frac{1}{9} \neq -9 \quad \text{False}$$

b. $x^y = z$ is $\log_x z = y$ True

c. $\log(x^{-1}) = \frac{1}{\log x}$

$$\log(x^{-1}) = -\log x$$
$$-\log x \neq \frac{1}{\log x} \quad \text{False}$$

d. $\log(x+y) = \log x + \log y$ False

e. $\log(x\cdot y) = \log x \cdot \log y$ False

f. $\log\left(\frac{x}{y}\right) = \log x - \log y$ True

g. $\frac{\log x}{\log y} = \frac{x}{y}$ False

h. If $\log x = \log y$, then $x = y$. True

SECTION 10.3

Objective A Exercises

1. $f(x) = \log_4 x$
   $y = \log_4 x$

   $y = \log_4 x$ is equivalent to $x = 4^y$.

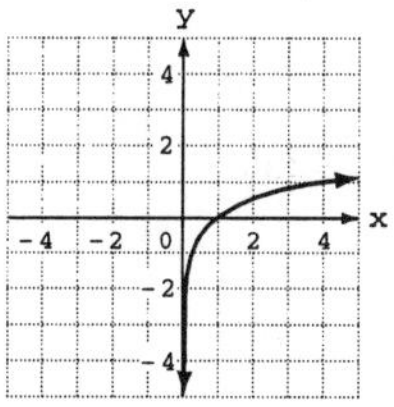

3. $f(x) = \log_3(2x-1)$
   $y = \log_3(2x-1)$

   $y = \log_3(2x-1)$ is equivalent to

   $(2x-1) = 3^y$, $2x = 3^y + 1$, or $x = \frac{1}{2}(3^y + 1)$.

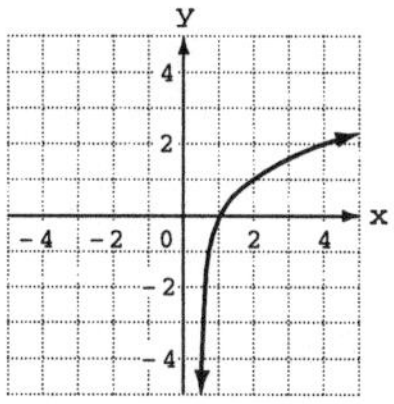

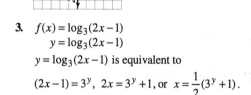

5. $f(x) = 3\log_2 x$
   $y = 3\log_2 x$
   $\frac{y}{3} = \log_2 x$

   $\frac{y}{3} = \log_2 x$ is equivalent to $x = 2^{\frac{y}{3}}$.

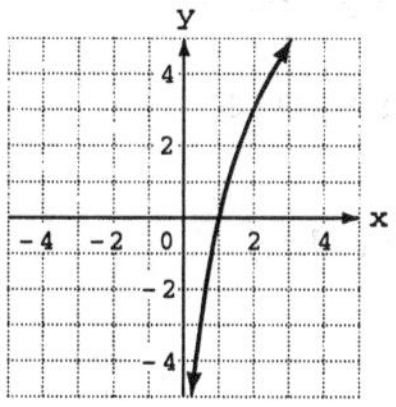

7. $f(x) = -\log_2 x$
   $y = -\log_2 x$
   $-y = \log_2 x$

   $-y = \log_2 x$ is equivalent to $x = 2^{-y}$.

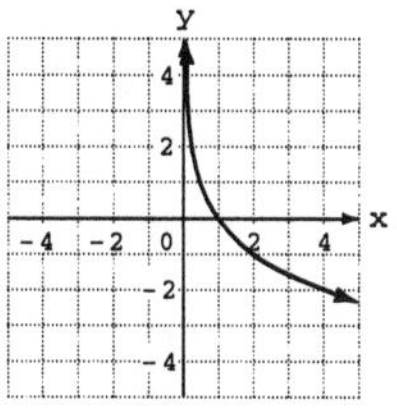

9. $f(x) = \log_2(x-1)$
   $y = \log_2(x-1)$

   $y = \log_2(x-1)$ is equivalent to $(x-1) = 2^y$, or $x = 2^y + 1$.

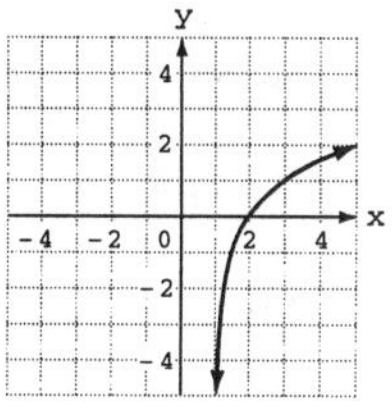

11. $f(x) = -\log_2(x-1)$
    $y = -\log_2(x-1)$
    $-y = \log_2(x-1)$

    $-y = \log_2(x-1)$ is equivalent to $(x-1) = 2^{-y}$, or $x = 2^{-y} + 1$.

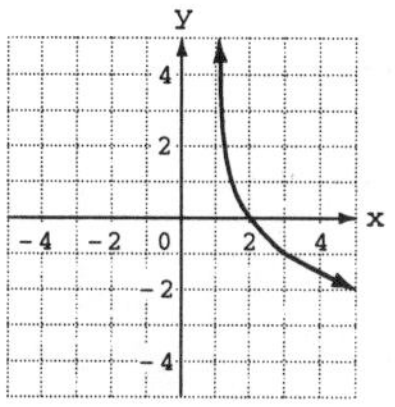

Applying the Concepts

13. $f(x) = \log_2 x - 3$
    $y = \log_2 x - 3$
    $y = \frac{\log x}{\log 2} - 3$
    $y = \frac{\log x}{0.3010} - 3$

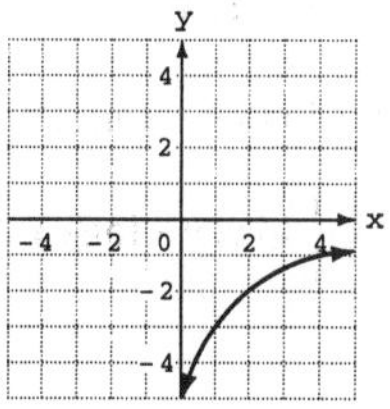

15. $f(x) = -\log_2 x + 2$
    $y = -\log_2 x + 2$
    $y = -\frac{\log x}{\log 2} + 2$
    $y = -\frac{\log x}{0.3010} + 2$

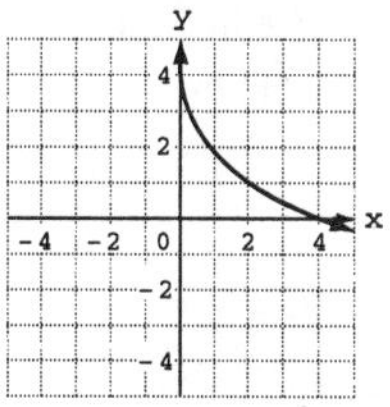

17. $f(x) = x - \log_2(1-x)$

$y = x - \log_2(1-x)$

$y = x - \dfrac{\log(1-x)}{\log 2}$

$y = x - \dfrac{\log(1-x)}{0.3010}$

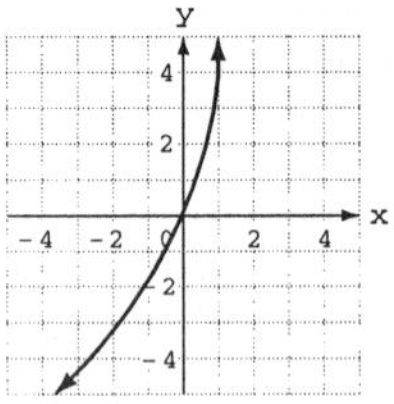

19. $f(x) = \dfrac{x}{2} - 2\log_2(x+1)$

$y = \dfrac{x}{2} - \log_2(x+1)^2$

$= \dfrac{x}{2} - \dfrac{\log(x+1)^2}{\log 2}$

$= \dfrac{x}{2} - \dfrac{\log(x+1)^2}{0.3010}$

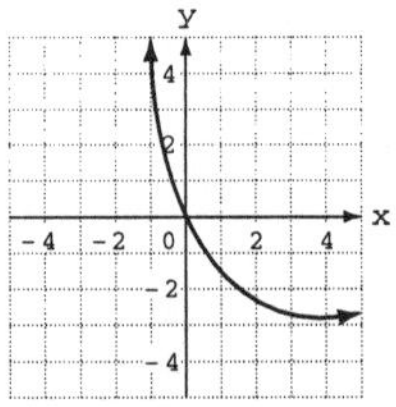

21. $f(x) = x^2 - 10\ln(x-1)$

$y = x^2 - 10\ln(x-1)$

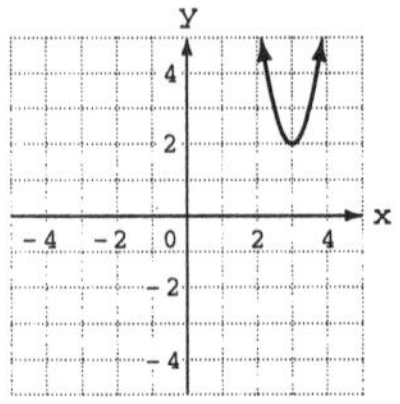

23. a. $M = 5\log s - 5$

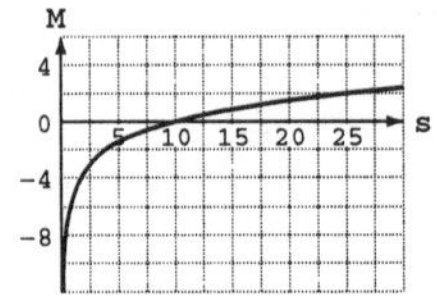

b. When a start has a distance modulus of $M = 2$, it is 25.1 parsecs away from the earth.

SECTION 10.4

Objective A Exercises

1. $5^{4x-1} = 5^{x-2}$

$4x - 1 = x - 2$

$3x - 1 = -2$

$3x = -1$

$x = -\dfrac{1}{3}$

The solution is $-\dfrac{1}{3}$.

3. $8^{x-4} = 8^{5x+8}$

$x - 4 = 5x + 8$

$-4x - 4 = 8$

$-4x = 12$

$x = -3$

The solution is –3.

5. $9^x = 3^{x+1}$

$3^{2x} = 3^{x+1}$

$2x = x + 1$

$x = 1$

The solution is 1.

7. $8^{x+2} = 16^x$

$(2^3)^{x+2} = 2^{4x}$

$2^{3x+6} = 2^{4x}$

$3x + 6 = 4x$

$6 = x$

The solution is 6.

9. $16^{2-x} = 32^{2x}$

$(2^4)^{2-x} = (2^5)^{2x}$

$2^{8-4x} = 2^{10x}$

$8 - 4x = 10x$

$8 = 14x$

$\dfrac{4}{7} = x$

The solution is $\dfrac{4}{7}$.

11. $25^{3-x} = 125^{2x-1}$

$(5^2)^{3-x} = (5^3)^{2x-1}$

$5^{6-2x} = 5^{6x-3}$

$6 - 2x = 6x - 3$

$9 = 8x$

$\dfrac{9}{8} = x$

The solution is $\dfrac{9}{8}$.

13. $5^x = 6$
$\log 5^x = \log 6$
$x \log 5 = \log 6$
$x = \frac{\log 6}{\log 5}$
$x = 1.1133$
The solution is 1.1133.

15. $e^x = 3$
$\ln e^x = \ln 3$
$x \ln e = \ln 3$
$x = \frac{\ln 3}{\ln e}$
$x = 1.0986$
The solution is 1.0986.

17. $10^x = 21$
$\log 10^x = \log 21$
$x \log 10 = \log 21$
$x = \frac{\log 21}{\log 10}$
$x = 1.3222$
The solution is 1.3222.

19. $2^{-x} = 7$
$\log 2^{-x} = \log 7$
$-x \log 2 = \log 7$
$-x = \frac{\log 7}{\log 2}$
$-x = 2.8074$
$x = -2.8074$

The solution is –2.8074.

21. $2^{x-1} = 6$
$\log 2^{x-1} = \log 6$
$(x-1)\log 2 = \log 6$
$x - 1 = \frac{\log 6}{\log 2}$
$x - 1 = 2.5850$
$x = 3.5850$

The solution is 3.5850.

23. $3^{2x-1} = 4$
$\log 3^{2x-1} = \log 4$
$(2x-1)\log 3 = \log 4$
$2x - 1 = \frac{\log 4}{\log 3}$
$2x - 1 = 1.26186$
$2x = 2.26186$
$x = 1.1309$

The solution is 1.1309

Objective B Exercises

25. $\log_2(2x-3) = 3$
Rewrite in exponential form.
$2^3 = 2x - 3$
$8 = 2x - 3$
$11 = 2x$
$\frac{11}{2} = x$
The solution is $\frac{11}{2}$.

27. $\log_2(x^2 + 2x) = 3$
Rewrite in exponential form.
$2^3 = x^2 + 2x$
$8 = x^2 + 2x$
$0 = x^2 + 2x - 8$
$0 = (x+4)(x-2)$
$x + 4 = 0 \quad x - 2 = 0$
$x = -4 \quad x = 2$
The solutions are –4 and 2.

29. $\log_5 \frac{2x}{x-1} = 1$
Rewrite in exponential form.
$5^1 = \frac{2x}{x-1}$
$(x-1)5 = (x-1)\frac{2x}{x-1}$
$5x - 5 = 2x$
$3x - 5 = 0$
$3x = 5$
$x = \frac{5}{3}$
The solution is $\frac{5}{3}$.

31. $\log x = \log(1-x)$
Use the fact that if $\log_b u = \log_b v$, then $u = v$.
$x = 1 - x$
$2x = 1$
$x = \frac{1}{2}$
The solution is $\frac{1}{2}$.

33. $\ln 5 = \ln(4x - 13)$
Use the fact that if $\ln u = \ln v$, then $u = v$.
$5 = 4x - 13$
$18 = 4x$
$\frac{18}{4} = x$
$\frac{9}{2} = x$
The solution is $\frac{9}{2}$.

35. $\ln(3x+2)=4$

This equation is equivalent to

$$e^4 = 3x+2$$
$$e^4 - 2 = 3x$$
$$\frac{e^4-2}{3} = x$$
$$17.5327 = x$$

The solution is 17.5327.

37. $\log_2 8x - \log_2(x^2-1) = \log_2 3$

$$\log_2\left(\frac{8x}{x^2-1}\right) = \log_2 3$$

Use the fact that if $\log_b u = \log_b v$, the $u = v$.

$$\frac{8x}{x^2-1} = 3$$
$$(x^2-1)\frac{8x}{x^2-1} = (x^2-1)3$$
$$8x = 3x^2 - 3$$
$$0 = 3x^2 - 8x - 3$$
$$0 = (3x+1)(x-3)$$

$3x+1=0 \qquad x-3=0$

$3x=-1 \qquad x=3$

$x=-\frac{1}{3}$

$-\frac{1}{3}$ does not check as a solution.

The solution is 3.

39. $\log_9 x + \log_9(2x-3) = \log_9 2$

$$\log_9 x(2x-3) = \log_9 2$$

Use the fact that if $\log_b u = \log_b v$, then $u = v$.

$$x(2x-3) = 2$$
$$2x^2 - 3x = 2$$
$$2x^2 - 3x - 2 = 0$$
$$(2x+1)(x-2) = 0$$

$2x+1=0 \qquad x-2=0$

$2x=-1 \qquad x=2$

$x=-\frac{1}{2}$

$-\frac{1}{2}$ does not check as a solution.

The solution is 2.

41. $\log_8 6x = \log_8 2 + \log_8(x-4)$

$\log_8 6x = \log_8 2(x-4)$

Use the fact that if $\log_b u = \log_b v$, then $u = v$.

$$6x = 2(x-4)$$
$$6x = 2x-8$$
$$4x = -8$$
$$x = -2$$

-2 does not check as a solution. The equation has no solution.

Applying the Concepts

43. $3^x = -x$

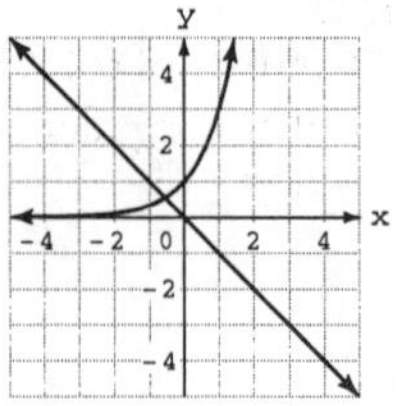

The solution is $x = -0.55$.

45. $2^{-x} = x-1$

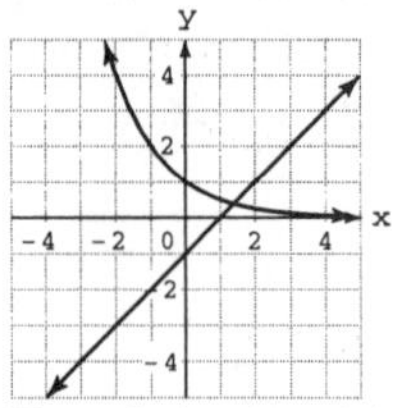

The solution is $x = 1.38$.

47. $\ln x = x^2$

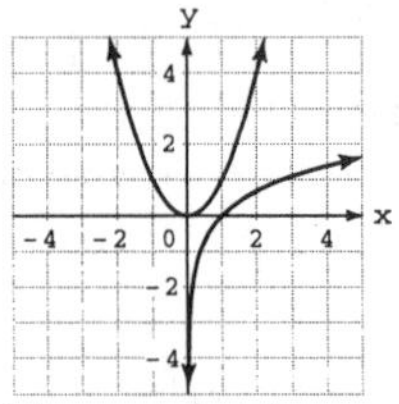

The equation has no solution.

49. $\log_3 x = -2x-2$

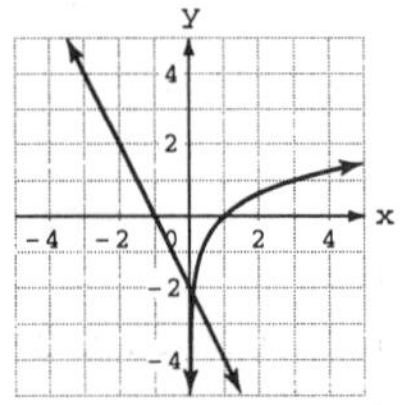

The solution is $x = 0.09$.

51. a. $s = 312.5\ln\left(\frac{e^{0.32t}+e^{-0.32t}}{2}\right)$

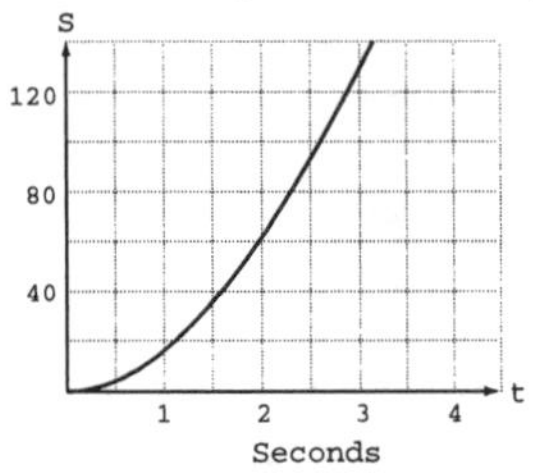

51. b. Use graphing calculator to find value of t when $s = 100$.

$t = 2.64$

It will take 2.64 seconds for the object to fall 100 feet.

53. Step 2 of the proof is incorrect. It states that
$1 \cdot \log(0.5) < 2\log(0.5)$
but $1 \cdot (-0.3010) < 2 \cdot (-0.3010)$
$-0.3010 < -0.6020$
is not true. It should be $-0.3010 > -0.6020$. With that inequality correctly written, the proof would proceed to show that $0.5 > 0.25$.

SECTION 10.5

Objective A Application Problems

1. Strategy To find the value of the investment, solve the compound interest formula for P. Use $A = 5000$, $n = 24$, and $i = \frac{9\%}{12} = \frac{0.09}{12} = 0.0075$

Solution
$$P = A(1+r)^n$$
$$P = 5000(1+0.0075)^{24}$$
$$P = 5000(1.0075)^{24}$$
$$P = 5982$$
The value of the investment after 2 years is \$5982.

3. Strategy To find the amount of money deposited, solve the compound interest formula for A. Use $P = 25{,}000$, $n = 48$, and $i = \frac{10\%}{12} = \frac{0.10}{12} = 0.008\overline{3}$

Solution
$$P = A(1+r)^n$$
$$25{,}000 = A(1+0.008\overline{3})^{48}$$
$$25{,}000 = A(1.008\overline{3})^{48}$$
$$\frac{25{,}000}{(1.008\overline{3})^{48}} = A$$
$$16{,}786 = A$$
\$16,786 must be deposited in the account.

5. Strategy To find the time, solve for t in the exponential decay equation. Use $k = 6$, $A_0 = 30$, and $A = 20$.

Solution
$$A = A_0\left(\frac{1}{2}\right)^{t/k}$$
$$20 = 30\left(\frac{1}{2}\right)^{t/6}$$
$$0.\overline{6} = \left(\frac{1}{2}\right)^{t/6}$$
$$0.\overline{6} = (0.5)^{t/6}$$
$$\log(0.\overline{6}) = \log(0.5)^{t/6}$$
$$\log(0.\overline{6}) = \frac{t}{6}\log(0.5)$$
$$\frac{\log(0.\overline{6})}{\log(0.5)} = \frac{t}{6}$$
$$0.5850 = \frac{t}{6}$$
$$3.510 = t$$

It will take 3.5 hours for the injection to decay to 20 mg.

7. Strategy To find the half-life, solve for k in the exponential decay equation. Use $A_0 = 25, A = 18.95$, and $t = 1$.

Solution
$$A = A_0\left(\frac{1}{2}\right)^{t/k}$$
$$18.95 = 25\left(\frac{1}{2}\right)^{1/k}$$
$$0.76 = \left(\frac{1}{2}\right)^{1/k}$$
$$0.76 = (0.5)^{1/k}$$
$$\log(0.76) = \log(0.5)^{1/k}$$
$$\log(0.76) = \frac{1}{k}\log(0.5)$$
$$k\log(0.76) = \log(0.5)$$
$$k = \frac{\log(0.5)}{\log(0.76)}$$
$$k = 2.5$$

The half-life is 2.5 years.

9. Strategy To find the number of weeks, replace P with its given value in the equation and solve for t.

Solution

$$P = 100[1-(0.75)^t]$$
$$80 = 100[1-(0.75)^t]$$
$$0.80 = 1-(0.75)^t$$
$$(0.75)^t = 0.20$$
$$\log(0.75)^t = \log(0.2)$$
$$t\log(0.75) = \log(0.2)$$
$$t = \frac{\log(0.2)}{\log(0.75)}$$
$$t = 5.59$$

After 6 weeks the student will make 80% of the welds correctly.

11. Strategy To find the pH, replace H^+ with its given value and solve for pH.

Solution

$$pH = -\log(H^+)$$
$$= -\log(0.045)$$
$$= 1.3468$$

The pH of the digestive solution is 1.35.

13. Strategy To find the thickness, solve the equation for d. Use $P = 75\% = 0.75$ and $k = 0.05$.

Solution

$$\log P = -kd$$
$$\log(0.75) = -0.05d$$
$$\frac{\log(0.75)}{-0.05} = d$$
$$2.499 \approx d$$

The depth is 2.5 m.

15. Strategy To find how many times stronger China's earthquake was, use the Richter equation to write a system of equations. Solve the system of equations for the ratio $\frac{I_1}{I_2}$.

Solution

$$8.2 = \log\frac{I_1}{I_0}$$
$$6.9 = \log\frac{I_2}{I_0}$$
$$8.2 = \log I_1 - \log I_0$$
$$6.9 = \log I_2 - \log I_0$$
$$1.3 = \log I_1 - \log I_2$$
$$1.3 = \log\frac{I_1}{I_2}$$
$$\frac{I_1}{I_2} = 10^{1.3} = 19.95$$

China's earthquake was 20 times stronger than Armenia's earthquake.

17. Strategy To determine the magnitude of the earthquake, solve for M in the given equation. Use 30 for A and 21 for t.

Solution

$$M = \log A + 3\log(8t) - 2.92$$
$$M = \log 30 + 3\log[(8)(21)] - 2.92$$
$$M = 1.4771 + 6.6759 - 2.92$$
$$M \approx 5.2$$

The earthquake has a magnitude of 5.2 on the Richter scale.

19. Strategy To find the number of decibels, replace I with its given value in the equation and solve for D.

Solution

$$D = 10(\log I + 16)$$
$$= 10[\log(3.2\times10^{-10}) + 16]$$
$$= 10(6.5051)$$
$$= 65.051$$

The number of decibels is 65.

21. Strategy To find the number of parsecs, use the distance modulus formula to solve for r. Use $M = 5.89$.

Solution

$$M = 5\log r - 5$$
$$5.89 = 5\log r - 5$$
$$10.89 = 5\log r$$
$$2.178 = \log r$$
$$10^{2.178} = r$$
$$150.66 = r$$

The star is 150.7 parsecs from the earth.

23. Strategy To find out how many times farther Antares is from the earth than Pollux is, use the distance modulus formula to write a system of equations. Let r_1 be the distance from Antares to the earth, and let r_2 be the distance from Pollux to Earth.

Solution

$$\begin{aligned} 5.4 &= 5\log r_1 - 5 \\ 2.7 &= 5\log r_2 - 5 \\ 2.7 &= 5\log r_1 - 5\log r_2 \\ 2.7 &= 5\log\frac{r_1}{r_2} \\ 0.54 &= \log\frac{r_1}{r_2} \\ 10^{0.54} &= \frac{r_1}{r_2} \\ 3.47 &= \frac{r_1}{r_2} \\ 3.47r_2 &= r_1 \end{aligned}$$

No, Antares is more than twice as far from the earth as Pollux is. Antares is 3.5 times as far from the earth as Pollux is.

25. Strategy To find the number of barrels, solve the equation for r. Use $T = 20$.

Solution

$$\begin{aligned} T &= 14.29\ln(0.00411r+1) \\ 20 &= 14.29\ln(0.00411r+1) \\ 1.3996 &= \ln(0.00411r+1) \\ e^{1.3996} &= 0.00411r+1 \\ 4.0535 &= 0.00411r+1 \\ 3.0535 &= 0.00411r \\ 742.94 &= r \end{aligned}$$

742.9 billion barrels of oil are necessary to last 20 years.

Applying the Concepts

27. Strategy To find the value of the investment, solve the continuous compounding formula for P. Use $A = 2500$, $t = 5$, and $r = 0.05$.

Solution

$$\begin{aligned} P &= Ae^{rt} \\ P &= 2500e^{0.05(5)} \\ P &= 2500e^{0.25} \\ P &= 2500(1.284) \\ P &= 3210.06 \end{aligned}$$

The investment has a value of \$3210.06 after 5 years.

29.

$$\begin{aligned} T &= 14.29\ln(0.00411r+1) \\ \frac{T}{14.29} &= \ln(0.00411r+1) \\ e^{T/14.29} &= 0.00411r+1 \\ e^{T/14.29} - 1 &= 0.00411r \\ \frac{e^{T/14.29}-1}{0.00411} &= r \text{ or } r = 243.31(e^{T/14.29}-1) \end{aligned}$$

31.

$$\begin{aligned} M &= 5\log r_1 - 5 \\ 2M &= 5\log r_2 - 5 \\ 2(5\log r_1 - 5) &= 5\log r_2 - 5 \\ 10\log r_1 - 10 &= 5\log r_2 - 5 \\ 10\log r_1 - 5\log r_2 &= 5 \\ 2\log r_1 - \log r_2 &= 1 \\ \log\frac{r_1^2}{r_2} &= 1 \\ \frac{r_1^2}{r_2} &= 10 \\ r_1^2 &= 10r_2 \\ r_1 &= \sqrt{10r_2} \end{aligned}$$

CHAPTER REVIEW

1. $f(x) = e^{x-2}$

$f(2) = e^{2-2} = e^0 = 1$

2. $\log_5 25 = 2$ is equivalent to $5^2 = 25$.

3. $f(x) = 3^{-x} + 2$

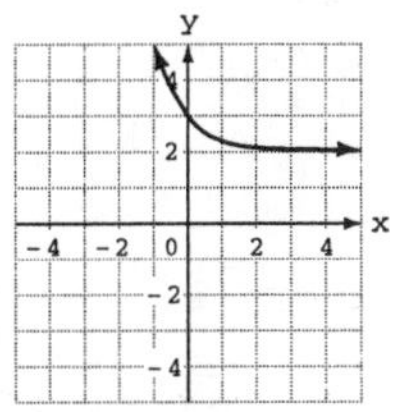

4. $f(x) = \log_3(x-1)$

$y = \log_3(x-1)$

$y = \log_3(x-1)$ is equivalent to

$3^y = x-1$ or $3^y + 1 = x$.

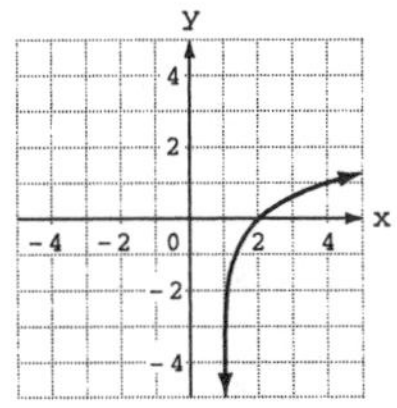

5.

$$\begin{aligned} \log_3\sqrt[5]{x^2y^4} &= \frac{1}{5}(\log_3 x^2 + \log_3 y^4) \\ &= \frac{1}{5}(2\log_3 x + 4\log_3 y) \\ &= \frac{2}{5}\log_3 x + \frac{4}{5}\log_3 y \end{aligned}$$

6. $2\log_3 x - 5\log_3 y = \log_3 x^2 - \log_3 y^5$
$= \log_3 \dfrac{x^2}{y^5}$

7. $27^{2x+4} = 81^{x-3}$
$3^{3(2x+4)} = 3^{4(x-3)}$
$6x + 12 = 4x - 12$
$2x = -24$
$x = -12$

8. $\log_5 \dfrac{7x+2}{3x} = 1$

Rewrite in exponential form.

$5^1 = \dfrac{7x+2}{3x}$
$15x = 7x + 2$
$8x = 2$
$x = \dfrac{1}{4}$

The solution is $\dfrac{1}{4}$.

9. $\log_6 22 = \dfrac{\log_{10} 22}{\log_{10} 6} = 1.7251$

10. $\log_2 x = 5$
$2^5 = x$
$32 = x$

11. $\log_3(x+2) = 4$

Rewrite in exponential form.

$3^4 = x + 2$
$81 = x + 2$
$79 = x$

The solution is 79.

12. $\log_{10} x = 3$
$10^3 = x$
$1000 = x$

13. $\dfrac{1}{3}(\log_7 x + 4\log_7 y) = \dfrac{1}{3}(\log_7 xy^4)$
$= \log_7 \sqrt[3]{xy^4}$

14. $\log_8 \sqrt{\dfrac{x^5}{y^3}} = \dfrac{1}{2}(\log_8 x^5 - \log_8 y^3)$
$= \dfrac{1}{2}(5\log_8 x - 3\log_8 y)$
$= \dfrac{5}{2}\log_8 x - \dfrac{3}{2}\log_8 y$

15. $2^5 = 32$ is equivalent to $\log_2 32 = 5$.

16. $\log_3 1.6 = \dfrac{\log_{10} 1.6}{\log_{10} 3} = 0.4278$

17. $3^{x+2} = 5$
$\log 3^{x+2} = \log 5$
$(x+2)\log 3 = \log 5$
$x + 2 = \dfrac{\log 5}{\log 3}$
$x = \dfrac{\log 5}{\log 3} - 2$
$= -0.535$

The solution is –0.535.

18. $f(x) = \left(\dfrac{2}{3}\right)^{x+2}$
$f(-3) = \left(\dfrac{2}{3}\right)^{-3+2} = \left(\dfrac{2}{3}\right)^{-1} = \dfrac{3}{2}$

19. $\log_8(x+2) - \log_8 x = \log_8 4$
$\log_8\left(\dfrac{x+2}{x}\right) = \log_8 4$

Use the fact that if $\log_b u = \log_b v$, then $u = v$.

$\dfrac{x+2}{x} = 4$
$x + 2 = 4x$
$2 = 3x$
$\dfrac{2}{3} = x$

The solution is $\dfrac{2}{3}$.

20. $\log_6 2x = \log_6 2 + \log_6(3x-4)$
$\log_6 2x = \log_6 2(3x-4)$

Use the fact that if $\log_b u = \log_b v$, then $u = v$.

$2x = 2(3x-4)$
$2x = 6x - 8$
$-4x = -8$
$x = 2$

The solution is 2.

21. $f(x) = \left(\dfrac{2}{3}\right)^{x+1}$

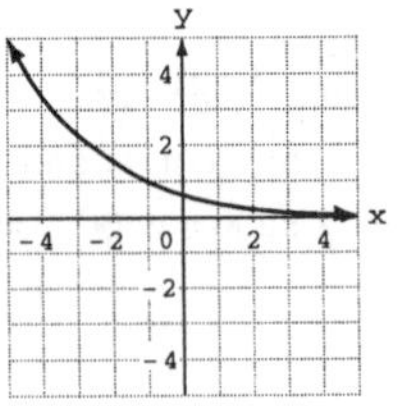

22. $f(x) = \log_2(2x-1)$
$y = \log_2(2x-1)$

is equivalent to $2^y = 2x-1$ or $\frac{1}{2}\cdot 2^y + \frac{1}{2} = x$.

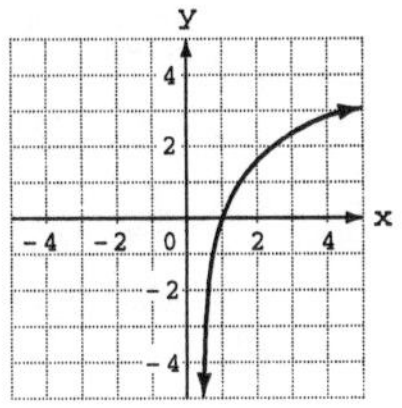

23. Strategy To find the value of the investment, solve the compound interest formula for P. Use $A = 4000$, $n = 24$, and $i = \frac{8\%}{12} = \frac{0.08}{12} = 0.00\overline{6}$

Solution
$$P = A(1+r)^n$$
$$P = 4000(1+0.0\overline{6})^{24}$$
$$= 4000(1.00\overline{6})^{24}$$
$$= 4691.55$$
The value of the investment in 2 years is \$4692.

24. Strategy To find how many times stronger the larger earthquake was, use the Richter equation to write a system of equations. Solve the system of equation for the ratio $\frac{I_1}{I_2}$.

Solution
$$6 = \log\frac{I_1}{I_0}$$
$$3 = \log\frac{I_2}{I_0}$$
$$6 = \log I_1 - \log I_0$$
$$3 = \log I_2 - \log I_0$$
$$3 = \log I_1 - \log I_2$$
$$3 = \log\frac{I_1}{I_2}$$
$$\frac{I_1}{I_2} = 10^3 = 1000$$
The larger earthquake was 1000 times stronger.

25. Strategy To find the half-life, solve for k in the exponential decay equation. Use $A_0 = 25, A = 15$, and $t = 20$.

Solution
$$A = A_0\left(\frac{1}{2}\right)^{t/k}$$
$$15 = 25\left(\frac{1}{2}\right)^{20/k}$$
$$0.6 = \left(\frac{1}{2}\right)^{20/k}$$
$$\log(0.6) = \log(0.5)^{20/k}$$
$$\log(0.6) = \frac{20}{k}\log(0.5)$$
$$k = \frac{20\log(0.5)}{\log(0.6)}$$
$$k = 27.14$$

The half-life is 27 days.

26. Strategy To find the number of decibels, replace I with its given value in the equation and solve for D.

Solution
$$D = 10(\log I + 16)$$
$$= 10\left[\log(5\times10^{-6}) + 16\right]$$
$$= 10(10.6990)$$
$$= 106.99$$
The number of decibels is 107.

CHAPTER TEST

1. $f(x) = \left(\frac{2}{3}\right)^x$
$f(0) = \left(\frac{2}{3}\right)^0 = 1$

2. $f(x) = 3^{x+1}$
$f(-2) = 3^{-2+1} = 3^{-1} = \frac{1}{3}$

3. $f(x) = 2^x - 3$

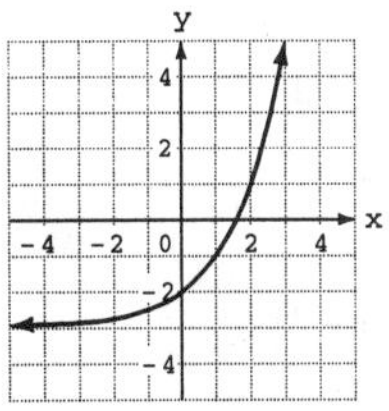

4. $f(x) = 2^x + 2$

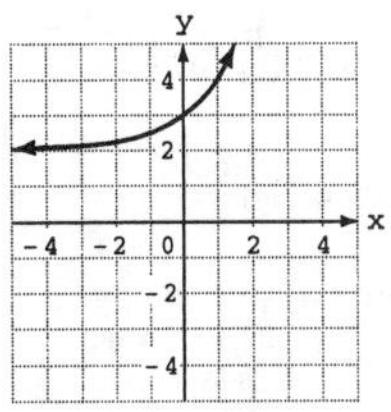

5. $\log_4 16 = x$

$4^x = 16$

$x = 2$

6. $\log_3 x = -2$

$3^{-2} = x$

$\frac{1}{9} = x$

7. $f(x) = \log_2(2x)$

$y = \log_2(2x)$

$2^y = 2x$

$\frac{1}{2} \cdot 2^y = x$

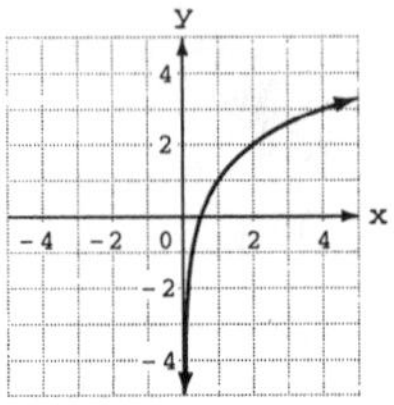

8. $f(x) = \log_3(x+1)$

$y = \log_3(x+1)$

$3^y = x+1$

$-1 + 3^y = x$

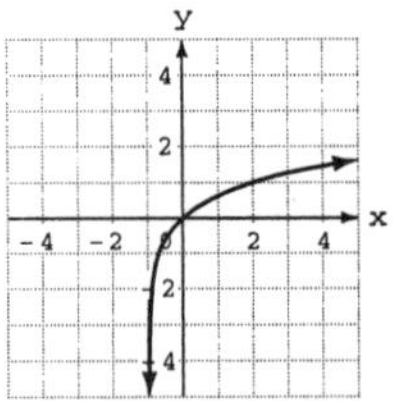

9. $\log_6 \sqrt{xy^3} = \frac{1}{2}\log_6(xy^3)$

$= \frac{1}{2}(\log_6 x + \log_6 y^3)$

$= \frac{1}{2}(\log_6 x + 3\log_6 y)$

$= \frac{1}{2}\log_6 x + \frac{3}{2}\log_6 y$

10. $\frac{1}{2}(\log_3 x - \log_3 y) = \frac{1}{2}\left(\log_3 \frac{x}{y}\right) = \log_3 \sqrt{\frac{x}{y}}$

11. $\ln\left(\frac{x}{\sqrt{z}}\right) = \ln x - \ln\sqrt{z}$

$= \ln x - \frac{1}{2}\ln z$

12. $3\ln x - \ln y - \frac{1}{2}\ln z = \ln x^3 - \ln y - \ln z^{1/2}$

$= \ln\frac{x^3}{y} - \ln z^{1/2}$

$= \ln\frac{x^3}{yz^{1/2}} = \ln\frac{x^3}{y\sqrt{z}}$

13. $3^{7x+1} = 3^{4x-5}$

$7x + 1 = 4x - 5$

$3x = -6$

$x = -2$

The solution is –2.

14. $8^x = 2^{x-6}$

$(2^3)^x = 2^{x-6}$

$3x = x - 6$

$2x = -6$

$x = -3$

The solution is –3.

15. $3^x = 17$

$\log 3^x = \log 17$

$x\log 3 = \log 17$

$x = \frac{\log 17}{\log 3}$

$x = 2.5789$

16. $\log x + \log(x-4) = \log 12$

$\log x(x-4) = \log 12$

Use the fact that if $\log_b u = \log_b v$, then $u = v$.

$x(x-4) = 12$

$x^2 - 4x - 12 = 0$

$(x-6)(x+2) = 0$

$x - 6 = 0 \quad x + 2 = 0$

$x = 6 \quad x = -2$

–2 does not check as a solution. The solution is 6.

17. $\log_6 x + \log_6(x-1) = 1$

$\log_6 x(x-1) = 1$

$x(x-1) = 6^1$

$x^2 - x - 6 = 0$

$(x-3)(x+2) = 0$

$x - 3 = 0 \quad x + 2 = 0$

$x = 3 \quad x = -2$

–2 does not check as a solution.

The solution is 3.

18. $\log_5 9 = \frac{\log_{10} 9}{\log_{10} 5} = 1.3652$

19. $\log_3 19 = \frac{\log 19}{\log 3} = 2.6801$

20. Strategy To find the half-life, solve for k in the exponential decay equation. Use $A_0 = 10, A = 9$, and $t = 5$.

Solution

$$A = A_0\left(\frac{1}{2}\right)^{t/k}$$
$$9 = 10\left(\frac{1}{2}\right)^{5/k}$$
$$0.9 = \left(\frac{1}{2}\right)^{5/k}$$
$$\log(0.9) = \log(0.5)^{5/k}$$
$$\log(0.9) = \frac{5}{k}\log(0.5)$$
$$k = \frac{5\log(0.5)}{\log(0.9)}$$
$$k = 32.9$$

The half-life is 33 h.

CUMULATIVE REVIEW

1.
$$4 - 2[x - 3(2 - 3x) - 4x] = 2x$$
$$4 - 2[x - 6 + 9x - 4x] = 2x$$
$$4 - 2[6x - 6] = 2x$$
$$4 - 12x + 12 = 2x$$
$$16 = 14x$$
$$\frac{8}{7} = x$$

2.
$$2x - y = 5$$
$$-y = -2x + 5$$
$$y = 2x - 5$$
$$m = 2$$
$$y - y_1 = m(x - x_1)$$
$$y - (-2) = 2(x - 2)$$
$$y + 2 = 2x - 4$$
$$y = 2x - 6$$

3. $4x^{2n} + 7x^n + 3 = (4x^n + 3)(x^n + 1)$

4.
$$\frac{1 - \frac{5}{x} + \frac{6}{x^2}}{1 + \frac{1}{x} - \frac{6}{x^2}} \cdot \frac{x^2}{x^2} = \frac{x^2 - 5x + 6}{x^2 + x - 6}$$
$$= \frac{(x-2)(x-3)}{(x+3)(x-2)}$$
$$= \frac{x-3}{x+3}$$

5.
$$\frac{\sqrt{xy}\cdot\left(\sqrt{x} + \sqrt{y}\right)}{\left(\sqrt{x} - \sqrt{y}\right)\cdot\left(\sqrt{x} + \sqrt{y}\right)} = \frac{\sqrt{x^2y} + \sqrt{xy^2}}{\sqrt{x^2} - \sqrt{y^2}}$$
$$= \frac{x\sqrt{y} + y\sqrt{x}}{x - y}$$

6.
$$x^2 - 4x - 6 = 0$$
$$x^2 - 4x + 4 = 6 + 4$$
$$(x-2)^2 = 10$$
$$\sqrt{(x-2)^2} = \sqrt{10}$$
$$x - 2 = \pm\sqrt{10}$$
$$x = 2 \pm \sqrt{10}$$

7.
$$(x - r_1)(x - r_2) = 0$$
$$\left(x - \frac{1}{3}\right)(x - (-3)) = 0$$
$$\left(x - \frac{1}{3}\right)(x + 3) = 0$$
$$x^2 + \frac{8}{3}x - 1 = 0$$
$$3x^2 + 8x - 3 = 0$$

8.
$$2x - y < 3 \qquad x + y < 1$$
$$-y < 3 - 2x \qquad y < 1 - x$$
$$y > -3 + 2x$$

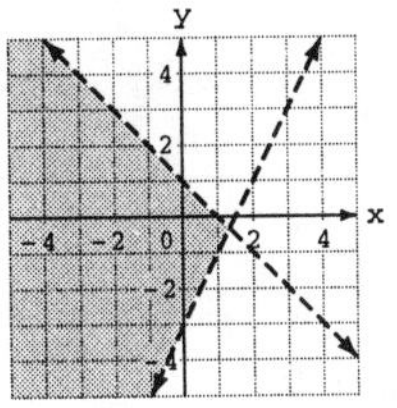

9. (1) $3x - y + z = 3$

(2) $x + y + 4z = 7$

(3) $3x - 2y + 3z = 8$

Eliminate y. Add Equation (1) to Equation (2).

$3x - y + z = 3$
$x + y + 4z = 7$

(4) $4x + 5z = 10$

Multiply Equation (2) by 2 and add to Equation (3).

$2(x + y + 4z) = 2(7)$
$3x - 2y + 3z = 8$

$2x + 2y + 8z = 14$
$3x - 2y + 3z = 8$

(5) $5x + 11z = 22$

Eliminate x. Multiply Equation (4) by –5 and Equation (5) by 4, and add.

$-5(4x + 5z) = -5(10)$
$4(5x + 11z) = 4(22)$

$-20x - 25z = -50$
$20x + 44z = 88$

$19z = 38$
$z = 2$

Replace z by 2 in Equation (4).

$4x + 5(2) = 10$
$4x + 10 = 10$
$4x = 0$
$x = 0$

Replace x by 0 and z by 2 in Equation (2).

$0 + y + 4(2) = 7$
$y + 8 = 7$
$y = -1$

The solution is (0, –1, 2).

10. $\dfrac{x-4}{2-x} - \dfrac{1-6x}{2x^2 - 7x + 6}$

$= \dfrac{x-4}{2-x} - \dfrac{1-6x}{(2x-3)(x-2)}$

$= \dfrac{x-4}{2-x} + \dfrac{1-6x}{(2x-3)(2-x)}$

$= \dfrac{(x-4)}{(2-x)} \cdot \dfrac{(2x-3)}{(2x-3)} + \dfrac{1-6x}{(2x-3)(2-x)}$

$= \dfrac{2x^2 - 11x + 12 + 1 - 6x}{(2-x)(2x-3)}$

$= \dfrac{2x^2 - 17x + 13}{(2-x)(2x-3)}$

11. $x^2 + 4x - 5 \le 0$

$(x+5)(x-1) \le 0$

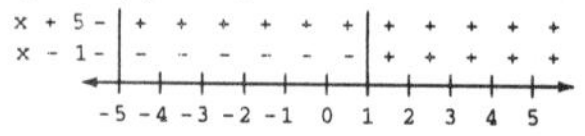

$\{x \mid -5 \le x \le 1\}$

12. $|2x - 5| \le 3$

$-3 \le 2x - 5 \le 3$
$-3 + 5 \le 2x \le 3 + 5$
$2 \le 2x \le 8$
$1 \le x \le 4$
$\{x \mid 1 \le x \le 4\}$

13. $f(x) = \left(\dfrac{1}{2}\right)^x + 1$

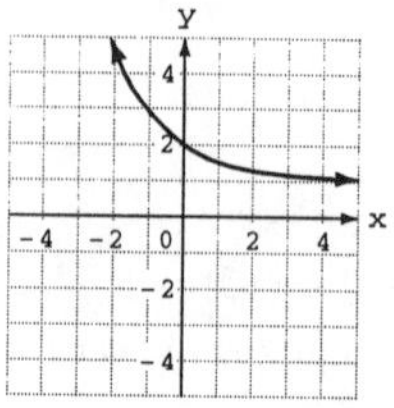

14. $f(x) = \log_2 x - 1$

$y = \log_2 x - 1$
$y + 1 = \log_2 x$
$2^{y+1} = x$

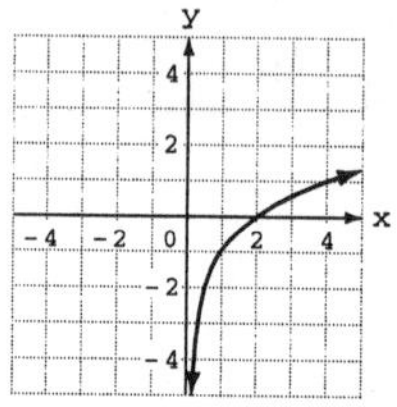

15. $f(x) = 2^{-x-1}$

$f(-3) = 2^{-(-3)-1} = 2^{3-1}$
$= 2^2 = 4$

16. $\log_5 x = 3$

$5^3 = x$
$125 = x$

17. $3\log_b x - 5\log_b y = \log_b x^3 - \log_b y^5$

$= \log_b \dfrac{x^3}{y^5}$

18. $\log_3 7 = \dfrac{\log 7}{\log 3} = 1.7712$

19. $4^{5x-2} = 4^{3x+2}$

$5x - 2 = 3x + 2$
$2x - 2 = 2$
$2x = 4$
$x = 2$

The solution is 2.

20. $\log x + \log(2x+3) = \log 2$
$\log x(2x+3) = \log 2$
Use the fact that if $\log_b u = \log_b v$, then $u = v$.
$x(2x+3) = 2$
$2x^2 + 3x - 2 = 0$
$(2x-1)(x+2) = 0$
$2x - 1 = 0 \quad x + 2 = 0$
$x = \frac{1}{2} \quad x = -2$
−2 does not check as a solution.
The solution is $\frac{1}{2}$.

21. Strategy To find the number of checks, write and solve an inequality using c to represent the number of checks.

Solution $5.00 + 0.02c > 2.00 + 0.08c$
$5 - 0.06c > 2$
$-0.06c > -3$
$\frac{-0.06c}{-0.06} < \frac{-3}{-0.06}$
$c < 50$
The customer can write at most 49 checks.

22. Strategy • Cost per pound of mixture: x

	Amount	Cost	Value
4.00 chocolate	16	4.00	16(4.00)
2.50 chocolate	24	2.50	24(2.50)
Mixture	40	x	$40x$

• The sum of the values before mixing equals the value after mixing.

Solution $16(4.00) + 24(2.50) = 40x$
$64 + 60 = 40x$
$124 = 40x$
$3.1 = x$
The cost per pound of the mixture is \$3.10.

23. Strategy • Rate of the wind: r

	Distance	Rate	Time
With wind	1000	$225 + r$	$\frac{1000}{225+r}$
Against wind	800	$225 - r$	$\frac{1000}{225-r}$

• The time flying with the wind equals the time flying against the wind.

Solution
$$\frac{1000}{225+r} = \frac{800}{225-r}$$
$$(225+r)(225-r)\frac{1000}{225+r} = (225+r)(225-r)\frac{800}{225-r}$$
$$(225-r)(1000) = (225+r)(800)$$
$$225000 - 1000r = 180000 + 800r$$
$$45000 = 1800r$$
$$25 = r$$

The rate of the wind is 25 mph.

24. Strategy To find how far the force will stretch the spring:
• Write the basic direct variation equation, replace the variable by the given values and solve for k.
• Write the direct variation equation, replacing k by its value. Substitute 34 for f and solve for d.

Solution $d = kf$
$6 = k(20)$
$0.3 = k$

$d = 0.3f$
$d = 0.3(34)$
$d = 10.2$
The spring will stretch 10.2 inches.

25. Strategy • Cost of redwood: x
Cost of fir: y
First purchase:

	Amount	Cost	Value
Redwood	80	x	$80x$
Fir	140	y	$140y$

Second purchase:

	Amount	Cost	Value
Redwood	140	x	$140x$
Fir	100	y	$100y$

• The total cost of the first purchase is \$67. The total cost of the second purchase is \$81.

$$80x+140y=67$$
$$140x+100y=81$$

Solution

$$80x+140y=67$$
$$140x+100y=81$$

$$-5(80x+140y)=-5(67)$$
$$7(140x+100y)=7(81)$$

$$-400x-700y=-335$$
$$980x+700y=567$$

$$580x=232$$
$$x=0.40$$

$$80x+140y=67$$
$$80(0.40)+140y=67$$
$$32+140y=67$$
$$140y=35$$
$$y=0.25$$

The cost of redwood is \$.40 per foot.
The cost of fir is \$.25 per foot.

26. Strategy To find the time, solve the compound interest formula for n. Use $P = 10{,}000$, $A = 5000$, and $i=\frac{9\%}{2}=\frac{0.09}{2}=0.045$.

Solution

$$P=A(1+r)^n$$
$$10{,}000=5000(1+0.045)^n$$
$$2=(1.045)^n$$
$$\log 2=\log(1.045)^n$$
$$\log 2=n\log(1.045)$$
$$\frac{\log 2}{\log(1.045)}=n$$
$$15.75=n$$

15.75 (6-month periods) ÷ 2
≈ 7.87 years
In approximately 8 years, the investment will be worth \$10,000.

Chapter 11: Conic Sections

SECTION 11.1

Objective A Exercises

1. $x = y^2 - 3y - 4$

$-\frac{b}{2a} = -\frac{-3}{2(1)} = \frac{3}{2}$

$x = \left(\frac{3}{2}\right)^2 - \left(\frac{3}{2}\right) - 4 = -\frac{25}{4}$

Vertex: $\left(-\frac{25}{4}, \frac{3}{2}\right)$

Axis of symmetry: $y = \frac{3}{2}$

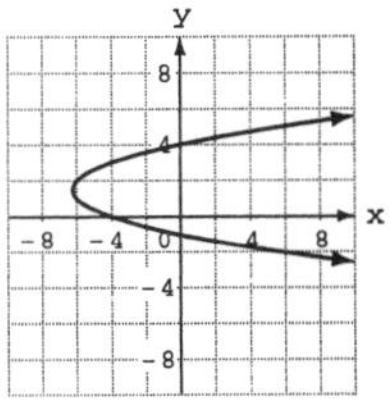

3. $y = x^2 + 2$

$-\frac{b}{2a} = -\frac{0}{2(1)} = 0$

$y = (0)^2 + 2 = 2$

Vertex: (0, 2)

Axis of symmetry: $x = 0$

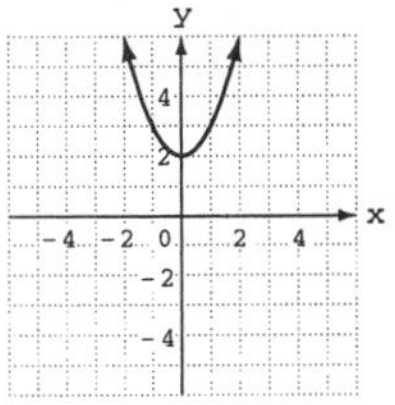

5. $x = -\frac{1}{4}y^2 - 1$

$-\frac{b}{2a} = -\frac{0}{2\left(-\frac{1}{4}\right)} = 0$

$x = -\frac{1}{4}(0)^2 - 1 = -1$

Vertex: (–1, 0)

Axis of symmetry: $y = 0$

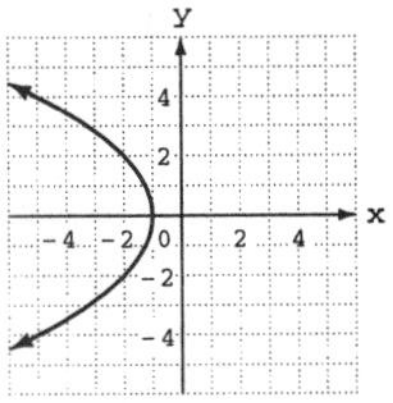

7. $x = -\frac{1}{2}y^2 + 2y - 3$

$-\frac{b}{2a} = -\frac{2}{2\left(-\frac{1}{2}\right)} = 2$

$x = -\frac{1}{2}(2)^2 + 2(2) - 3 = -1$

Vertex: (–1, 2)

Axis of symmetry: $y = 2$

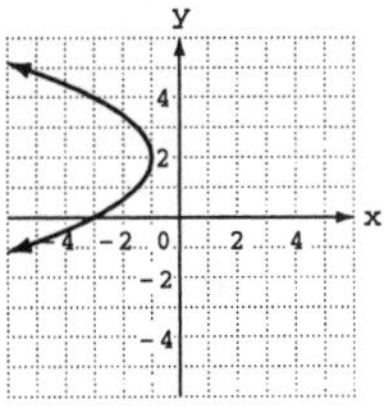

9. $y = \frac{1}{2}x^2 + x - 3$

$-\frac{b}{2a} = -\frac{1}{2\left(\frac{1}{2}\right)} = -1$

$y = -\frac{1}{2}(-1)^2 + (-1) - 3 = -\frac{7}{2}$

Vertex: $\left(-1, -\frac{7}{2}\right)$

Axis of symmetry: $x = -1$

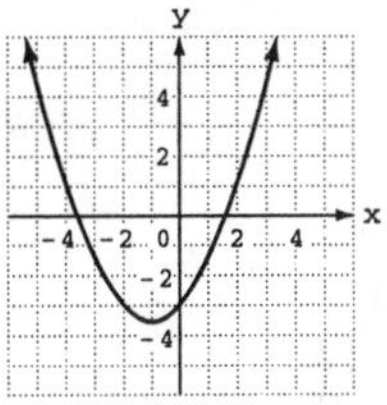

11. $x = y^2 - y - 6$

$-\frac{b}{2a} = -\frac{-1}{2(1)} = \frac{1}{2}$

$x = \left(\frac{1}{2}\right)^2 - \left(\frac{1}{2}\right) - 6 = -\frac{25}{4}$

Vertex: $\left(-\frac{25}{4}, \frac{1}{2}\right)$

Axis of symmetry: $y = \frac{1}{2}$

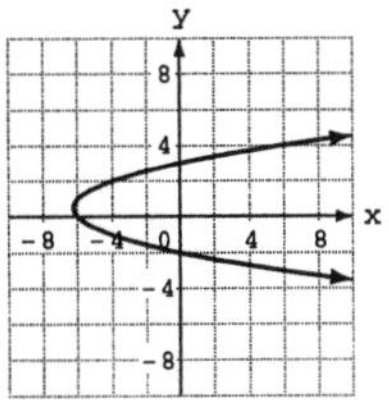

13. $y = 2x^2 + 4x - 5$

$-\frac{b}{2a} = -\frac{4}{2(2)} = -1$

$y = 2(-1)^2 + 4(-1) - 5 = -7$

Vertex: $(-1, -7)$

Axis of symmetry: $x = -1$

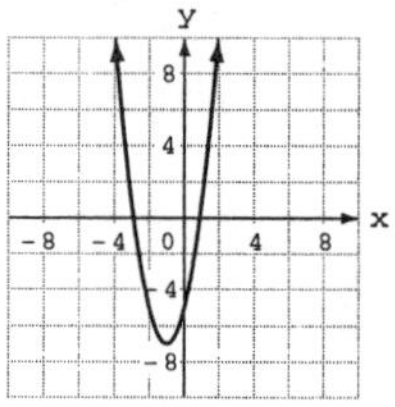

15. $y = 2x^2 - x - 3$

$-\frac{b}{2a} = -\frac{-1}{2(2)} = \frac{1}{4}$

$y = 2\left(\frac{1}{4}\right)^2 - \frac{1}{4} - 3 = -\frac{25}{8}$

Vertex: $\left(\frac{1}{4}, -\frac{25}{8}\right)$

Axis of symmetry: $x = \frac{1}{4}$

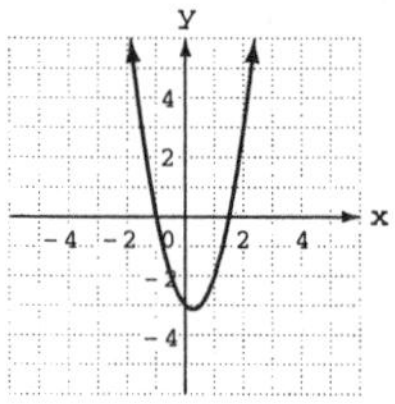

17. $y = x^2 + 5x + 6$

$-\frac{b}{2a} = -\frac{5}{2(1)} = -\frac{5}{2}$

$y = \left(-\frac{5}{2}\right)^2 + 5\left(-\frac{5}{2}\right) + 6 = -\frac{1}{4}$

Vertex: $\left(-\frac{5}{2}, -\frac{1}{4}\right)$

Axis of symmetry: $x = -\frac{5}{2}$

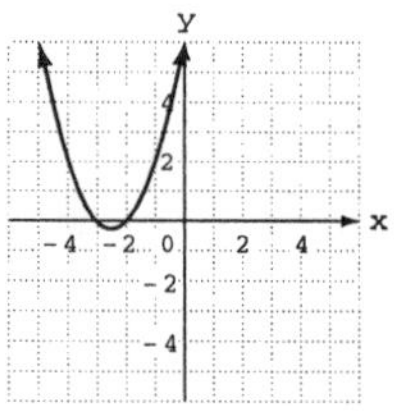

Applying the Concepts

19. a. Sometimes true.

b. Always true.

c. Sometimes true.

21. It means that the graph has no x-intercepts.

SECTION 11.2

Objective A Exercises

1.

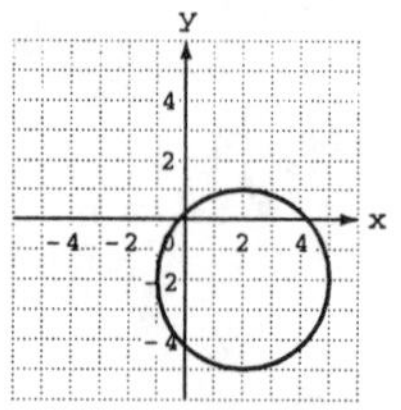

3.

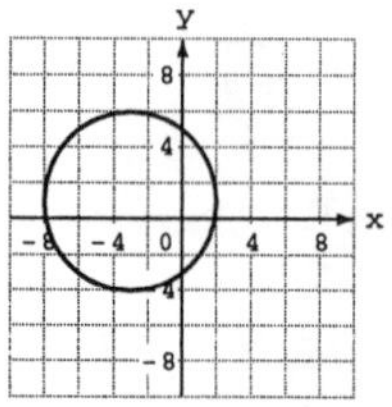

5.

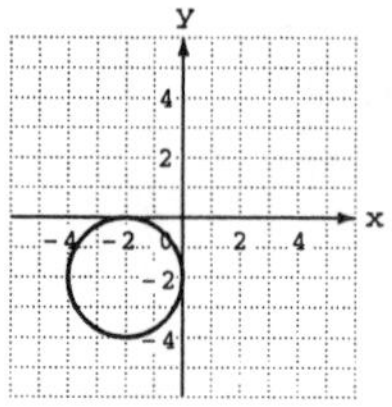

7. $(x-h)^2 + (y-k)^2 = r^2$

$(x-2)^2 + [y-(-1)]^2 = 2^2$

$(x-2)^2 + (y+1)^2 = 4$

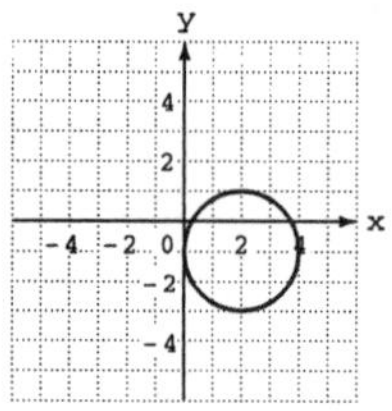

9. $(x_1, y_1) = (1, 2)$ $(x_2, y_2) = (-1, 1)$

$d = \sqrt{(x_1 - x_2)^2 + (y_1 - y_2)^2}$

$= \sqrt{[1-(-1)]^2 + (2-1)^2}$

$= \sqrt{2^2 + 1^2} = \sqrt{4+1} = \sqrt{5}$

$(x-h)^2 + (y-k)^2 = r^2$

$[x-(-1)]^2 + (y-1)^2 = (\sqrt{5})^2$

$(x+1)^2 + (y-1)^2 = 5$

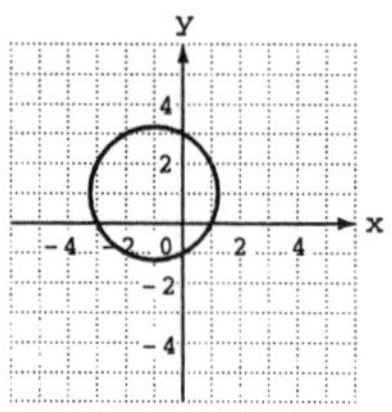

Objective B Exercises

11.
$$x^2+y^2-2x+4y-20=0$$
$$(x^2-2x)+(y^2+4y)=20$$
$$(x^2-2x+1)+(y^2+4y+4)=20+1+4$$
$$(x-1)^2+(y+2)^2=25$$

Center: (1, –2)
Radius: 5

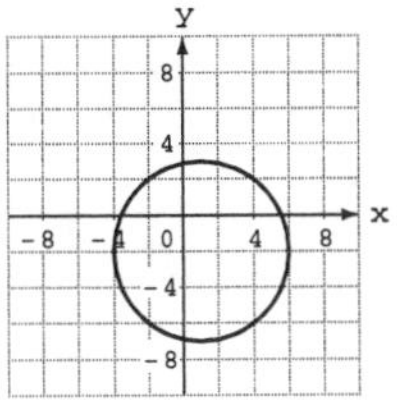

13.
$$x^2+y^2+6x+8y+9=0$$
$$(x^2+6x)+(y^2+8y)=-9$$
$$(x^2+6x+9)+(y^2+8y+16)=-9+9+16$$
$$(x+3)^2+(y+4)^2=16$$

Center: (–3, –4)
Radius: 4

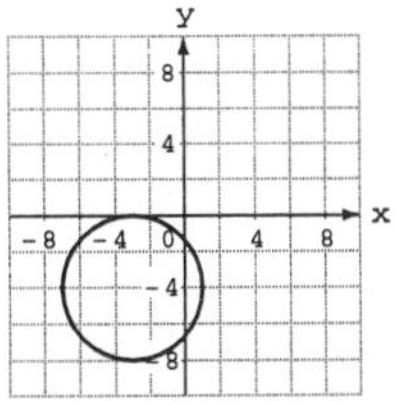

15.
$$x^2+y^2-2x+2y-23=0$$
$$(x^2-2x)+(y^2+2y)=23$$
$$(x^2-2x+1)+(y^2+2y+1)=23+1+1$$
$$(x-1)^2+(y+1)^2=25$$

Center: (1, –1)
Radius: 5

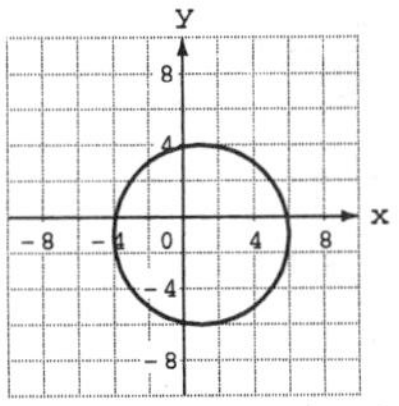

Applying the Concepts, page 570

17. $(x_1, y_1)=(4, 0)\ (x_2, y_2)=(0, 0)$
$$r=\sqrt{(x_1-x_2)^2+(y_1-y_2)^2}$$
$$=\sqrt{(4-0)^2+(0-0)^2}$$
$$=\sqrt{4^2+0^2}=4$$
$$(x-h)^2+(y-k)^2=r^2$$
$$(x-4)^2+(y-0)^2=4^2$$
$$(x-4)^2+y^2=16$$

19. The radius of the circle will be $6\sqrt{3}$ inches.
$$r^2+6^2=12^2$$
$$r^2+36=144$$
$$r^2=108$$
$$r=\sqrt{108}=6\sqrt{3}$$

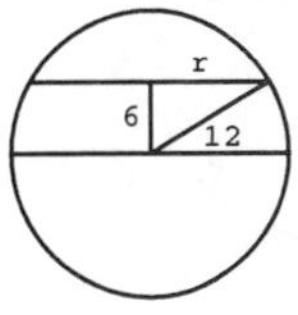

21.
$$x^2+y^2+4x+8y+24=0$$
$$(x^2+4x)+(y^2+8y)=-24$$
$$(x^2+4x+4)+(y^2+8y+16)=-24+4+16$$
$$(x+2)^2+(y+4)^2=-4$$

This equation is not the equation of a circle because the r^2 term is negative $(r^2=-4)$.

SECTION 11.3

Objective A Exercises

1. x-intercepts (2, 0) and (–2, 0)
y-intercepts: (0, 3) and (0, –3).

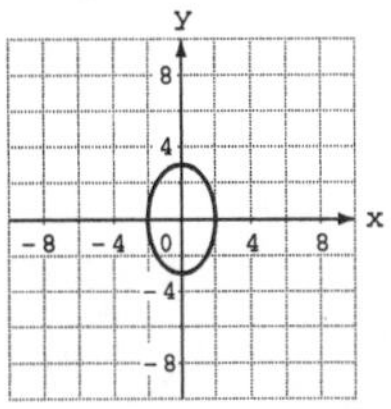

3. x-intercepts: (5, 0) and (–5, 0)
y-intercepts: (0, 3) and (0, –3).

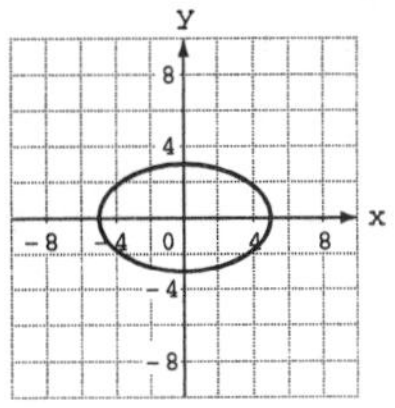

5. x-intercepts: (6, 0) and (–6, 0)
y-intercepts: (0, 4) and (0, –4).

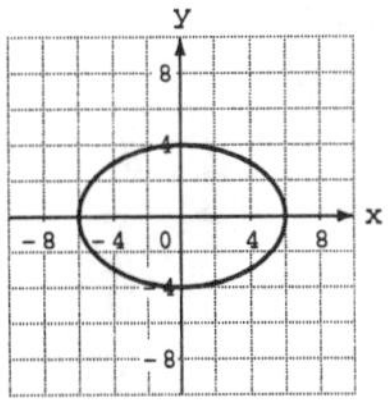

7. x-intercepts: (4, 0) and (–4, 0)
y-intercepts: (0, 7) and (0, –7).

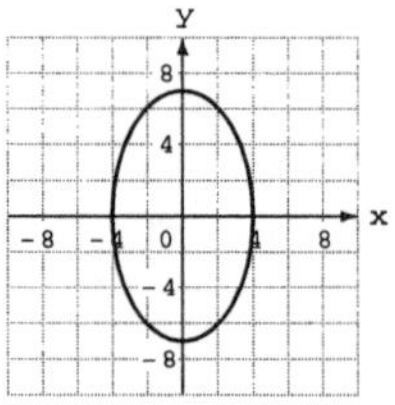

9. x-intercepts: (2, 0) and (–2, 0)
y-intercepts: (0, 5) and (0, –5).

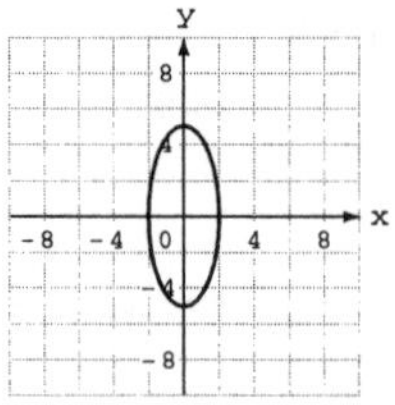

Objective B Exercises

11. Axis of symmetry: x-axis
Vertices: (5, 0) and (–5, 0)
Asymptotes: $y = \frac{2}{5}x$ and $y = -\frac{2}{5}x$

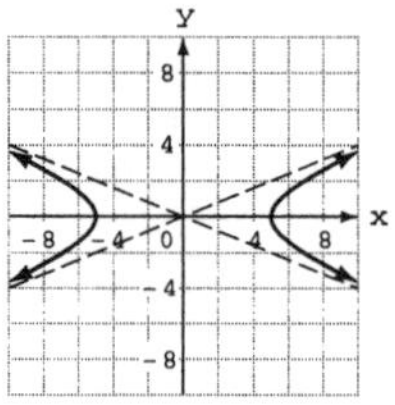

13. Axis of symmetry: y-axis
Vertices: (0, 4) and (0, –4)
Asymptotes: $y = \frac{4}{5}x$ and $y = -\frac{4}{5}x$

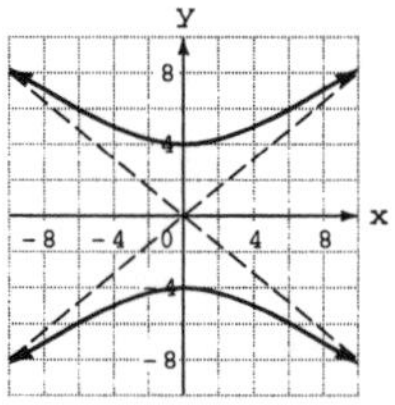

15. Axis of symmetry: x-axis
Vertices: (3, 0) and (–3, 0)
Asymptotes: $y = \frac{7}{3}x$ and $y = -\frac{7}{3}x$

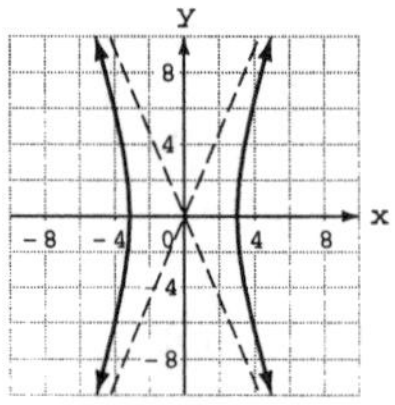

17. Axis of symmetry: y-axis
Vertices: (0, 2) and (0, –2)
Asymptotes: $y = \frac{1}{2}x$ and $y = -\frac{1}{2}x$

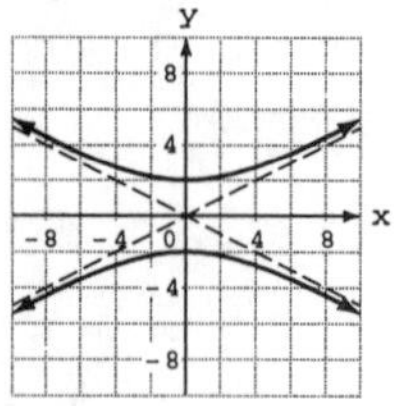

19. Axis of symmetry: x-axis
Vertices: (6, 0) and (–6, 0)
Asymptotes: $y = \frac{1}{2}x$ and $y = -\frac{1}{2}x$

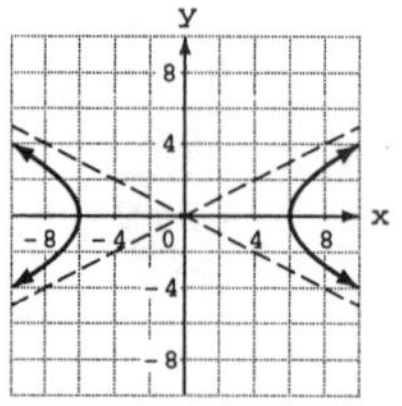

21. Axis of symmetry: y-axis
Vertices: (0, 5) and (0, –5)
Asymptotes: $y = \frac{5}{2}x$ and $y = -\frac{5}{2}x$

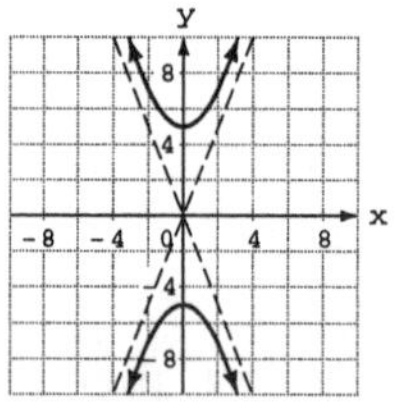

Applying the Concepts

23.
$$16x^2 + 25y^2 = 400$$
$$\frac{1}{400}(16x^2 + 25y^2) = \frac{1}{400} \cdot 400$$
$$\frac{x^2}{25} + \frac{y^2}{16} = 1 \text{ ellipse}$$
x-intercepts: (5, 0) and (–5, 0)
y-intercepts: (0, 4) and (0, –4)

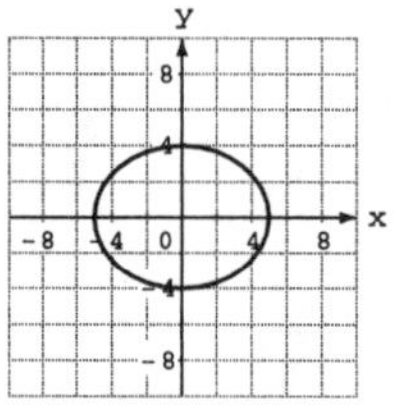

25. $25y^2 - 4x^2 = -100$

$-\frac{1}{100}(25y^2 - 4x^2) = -\frac{1}{100}(-100)$

$\frac{x^2}{25} - \frac{y^2}{4} = 1$ hyperbola

Axis of symmetry: x-axis

Vertices: (5, 0) and (–5, 0)

Asymptotes: $y = \frac{2}{5}x$ and $y = -\frac{2}{5}x$

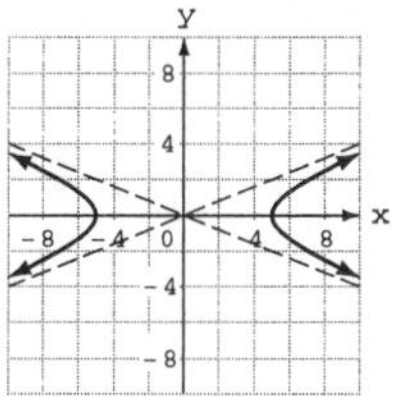

SECTION 11.4

Objective A Exercises

1. (1) $y = x^2 - x - 1$

(2) $y = 2x + 9$

Use the substitution method.

$y = x^2 - x - 1$
$2x + 9 = x^2 - x - 1$
$0 = x^2 - 3x - 10$
$0 = (x - 5)(x + 2)$
$x - 5 = 0 \quad x + 2 = 0$
$x = 5 \quad x = -2$

Substitute into Equation (2).

$y = 2x + 9$	$y = 2x + 9$
$y = 2(5) + 9$	$y = 2(-2) + 9$
$y = 10 + 9$	$y = -4 + 9$
$y = 19$	$y = 5$

The solutions are (5, 19) and (–2, 5).

3. (1) $y^2 = -x + 3$

(2) $x - y = 1$

Solve Equation (2) for x.

$x - y = 1$
$x = y + 1$

Use the substitution method.

$y^2 = -x + 3$
$y^2 = -(y + 1) + 3$
$y^2 = -y - 1 + 3$
$y^2 = -y + 2$
$y^2 + y - 2 = 0$
$(y + 2)(y - 1) = 0$
$y + 2 = 0 \quad y - 1 = 0$
$y = -2 \quad y = 1$

Substitute into Equation (2).

$x - y = 1$	$x - y = 1$
$x - (-2) = 1$	$x - 1 = 1$
$x + 2 = 1$	$x = 2$
$x = -1$	

The solutions are (–1, –2) and (2, 1).

5. (1) $y^2 = 2x$

(2) $x + 2y = -2$

Solve Equation (2) for x.

$x + 2y = -2$
$x = -2y - 2$

Use the substitution method.

$y^2 = 2x$
$y^2 = 2(-2y - 2)$
$y^2 = -4y - 4$
$y^2 + 4y + 4 = 0$
$(y + 2)(y + 2) = 0$
$y + 2 = 0 \quad y + 2 = 0$
$y = -2 \quad y = -2$

Substitute into Equation (2).

$x + 2y = -2$	$x + 2y = -2$
$x + 2(-2) = -2$	$x + 2(-2) = -2$
$x - 4 = -2$	$x - 4 = -2$
$x = 2$	$x = 2$

The solution is a double root.

The solution is (2, –2)

7. (1) $x^2 + 2y^2 = 12$

(2) $2x - y = 2$

Solve Equation (2) for y.

$$2x - y = 2$$
$$-y = -2x + 2$$
$$y = 2x - 2$$

Use the substitution method.

$$x^2 + 2y^2 = 12$$
$$x^2 + 2(2x-2)^2 = 12$$
$$x^2 + 2(4x^2 - 8x + 4) = 12$$
$$x^2 + 8x^2 - 16x + 8 = 12$$
$$9x^2 - 16x - 4 = 0$$
$$(x-2)(9x+2) = 0$$
$$x - 2 = 0 \quad 9x + 2 = 0$$
$$x = 2 \quad 9x = -2$$
$$x = -\frac{2}{9}$$

Substitute into Equation (2).

$$2x - y = 2 \qquad 2x - y = 2$$
$$2(2) - y = 2 \qquad 2\left(-\frac{2}{9}\right) - y = 2$$
$$4 - y = 2 \qquad -\frac{4}{9} - y = 2$$
$$-y = -2 \qquad -y = \frac{22}{9}$$
$$y = 2 \qquad y = -\frac{22}{9}$$

The solutions are (2, 2) and $\left(-\frac{2}{9}, -\frac{22}{9}\right)$.

9. (1) $x^2 + y^2 = 13$

(2) $x + y = 5$

Solve Equation (2) for y.

$$x + y = 5$$
$$y = -x + 5$$

Use the substitution method.

$$x^2 + y^2 = 13$$
$$x^2 + (-x+5)^2 = 13$$
$$x^2 + x^2 - 10x + 25 = 13$$
$$2x^2 - 10x + 12 = 0$$
$$2(x^2 - 5x + 6) = 0$$
$$2(x-3)(x-2) = 0$$
$$x - 3 = 0 \quad x - 2 = 0$$
$$x = 3 \quad x = 2$$

Substitute into Equation (2).

$$x + y = 5 \quad x + y = 5$$
$$3 + y = 5 \quad 2 + y = 5$$
$$y = 2 \quad y = 3$$

The solutions are (3, 2) and (2, 3).

11. (1) $4x^2 + y^2 = 12$

(2) $y = 4x^2$

Use the substitution method.

$$4x^2 + y^2 = 12$$
$$4x^2 + (4x^2)^2 = 12$$
$$4x^2 + 16x^4 = 12$$
$$16x^4 + 4x^2 - 12 = 0$$
$$4(4x^4 + x^2 - 3) = 0$$
$$4(4x^2 - 3)(x^2 + 1) = 0$$
$$4x^2 - 3 = 0 \qquad x^2 + 1 = 0$$
$$4x^2 = 3 \qquad x^2 = -1$$
$$x^2 = \frac{3}{4} \qquad x = \pm\sqrt{-1}$$
$$x = \pm\frac{\sqrt{3}}{2}$$

Substitute the real number solutions into Equation (2).

$$y = 4x^2 \qquad y = 4x^2$$
$$y = 4\left(\frac{\sqrt{3}}{2}\right)^2 \qquad y = 4\left(-\frac{\sqrt{3}}{2}\right)^2$$
$$y = 4\left(\frac{3}{4}\right) \qquad y = 4\left(\frac{3}{4}\right)$$
$$y = 3 \qquad y = 3$$

The solutions are $\left(\frac{\sqrt{3}}{2}, 3\right)$ and $\left(-\frac{\sqrt{3}}{2}, 3\right)$.

13. (1) $y = x^2 - 2x - 3$

(2) $y = x - 6$

Use the substitution method.

$$y = x^2 - 2x - 3$$
$$x - 6 = x^2 - 2x - 3$$
$$0 = x^2 - 3x + 3$$
$$x = \frac{-b \pm \sqrt{b^2 - 4ac}}{2a}$$
$$= \frac{-(-3) \pm \sqrt{(-3)^2 - 4(1)(3)}}{2(1)}$$
$$= \frac{3 \pm \sqrt{9 - 12}}{2}$$
$$= \frac{3 \pm \sqrt{-3}}{2}$$

The system of equations has no real number solution.

15. (1) $3x^2 - y^2 = -1$

(2) $x^2 + 4y^2 = 17$

Use the addition method.

Multiply Equation (1) by 4.

$$12x^2 - 4y^2 = -4$$
$$x^2 + 4y^2 = 17$$
$$13x^2 = 13$$
$$x^2 = 1$$
$$x = \pm\sqrt{1} = \pm 1$$

Substitute into Equation (2).

$$x^2 + 4y^2 = 17 \qquad x^2 + 4y^2 = 17$$
$$1^2 + 4y^2 = 17 \qquad (-1)^2 + 4y^2 = 17$$
$$1 + 4y^2 = 17 \qquad 1 + 4y^2 = 17$$
$$4y^2 = 16 \qquad 4y^2 = 16$$
$$y^2 = 4 \qquad y^2 = 4$$
$$y = \pm\sqrt{4} \qquad y = \pm\sqrt{4}$$
$$y = \pm 2 \qquad y = \pm 2$$

The solutions are (1, 2), (1, –2), (–1, 2), and (–1, –2).

17. (1) $2x^2 + 3y^2 = 30$

(2) $x^2 + y^2 = 13$

Use the addition method.

Multiply Equation (2) by –2.

$$2x^2 + 3y^2 = 30$$
$$-2x^2 - 2y^2 = -26$$
$$y^2 = 4$$
$$y = \pm\sqrt{4} = \pm 2$$

Substitute into Equation (2).

$$x^2 + y^2 = 13 \qquad x^2 + y^2 = 13$$
$$x^2 + 2^2 = 13 \qquad x^2 + (-2)^2 = 13$$
$$x^2 + 4 = 13 \qquad x^2 + 4 = 13$$
$$x^2 = 9 \qquad x^2 = 9$$
$$x = \pm\sqrt{9} \qquad x = \pm\sqrt{9}$$
$$x = \pm 3 \qquad x = \pm 3$$

The solutions are (3, 2), (3, –2), (–3, 2), and (–3, –2).

19. (1) $y = 2x^2 - x + 1$

(2) $y = x^2 - x + 5$

Use the substitution method.

$$y = 2x^2 - x + 1$$
$$x^2 - x + 5 = 2x^2 - x + 1$$
$$0 = x^2 - 4$$
$$0 = (x+2)(x-2)$$
$$x + 2 = 0 \qquad x - 2 = 0$$
$$x = -2 \qquad x = 2$$

Substitute into Equation (2).

$$y = x^2 - x + 5 \qquad y = x^2 - x + 5$$
$$y = (-2)^2 - (-2) + 5 \qquad y = 2^2 - 2 + 5$$
$$y = 4 + 2 + 5 \qquad y = 4 - 2 + 5$$
$$y = 11 \qquad y = 7$$

The solutions are (2, 7) and (–2, 11).

21. (1) $2x^2 + 3y^2 = 24$

(2) $x^2 - y^2 = 7$

Use the addition method.

Multiply Equation (2) by 3.

$$2x^2 + 3y^2 = 24$$
$$3x^2 - 3y^2 = 21$$
$$5x^2 = 45$$
$$x^2 = 9$$
$$x = \pm\sqrt{9} = \pm 3$$

Substitute into Equation (2).

$$x^2 - y^2 = 7 \qquad x^2 - y^2 = 7$$
$$3^2 - y^2 = 7 \qquad (-3)^2 - y^2 = 7$$
$$9 - y^2 = 7 \qquad 9 - y^2 = 7$$
$$-y^2 = -2 \qquad -y^2 = -2$$
$$y^2 = 2 \qquad y^2 = 2$$
$$y = \pm\sqrt{2} \qquad y = \pm\sqrt{2}$$

The solutions are

$(3, \sqrt{2})$, $(3, -\sqrt{2})$, $(-3, \sqrt{2})$, and $(-3, -\sqrt{2})$.

23. (1) $x^2 + y^2 = 36$

(2) $4x^2 + 9y^2 = 36$

Use the addition method.

Multiply Equation (1) by –4.

$$-4x^2 - 4y^2 = -144$$
$$4x^2 + 9y^2 = 36$$
$$5y^2 = -108$$
$$y^2 = -\frac{108}{5}$$
$$y = \pm\sqrt{-\frac{108}{5}}$$

The system of equations has no real number solution.

25. (1) $11x^2 - 2y^2 = 4$

(2) $3x^2 + y^2 = 15$

Use the addition method.

Multiply Equation (2) by 2.

$$11x^2 - 2y^2 = 4$$
$$6x^2 + 2y^2 = 30$$
$$17x^2 = 34$$
$$x^2 = 2$$
$$x = \pm\sqrt{2}$$

Substitute into Equation (2).

$$3x^2 + y^2 = 15 \qquad 3x^2 + y^2 = 15$$
$$3(\sqrt{2})^2 + y^2 = 15 \qquad 3(-\sqrt{2})^2 + y^2 = 15$$
$$3(2) + y^2 = 15 \qquad 3(2) + y^2 = 15$$
$$6 + y^2 = 15 \qquad 6 + y^2 = 15$$
$$y^2 = 9 \qquad y^2 = 9$$
$$y = \pm\sqrt{9} \qquad y = \pm\sqrt{9}$$
$$y = \pm 3 \qquad y = \pm 3$$

The solutions are

$(\sqrt{2}, 3)$, $(\sqrt{2}, -3)$, $(-\sqrt{2}, 3)$, and $(-\sqrt{2}, -3)$.

27. (1) $2x^2 - y^2 = 7$

(2) $2x - y = 5$

Solve Equation (2) for y.

$$2x - y = 5$$
$$-y = -2x + 5$$
$$y = 2x - 5$$

Use the substitution method.

$$2x^2 - y^2 = 7$$
$$2x^2 - (2x - 5)^2 = 7$$
$$2x^2 - (4x^2 - 20x + 25) = 7$$
$$2x^2 - 4x^2 + 20x - 25 = 7$$
$$-2x^2 + 20x - 32 = 0$$
$$-2(x^2 - 10x + 16) = 0$$
$$-2(x - 2)(x - 8) = 0$$
$$x - 2 = 0 \qquad x - 8 = 0$$
$$x = 2 \qquad x = 8$$

Substitute into Equation (2).

$$2x - y = 5 \qquad 2x - y = 5$$
$$2(2) - y = 5 \qquad 2(8) - y = 5$$
$$4 - y = 5 \qquad 16 - y = 5$$
$$-y = 1 \qquad -y = -11$$
$$y = -1 \qquad y = 11$$

The solutions are $(2, -1)$ and $(8, 11)$.

29. (1) $y = 3x^2 + x - 4$

(2) $y = 3x^2 - 8x + 5$

Use the substitution method.

$$y = 3x^2 + x - 4$$
$$3x^2 - 8x + 5 = 3x^2 + x - 4$$
$$0 = 9x - 9$$
$$0 = 9(x - 1)$$
$$x - 1 = 0$$
$$x = 1$$

Substitute into Equation (1).

$$y = 3x^2 + x - 4$$
$$y = 3(1)^2 + 1 - 4$$
$$y = 3 + 1 - 4$$
$$y = 0$$

The solution is $(1, 0)$.

31. (1) $x = y + 3$

(2) $x^2 + y^2 = 5$

Use the substitution method.

$$x^2 + y^2 = 5$$
$$(y + 3)^2 + y^2 = 5$$
$$y^2 + 6y + 9 + y^2 = 5$$
$$2y^2 + 6y + 9 = 5$$
$$2y^2 + 6y + 4 = 0$$
$$2(y^2 + 3y + 2) = 0$$
$$2(y + 1)(y + 2) = 0$$
$$y + 1 = 0 \qquad y + 2 = 0$$
$$y = -1 \qquad y = -2$$

Substitute into Equation (1).

$$x = y + 3 \qquad x = y + 3$$
$$x = -1 + 3 \qquad x = -2 + 3$$
$$x = 2 \qquad x = 1$$

The solutions are $(2, -1)$ and $(1, -2)$.

33. (1) $y = x^2 + 4x + 4$

(2) $x + 2y = 4$

Use the substitution method.

$$x + 2y = 4$$
$$x + 2(x^2 + 4x + 4) = 4$$
$$x + 2x^2 + 8x + 8 = 4$$
$$2x^2 + 9x + 8 = 4$$
$$2x^2 + 9x + 4 = 0$$
$$(2x+1)(x+4) = 0$$

$2x + 1 = 0$ $\quad$ $x + 4 = 0$

$2x = -1$ $\quad$ $x = -4$

$x = -\frac{1}{2}$

Substitute into Equation (2).

$x + 2y = 4$ $\quad$ $x + 2y = 4$

$-\frac{1}{2} + 2y = 4$ $\quad$ $-4 + 2y = 4$

$2y = 4 + \frac{1}{2}$ $\quad$ $2y = 8$

$2y = \frac{9}{2}$ $\quad$ $y = 4$

$y = \frac{9}{4}$

The solutions are $\left(-\frac{1}{2}, \frac{9}{4}\right)$ and (–4, 4).

Applying the Concepts

35. $y = 2^x$

$x + y = 3$

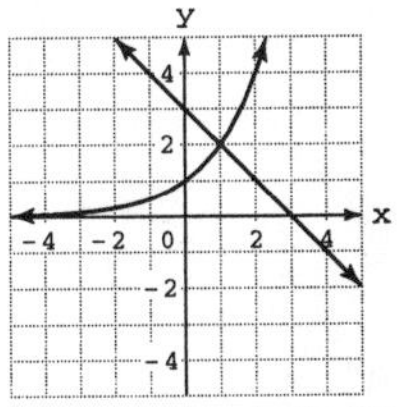

The solution is (1.000, 2.000).

37. $y = \log_2 x$

$\frac{x^2}{9} + \frac{y^2}{1} = 1$

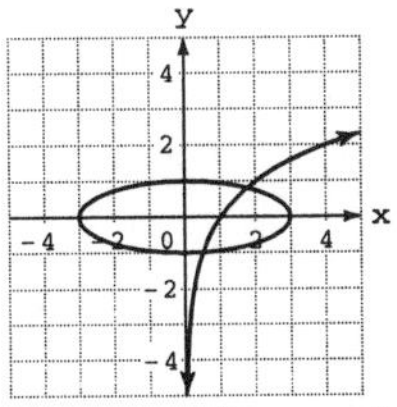

The approximate solutions are (1.755, 0.811), (0.505, –0.986).

39. $y = -\log_3 x$

$x + y = 4$

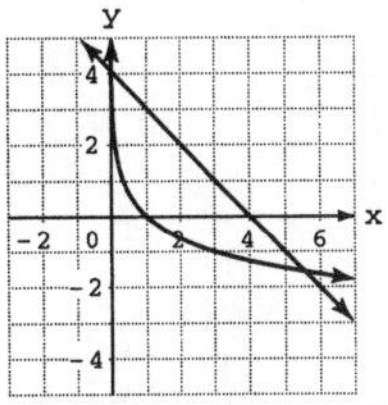

The approximate solutions are (5.562, –1.562), (0.013, 3.987)

SECTION 11.5

Objective A Exercises

1. $y \le x^2 - 4x + 3$

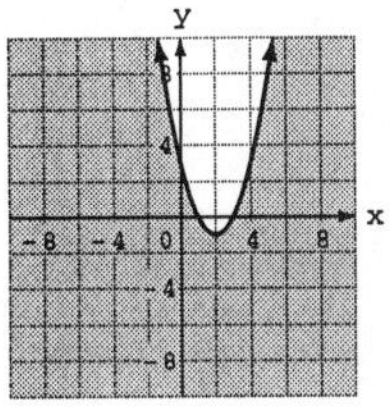

3. $(x-1)^2 + (y+2)^2 \le 9$

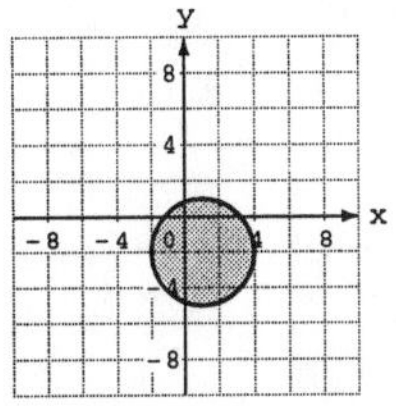

5. $(x+3)^2 + (x-2)^2 \ge 9$

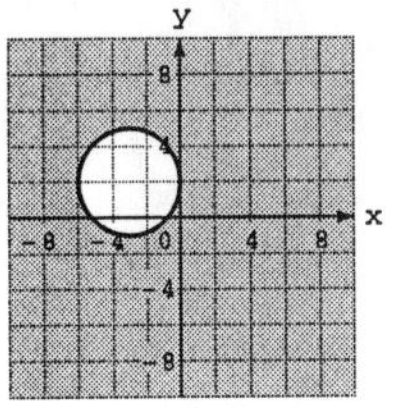

7. $\frac{x^2}{16} + \frac{y^2}{25} < 1$

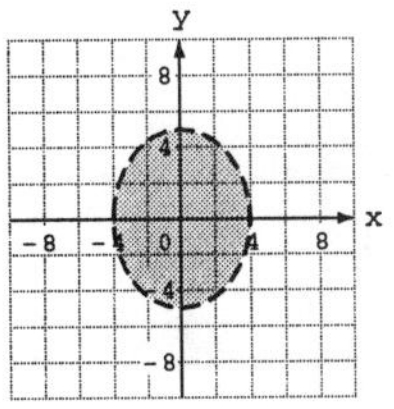

9. $\frac{x^2}{25}-\frac{y^2}{9}\le 1$

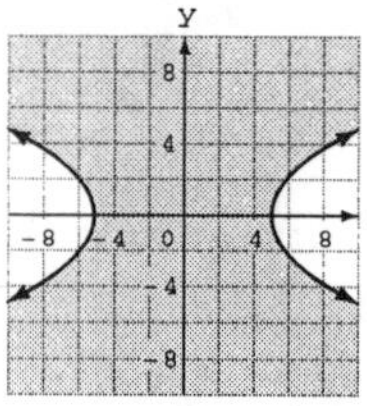

11. $\frac{x^2}{4}+\frac{y^2}{16}\ge 1$

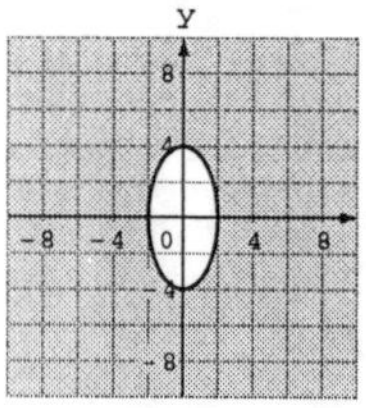

13. $y\le x^2-2x+3$

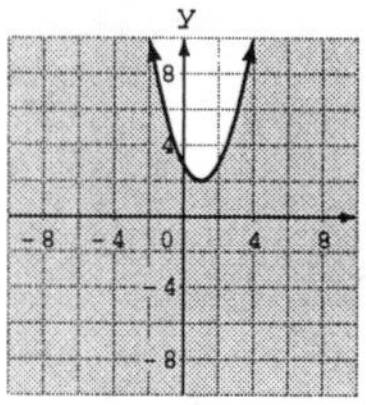

15. $\frac{y^2}{9}-\frac{x^2}{16}\le 1$

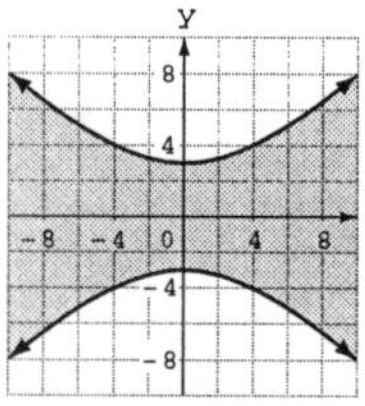

17. $\frac{x^2}{9}+\frac{y^2}{1}\le 1$

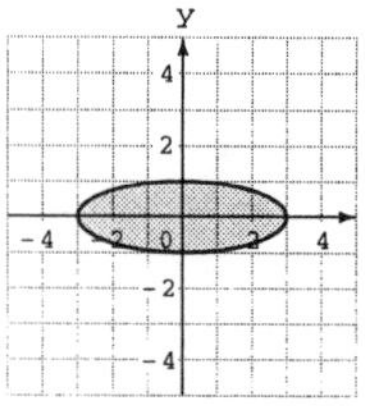

19. $(x-1)^2+(y+3)^2\le 25$

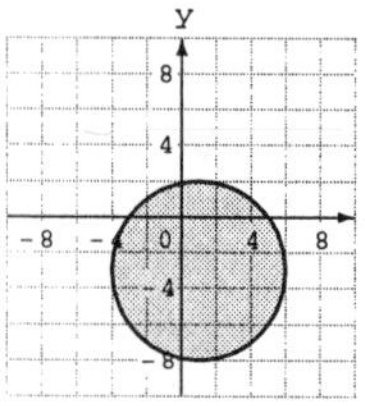

21. $\frac{y^2}{25}-\frac{x^2}{4}\le 1$

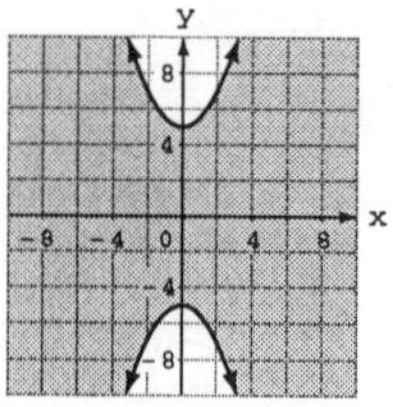

23. $\frac{x^2}{25}+\frac{y^2}{9}\le 1$

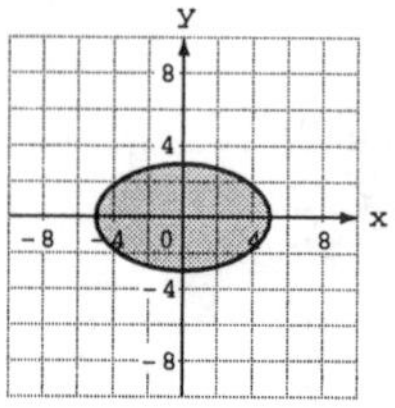

Objective B Exercises

25. $y\le (x-2)^2$
$y+x>4$

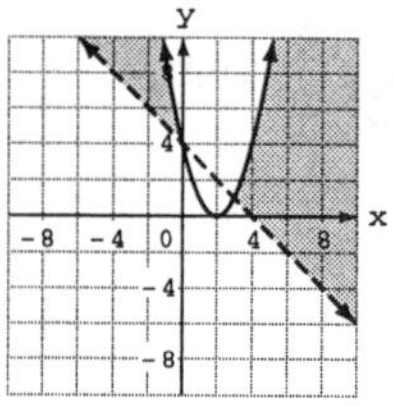

27. $x^2+y^2<16$
$y>x+1$

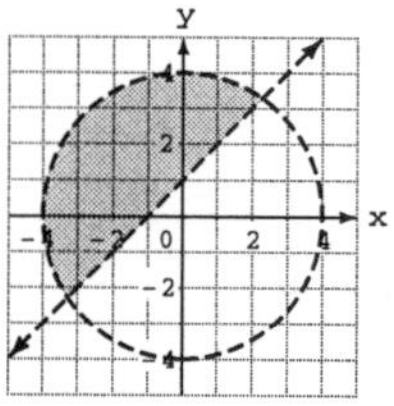

29. $\frac{x^2}{4}+\frac{y^2}{16}\le 1$
$y\le -\frac{1}{2}x+2$

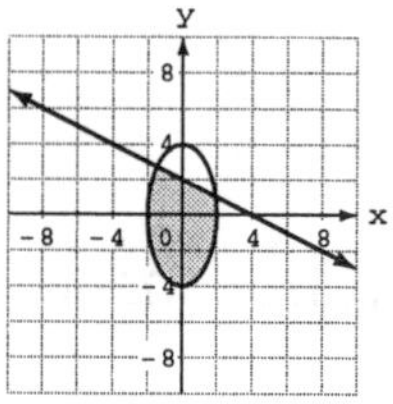

31. $x \geq y^2 - 3y + 2$
$y \geq 2x - 2$

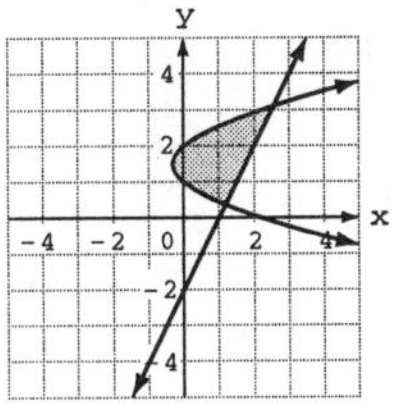

33. $x^2 + y^2 < 25$
$\frac{x^2}{9} + \frac{y^2}{36} < 1$

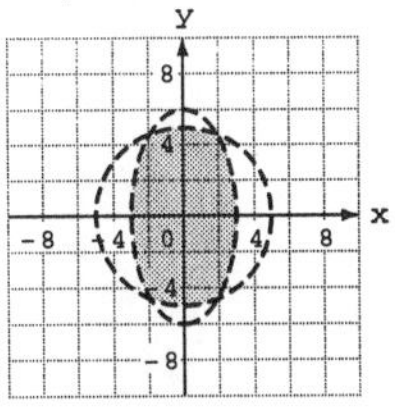

35. $x^2 + y^2 > 4$
$x^2 + y^2 < 25$

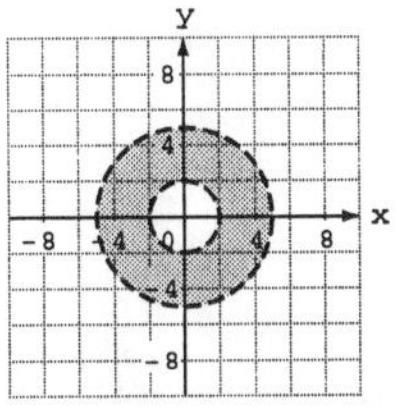

Applying the Concepts

37. $y > x^2 - 3$
$y < x + 3$
$x \leq 0$

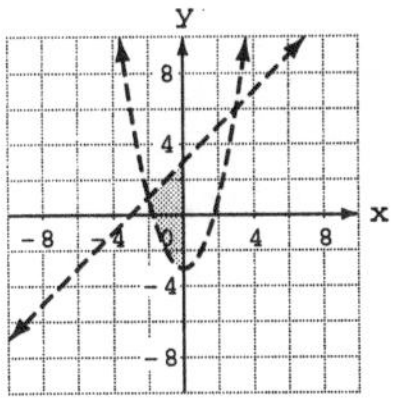

39. $x^2 + y^2 < 3$
$x > y^2 - 1$
$y \geq 0$

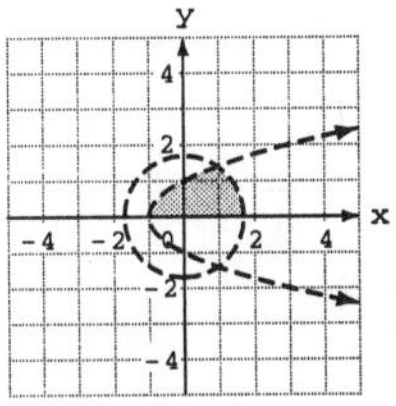

41. $\frac{x^2}{16} + \frac{y^2}{4} \leq 1$
$x^2 + y^2 \leq 4$
$x \geq 0$
$y \leq 0$

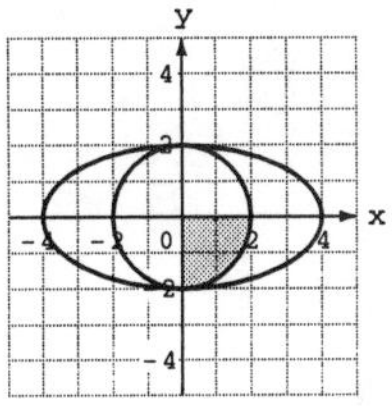

43. $y > 2^x$
$x + y < 4$

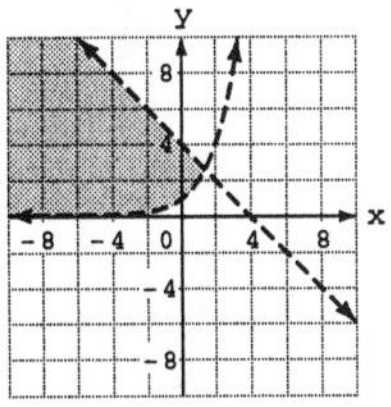

45. $y \geq \log_2 x$
$x^2 + y^2 < 9$

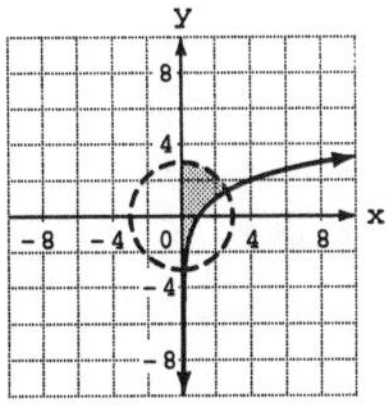

47. $y < 3^{-x}$
$\frac{x^2}{4} - \frac{y^2}{1} \geq 1$

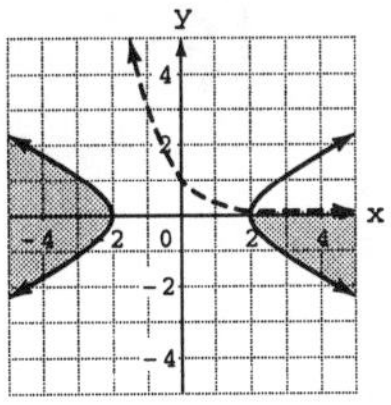

CHAPTER REVIEW

1. $y = -2x^2 + x - 2$

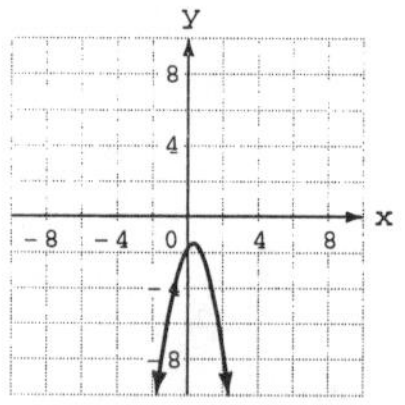

2. x-intercepts: (1, 0) and (–1, 0)
y-intercepts: (0, 3) and (0, –3)

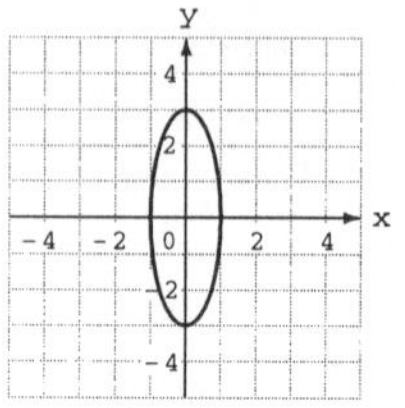

3. $\frac{x^2}{9} - \frac{y^2}{16} < 1$

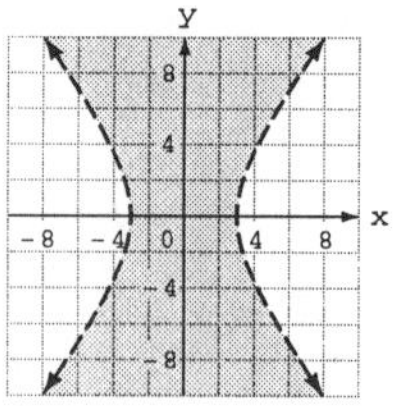

4. $(x+3)^2 + (y+1)^2 = 1$

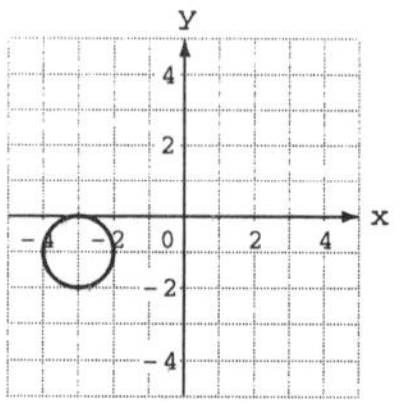

Center: (–3, –1)
Radius: 1

5. $y = x^2 - 4x + 8$
$-\frac{b}{2a} = -\frac{-4}{2(1)} = \frac{4}{2} = 2$
$y = 2^2 - 4(2) + 8 = 4$
Vertex: (2, 4)
Axis of symmetry: $x = 2$

6. (1) $y^2 = 2x^2 - 3x + 6$
(2) $y^2 = 2x^2 + 5x - 2$
Use the subtraction method.
$$y^2 = 2x^2 - 3x + 6$$
$$-y^2 = -2x^2 - 5x + 2$$
$$0 = -8x + 8$$
$$8x = 8$$
$$x = 1$$
Substitute into Equation (1).
$$y^2 = 2x^2 - 3x + 6$$
$$y^2 = 2(1)^2 - 3(1) + 6$$
$$y^2 = 2 - 3 + 6$$
$$y^2 = 5$$
$$y = \pm\sqrt{5}$$
The solutions are $(1, \sqrt{5})$ and $(1, -\sqrt{5})$.

7. $\frac{x^2}{25} + \frac{y^2}{16} \le 1$
$\frac{y^2}{4} - \frac{x^2}{4} \ge 1$

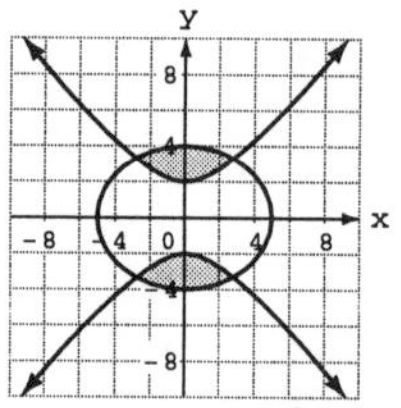

8. Axis of symmetry: x-axis
Vertices: (5, 0) and (–5, 0)
Asymptotes: $y = \frac{1}{5}x$ and $y = -\frac{1}{5}x$

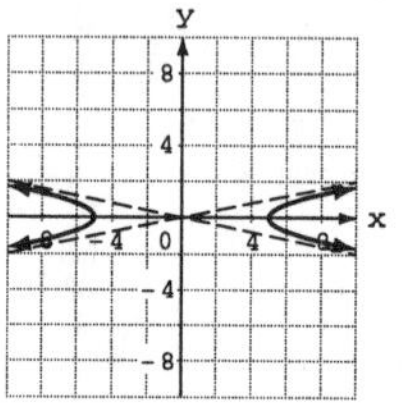

9. $(x_1, y_1) = (2, -1)$ $(x_2, y_2) = (-1, 2)$
$$r = \sqrt{(x_1 - x_2)^2 + (y_1 - y_2)^2}$$
$$= \sqrt{[2-(-1)]^2 + (-1-2)^2}$$
$$= \sqrt{3^2 + (-3)^2}$$
$$= \sqrt{9+9} = \sqrt{18}$$
$$(x-h)^2 + (y-k)^2 = r^2$$
$$[x-(-1)]^2 + (y-2)^2 = (\sqrt{18})^2$$
$$(x+1)^2 + (y-2)^2 = 18$$

10. $y = -x^2 + 7x - 8$

$$-\frac{b}{2a} = \frac{-7}{2(-1)} = \frac{7}{2}$$

$$y = -\left(\frac{7}{2}\right)^2 + 7\left(\frac{7}{2}\right) - 8 = \frac{17}{4}$$

Vertex: $\left(\frac{7}{2}, \frac{17}{4}\right)$

Axis of symmetry: $x = \frac{7}{2}$

11. (1) $x = 2y^2 - 3y + 1$

(2) $3x - 2y = 0$

Solve Equation (2) for x.

$$3x - 2y = 0$$
$$3x = 2y$$
$$x = \frac{2}{3}y$$

Use the substitution method.

$$\frac{2}{3}y = 2y^2 - 3y + 1$$
$$2y = 6y^2 - 9y + 3$$
$$0 = 6y^2 - 11y + 3$$
$$0 = (2y - 3)(3y - 1)$$
$$0 = 2y - 3 \quad 0 = 3y - 1$$
$$2y = 3 \quad 3y = 1$$
$$y = \frac{3}{2} \quad y = \frac{1}{3}$$

Substitute into Equation (2).

$$3x - 2\left(\frac{3}{2}\right) = 0 \quad 3x - 2\left(\frac{1}{3}\right) = 0$$
$$3x = 3 \quad 3x = \frac{2}{3}$$
$$x = 1 \quad x = \frac{2}{9}$$

The solutions are $\left(1, \frac{3}{2}\right)$ and $\left(\frac{2}{9}, \frac{1}{3}\right)$.

12. $(x_1, y_1) = (4, 6)$ $(x_2, y_2) = (0, -3)$

$$d = \sqrt{(x_1 - x_2)^2 + (y_1 - y_2)^2}$$
$$= \sqrt{(4-0)^2 + (6-(-3))^2}$$
$$= \sqrt{4^2 + 9^2}$$
$$= \sqrt{16 + 81} = \sqrt{97}$$
$$(x-h)^2 + (y-k)^2 = r^2$$
$$(x-0)^2 + (y-(-3))^2 = (\sqrt{97})^2$$
$$x^2 + (y+3)^2 = 97$$

13. $(x-h)^2 + (y-k)^2 = r^2$

$$(x-(-1))^2 + (y-5)^2 = 6^2$$
$$(x+1)^2 + (y-5)^2 = 36$$

14. (1) $2x^2 + y^2 = 19$

(2) $3x^2 - y^2 = 6$

Use the addition method.

$$2x^2 + y^2 = 19$$
$$3x^2 - y^2 = 6$$
$$5x^2 = 25$$
$$x^2 = 5$$
$$x = \pm\sqrt{5}$$

Substitute the Equation (1).

$$2x^2 + y^2 = 19 \quad 2x^2 + y^2 = 19$$
$$2(\sqrt{5})^2 + y^2 = 19 \quad 2(-\sqrt{5})^2 + y^2 = 19$$
$$10 + y^2 = 19 \quad 10 + y^2 = 19$$
$$y^2 = 9 \quad y^2 = 9$$
$$y = \pm\sqrt{9} \quad y = \pm\sqrt{9}$$
$$y = \pm 3 \quad y = \pm 3$$

The solutions are $(\sqrt{5}, 3)$, $(\sqrt{5}, -3)$, $(-\sqrt{5}, 3)$, and $(-\sqrt{5}, -3)$.

15. $x^2 + y^2 + 4x - 2y = 4$

$$(x^2 + 4x) + (y^2 - 2y) = 4$$
$$(x^2 + 4x + 4) + (y^2 - 2y + 1) = 4 + 4 + 1$$
$$(x+2)^2 + (y-1)^2 = 9$$

16. (1) $y = x^2 + 5x - 6$

(2) $y = x - 10$

Use the substitution method.

$$x - 10 = x^2 + 5x - 6$$
$$0 = x^2 + 4x + 4$$
$$0 = (x+2)^2$$
$$x + 2 = 0 \quad x + 2 = 0$$
$$x = -2 \quad x = -2$$

Substitute into Equation (2).

$$y = -2 - 10 \quad y = -2 - 10$$
$$y = -12 \quad y = -12$$

The solution is $(-2, -12)$.

17. $\frac{x^2}{16} + \frac{y^2}{4} > 1$

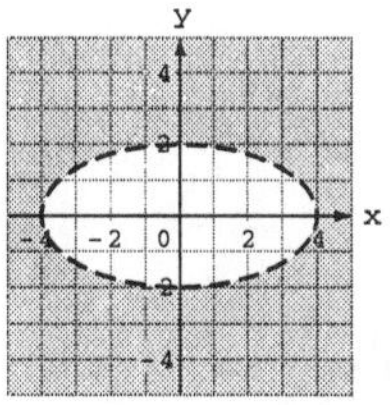

18. Axis of symmetry: y-axis
Vertices: (0, 4) and (0, –4)
Asymptotes: $y = \frac{4}{3}x$ and $y = -\frac{4}{3}x$

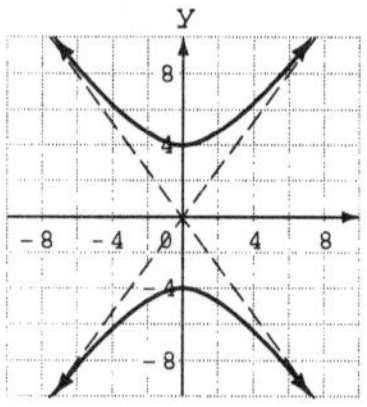

19. $(x-2)^2 + (y+1)^2 \le 16$

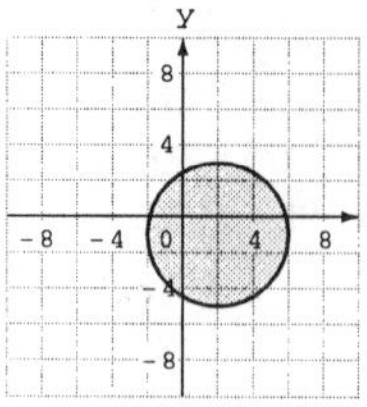

20. $x^2 + (y-2)^2 = 9$

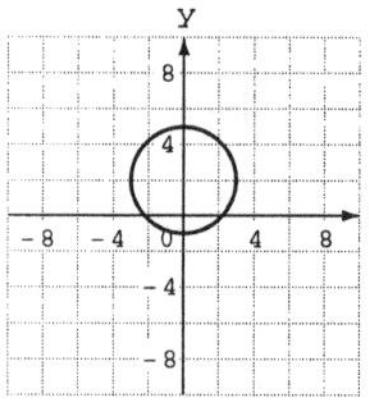

Center: (0, 2)
Radius: 3

21. x-intercepts: (5, 0) and (–5, 0)
y-intercepts: (0, 3) and (0, –3).

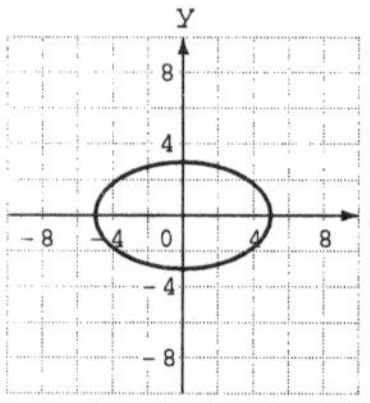

22. $y \ge -x^2 - 2x + 3$

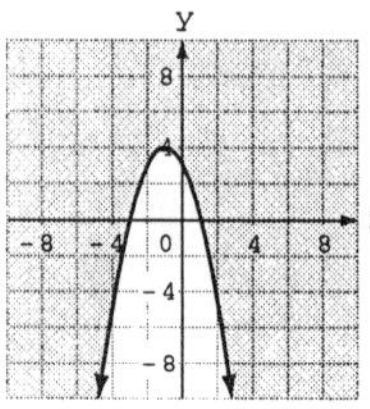

23. $\frac{x^2}{16} + \frac{y^2}{4} < 1$
$x^2 + y^2 > 9$

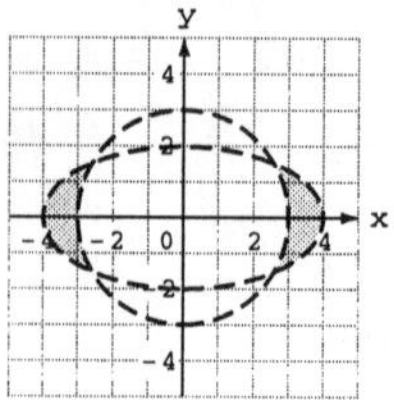

24. (1) $y \ge x^2 - 4x + 2$
(2) $y \le \frac{1}{3}x - 1$

Write Equation (1) in standard form.

$y \ge (x^2 - 4x + 4) - 4 + 2$
$y \ge (x-2)^2 - 2$

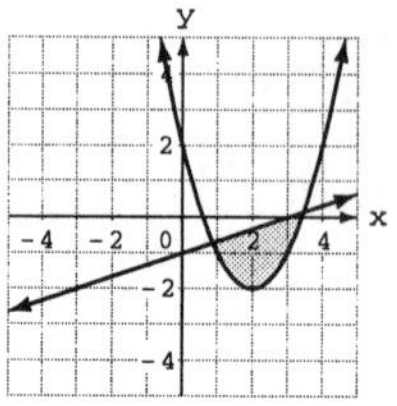

25. $x = 2y^2 - 6y + 5$

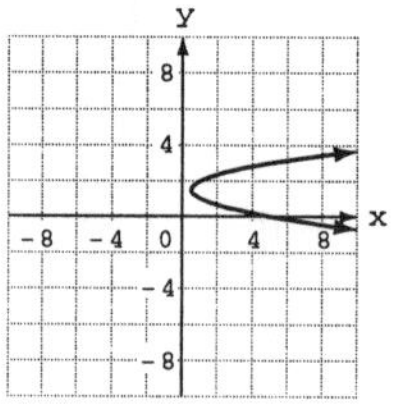

26. $\frac{x^2}{9} + \frac{y^2}{1} \ge 1$
$\frac{x^2}{4} - \frac{y^2}{1} \le 1$

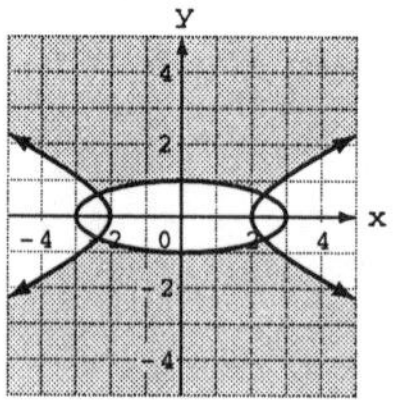

CHAPTER TEST

1. $(x-h)^2+(y-k)^2=r^2$

$[x-(-3)]^2+[y-(-3)]^2=4^2$

$(x+3)^2+(y+3)^2=16$

2. $(x_1, y_1)=(2, 5)\ (x_2, y_2)=(-2, 1)$

$d=\sqrt{(x_1-x_2)^2+(y_1-y_2)^2}$

$=\sqrt{2-(-2))^2+(5-1)^2}$

$=\sqrt{4^2+4^2}=\sqrt{16+16}$

$=\sqrt{32}=4\sqrt{2}$

$(x-h)^2+(y-k)^2=r^2$

$(x-(-2))^2+(y-1)^2=(4\sqrt{2})^2$

$(x+2)^2+(y-1)^2=32$

3. Axis of symmetry: y-axis

Vertices: (0, 5) and (0, –5)

Asymptotes: $y=\dfrac{5}{4}x$ and $y=-\dfrac{5}{4}x$

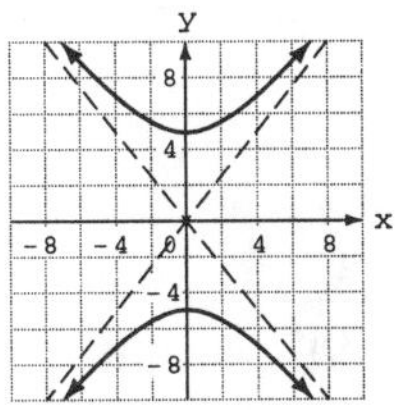

4. $x^2+y^2<36$

$x+y>4$

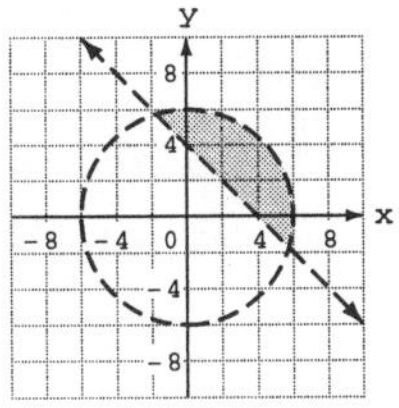

5. $y=-x^2+6x-5$

$-\dfrac{b}{2a}=-\dfrac{6}{2(-1)}=3$

Axis of symmetry: $x=3$

6. (1) $x^2-y^2=24$

(2) $2x^2+5y^2=55$

Use the addition method.

Multiply Equation (1) by –2.

$-2x^2+2y^2=-48$

$2x^2+5y^2=55$

$7y^2=7$

$y^2=1$

$y=\pm\sqrt{1}$

$y=\pm 1$

Substitute into Equation (1).

$x^2-y^2=24$	$x^2-y^2=24$
$x^2-(1)^2=24$	$x^2-(-1)^2=24$
$x^2-1=24$	$x^2-1=24$
$x^2=25$	$x^2=25$
$x=\pm\sqrt{25}$	$x=\pm\sqrt{25}$
$x=\pm 5$	$x=\pm 5$

The solutions are (5, 1), (–5, 1), (5, –1), and (–5, –1).

7. $y=-x^2+3x-2$

$-\dfrac{b}{2a}=-\dfrac{3}{2(-1)}=\dfrac{3}{2}$

$y=-\left(\dfrac{3}{2}\right)^2+3\left(\dfrac{3}{2}\right)-2=\dfrac{1}{4}$

Vertex: $\left(\dfrac{3}{2}, \dfrac{1}{4}\right)$

8. $x=y^2-y-2$

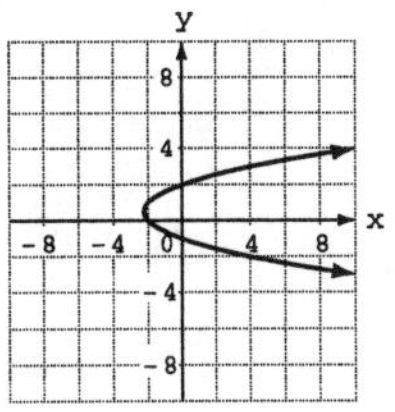

9. x-intercepts: (4, 0) and (–4, 0)

y-intercepts: (0, 2) and (0, –2)

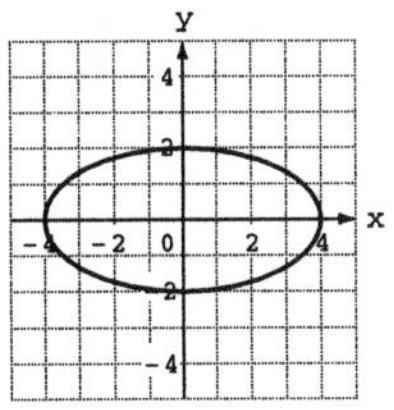

10. $\frac{x^2}{25}+\frac{y^2}{4}\le 1$

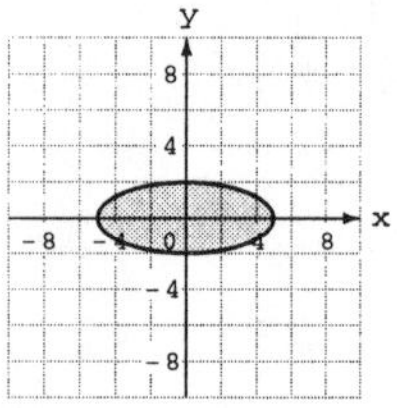

11. $(x-h)^2+(y-k)^2=r^2$

$[(x-(-2)]^2+(y-4)^2=3^2$

$(x+2)^2+(y-4)^2=9$

12. (1) $x=3y^2+2y-4$

(2) $x=y^2-5y$

Use the addition method.

Multiply Equation (1) by –1.

$x=3y^2+2y-4$

$-x=-y^2+5y$

$0=2y^2+7y-4$

$0=(2y-1)(y+4)$

$2y-1=0 \quad y+4=0$

$y=\frac{1}{2} \quad y=-4$

Substitute into Equation (2).

$x=y^2-5y$

$x=\left(\frac{1}{2}\right)^2-5\left(\frac{1}{2}\right)$

$x=\frac{1}{4}-\frac{5}{2}$

$x=-\frac{9}{4}$

$x=y^2-5y$

$x=(-4)^2-5(-4)$

$x=16+20$

$x=36$

The solutions are $\left(-\frac{9}{4},\frac{1}{2}\right)$ and (36, –4).

13. (1) $x^2+2y^2=4$

(2) $x+y=2$

Solve Equation (2) for y.

$x+y=2$

$y=2-x$

Use the substitution method.

$x^2+2(2-x)^2=4$

$x^2+2(4-4x+x^2)=4$

$x^2+8-8x+2x^2=4$

$3x^2-8x+4=0$

$(3x-2)(x-2)=0$

$3x-2=0 \quad x-2=0$

$x=\frac{2}{3} \quad x=2$

Substitute into Equation (2).

$x+y=2$

$\frac{2}{3}+y=2$

$y=\frac{4}{3}$

$x+y=2$

$2+y=2$

$y=0$

The solutions are $\left(\frac{2}{3},\frac{4}{3}\right)$ and (2, 0).

14. $(x_1,y_1)=(2,4)\ (x_2,y_2)=(-1,-3)$

$r=\sqrt{(x_1-x_2)^2+(y_1-y_2)^2}$

$=\sqrt{[2-(-1)]^2+[4-(-3)]^2}$

$=\sqrt{3^2+7^2}$

$=\sqrt{9+49}=\sqrt{58}$

$(x-h)^2+(y-k)^2=r^2$

$[x-(-1)]^2+[y-(-3)]^2=(\sqrt{58})^2$

$(x+1)^2+(y+3)^2=58$

15. $\frac{x^2}{25}-\frac{y^2}{16}>1$

$x^2+y^2<3$

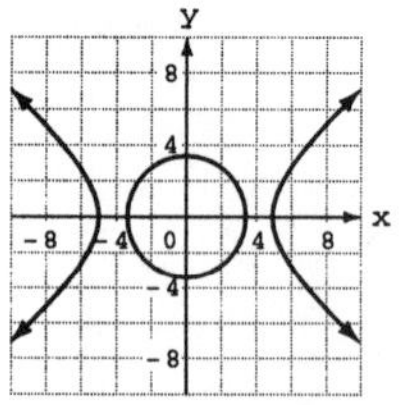

The solution sets of these inequalities do not intersect, so the system has no real number solution.

16.
$$x^2 + y^2 - 4x + 2y + 1 = 0$$
$$(x^2 - 4x) + (y^2 + 2y) = -1$$
$$(x^2 - 4x + 4) + (y^2 + 2y + 1) = -1 + 4 + 1$$
$$(x-2)^2 + (y+1)^2 = 4$$

Center: (2, –1)
Radius: 2

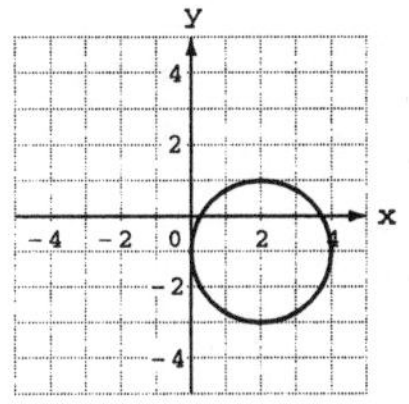

17. $y = \frac{1}{2}x^2 + x - 4$

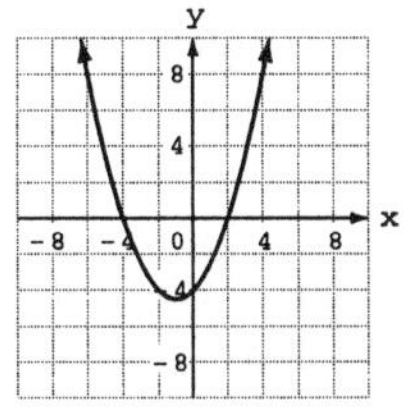

18. $(x-2)^2 + (y+1)^2 = 9$

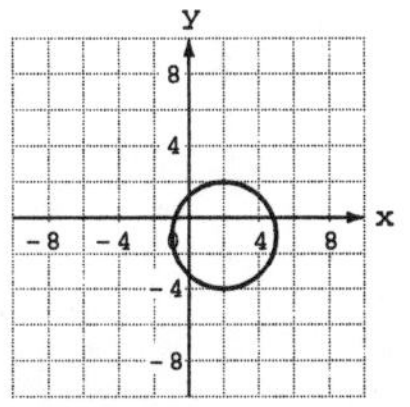

19. Axis of symmetry: x-axis
Vertices: (3, 0) and (–3, 0)
Asymptotes: $y = \frac{2}{3}x$ and $y = -\frac{2}{3}x$

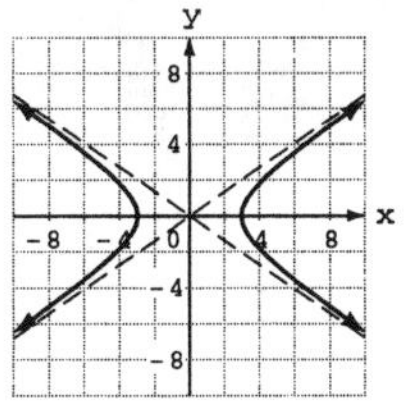

20. $\frac{x^2}{16} - \frac{y^2}{25} < 1$

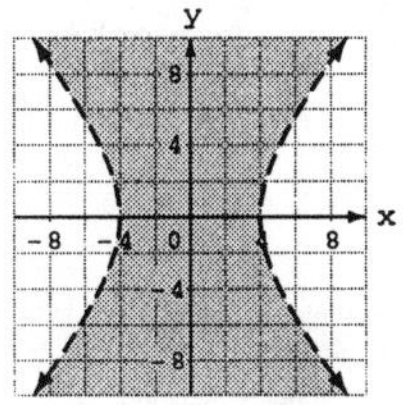

CUMULATIVE REVIEW

1. $\{x|x < 4\} \cap \{x|x > 2\} = \{x|2 < x < 4\}$

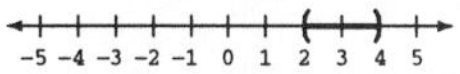

2.
$$\frac{5x-2}{3} - \frac{1-x}{5} = \frac{x+4}{10}$$
$$30\left(\frac{5x-2}{3} - \frac{1-x}{5}\right) = 30\left(\frac{x+4}{10}\right)$$
$$10(5x-2) - 6(1-x) = 3(x+4)$$
$$50x - 20 - 6 + 6x = 3x + 12$$
$$56x - 26 = 3x + 12$$
$$53x - 26 = 12$$
$$53x = 38$$
$$x = \frac{38}{53}$$

The solution is $\frac{38}{53}$.

3.
$$4 + |3x+2| < 6$$
$$|3x+2| < 2$$
$$-2 < 3x + 2 < 2$$
$$-4 < 3x < 0$$
$$-\frac{4}{3} < x < 0$$
$$\left\{x \middle| -\frac{4}{3} < x < 0\right\}$$

4. $(x_1, y_1) = (2, -3)$ $m = -\frac{3}{2}$
$$y - y_1 = m(x - x_1)$$
$$y - (-3) = -\frac{3}{2}(x-2)$$
$$y + 3 = -\frac{3}{2}x + 3$$
$$y = -\frac{3}{2}x$$

5. The product of the slopes of two perpendicular lines is –1.

$m_1 \cdot m_2 = -1$ $\quad y - y_1 = m(x - x_1)$
$m_1 \cdot -1 = -1$ $\quad y - (-2) = 1(x - 4)$
$m_1 = 1$ $\quad y + 2 = x - 4$
$\quad y = x - 6$

6. $x^{2n}(x^{2n} + 2x^n - 3x) = x^{4n} + 2x^{3n} - 3x^{2n+1}$

7.
$$(x-1)^3 - y^3$$
$$= [(x-1) - y][(x-1)^2 + (x-1)y + y^2]$$
$$= (x - 1 - y)(x^2 - 2x + 1 + xy - y + y^2)$$
$$= (x - y - 1)(x^2 - 2x + xy - y + y^2 + 1)$$

8.

$$\frac{3x-2}{x+4} \le 1$$
$$\frac{3x-2}{x+4} - 1 \le 0$$
$$\frac{3x-2}{x+4} - \frac{x+4}{x+4} \le 0$$
$$\frac{2x-6}{x+4} \le 0$$

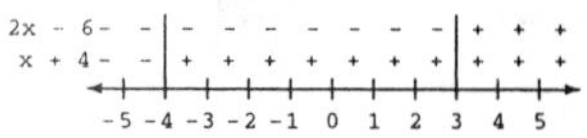

$\{x \mid -4 < x \le 3\}$

9.

$$\frac{ax-bx}{ax+ay-bx-by} = \frac{x(a-b)}{(ax+ay)+(-bx-by)}$$
$$= \frac{x(a-b)}{a(x+y)-b(x+y)}$$
$$= \frac{x(a-b)}{(x+y)(a-b)} = \frac{x}{x+y}$$

10.

$$\frac{x-4}{3x-2} - \frac{1+x}{3x^2+x-2} = \frac{x-4}{3x-2} - \frac{1+x}{(3x-2)(x+1)}$$
$$= \frac{x-4}{3x-2} \cdot \frac{x+1}{x+1} - \frac{1+x}{(3x-2)(x+1)}$$
$$= \frac{x^2-3x-4}{(3x-2)(x+1)} - \frac{1+x}{(3x-2)(x+1)}$$
$$= \frac{(x^2-3x-4)-(1+x)}{(3x-2)(x+1)}$$
$$= \frac{x^2-3x-4-1-x}{(3x-2)(x+1)}$$
$$= \frac{x^2-4x-5}{(3x-2)(x+1)}$$
$$= \frac{(x-5)(x+1)}{(3x-2)(x+1)} = \frac{x-5}{3x-2}$$

11.

$$\frac{6x}{2x-3} - \frac{1}{2x-3} = 7$$
$$(2x-3)\left(\frac{6x}{2x-3} - \frac{1}{2x-3}\right) = (2x-3)(7)$$
$$6x-1 = 14x-21$$
$$-8x-1 = -21$$
$$-8x = -20$$
$$x = \frac{5}{2}$$

The solution is $\frac{5}{2}$.

12.

$$5x+2y > 10$$
$$2y > -5x+10$$
$$y > -\frac{5}{2}x+5$$

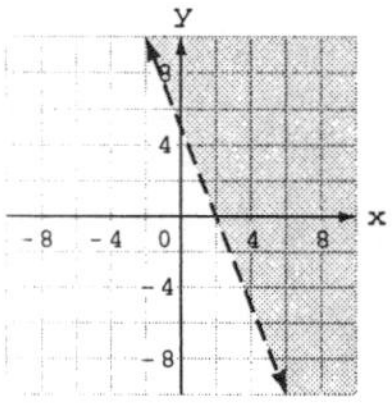

13. $\left(\frac{12a^2b^2}{a^{-3}b^{-4}}\right)^{-1}\left(\frac{ab}{4^{-1}a^{-2}b^4}\right)^2 = (12a^5b^6)^{-1}\left(\frac{4a^3}{b^3}\right)^2$

$= (12^{-1}a^{-5}b^{-6})\left(\frac{4^2a^6}{b^6}\right)$

$= \left(\frac{1}{12a^5b^6}\right)\left(\frac{4^2a^6}{b^6}\right) = \frac{16a^6}{12a^5b^{12}} = \frac{4a}{3b^{12}}$

14. $2\sqrt[4]{x^3} = 2x^{3/4}$

15. $\sqrt{18} - \sqrt{-25} = \sqrt{18} - i\sqrt{25}$

$= 3\sqrt{2} - 5i$

16. $2x^2 + 2x - 3 = 0$

$x = \frac{-b \pm \sqrt{b^2 - 4ac}}{2a} = \frac{-2 \pm \sqrt{2^2 - 4(2)(-3)}}{2(2)}$

$= \frac{-2 \pm \sqrt{4+24}}{4} = \frac{-2 \pm \sqrt{28}}{4}$

$= \frac{-2 \pm 2\sqrt{7}}{4} = \frac{-1 \pm \sqrt{7}}{2}$

The solutions are $\frac{-1+\sqrt{7}}{2}$ and $\frac{-1-\sqrt{7}}{2}$.

17. (1) $x^2 + y^2 = 20$

(2) $x^2 - y^2 = 12$

Use the addition method.

$x^2 + y^2 = 20$

$x^2 - y^2 = 12$

$2x^2 = 32$

$x^2 = 16$

$x = \pm\sqrt{16}$

$x = \pm 4$

Substitute into Equation (1).

$x^2 + y^2 = 20$	$x^2 + y^2 = 20$
$(4)^2 + y^2 = 20$	$(-4)^2 + y^2 = 20$
$16 + y^2 = 20$	$16 + y^2 = 20$
$y^2 = 4$	$y^2 = 4$
$y = \pm\sqrt{4}$	$y = \pm\sqrt{4}$
$y = \pm 2$	$y = \pm 2$

The solutions are (4, 2), (4, –2), (–4, 2), and (–4, –2).

18. $x - \sqrt{2x-3} = 3$

$-\sqrt{2x-3} = -x + 3$

$\sqrt{2x-3} = x - 3$

$(\sqrt{2x-3})^2 = (x-3)^2$

$2x - 3 = x^2 - 6x + 9$

$0 = x^2 - 8x + 12$

$0 = (x-6)(x-2)$

$x - 6 = 0 \quad x - 2 = 0$

$x = 6 \quad\quad x = 2$

Check:

$x - \sqrt{2x-3}$	$= 3$
$6 - \sqrt{2(6)-3}$	3
$6 - \sqrt{9}$	
$6 - 3$	
$3 = 3$	

$x - \sqrt{2x-3}$	$= 3$
$2 - \sqrt{2(2)-3}$	3
$2 - \sqrt{1}$	
$2 - 1$	
$1 \neq 3$	

The solution is 6.

19. $f(x) = -x^2 + 3x - 2$

$$\begin{aligned} f(-3) &= -(-3)^2 + 3(-3) - 2 \\ &= -9 - 9 - 2 \\ &= -20 \end{aligned}$$

20.

$$\begin{aligned} f(x) &= 4x + 8 \\ y &= 4x + 8 \\ x &= 4y + 8 \\ x - 8 &= 4y \\ \frac{1}{4}x - 2 &= y \end{aligned}$$

The inverse of the function is $f^{-1}(x) = \frac{1}{4}x - 2$.

21. $f(x) = -2x^2 + 4x - 2$

$$x = -\frac{b}{2a} = -\frac{4}{2(-2)} = \frac{-4}{-4} = 1$$

$$\begin{aligned} f(x) &= -2x^2 + 4x - 2 \\ f(1) &= -2(1)^2 + 4(1) - 2 \\ &= -2 + 4 - 2 \\ &= 0 \end{aligned}$$

The maximum value of the function is 0.

22. Strategy

- Let x represent one number. Since the sum of the two numbers is 40, $40 - x$ represents the other number. Then their product is represented by $-x^2 + 40x$.
- To find the first of the two numbers, find the x-coordinate of the vertex of the function $f(x) = -x^2 + 40x$.
- To find the other number, replace x in $40 - x$ by the x-coordinate of the vertex and evaluate.

Solution $x = -\frac{b}{2a} = -\frac{40}{2(-1)} = \frac{-40}{-2} = 20$

$40 - x = 40 - 20 = 20$

$20 \cdot 20 = 400$

The maximum product of the two numbers whose sum is 40 is 400.

23. $(x_1, y_1) = (2, 4)$ $(x_2, y_2) = (-1, 0)$

$$\begin{aligned} d &= \sqrt{(x_1 - x_2)^2 + (y_1 - y_2)^2} \\ &= \sqrt{[2 - (-1)^2] + (4 - 0)^2} \\ &= \sqrt{3^2 + 4^2} \\ &= \sqrt{9 + 16} = \sqrt{25} = 5 \end{aligned}$$

24. $(x_1, y_1) = (3, 1)$ $(x_2, y_2) = (-1, 2)$

$$\begin{aligned} r &= \sqrt{(x_1 - x_2)^2 + (y_1 - y_2)^2} \\ &= \sqrt{[3 - (-1)]^2 + (1 - 2)^2} \\ &= \sqrt{4^2 + (-1)^2} \\ &= \sqrt{16 + 1} = \sqrt{17} \end{aligned}$$

$$(x - h)^2 + (y - k)^2 = r^2$$
$$[x - (-1)]^2 + (y - 2)^2 = (\sqrt{17})^2$$
$$(x + 1)^2 + (y - 2)^2 = 17$$

25. $x = y^2 - 2y + 3$

$$-\frac{b}{2a} = -\frac{-2}{2(1)} = \frac{2}{2} = 1$$

$x = (1)^2 - 2(1) + 3 = 2$

Vertex: (2, 1)

Axis of symmetry: $y = 1$

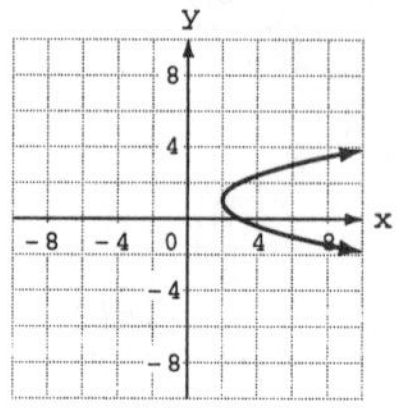

26. $\frac{x^2}{25} + \frac{y^2}{4} = 1$

x-intercepts: (5, 0) and (–5, 0)

y-intercepts: (0, 2) and (0, –2).

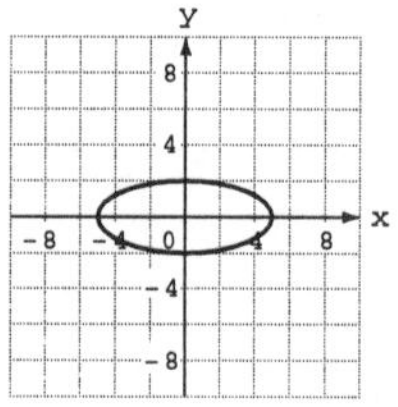

27. $\frac{y^2}{4} - \frac{x^2}{25} < 1$

Axis of symmetry: y-axis

Vertices: (0, 2) and (0, –2)

Asymptotes: $y = \frac{2}{5}x$ and $y = -\frac{2}{5}x$

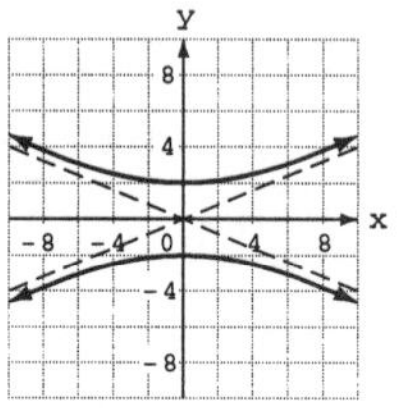

28. $(x-1)^2 + y^2 \le 25$

$y^2 < x$

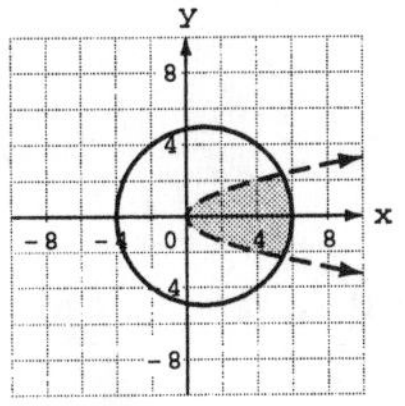

29. Strategy • Number of adult tickets: x
Number of child tickets: $192 - x$

	Amount	Cost	Value
Adult tickets	x	4.00	$4x$
Child tickets	$192 - x$	1.50	$1.5(192 - x)$

• The sum of the values of each type of ticket sold equals the total value of all the tickets sold ($493).

Solution

$$4x + 1.5(192 - x) = 493$$
$$4x + 288 - 1.5x = 493$$
$$2.5x + 288 = 493$$
$$2.5x = 205$$
$$x = 82$$

There were 82 adult tickets sold.

30. Strategy • The unknown rate of the motorcycle: r
The unknown rate of the car: $r - 12$

	Distance	Rate	Time
Motorcycle	180	r	$\frac{180}{r}$
Car	144	$r - 12$	$\frac{144}{r-12}$

• The time traveled by the motorcycle is the same as the time traveled by the car.

Solution

$$\frac{180}{r} = \frac{144}{r-12}$$
$$r(r-12)\left(\frac{180}{r}\right) = r(r-12)\left(\frac{144}{r-12}\right)$$
$$(r-12)(180) = r(144)$$
$$180r - 2160 = 144r$$
$$36r - 2160 = 0$$
$$36r = 2160$$
$$r = 60$$

The rate of the motorcycle is 60 mph.

31. Strategy • The unknown rowing rate of the crew in calm water: r

	Distance	Rate	Time
With current	12	$r+1.5$	$\frac{12}{r+1.5}$
Against current	12	$r-1.5$	$\frac{12}{r-1.5}$

• The sum of the time traveling upriver and the time traveling downriver equals the total time traveled (6 h).

Solution

$$\frac{12}{r+1.5}+\frac{12}{r-1.5}=6$$
$$(r+1.5)(r-1.5)\left(\frac{12}{r+1.5}+\frac{12}{r-1.5}\right)=(r+1.5)(r-1.5)(6)$$
$$(r-1.5)(12)+(r+1.5)(12)=(r^2-2.25)(6)$$
$$12r-18+12r+18=6r^2-13.5$$
$$24r=6r^2-13.5$$
$$0=6r^2-24r-13.5$$
$$0=12r^2-48r-27$$
$$0=3(4r^2-16r-9)$$
$$0=4r^2-16r-9$$
$$0=(2r+1)(2r-9)$$

$$2r+1=0 \qquad 2r-9=0$$
$$2r=-1 \qquad 2r=9$$
$$r=-\frac{1}{2} \qquad r=\frac{9}{2}$$

Since rate cannot be a negative number, the solution $-\frac{1}{2}$ is not possible. The rowing rate of the crew is 4.5 mph.

32. Strategy To find the speed:

• Write the basic inverse variation equation, replace the variables by the given values, and solve for k.
• Write the inverse variation equation, replacing k by its value. Substitute 60 for t and solve for v.

Solution

$$v=\frac{k}{t} \qquad v=\frac{1080}{t}$$
$$30=\frac{k}{36} \qquad =\frac{1080}{60}$$
$$1080=k \qquad =18$$

The gear will make 18 revolutions per minute.

Chapter 12: Sequences and Series

SECTION 12.1

Objective A Exercises

1. $a_n = n+1$

$a_1 = 1+1 = 2$ The first term is 2.

$a_2 = 2+1 = 3$ The second term is 3.

$a_3 = 3+1 = 4$ The third term is 4.

$a_4 = 4+1 = 5$ The fourth term is 5.

3. $a_n = 2n+1$

$a_1 = 2(1)+1 = 3$ The first term is 3.

$a_2 = 2(2)+1 = 5$ The second term is 5.

$a_3 = 2(3)+1 = 7$ The third term is 7.

$a_4 = 2(4)+1 = 9$ The fourth term is 9.

5. $a_n = 2-2n$

$a_1 = 2-2(1) = 0$ The first term is 0.

$a_2 = 2-2(2) = -2$ The second term is -2.

$a_3 = 2-2(3) = -4$ The third term is -4.

$a_4 = 2-2(4) = -6$ The fourth term is -6.

7. $a_n = 2^n$

$a_1 = 2^1 = 2$ The first term is 2.

$a_2 = 2^2 = 4$ The second term is 4.

$a_3 = 2^3 = 8$ The third term is 8.

$a_4 = 2^4 = 16$ The fourth term is 16.

9. $a_n = n^2+1$

$a_1 = 1^2+1 = 2$ The first term is 2.

$a_2 = 2^2+1 = 5$ The second term is 5.

$a_3 = 3^2+1 = 10$ The third term is 10.

$a_4 = 4^2+1 = 17$ The fourth term is 17.

11. $a_n = n^2 - \frac{1}{n}$

$a_1 = 1^2 - \frac{1}{1}$ The first term is 0.

$a_2 = 2^2 - \frac{1}{2} = \frac{7}{2}$ The second term is $\frac{7}{2}$.

$a_3 = 3^2 - \frac{1}{3} = \frac{26}{3}$ The third term is $\frac{26}{3}$.

$a_4 = 4^2 - \frac{1}{4} = \frac{63}{4}$ The fourth term is $\frac{63}{4}$.

13. $a_n = 3n+4$

$a_{12} = 3(12)+4 = 40$

The twelfth term is 40.

15. $a_n = n(n-1)$

$a_{11} = 11(11-1) = 110$

The eleventh term is 110.

17. $a_n = (-1)^{n-1}n^2$

$a_{15} = (-1)^{14}(15)^2 = 225$

The fifteenth term is 225.

19. $a_n = \left(\frac{1}{2}\right)^n$

$a_8 = \left(\frac{1}{2}\right)^8 = \frac{1}{256}$

The eighth term is $\frac{1}{256}$.

21. $a_n = (n+2)(n+3)$

$a_{17} = (17+2)(17+3) = (19)(20) = 380$

The seventeenth term is 380.

23. $a_n = \frac{(-1)^{2n-1}}{n^2}$

$a_6 = \frac{(-1)^{11}}{(6)^2} = -\frac{1}{36}$

The sixth term is $-\frac{1}{36}$.

Objective B Exercises

25. $\sum_{n=1}^{5}(2n+3) = (2\cdot1+3)+(2\cdot2+3)+(2\cdot3+3)+(2\cdot4+3)+(2\cdot5+3)$

$= 5+7+9+11+13$

$= 45$

27. $\sum_{i=1}^{4} 2i = 2(1)+2(2)+2(3)+2(4) = 2+4+6+8 = 20$

29. $\sum_{i=1}^{6} i^2 = 1^2+2^2+3^2+4^2+5^2+6^2 = 1+4+9+16+25+36 = 91$

31. $\sum_{n=1}^{6}(-1)^n = (-1)^1 + (-1)^2 + (-1)^3 + (-1)^4 + (-1)^5 + (-1)^6$
$= -1+1-1+1-1+1 = 0$

33. $\sum_{i=3}^{6} i^3 = 3^3 + 4^3 + 5^3 + 6^3 = 27 + 64 + 125 + 216 = 432$

35. $\sum_{n=3}^{5} \frac{(-1)^{n-1}}{n-2} = \frac{(-1)^2}{3-2} + \frac{(-1)^3}{4-2} + \frac{(-1)^4}{5-2} = 1 - \frac{1}{2} + \frac{1}{3} = \frac{5}{6}$

37. $\sum_{n=1}^{5} 2x^n = 2x + 2x^2 + 2x^3 + 2x^4 + 2x^5$

39. $\sum_{i=1}^{5} \frac{x^i}{i} = x + \frac{x^2}{2} + \frac{x^3}{3} + \frac{x^4}{4} + \frac{x^5}{5}$

41. $\sum_{i=3}^{5} \frac{x^i}{2i} = \frac{x^3}{2(3)} + \frac{x^4}{2(4)} + \frac{x^5}{2(5)} = \frac{x^3}{6} + \frac{x^4}{8} + \frac{x^5}{10}$

43. $\sum_{n=1}^{5} x^{2n} = x^{2(1)} + x^{2(2)} + x^{2(3)} + x^{2(4)} + x^{2(5)} = x^2 + x^4 + x^6 + x^8 + x^{10}$

45. $\sum_{i=1}^{4} \frac{x^i}{i^2} = \frac{x^1}{1^2} + \frac{x^2}{2^2} + \frac{x^3}{3^2} + \frac{x^4}{4^2} = x + \frac{x^2}{4} + \frac{x^3}{9} + \frac{x^4}{16}$

47. $\sum_{n=1}^{4} nx^{n-1} = 1x^{1-1} + 2x^{2-1} + 3x^{3-1} + 4x^{4-1} = 1 + 2x + 3x^2 + 4x^3$

Applying the Concepts

49. The infinite sum of $\frac{1}{2} + \frac{1}{4} + \frac{1}{8} + \frac{1}{16} + \ldots$ is 1.

51. a. False.

b. False.

53. The Fibonacci Sequence is named after a thirteen-century mathematician, Leonardo Fibonacci of Pisa, who was the first mathematician to bring Arabic numerals into Europe. The Fibonacci Sequence consists of the numbers 0, 1, 1, 2, 3, 5, 8, 13, ... Every Fibonacci number is the sum of its two predecessors; that is, $F_{k+2} = F_k + F_{k+1}$. The sequence shows up in a startling number of applications in nature (in botany, for example).

SECTION 12.2

Objective A Exercises

1. $d = a_2 - a_1 = 11 - 1 = 10$
$a_n = a_1 + (n-1)d$
$a_{15} = 1 + (15-1)(10)$
$= 1 + 14(10) = 1 + 140$
$a_{15} = 141$

3. $d = a_2 - a_1 = -2 - (-6) = 4$
$a_n = a_1 + (n-1)d$
$a_{15} = -6 + (15-1)4$
$= -6 + 14(4) = -6 + 56$
$a_{15} = 50$

5. $d = a_2 - a_1 = \frac{5}{2} - 2 = \frac{1}{2}$
$a_n = a_1 + (n-1)d$
$a_{31} = 2 + (31-1)\frac{1}{2} = 2 + 30\left(\frac{1}{2}\right) = 2 + 15$
$a_{31} = 17$

7.
$$d = a_2 - a_1 = -\frac{5}{2} - (-4) = \frac{3}{2}$$
$$a_n = a_1 + (n-1)d$$
$$a_{12} = -4 + (12-1)\frac{3}{2} = -4 + 11\left(\frac{3}{2}\right) = -4 + \frac{33}{2}$$
$$a_{12} = \frac{25}{2} = 12\frac{1}{2}$$

9.
$$d = a_2 - a_1 = 5 - 8 = -3$$
$$a_n = a_1 + (n-1)d$$
$$a_{40} = 8 + (40-1)(-3) = 8 + 39(-3) = 8 - 117$$
$$a_{40} = -109$$

11.
$$d = a_2 - a_1 = 4 - 1 = 3$$
$$a_n = a_1 + (n-1)d$$
$$a_n = 1 + (n-1)3$$
$$a_n = 1 + 3n - 3$$
$$a_n = 3n - 2$$

13.
$$d = a_2 - a_1 = 0 - 3 = -3$$
$$a_n = a_1 + (n-1)d$$
$$a_n = 3 + (n-1)(-3)$$
$$a_n = 3 - 3n + 3$$
$$a_n = -3n + 6$$

15.
$$d = a_2 - a_1 = 4.5 - 7 = -2.5$$
$$a_n = a_1 + (n-1)d$$
$$a_n = 7 + (n-1)(-2.5)$$
$$a_n = 7 - 2.5n + 2.5$$
$$a_n = -2.5n + 9.5$$

17.
$$d = a_2 - a_1 = 8 - 3 = 5$$
$$a_n = a_1 + (n-1)d$$
$$98 = 3 + (n-1)5$$
$$98 = 3 + 5n - 5$$
$$98 = 5n - 2$$
$$100 = 5n$$
$$20 = n$$

There are 20 terms in the sequence.

19.
$$d = a_2 - a_1 = -3 - 1 = -4$$
$$a_n = a_1 + (n-1)d$$
$$-75 = 1 + (n-1)(-4)$$
$$-75 = 1 - 4n + 4$$
$$-75 = 5 - 4n$$
$$-80 = -4n$$
$$20 = n$$

There are 20 terms in the sequence.

21.
$$d = a_2 - a_1 = \frac{13}{3} - \frac{7}{3} = 2$$
$$a_n = a_1 + (n-1)d$$
$$\frac{79}{3} = \frac{7}{3} + (n-1)2$$
$$\frac{79}{3} = \frac{7}{3} + 2n - 2$$
$$\frac{79}{3} = 2n + \frac{1}{3}$$
$$26 = 2n$$
$$13 = n$$

There are 13 terms in the sequence.

23.
$$d = a_2 - a_1 = 2 - 3.5 = -1.5$$
$$a_n = a_1 + (n-1)d$$
$$-25 = 3.5 + (n-1)(-1.5)$$
$$-25 = 3.5 - 1.5n + 1.5$$
$$-25 = 5 - 1.5n$$
$$-30 = -1.5n$$
$$20 = n$$

There are 20 terms in the sequence.

Objective B Exercises

25.
$$d = a_2 - a_1 = 3 - 1 = 2$$
$$a_n = a_1 + (n-1)d$$
$$a_n = 1 + (50-1)2 = 1 + 49(2) = 99$$
$$S_n = \frac{n}{2}(a_1 + a_2)$$
$$S_n = \frac{50}{2}(1 + 99) = 25(100) = 2500$$

27.
$$d = a_2 - a_1 = 18 - 20 = -2$$
$$a_n = a_1 + (n-1)d$$
$$a_n = 20 + (40-1)(-2) = 20 + 39(-2)$$
$$= 20 - 78 = -58$$
$$S_n = \frac{n}{2}(a_1 + a_n)$$
$$S_n = \frac{40}{2}[20 + (-58)] = \frac{40}{2}(-38) = -760$$

29.
$$d = a_2 - a_1 = 1 - \frac{1}{2} = \frac{1}{2}$$
$$a_n = a_1 + (n-1)d$$
$$a_n = \frac{1}{2} + (27-1)\frac{1}{2} = \frac{1}{2} + (26)\frac{1}{2} = \frac{27}{2}$$
$$S_n = \frac{n}{2}(a_1 + a_n)$$
$$S_n = \frac{27}{2}\left(\frac{1}{2} + \frac{27}{2}\right) = \frac{27}{2}(14) = 189$$

31.
$$a_i = 3i - 1$$
$$a_1 = 3(1) - 1 = 2$$
$$a_{15} = 3(15) - 1 = 44$$
$$S_i = \frac{i}{2}(a_1 + a_i)$$
$$S_i = \frac{15}{2}(2 + 44) = \frac{15}{2}(46) = 345$$

33.
$$a_n = \frac{1}{2}n + 1$$
$$a_1 = \frac{1}{2}(1) + 1 = \frac{3}{2}$$
$$a_{17} = \frac{1}{2}(17) + 1 = \frac{19}{2}$$
$$S_n = \frac{n}{2}(a_1 + a_n)$$
$$S_n = \frac{17}{2}\left(\frac{3}{2} + \frac{19}{2}\right) = \frac{17}{2}(11) = \frac{187}{2}$$

35.
$$a_i = 4 - 2i$$
$$a_1 = 4 - 2(1) = 2$$
$$a_{15} = 4 - 2(15) = -26$$
$$S_i = \frac{i}{2}(a_1 + a_i)$$
$$S_i = \frac{15}{2}(2 - 26) = \frac{15}{2}(-24) = -180$$

Objective C Application Problems

37. Strategy To find the number of weeks:

- Write the arithmetic sequence.
- Find the common difference of the arithmetic sequence.
- Use the Formula for the nth Term of an Arithmetic Sequence to find the number of terms in the sequence.

Solution 10, 15, 20, …, 60
$$d = a_2 - a_1 = 15 - 10 = 5$$
$$a_n = a_1 + (n-1)d$$
$$60 = 10 + (n-1)5$$
$$60 = 10 + 5n - 5$$
$$60 = 5 + 5n$$
$$55 = 5n$$
$$11 = n$$
In 11 weeks the person will walk 60 min per day.

39. Strategy To find the distance the object will fall during the fifth second:

- Write the common difference of the arithmetic sequence.
- Find the common difference of the arithmetic sequence.
- Use the Formula for the nth Term of an arithmetic Sequence to find the 5th term.

Solution 16, 48, 80, …
$$d = a_2 - a_1 = 48 - 16 = 32$$
$$a_n = a_1 + (n-1)d$$
$$a_5 = 16 + (5-1)32$$
$$a_5 = 16 + 4(32)$$
$$a_5 = 16 + 128 = 144$$
The object will drop 144 ft during the 5th second.

41. Strategy To find the monthly salary during the eighth month and to find the total salary for the eight month period:

- Write the arithmetic sequence.
- Find the common difference of the arithmetic sequence.
- Use the Formula for the nth term of an Arithmetic Sequence to find the salary during the eighth month
- Use the Formula for the Sum of n Terms of an Arithmetic Sequence to find the total salary for the eight months.

Solution 1500, 1800, 2100 …
$$d = a_1 - a_2 = 1800 - 1500 = 300$$
$$a_8 = a_1 + (n-1)d$$
$$a_8 = 1500 + (8-1)(300)$$
$$a_8 = 1500 + 7(300) = 1500 + 2100$$
$$a_8 = 3600$$

$$S_n = \frac{n}{2}(a_1 + a_n)$$
$$S_8 = \frac{8}{2}(1500 + 3600)$$
$$S_8 = 4(5100) = 20{,}400$$
The salary for the eighth month is \$3600. The total salary for eight months is \$20,400.

Applying the Concepts

43.
$$\sum_{i=1}^{2} \log 2i = \log 2(1) + \log 2(2)$$
$$= \log 2 + \log 4$$
$$= \log(2 \cdot 4)$$
$$= \log 8$$

SECTION 12.3

Objective A Exercises

1. $r = \frac{a_2}{a_1} = \frac{8}{2} = 4$

$a_n = a_1 r^{n-1}$
$a_9 = 2(4)^{9-1}$
$= 2(4)^8$
$= 2(65,536) = 131,072$

3. $r = \frac{a_2}{a_1} = \frac{-4}{6} = -\frac{2}{3}$

$a_n = a_1 r^{n-1}$
$a_7 = 6\left(-\frac{2}{3}\right)^{7-1}$
$= 6\left(-\frac{2}{3}\right)^6$
$= 6\left(\frac{64}{729}\right) = \frac{128}{243}$

5. $r = \frac{a_2}{a_1} = \frac{\frac{1}{8}}{-\frac{1}{16}} = -2$

$a_n = a_1 r^{n-1}$
$a_{10} = -\frac{1}{16}(-2)^{10-1}$
$= -\frac{1}{16}(-2)^9$
$= -\frac{1}{16}(-512) = 32$

7. $a_n = a_1 r^{n-1}$
$a_4 = 9r^{4-1}$
$\frac{8}{3} = 9r^{4-1}$
$\frac{8}{3} = 9r^3$
$\frac{8}{27} = r^3$
$\frac{2}{3} = r$
$a_n = a_1 r^{n-1}$
$a_2 = 9\left(\frac{2}{3}\right)^{2-1} = 9\left(\frac{2}{3}\right) = 6$
$a_3 = 9\left(\frac{2}{3}\right)^{3-1} = 9\left(\frac{2}{3}\right)^2 = 9\left(\frac{4}{9}\right) = 4$

9. $a_n = a_1 r^{n-1}$
$a_4 = 3r^{4-1}$
$-\frac{8}{9} = 3r^{4-1}$
$-\frac{8}{9} = 3r^3$
$-\frac{8}{27} = r^3$
$-\frac{2}{3} = r$
$a_n = a_1 r^{n-1}$
$a_2 = 3\left(-\frac{2}{3}\right)^{2-1} = 3\left(-\frac{2}{3}\right) = -2$
$a_3 = 3\left(-\frac{2}{3}\right)^{3-1} = 3\left(-\frac{2}{3}\right)^2 = 3\left(\frac{4}{9}\right) = \frac{4}{3}$

11. $a_n = a_1 r^{n-1}$
$a_4 = (-3)r^{4-1}$
$192 = (-3)r^{4-1}$
$192 = (-3)r^3$
$-64 = r^3$
$-4 = r$
$a_n = a_1 r^{n-1}$
$a_2 = -3(-4)^{2-1} = -3(-4) = 12$
$a_3 = -3(-4)^{3-1} = -3(-4)^2 = -3(16) = -48$

Objective B Exercises

13. $r = \frac{a_2}{a_1} = \frac{6}{2} = 3$

$S_n = \frac{a_1(1-r^n)}{1-r}$
$S_7 = \frac{2(1-3^7)}{1-3} = \frac{2(1-2187)}{-2}$
$= \frac{2(-2186)}{-2} = 2186$

15. $r = \frac{a_2}{a_1} = \frac{9}{12} = \frac{3}{4}$

$S_n = \frac{a_1(1-r^n)}{1-r}$
$S_5 = \frac{12\left[1-\left(\frac{3}{4}\right)^5\right]}{1-\frac{3}{4}}$
$= \frac{12\left(1-\frac{243}{1024}\right)}{\frac{1}{4}}$
$= 48\left(\frac{781}{1024}\right) = \frac{2343}{64}$

17. $a_n = (2)^i$

$a_1 = (2)^1 = 2$

$a_2 = (2)^2 = 4$

$r = \frac{a_2}{a_1} = \frac{4}{2} = 2$

$S_n = \frac{a_1(1-r^n)}{1-r}$

$S_5 = \frac{2(1-2^5)}{1-2} = \frac{2(1-32)}{-1}$
$= -2(-31) = 62$

19. $a_n = \left(\frac{1}{3}\right)^i$

$a_1 = \left(\frac{1}{3}\right)^1 = \frac{1}{3}$

$a_2 = \left(\frac{1}{3}\right)^2 = \frac{1}{9}$

$r = \frac{a_2}{a_1} = \frac{1}{9} \div \frac{1}{3} = \frac{1}{9} \cdot \frac{3}{1} = \frac{1}{3}$

$S_n = \frac{a_1(1-r^n)}{1-r}$

$S_5 = \frac{\frac{1}{3}\left[1-\left(\frac{1}{3}\right)^5\right]}{1-\frac{1}{3}} = \frac{\frac{1}{3}\left(1-\frac{1}{243}\right)}{\frac{2}{3}}$

$= \frac{\frac{1}{3}\left(\frac{242}{243}\right)}{\frac{2}{3}} = \frac{\frac{242}{729}}{\frac{2}{3}} = \frac{121}{243}$

Objective C Exercises

21. $r = \frac{a_2}{a_1} = \frac{2}{3}$

$S = \frac{a_1}{1-r} = \frac{3}{1-\frac{2}{3}} = \frac{3}{\frac{1}{3}} = 9$

23. $r = \frac{a_2}{a_1} = \frac{\frac{7}{100}}{\frac{7}{10}} = \frac{1}{10}$

$S = \frac{a_1}{1-r} = \frac{\frac{7}{10}}{1-\frac{1}{10}} = \frac{\frac{7}{10}}{\frac{9}{10}} = \frac{7}{9}$

25. $0.88\overline{8} = 0.8 + 0.08 + 0.008 + \ldots$
$= \frac{8}{10} + \frac{8}{100} + \frac{8}{1000} + \ldots$

$S = \frac{a_1}{1-r} = \frac{\frac{8}{10}}{1-\frac{1}{10}} = \frac{\frac{8}{10}}{\frac{9}{10}} = \frac{8}{9}$

An equivalent fraction is $\frac{8}{9}$.

27. $0.22\overline{2} = 0.2 + 0.02 + 0.002 + \ldots$
$= \frac{2}{10} + \frac{2}{100} + \frac{2}{1000} + \ldots$

$S = \frac{a_1}{1-r} = \frac{\frac{2}{10}}{1-\frac{1}{10}} = \frac{\frac{2}{10}}{\frac{9}{10}} = \frac{2}{9}$

An equivalent fraction is $\frac{2}{9}$.

29. $0.45\overline{45} = 0.45 + 0.0045 + 0.000045 + \ldots$
$= \frac{45}{100} + \frac{45}{10{,}000} + \frac{45}{1{,}000{,}000} + \ldots$

$S = \frac{a_1}{1-r} = \frac{\frac{45}{100}}{1-\frac{1}{100}} = \frac{\frac{45}{100}}{\frac{99}{100}} = \frac{45}{99} = \frac{5}{11}$

An equivalent fraction is $\frac{5}{11}$.

31. $0.166\overline{6} = 0.1 + 0.06 + 0.006 + 0.0006 + \ldots$
$= \frac{1}{10} + \frac{6}{100} + \frac{6}{1000} + \frac{6}{10{,}000} + \ldots$

$S = \frac{a_1}{1-r} = \frac{\frac{6}{100}}{1-\frac{1}{10}} = \frac{\frac{6}{100}}{\frac{9}{10}} = \frac{6}{90} = \frac{1}{15}$

$0.166\overline{6} = \frac{1}{10} + \frac{1}{15} = \frac{5}{30} = \frac{1}{6}$

An equivalent fraction is $\frac{1}{6}$.

Objective D Application Problems

33. Strategy To find the amount of radioactive material at the beginning of the fourth hour, use the Formula for the nth Term of a Geometric Sequence.

Solution $n = 4,\ a_1 = 400,\ r = \frac{1}{2}$

$a_n = a_1 r^{n-1}$

$a_4 = 400\left(\frac{1}{2}\right)^{4-1}$
$= 400\left(\frac{1}{2}\right)^3 = 400\left(\frac{1}{8}\right) = 50$

There will be 50 mg of radioactive material in the sample at the beginning of the fourth hour.

35. Strategy To find the height of the ball on the sixth bounce, use the Formula for the nth Term of a Geometric Sequence.

Solution $n = 6,\ a_1 = 75\%$ of $10 = 7.5$,
$r = 75\% = \frac{3}{4}$

$a_n = a_1 r^{n-1}$

$a_6 = 7.5\left(\frac{3}{4}\right)^{6-1}$
$= 7.5\left(\frac{3}{4}\right)^5 = 7.5\left(\frac{243}{1024}\right) \approx 1.8$

The ball bounces to a height of 1.8 ft on the sixth bounce.

37. Strategy To find the total amount of money earned in 30 days, use the Formula for the Sum of n Terms of a Finite Geometric Series.

Solution $n = 30,\ a_1 = 1,\ r = 2$

$$S_n = \frac{a_1(1-r^n)}{1-r}$$

$$S_{30} = \frac{1(1-2^{30})}{1-2}$$

$$= \frac{1(1-1{,}073{,}741{,}824)}{-1}$$

$$= \frac{-1{,}073{,}741{,}823}{-1} = 1{,}073{,}741{,}823$$

The total amount earned in 30 days is 1,073,741,823 cents, or \$10,737,418.23.

Applying the Concepts

39. $a_1,\ a_2,\ 3\ \ a_4,\ a_5,\ \frac{1}{9}$

Use the two known terms in the Formula for the nth Term of a Geometric Sequence, and solve for r.

$$a_3 = a_1 r^{3-1} \qquad a_6 = a_1 r^{6-1}$$

$$3 = a_1 r^2 \qquad (2)\ \ \frac{1}{9} = a_1 r^5$$

$$a_1 = \frac{3}{r^2}$$

(1) $a_1 = 3r^{-2}$

Substitute Equation (1) into Equation (2).

$$\frac{1}{9} = a_1 r^5$$

$$\frac{1}{9} = (3r^{-2})r^5$$

$$\frac{1}{9} = 3r^3$$

$$\frac{1}{27} = r^3$$

$$\frac{1}{3} = r$$

Substitute r into Equation (1) to find a_1.

$$a_1 = 3r^{-2}$$

$$a_1 = 3\left(\frac{1}{3}\right)^{-2}$$

$$a_1 = 27$$

The first term is 27.

41. An arithmetic sequence has a constant term *added* to each successive term in the sequence. A geometric sequence has a constant term *multiplied* by each successive term in the sequence.

SECTION 12.4

Objective A Exercises

1. $3! = 3\cdot 2\cdot 1 = 6$

3. $8! = 8\cdot 7\cdot 6\cdot 5\cdot 4\cdot 3\cdot 2\cdot 1 = 40{,}320$

5. $0! = 1$

7. $\frac{5!}{2!3!} = \frac{5\cdot 4\cdot 3\cdot 2\cdot 1}{(2\cdot 1)(3\cdot 2\cdot 1)} = 10$

9. $\frac{6!}{6!0!} = \frac{6\cdot 5\cdot 4\cdot 3\cdot 2\cdot 1}{(6\cdot 5\cdot 4\cdot 3\cdot 2\cdot 1)(1)} = 1$

11. $\frac{9!}{6!3!} = \frac{9\cdot 8\cdot 7\cdot 6\cdot 5\cdot 4\cdot 3\cdot 2\cdot 1}{(6\cdot 5\cdot 4\cdot 3\cdot 2\cdot 1)(3\cdot 2\cdot 1)} = 84$

13. $\binom{7}{2} = \frac{7!}{(7-2)!2!} = \frac{7!}{5!2!} = \frac{7\cdot 6\cdot 5\cdot 4\cdot 3\cdot 2\cdot 1}{(5\cdot 4\cdot 3\cdot 2\cdot 1)(2\cdot 1)} = 21$

15. $\binom{10}{2} = \frac{10!}{(10-2)!2!} = \frac{10!}{8!2!} = \frac{10\cdot9\cdot8\cdot7\cdot6\cdot5\cdot4\cdot3\cdot2\cdot1}{(8\cdot7\cdot6\cdot5\cdot4\cdot3\cdot2\cdot1)(2\cdot1)} = 45$

17. $\binom{9}{0} = \frac{9!}{(9-0)!0!} = \frac{9!}{9!0!} = \frac{9\cdot8\cdot7\cdot6\cdot5\cdot4\cdot3\cdot2\cdot1}{(9\cdot8\cdot7\cdot6\cdot5\cdot4\cdot3\cdot2\cdot1)(1)} = 1$

19. $\binom{6}{3} = \frac{6!}{(6-3)!3!} = \frac{6!}{3!3!} = \frac{6\cdot5\cdot4\cdot3\cdot2\cdot1}{(3\cdot2\cdot1)(3\cdot2\cdot1)} = 20$

21. $\binom{11}{1} = \frac{11!}{(11-1)!1!} = \frac{11!}{10!1!} = \frac{11\cdot10\cdot9\cdot8\cdot7\cdot6\cdot5\cdot4\cdot3\cdot2\cdot1}{(10\cdot9\cdot8\cdot7\cdot6\cdot5\cdot4\cdot3\cdot2\cdot1)(1)} = 11$

23. $\binom{4}{2} = \frac{4!}{(4-2)!2!} = \frac{4!}{2!2!} = \frac{4\cdot3\cdot2\cdot1}{(2\cdot1)(2\cdot1)} = 6$

25. $$\begin{aligned}(x+y)^4 &= \binom{4}{0}x^4 + \binom{4}{1}x^3y + \binom{4}{2}x^2y^2 + \binom{4}{3}xy^3 + \binom{4}{4}y^4 \\ &= x^4 + 4x^3y + 6x^2y^2 + 4xy^3 + y^4\end{aligned}$$

27. $$\begin{aligned}(x-y)^5 &= \binom{5}{0}x^5 + \binom{5}{1}x^4(-y) + \binom{5}{2}x^3(-y)^2 + \binom{5}{3}x^2(-y)^3 + \binom{5}{4}x(-y)^4 + \binom{5}{5}(-y)^5 \\ &= x^5 - 5x^4y + 10x^3y^2 - 10x^2y^3 + 5xy^4 - y^5\end{aligned}$$

29. $$\begin{aligned}(2m+1)^4 &= \binom{4}{0}(2m)^4 + \binom{4}{1}(2m)^3(1) + \binom{4}{2}(2m)^2(1)^2 + \binom{4}{3}(2m)(1)^3 + \binom{4}{4}(1)^4 \\ &= 1(16m^4) + 4(8m^3) + 6(4m^2) + 4(2m) + 1(1) \\ &= 16m^4 + 32m^3 + 24m^2 + 8m + 1\end{aligned}$$

31. $$\begin{aligned}(2r-3)^5 &= \binom{5}{0}(2r)^5 + \binom{5}{1}(2r)^4(-3) + \binom{5}{2}(2r)^3(-3)^2 + \binom{5}{3}(2r)^2(-3)^3 + \binom{5}{4}(2r)(-3)^4 + \binom{5}{5}(-3)^5 \\ &= 1(32r^5) + 5(16r^4)(-3) + 10(8r^3)(9) + 10(4r^2)(-27) + 5(2r)(81) + 1(-243) \\ &= 32r^5 - 240r^4 + 720r^3 - 1080r^2 + 810r - 243\end{aligned}$$

33. $$\begin{aligned}(a+b)^{10} &= \binom{10}{0}a^{10} + \binom{10}{1}a^9b + \binom{10}{2}a^8b^2 + \ldots \\ &= a^{10} + 10a^9b + 45a^8b^2 + \ldots\end{aligned}$$

35. $$\begin{aligned}(a-b)^{11} &= \binom{11}{0}a^{11} + \binom{11}{1}a^{10}(-b) + \binom{11}{2}a^9(-b)^2 + \ldots \\ &= (1)a^{11} + 11a^{10}(-b) + 55a^9b^2 + \ldots \\ &= a^{11} - 11a^{10}b + 55a^9b^2 + \ldots\end{aligned}$$

37. $$\begin{aligned}(2x+y)^8 &= \binom{8}{0}(2x)^8 + \binom{8}{1}(2x)^7y + \binom{8}{2}(2x)^6y^2 + \ldots \\ &= 1(256x^8) + 8(128x^7)y + 28(64x^6)y^2 + \ldots \\ &= 256x^8 + 1024x^7y + 1792x^6y^2 + \ldots\end{aligned}$$

39. $$\begin{aligned}(4x-3y)^8 &= \binom{8}{0}(4x)^8 + \binom{8}{1}(4x)^7(-3y) + \binom{8}{2}(4x)^6(-3y)^2 + \ldots \\ &= 1(65{,}536x^8) + 8(16{,}384x^7)(-3y) + 28(4096x^6)(9y^2) + \ldots \\ &= 65{,}536x^8 - 393{,}216x^7y + 1{,}032{,}192x^6y^2 + \ldots\end{aligned}$$

41. $\left(x+\frac{1}{x}\right)^7 = \binom{7}{0}x^7 + \binom{7}{1}x^6\left(\frac{1}{x}\right) + \binom{7}{2}x^5\left(\frac{1}{x}\right)^2 + \ldots$

$= 1(x^7) + 7x^6\left(\frac{1}{x}\right) + 21x^5\left(\frac{1}{x^2}\right) + \ldots$

$= x^7 + 7x^5 + 21x^3 + \ldots$

43. $n = 7,\ a = 2x, b = -1,\ r = 4$

$\binom{7}{4-1}(2x)^{7-4+1}(-1)^{4-1} = \binom{7}{3}(2x)^4(-1)^3 = 35(16x^4)(-1) = -560x^4$

45. $n = 6,\ a = x^2,\ b = (-y^2), r = 2$

$\binom{6}{2-1}(x^2)^{6-2+1}(-y^2)^{2-1} = \binom{6}{1}(x^2)^5(-y^2) = 6x^{10}(-y^2) = -6x^{10}y^2$

47. $n = 9,\ a = y,\ b = -1,\ r = 5$

$\binom{9}{5-1}y^{9-5+1}(-1)^{5-1} = \binom{9}{4}y^5(-1)^4 = 126y^5(1) = 126y^5$

49. $n = 5,\ a = n,\ b = \frac{1}{n}, r = 2$

$\binom{5}{2-1}n^{5-2+1}\left(\frac{1}{n}\right)^{2-1} = \binom{5}{1}n^4\left(\frac{1}{n}\right) = 5n^4\left(\frac{1}{n}\right) = 5n^3$

Applying the Concepts

51. **a.** False; $0! \cdot 4! = 1 \cdot 4! = 24$

b. False; $\frac{4!}{0!} = \frac{4!}{1} = 24$

c. False.

d. False.

e. False.

f. True.

CHAPTER REVIEW

1. $\sum_{i=1}^{4} 2x^{i-1} = 2x^{1-1} + 2x^{2-1} + 2x^{3-1} + 2x^{4-1}$

$= 2 + 2x + 2x^2 + 2x^3$

2. $a_n = 3n - 2$

$a_{10} = 3(10) - 2 = 30 - 2 = 28$

The tenth term is 28.

3. $0.633\overline{3} = 0.6 + 0.03 + 0.003 + \ldots$

$= \frac{6}{10} + \frac{3}{100} + \frac{3}{1000} + \ldots$

$S = \frac{a_1}{1-r} = \frac{\frac{3}{100}}{1-\frac{1}{10}} = \frac{\frac{3}{100}}{\frac{9}{10}} = \frac{3}{100}\cdot\frac{10}{9} = \frac{1}{30}$

$0.633\overline{3} = \frac{6}{10} + \frac{1}{30} = \frac{19}{30}$

An equivalent fraction is $\frac{19}{30}$.

4. $r = \frac{a_2}{a_1} = \frac{\frac{3}{100}}{\frac{3}{10}} = \frac{1}{10}$

$S = \frac{a_1}{1-r} = \frac{\frac{3}{10}}{1-\frac{1}{10}} = \frac{\frac{3}{10}}{\frac{9}{10}} = \frac{1}{3}$

5. $\sum_{i=1}^{30} 4i-1 = 3, 7, 11, \ldots, 119$

$S_n = \frac{30}{2}(3+119) = 15(122) = 1830$

6. $\sum_{n=1}^{5}(3n-2) = [3(1)-2]+[3(2)-2]$
$+[3(3)-2]+[3(4)-2]+[3(5)-2]$
$=1+4+7+10+13$
$=35$

7. $0.23\overline{23} = 0.23+0.0023+0.000023+\ldots$
$= \frac{23}{100}+\frac{23}{10{,}000}+\frac{23}{1{,}000{,}000}+\ldots$
$S = \frac{a_1}{1-r} = \frac{\frac{23}{100}}{1-\frac{1}{100}} = \frac{\frac{23}{100}}{\frac{99}{100}} = \frac{23}{99}$
An equivalent fraction is $\frac{23}{99}$.

8. $\binom{9}{3} = \frac{9!}{(9-3)!3!}$
$= \frac{9!}{6!3!}$
$= \frac{9\cdot8\cdot7\cdot6\cdot5\cdot4\cdot3\cdot2\cdot1}{(6\cdot5\cdot4\cdot3\cdot2\cdot1)(3\cdot2\cdot1)} = 84$

9. $\sum_{n=1}^{5} 2(3)^n = 6, 18, 54, \ldots$
$r = \frac{a_2}{a_1} = \frac{18}{6} = 3$
$S_n = \frac{a_1(1-r^n)}{1-r}$
$= \frac{6(1-3^5)}{1-3}$
$= \frac{6(1-243)}{-2} = -3(-242) = 726$

10. $d = a_2 - a_1 = 2-8 = -6$
$a_n = a_1 + (n-1)d$
$-118 = 8+(n-1)(-6)$
$-126 = -6(n-1)$
$21 = n-1$
$22 = n$
There are 22 terms in the sequence.

11. $\sum_{n=1}^{8}\left(\frac{1}{2}\right)^n = \frac{1}{2}, \frac{1}{4}, \frac{1}{8}, \ldots$
$r = \frac{a_2}{a_1} = \frac{\frac{1}{4}}{\frac{1}{2}} = \frac{1}{4}\cdot\frac{2}{1} = \frac{1}{2}$
$S_n = \frac{a_1(1-r^n)}{1-r}$
$= \frac{\frac{1}{2}\left(1-\left(\frac{1}{2}\right)^8\right)}{1-\frac{1}{2}}$
$= \frac{\frac{1}{2}\left(1-\frac{1}{256}\right)}{\frac{1}{2}}$
$= \frac{255}{256} \approx 0.996$

12. $n=8,\ a=3x,\ b=-y,\ r=5$
$\binom{8}{5-1}(3x)^{8-5+1}(-y)^{5-1} = \binom{8}{4}(3x)^4(-y)^4$
$= 70(81x^4)y^4$
$= 5670x^4y^4$

13. $a_n = \frac{(-1)^{2n-1}n}{n^2+2}$
$a_5 = \frac{(-1)^{2(5)-1}\cdot 5}{(5)^2+2} = \frac{(-1)^9\cdot 5}{25+2} = \frac{-5}{27}$
The fifth term is $-\frac{5}{27}$.

14. $r = \frac{a_2}{a_1} = \frac{5\sqrt{5}}{5} = \sqrt{5}$
$S_n = \frac{a_1(1-r^n)}{1-r}$
$S_7 = \frac{5(1-(\sqrt{5})^7)}{1-\sqrt{5}} = \frac{5(1-125\sqrt{5})}{1-\sqrt{5}}$
$= \frac{5-625\sqrt{5}}{1-\sqrt{5}}$
$= \frac{5-625\sqrt{5}}{1-\sqrt{5}}\cdot\frac{1+\sqrt{5}}{1+\sqrt{5}}$
$= \frac{5+5\sqrt{5}-625\sqrt{5}-3125}{1-5}$
$= \frac{-620\sqrt{5}-3120}{-4} \approx 1127$

15. $d = a_2 - a_1 = -2-(-7) = -2+7 = 5$
$a_n = a_1 + (n-1)d$
$a_n = -7+(n-1)5 = -7+5n-5 = 5n-12$
$a_n = 5n-12$

16. $n=11,\ a=x,\ b=-2y,\ r=8$
$\binom{11}{8-1}(x)^{11-8+1}(-2y)^{8-1} = \binom{11}{7}x^4(-2y)^7$
$= 330x^4(-128y^7)$
$= -42{,}240x^4y^7$

17. $r = \frac{a_2}{a_1} = \frac{\sqrt{3}}{1} = \sqrt{3}$

$a_n = a_1 r^{n-1}$

$a_{12} = 1 \cdot (\sqrt{3})^{12-1} = (\sqrt{3})^{11} = 243\sqrt{3}$

18. $d = a_2 - a_1 = 13 - 11 = 2$

$a_n = a_1 + (n-1)d$

$a_{40} = 11 + 2(40-1) = 11 + 2(39) = 89$

$S_n = \frac{n}{2}(a_1 + a_n)$

$S_{40} = \frac{40}{2}(11+89) = 20(100) = 2000$

19. $\binom{12}{9} = \frac{12!}{(12-9)!9!}$

$= \frac{12!}{3!9!}$

$= \frac{12 \cdot 11 \cdot 10 \cdot 9 \cdot 8 \cdot 7 \cdot 6 \cdot 5 \cdot 4 \cdot 3 \cdot 2 \cdot 1}{(3 \cdot 2 \cdot 1)(9 \cdot 8 \cdot 7 \cdot 6 \cdot 5 \cdot 4 \cdot 3 \cdot 2 \cdot 1)} = 220$

20. $\sum_{n=1}^{4} \frac{(-1)^{n-1} n}{n+1} = \frac{(-1)^{1-1} \cdot 1}{1+1} + \frac{(-1)^{2-1} \cdot 2}{2+1}$

$+ \frac{(-1)^{3-1} \cdot 3}{3+1} + \frac{(-1)^{4-1} \cdot 4}{4+1}$

$= \left(\frac{1}{2}\right) + \left(-\frac{2}{3}\right) + \frac{3}{4} + \left(-\frac{4}{5}\right) = -\frac{13}{60}$

21. $\sum_{i=1}^{5} \frac{(2x)^i}{i} = \frac{(2x)^1}{1} + \frac{(2x)^2}{2} + \frac{(2x)^3}{3} + \frac{(2x)^4}{4} + \frac{(2x)^5}{5}$

$= 2x + \frac{4x^2}{2} + \frac{8x^3}{3} + \frac{16x^4}{4} + \frac{32x^5}{5}$

$= 2x + 2x^2 + \frac{8}{3}x^3 + 4x^4 + \frac{32}{5}x^5$

22. $r = \frac{a_2}{a_1} = \frac{1}{3}$

$a_n = a_1 r^{n-1}$

$a_8 = 3\left(\frac{1}{3}\right)^7 = \frac{1}{729}$

23. $(x - 3y^2)^5 = \binom{5}{0}x^5 + \binom{5}{1}x^4(-3y^2) + \binom{5}{2}x^3(-3y^2)^2 + \binom{5}{3}x^2(-3y^2)^3 + \binom{5}{4}x(-3y^2)^4 + \binom{5}{5}(-3y^2)^5$

$= x^5 - 15x^4y^2 + 90x^3y^4 - 270x^2y^6 + 405xy^8 - 243y^{10}$

24. $r = \frac{a_2}{a_1} = -\frac{1}{4}$

$S = \frac{a_1}{1-r} = \frac{4}{1-\left(-\frac{1}{4}\right)} = \frac{4}{\frac{5}{4}} = \frac{16}{5}$

25. $r = \frac{a_2}{a_1} = \frac{\frac{4}{3}}{2} = \frac{2}{3}$

$S = \frac{a_1}{1-r} = \frac{2}{1-\frac{2}{3}} = \frac{2}{\frac{1}{3}} = 6$

26. $\frac{12!}{5!8!} = \frac{12 \cdot 11 \cdot 10 \cdot 9 \cdot 8 \cdot 7 \cdot 6 \cdot 5 \cdot 4 \cdot 3 \cdot 2 \cdot 1}{(5 \cdot 4 \cdot 3 \cdot 2 \cdot 1)(8 \cdot 7 \cdot 6 \cdot 5 \cdot 4 \cdot 3 \cdot 2 \cdot 1)} = 99$

27. $d = a_2 - a_1 = 5 - 1 = 4$

$a_n = a_1 + (n-1)d$

$a_{20} = 1 + (20-1)4 = 1 + 19(4) = 77$

$a_{20} = 77$

28. Strategy To find the temperature of the spa after 8 hours, use the Formula for the nth Term of a Geometric Sequence.

Solution $n = 8,\ a_1 = 0.95(102) = 96.9,\ r = 0.95$

$$a_n = a_1 r^{n-1}$$
$$a_8 = 96.9(0.95)^7 = 67.7$$

The temperature is 67.7°F.

29. Strategy To find the total salary for the nine-month period:

- Write the arithmetic sequence.
- Find the common difference of the arithmetic sequence.
- Use the Formula for the nth Term of an Arithmetic Sequence to find the 9th term.
- Use the Formula for the Sum of n Terms of an Arithmetic Sequence to find the sum of 9 terms of the sequence.

Solution \$1200, \$1240, \$1280, ...

$$d = a_2 - a_1 = 1240 - 1200 = 40$$
$$a_n = a_1 + (n-1)d$$
$$a_9 = 1200 + (9-1)40 = 1520$$
$$S_n = \frac{n}{2}(a_1 + a_n)$$
$$S_9 = \frac{9}{2}(1200 + 1520) = \$12,240$$

The total salary for the nine-month period is \$12,240.

30. Strategy To find the amount of radioactive material at the beginning of the seventh hour, use the Formula for the nth Term of a Geometric Sequence.

Solution $n = 7,\ a_1 = 200,\ r = \frac{1}{2}$

$$a_n = a_1 r^{n-1}$$
$$a = 200\left(\frac{1}{2}\right)^{7-1}$$
$$= 200\left(\frac{1}{2}\right)^6 = \frac{200}{64} = 3.125$$

There will be a 3.125 mg of radioactive material in the sample at the beginning of the seventh hour.

CHAPTER TEST

1. $\sum_{n=1}^{4}(3n+1) = 4 + 7 + 10 + 13 = 34$

2. $$\binom{9}{6} = \frac{9!}{(9-6)!6!} = \frac{9!}{3!6!} = \frac{9\cdot8\cdot7\cdot6\cdot5\cdot4\cdot3\cdot2\cdot1}{(3\cdot2\cdot1)(6\cdot5\cdot4\cdot3\cdot2\cdot1)} = 84$$

3. $r = \frac{a_2}{a_1} = \frac{4\sqrt{2}}{4} = \sqrt{2}$

$$a_n = ar^{n-1}$$
$$a_7 = 4\left(\sqrt{2}\right)^{7-1} = 4\cdot\left(\sqrt{2}\right)^6 = 32$$

4. $a_n = \frac{8}{n+2}$

$$a_{14} = \frac{8}{14+2} = \frac{8}{16} = \frac{1}{2}$$

The fourteenth term is $\frac{1}{2}$.

5. $$\sum_{i=1}^{4} 3x^i = 3x^1 + 3x^2 + 3x^3 + 3x^4 = 3x + 3x^2 + 3x^3 + 3x^4$$

6. $d = a_2 - a_1 = -19 - (-25) = -19 + 25 = 6$

$$a_n = a_1 + (n-1)d$$
$$a_{18} = -25 + (18-1)6 = -25 + 17(6) = 77$$
$$S_n = \frac{n}{2}(a_1 + a_n)$$
$$S_{18} = \frac{18}{2}(-25 + 77) = 468$$

7. $r = \frac{a_2}{a_1} = \frac{3}{4}$

$$S_n = \frac{a_1}{1-r} = \frac{4}{1-\frac{3}{4}} = \frac{4}{\frac{1}{4}} = 16$$

8. $d = a_2 - a_1 = -8 - (-5) = -8 + 5 = -3$

$$a_n = a_1 + (n-1)d$$
$$-50 = -5 + (n-1)(-3)$$
$$-45 = -3(n-1)$$
$$15 = n - 1$$
$$16 = n$$

9. $0.233\overline{3} = 0.2 + 0.03 + 0.003 + \ldots$

$$= \frac{2}{10} + \frac{3}{100} + \frac{3}{1000} + \ldots$$
$$S = \frac{a_1}{1-r} = \frac{\frac{3}{100}}{1-\frac{1}{10}} = \frac{\frac{3}{100}}{\frac{9}{10}} = \frac{3}{90} = \frac{1}{30}$$
$$0.233\overline{3} = \frac{2}{10} + \frac{1}{30} = \frac{7}{30}$$

An equivalent fraction is $\frac{7}{30}$.

10. $$\frac{8!}{4!4!} = \frac{8\cdot7\cdot6\cdot5\cdot4\cdot3\cdot2\cdot1}{(4\cdot3\cdot2\cdot1)(4\cdot3\cdot2\cdot1)} = 70$$

11. $r = \dfrac{a_2}{a_1} = \dfrac{2}{6} = \dfrac{1}{3}$

$a_n = a_1 r^{n-1}$

$a_5 = 6 \cdot \left(\dfrac{1}{3}\right)^{5-1} = 6 \cdot \left(\dfrac{1}{3}\right)^4 = 6 \cdot \dfrac{1}{81} = \dfrac{2}{27}$

12. $n = 7,\ a = x,\ b = -2y, r = 4$

$\binom{7}{4-1} x^{7-4+1}(-2y)^{4-1} = \binom{7}{3} x^4(-2y)^3$

$= 35x^4(-8y^3)$

$= -280x^4y^3$

13. $d = a_2 - a_1 = -16 - (-13) = -16 + 13 = -3$

$a_n = a_1 + (n-1)d$

$a_{35} = -13 + (35-1)(-3) = -13 + 34(-3) = -115$

14. $d = a_2 - a_1 = 9 - 12 = -3$

$a_n = a_1 + (n-1)d$

$a_n = 12 + (n-1)(-3)$

$= 12 - 3n + 3 = -3n + 15$

$a_n = -3n + 15$

15. $r = \dfrac{a_2}{a_1} = \dfrac{12}{-6} = -2$

$S_n = \dfrac{a_1(1-r^n)}{1-r}$

$S_5 = \dfrac{-6(1-(-2)^5)}{1-(-2)}$

$= \dfrac{-6(1-(-32))}{3}$

$= -2(33) = -66$

16. $a_n = \dfrac{n+1}{n}$

$a_6 = \dfrac{6+1}{6} = \dfrac{7}{6}$ The sixth term is $\dfrac{7}{6}$.

$a_7 = \dfrac{7+1}{7} = \dfrac{8}{7}$ The seventh term is $\dfrac{8}{7}$.

17. $r = \dfrac{a_2}{a_1} = \dfrac{\frac{3}{2}}{1} = \dfrac{3}{2}$

$S_n = \dfrac{a_1(1-r^n)}{1-r}$

$S_6 = \dfrac{1\left(1-\left(\frac{3}{2}\right)^6\right)}{1-\frac{3}{2}} = \dfrac{1-\frac{729}{64}}{-\frac{1}{2}} = \dfrac{-\frac{665}{64}}{-\frac{1}{2}} = \dfrac{665}{32}$

18. $d = a_2 - a_1 = 12 - 5 = 7$

$a_n = a_1 + (n-1)d$

$a_{21} = 5 + (21-1)7 = 5 + 20(7) = 145$

$S_n = \dfrac{n}{2}(a_1 + a_n)$

$S_{21} = \dfrac{21}{2}(5 + 145) = 1575$

19. Strategy To find how much material was in stock after the shipment on October 1:

- Write the arithmetic sequence.
- Find the common difference of the arithmetic sequence.
- Use the Formula for the nth term of an Arithmetic Sequence to find the tenth term.

Solution 7500, 6950, 6400, ...

$d = a_2 - a_1 = 6950 - 7500 = -500$

$a_n = a_1 + (n-1)d$

$a_{10} = 7500 + (10-1)(-550) = 2550$

The inventory after the October 1 shipment was 2550 yd.

20. Strategy To find the amount of radioactive material at the beginning of the fifth day, use the Formula for the nth Term of a Geometric Sequence.

Solution $n = 5,\ a_1 = 320,\ r = \dfrac{1}{2}$

$a_n = a_1 r^{n-1}$

$a_5 = 320\left(\dfrac{1}{2}\right)^{5-1} = 320\left(\dfrac{1}{2}\right)^4 = 20$

There will be 20 mg of radioactive material in the sample at the beginning of the fifth day.

CUMULATIVE REVIEW

1. $3x - 2y = -4$

$-2y = -3x - 4$

$y = \dfrac{3}{2}x + 2$

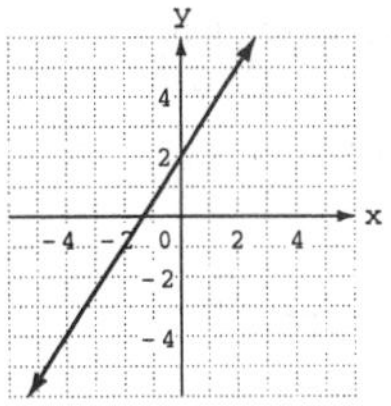

2. $2x^6 + 16 = 2(x^6 + 8)$

$= 2((x^2)^3 + 2^3)$

$= 2(x^2 + 2)(x^4 - 2x^2 + 4)$

3. $\dfrac{4x^2}{x^2 + x - 2} - \dfrac{3x-2}{x+2}$

$= \dfrac{4x^2}{(x+2)(x-1)} - \dfrac{3x-2}{x+2} \cdot \dfrac{x-1}{x-1}$

$= \dfrac{4x^2 - (3x^2 - 5x + 2)}{(x+2)(x-1)}$

$= \dfrac{x^2 + 5x - 2}{(x+2)(x-1)}$

4. $f(x) = 2x^2 - 3x$
$f(-2) = 2(-2)^2 - 3(-2)$
$f(-2) = 2 \cdot 4 + 6$
$f(-2) = 14$

5. $\sqrt{2y}\left(\sqrt{8xy} - \sqrt{y}\right) = \sqrt{16xy^2} - \sqrt{2y^2}$
$= \sqrt{16y^2(x)} - \sqrt{y^2(2)}$
$= 4y\sqrt{x} - y\sqrt{2}$

6. $2x^2 - x + 7 = 0$
$a = 2,\ b = -1,\ c = 7$
$$x = \frac{-b \pm \sqrt{b^2 - 4ac}}{2a}$$
$$= \frac{-(-1) \pm \sqrt{(-1)^2 - 4(2)(7)}}{2(2)}$$
$$= \frac{1 \pm \sqrt{1 - 56}}{4}$$
$$= \frac{1 \pm \sqrt{-55}}{4}$$
$$= \frac{1}{4} \pm \frac{\sqrt{55}}{4}i$$
The solutions are $\frac{1}{4} + \frac{\sqrt{55}}{4}i$ and $\frac{1}{4} - \frac{\sqrt{55}}{4}i$.

7. $5 - \sqrt{x} = \sqrt{x+5}$
$\left(5 - \sqrt{x}\right)^2 = \left(\sqrt{x+5}\right)^2$
$25 - 10\sqrt{x} + x = x + 5$
$-10\sqrt{x} = -20$
$\sqrt{x} = 2$
$\left(\sqrt{x}\right)^2 = 2^2$
$x = 4$

Check:

$5 - \sqrt{x} =$	$\sqrt{x+5}$
$5 - \sqrt{4}$	$\sqrt{4+5}$
$5 - 2$	$\sqrt{9}$
$3 =$	3

The solution is 4.

8. $(x_1, y_2) = (4, 2),\ (x_2, y_2) = (-1, -1)$
$d = \sqrt{(x_1 - x_2)^2 + (y_1 - y_2)^2}$
$= \sqrt{(4 - (-1))^2 + (2 - (-1))^2}$
$= \sqrt{5^2 + 3^2}$
$= \sqrt{25 + 9}$
$= \sqrt{34}$
$(x - h)^2 + (y - k)^2 = r^2$
$(x - (-1))^2 + (y - (-1))^2 = (\sqrt{34})^2$
$(x + 1)^2 + (y + 1)^2 = 34$

9. (1) $3x - 3y = 2$
(2) $6x - 4y = 5$
Eliminate x.
Multiply Equation (1) by –2 and add Equation (2).
$-6x + 6y = -4$
$6x - 4y = 5$
$2y = 1$
$y = \frac{1}{2}$
Substitute $\frac{1}{2}$ for y in Equation (2).
$6x - 4\left(\frac{1}{2}\right) = 5$
$6x - 2 = 5$
$6x = 7$
$x = \frac{7}{6}$
The solution is $\left(\frac{7}{6}, \frac{1}{2}\right)$.

10. $\begin{vmatrix} -3 & 1 \\ 4 & 2 \end{vmatrix} = -3(2) - 4(1) = -6 - 4 = -10$

11. $2x - 1 > 3$ or $1 - 3x > 7$
$2x > 4$ $\qquad -3x > 6$
$x > 2$ $\qquad x < -2$
$\{x | x > 2\}$ or $\{x | x < -2\}$
$\{x | x < -2 \text{ or } x > 2\}$

12. $2x - 3y < 9$
$-3y < -2x + 9$
$y > \frac{2}{3}x - 3$

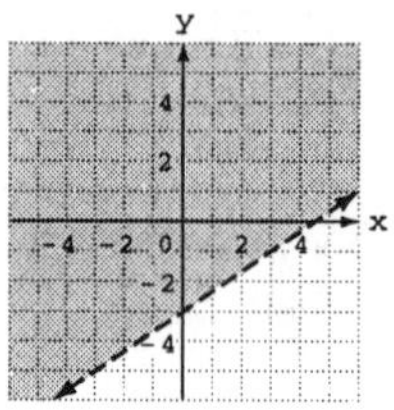

13. $\log_5 \sqrt{\dfrac{x}{y}} = \dfrac{1}{2}[\log_5 x - \log_5 y]$

$= \dfrac{1}{2}\log_5 x - \dfrac{1}{2}\log_5 y$

14.
$$\begin{aligned} 4^x &= 8^{x-1} \\ (2^2)^x &= (2^3)^{x-1} \\ 2^{2x} &= 2^{3(x-1)} \\ 2x &= 3(x-1) \\ 2x &= 3x-3 \\ -x &= -3 \\ x &= 3 \end{aligned}$$

The solution is 3.

15. $a_n = n(n-1)$

$a_5 = 5(5-1) = 5(4) = 20$ The fifth term is 20.

$a_6 = 6(6-1) = 6(5) = 30$ The sixth term is 30.

16.
$$\begin{aligned} \sum_{n=1}^{7}(-1)^{n-1}(n+2) &= (-1)^{1-1}(1+2)+(-1)^{2-1}(2+2)+(-1)^{3-1}(3+2)+(-1)^{4-1}(4+2)+(-1)^{5-1}(5+2) \\ &\quad +(-1)^{6-1}(6+2)+(-1)^{7-1}(7+2) \\ &= (-1)^0(3)+(-1)^1(4)+(-1)^2(5)+(-1)^3(6)+(-1)^4(7)+(-1)^5(8)+(-1)^6(9) \\ &= 3-4+5-6+7-8+9 = 6 \end{aligned}$$

17.
$$\begin{aligned} d &= a_2 - a_1 = -10-(-7) = -10+7 = -3 \\ a_n &= a_1 + (n-1)d \\ a_{33} &= -7+(33-1)(-3) = -7+32(-3) = -103 \end{aligned}$$

The thirty-third term is −103.

18. $r = \dfrac{a_2}{a_1} = -\dfrac{2}{3}$

$S = \dfrac{a_1}{1-r} = \dfrac{3}{1-\left(-\frac{2}{3}\right)} = \dfrac{3}{\frac{5}{3}} = \dfrac{9}{5}$

19.
$$\begin{aligned} 0.4\overline{6} &= 0.4+0.06+0.006+\ldots \\ &= \frac{4}{10}+\frac{6}{100}+\frac{6}{1000}+\ldots \end{aligned}$$

$S = \dfrac{a_1}{1-r} = \dfrac{\frac{6}{100}}{1-\frac{1}{10}} = \dfrac{\frac{6}{100}}{\frac{9}{10}} = \dfrac{6}{100}\cdot\dfrac{10}{9} = \dfrac{1}{15}$

$0.4\overline{6} = \dfrac{4}{10}+\dfrac{1}{15} = \dfrac{14}{30} = \dfrac{7}{15}$

An equivalent fraction is $\dfrac{7}{15}$.

20. $n=6,\ a=2x, b=y,\ r=6$

$$\begin{aligned} \binom{6}{6-1}(2x)^{6-6+1}(y)^{6-1} &= \binom{6}{5}(2x)^1 y^5 \\ &= 6\cdot 2x\cdot y^5 \\ &= 12xy^5 \end{aligned}$$

21. Strategy Amount of pure water: x

	Amount	Percent	Value
Water	x	0	$0\cdot x$
8%	200	0.08	200(0.08)
5%	$x+200$	0.05	$(x+200)(0.05)$

- The sum of the values before mixing equals the value after mixing.

$0\cdot x + 200(0.08) = (x+200)(0.05)$

Solution
$$\begin{aligned} 0\cdot x+16 &= 0.05x+10 \\ 16 &= 0.05x+10 \\ 6 &= 0.05x \\ 120 &= x \end{aligned}$$

The amount of water that must be added is 120 oz.

22. Strategy
- Time required for the older computer: t
  Time required for the new computer: $t-16$

	Rate	Time	Part
Older Computer	$\frac{1}{t}$	15	$\frac{15}{t}$
New computer	$\frac{1}{t-16}$	15	$\frac{15}{t-16}$

- The sum of the part of the task completed by the older computer and the part of the task completed by the new computer is 1.

Solution

$$\frac{15}{t}+\frac{15}{t-16}=1$$
$$t(t-16)\left(\frac{15}{t}+\frac{15}{t-16}\right)=1(t)(t-16)$$
$$15(t-16)+15t=t^2-16t$$
$$15t-240+15t=t^2-16t$$
$$0=t^2-46t+240$$
$$0=(t-40)(t-6)$$

$t-40=0 \quad t-6=0$
$t=40 \quad t=6$

$t=6$ does not check as a solution since $t-16=6-16=-10$.

$t=40,\ t-16=24$

The new computer takes 24 min to complete the payroll. The older computer takes 40 min to complete the payroll.

23. Strategy
- Rate of boat in calm water: x
  Rate of current: y

	Rate	Time	Distance
With current	$x+y$	2	$2(x+y)$
Against current	$x-y$	3	$3(x-y)$

- The distance traveled with the current is 15 mi. The distance traveled against the current is 15 mi.
  $2(x+y)=15$
  $3(x-y)=15$

Solution

$$2(x+y)=15 \quad \frac{1}{2}\cdot 2(x+y)=\frac{1}{2}\cdot 15$$
$$3(x-y)=15 \quad \frac{1}{3}\cdot 3(x-y)=\frac{1}{3}\cdot 15$$

$$x+y=7.5$$
$$x-y=5$$

$$2x=12.5$$
$$x=6.25$$

$$x+y=7.5$$
$$6.25+y=7.5$$
$$y=1.25$$

The boat was traveling 6.25 mph and the current was traveling 1.25 mph.

24. Strategy

To find the half-life, solve for k in the exponential decay equation.
Use $A_0=80,\ A=55,\ t=30$

Solution

$$A=A_0\left(\frac{1}{2}\right)^{t/k}$$
$$55=80\left(\frac{1}{2}\right)^{30/k}$$
$$0.6875=(0.5)^{30/k}$$
$$\log 0.6875=\frac{30}{k}\log(0.5)$$
$$k=\frac{30\log 0.5}{\log 0.6875}=55.49$$

The half-life is 55 days.

25\. Strategy To find the total number of seats in the 12 rows of the theater:

- Write the arithmetic sequence.
- Use the Formula for the nth Term of an Arithmetic Sequence to find the 12th term.
- Use the Formula for the Sum of n Terms of an Arithmetic Sequence to find the sum of the 12 terms of the sequence.

Solution 62, 74, 86, ...

$d = a_2 - a_1 = 74 - 62 = 12$

$a_{12} = 62 + (12-1)12 = 62 + 132 = 194$

$S_n = \frac{n}{2}(a_1 + a_n)$

$S_{12} = \frac{12}{2}(62 + 194) = 1536$

The total number of seats in the theater is 1536.

26\. Strategy To find the height of the ball on the fifth bounce, use the Formula for the nth Term of a Geometric Sequence.

Solution $n = 5,\ a_1 = 80\% \text{ of } 8 = 6.4,$

$r = 80\% = 0.8$

$a_n = a_1 r^{n-1}$

$a_5 = 6.4(0.8)^{5-1}$

$= 6.4(0.4096) = 2.62144$

The height of the fifth bounce is 2.6 ft.

Final Exam

FINAL EXAM

1. $12-8[3-(-2)]^2 \div 5-3 = 12-8[5]^2 \div 5-3$
$= 12-8(25)\div 5-3$
$= 12-200\div 5-3$
$= 12-40-3$
$= -31$

2. $\dfrac{3^2-(-4)^2}{3-(-4)} = \dfrac{9-16}{3+4} = \dfrac{-7}{7} = -1$

3. $5-2[3x-7(2-x)-5x] = 5-2[3x-14+7x-5x]$
$= 5-2[5x-14]$
$= 5-10x+28$
$= 33-10x$

4. $\dfrac{3}{4}x-2=4$
$\dfrac{3}{4}x=6$
$\dfrac{4}{3}\cdot\dfrac{3}{4}x=\dfrac{4}{3}\cdot 6$
$x=8$

5. $\dfrac{2-4x}{3}-\dfrac{x-6}{12}=\dfrac{5x-2}{6}$
$12\left(\dfrac{2-4x}{3}-\dfrac{x-6}{12}\right)=12\left(\dfrac{5x-2}{6}\right)$
$4(2-4x)-(x-6)=2(5x-2)$
$8-16x-x+6=10x-4$
$14-17x=10x-4$
$-27x=-18$
$x=\dfrac{2}{3}$

6. $8-|5-3x|=1$
$-|5-3x|=-7$
$|5-3x|=7$
$5-3x=7 \qquad 5-3x=-7$
$-3x=2 \qquad -3x=-12$
$x=-\dfrac{2}{3} \qquad x=4$
The solutions are $-\dfrac{2}{3}$ and 4.

7. x-intercept:
$2x-3y=9$
$2x-3(0)=9$
$2x=9$
$x=\dfrac{9}{2}$
$\left(\dfrac{9}{2}, 0\right)$

y-intercept:
$2x-3y=9$
$2(0)-3y=9$
$-3y=9$
$y=-3$
$(0, -3)$

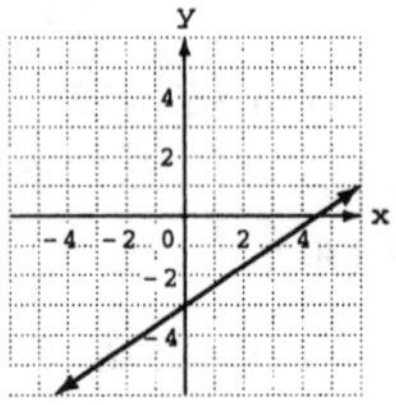

8. $(x_1, y_1)=(3,-2),\ (x_2, y_2)=(1,4)$
$m=\dfrac{y_2-y_1}{x_2-x_1}=\dfrac{4-(-2)}{1-3}=\dfrac{6}{-2}=-3$
$y-y_1=m(x-x_1)$
$y-(-2)=-3(x-3)$
$y+2=-3x+9$
$y=-3x+7$
The equation of the line is $y=-3x+7$.

9. $3x-2y=6$
$-2y=-3x+6$
$y=\dfrac{3}{2}x-3$
$m_1=\dfrac{3}{2}$
$m_1\cdot m_2=-1$
$\dfrac{3}{2}m_2=-1$
$m_2=-\dfrac{2}{3} \quad (x_1, y_1)=(-2, 1)$
$y-y_1=m(x-x_1)$
$y-1=-\dfrac{2}{3}(x-(-2))$
$y-1=-\dfrac{2}{3}(x+2)$
$y-1=-\dfrac{2}{3}x-\dfrac{4}{3}$
$y=-\dfrac{2}{3}x-\dfrac{1}{3}$
The equation of the line is $y=-\dfrac{2}{3}x-\dfrac{1}{3}$.

10. $2a[5-a(2-3a)-2a]+3a^2$
$= 2a[5-2a+3a^2-2a]+3a^2$
$= 2a[5-4a+3a^2]+3a^2$
$= 10a-8a^2+6a^3+3a^2$
$= 6a^3-5a^2+10a$

11. $8-x^3y^3=2^3-(xy)^3$
$=(2-xy)(4+2xy+x^2y^2)$

12. $x-y-x^3+x^2y=x-y-x^2(x-y)$
$=1(x-y)-x^2(x-y)$
$=(x-y)(1-x^2)$
$=(x-y)(1-x)(1+x)$

13.
$$\begin{array}{r|l} & x^2-2x-3 \\ 2x-3 & 2x^3-7x^2+0x+4 \\ & \underline{2x^3-3x^2} \\ & -4x^2+0x \\ & \underline{-4x^2+6x} \\ & -6x+4 \\ & \underline{-6x+9} \\ & -5 \end{array}$$

$$\frac{2x^3-7x^2+4}{2x-3}=x^2-2x-3-\frac{5}{2x-3}$$

14. $\dfrac{x^2-3x}{2x^2-3x-5}\div\dfrac{4x-12}{4x^2-4}$
$=\dfrac{x^2-3x}{2x^2-3x-5}\cdot\dfrac{4x^2-4}{4x-12}$
$=\dfrac{x(x-3)}{(2x-5)(x+1)}\cdot\dfrac{4(x+1)(x-1)}{4(x-3)}$
$=\dfrac{x(x-3)(x+1)(x-1)}{(2x-5)(x+1)(x-3)}$
$=\dfrac{x(x-1)}{2x-5}$

15. $\dfrac{x-2}{x+2}-\dfrac{x+3}{x-3}=\dfrac{x-2}{x+2}\cdot\dfrac{x-3}{x-3}-\dfrac{x+3}{x-3}\cdot\dfrac{x+2}{x+2}$
$=\dfrac{x^2-5x+6-(x^2+5x+6)}{(x+2)(x-3)}$
$=\dfrac{x^2-5x+6-x^2-5x-6}{(x+2)(x-3)}$
$=\dfrac{-10x}{(x+2)(x-3)}$

16. $\dfrac{\frac{3}{x}+\frac{1}{x+4}}{\frac{1}{x}+\frac{3}{x+4}}=\dfrac{\frac{3}{x}+\frac{1}{x+4}}{\frac{1}{x}+\frac{3}{x+4}}\cdot\dfrac{x(x+4)}{x(x+4)}$
$=\dfrac{3(x+4)+x}{x+4+3x}$
$=\dfrac{3x+12+x}{4x+4}$
$=\dfrac{4x+12}{4x+4}$
$=\dfrac{4(x+3)}{4(x+1)}=\dfrac{x+3}{x+1}$

17.
$$\frac{5}{x-2}-\frac{5}{x^2-4}=\frac{1}{x+2}$$
$$(x+2)(x-2)\left(\frac{5}{x-2}-\frac{5}{(x+2)(x-2)}\right)=\frac{1}{x+2}(x+2)(x-2)$$
$$5(x+2)-5=x-2$$
$$5x+10-5=x-2$$
$$5x+5=x-2$$
$$4x=-7$$
$$x=-\frac{7}{4}$$

The solution is $-\dfrac{7}{4}$.

18. $a_n=a_1+(n-1)d$
$a_n-a_1=(n-1)d$
$\dfrac{a_n-a_1}{n-1}=d$

19. $\left(\dfrac{4x^2y^{-1}}{3x^{-1}y}\right)^{-2}\left(\dfrac{2x^{-1}y^2}{9x^{-2}y^2}\right)^3$
$=\dfrac{4^{-2}x^{-4}y^2}{3^{-2}x^2y^{-2}}\cdot\dfrac{2^3x^{-3}y^6}{9^3x^{-6}y^6}$
$=4^{-2}\cdot 3^{-(-2)}\cdot x^{-4-2}y^{2-(-2)}\cdot 2^3\cdot 9^{-3}x^{-3-(-6)}y^{6-6}$
$=4^{-2}\cdot 3^2x^{-6}y^4\cdot 2^3\cdot 9^{-3}x^3y^0$
$=\dfrac{9x^{-3}y^4\cdot 8}{16\cdot 729}=\dfrac{y^4}{162x^3}$

20. $\left(\dfrac{3x^{2/3}y^{1/2}}{6x^2y^{4/3}}\right)^6 = \dfrac{3^6x^4y^3}{6^6x^{12}y^8}$

$= \dfrac{729x^{4-12}y^{3-8}}{46656}$

$= \dfrac{1x^{-8}y^{-5}}{64}$

$= \dfrac{1}{64x^8y^5}$

21. $x\sqrt{18x^2y^3} - y\sqrt{50x^4y}$

$= x\sqrt{3^2x^2y^2(2y)} - y\sqrt{5^2x^4(2y)}$

$= 3x^2y\sqrt{2y} - 5x^2y\sqrt{2y}$

$= -2x^2y\sqrt{2y}$

22. $\dfrac{\sqrt{16x^5y^4}}{\sqrt{32xy^7}} = \sqrt{\dfrac{16x^5y^4}{32xy^7}}$

$= \sqrt{\dfrac{x^4}{2y^3}}$

$= \sqrt{\dfrac{x^4}{y^2(2y)}}$

$= \dfrac{x^2}{y}\sqrt{\dfrac{1}{2y}}\cdot\sqrt{\dfrac{2y}{2y}}$

$= \dfrac{x^2}{y}\sqrt{\dfrac{1\cdot 2y}{(2y)^2}}$

$= \dfrac{x^2\sqrt{2y}}{2y^2}$

23. $\dfrac{3}{2+i}\cdot\dfrac{2-i}{2-i} = \dfrac{6-3i}{4+1} = \dfrac{6-3i}{5} = \dfrac{6}{5} - \dfrac{3}{5}i$

24. $(x-r_1)(x-r_2) = 0$

$\left(x - \left(-\dfrac{1}{2}\right)\right)(x-2) = 0$

$\left(x + \dfrac{1}{2}\right)(x-2) = 0$

$x^2 - \dfrac{3}{2}x - 1 = 0$

$2\left(x^2 - \dfrac{3}{2}x - 1\right) = 2(0)$

$2x^2 - 3x - 2 = 0$

25. $2x^2 - 3x - 1 = 0$

$a = 2,\ b = -3,\ c = -1$

$x = \dfrac{-b \pm \sqrt{b^2 - 4ac}}{2a}$

$= \dfrac{-(-3) \pm \sqrt{(-3)^2 - 4(2)(-1)}}{2(2)}$

$= \dfrac{3 \pm \sqrt{9+8}}{4} = \dfrac{3 \pm \sqrt{17}}{4}$

The solutions are $\dfrac{3+\sqrt{17}}{4}$ and $\dfrac{3-\sqrt{17}}{4}$.

26. $x^{2/3} - x^{1/3} - 6 = 0$

$(x^{1/3})^2 - x^{1/3} - 6 = 0$

Let $u = x^{1/3}$.

$u^2 - u - 6 = 0$

$(u-3)(u+2) = 0$

$u - 3 = 0 \qquad u + 2 = 0$

$u = 3 \qquad u = -2$

$x^{1/3} = 3 \qquad x^{1/3} = -2$

$(x^{1/3})^3 = 3^3 \qquad (x^{1/3})^3 = (-2)^3$

$x = 27 \qquad x = -8$

The solutions are 27 and –8.

27. $\dfrac{2}{x} - \dfrac{2}{2x+3} = 1$

$x(2x+3)\left(\dfrac{2}{x} - \dfrac{2}{2x+3}\right) = 1[x(2x+3)]$

$2(2x+3) - 2x = 2x^2 + 3x$

$4x + 6 - 2x = 2x^2 + 3x$

$2x + 6 = 2x^2 + 3x$

$0 = 2x^2 + x - 6$

$0 = (2x-3)(x+2)$

$2x - 3 = 0 \qquad x + 2 = 0$

$x = \dfrac{3}{2} \qquad x = -2$

The solutions are $\dfrac{3}{2}$ and –2.

28. $f(x) = -x^2 + 4$

$-\dfrac{b}{2a} = -\dfrac{0}{2(-1)} = 0$

$f(x) = -0^2 + 4 = 4$

Vertex: (0, 4)

Axis of symmetry: ($x = 0$)

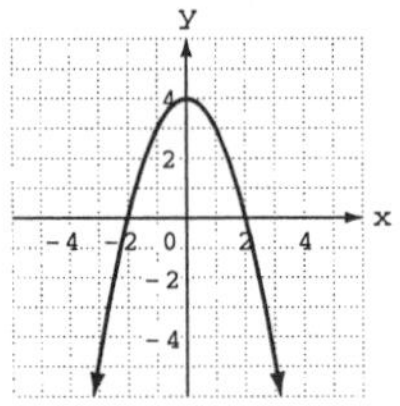

29. x-intercepts: (4, 0) and (–4, 0)
y-intercepts: (0, 2) and (0, –2)

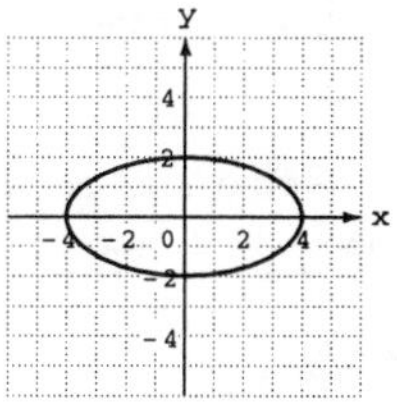

30.

$$f(x)=\frac{2}{3}x-4$$
$$y=\frac{2}{3}x-4$$
$$x=\frac{2}{3}y-4$$
$$x+4=\frac{2}{3}y$$
$$\frac{3}{2}(x+4)=\frac{3}{2}\cdot\frac{2}{3}y$$
$$\frac{3}{2}x+6=y$$

The inverse function is $f^{-1}(x)=\frac{3}{2}x+6$.

31. (1) $3x-2y=1$
(2) $5x-3y=3$
Eliminate y.
Multiply Equation (1) by –3 and Equation (2) by 2. Add the two new equations.

$$-3(3x-2y)=-3(1) \quad -9x+6y=-3$$
$$2(5x-3y)=2(3) \quad 10x-6y=6$$
$$x=3$$

Substitute 3 for x in Equation (1).

$$3x-2y=1$$
$$3(3)-2y=1$$
$$9-2y=1$$
$$-2y=-8$$
$$y=4$$

The solution is (3, 4).

32. $\begin{vmatrix}3 & 4\\ -1 & 2\end{vmatrix}=3(2)-(-1)(4)=6+4=10$

33. (1) $x^2-y^2=4$
(2) $x+y=1$
Solve Equation (2) for y and substitute into Equation (1).

$$x+y=1$$
$$y=-x+1$$
$$x^2-y^2=4$$
$$x^2-(-x+1)^2=4$$
$$x^2-(x^2-2x+1)=4$$
$$x^2-x^2+2x-1=4$$
$$2x=5$$
$$x=\frac{5}{2}$$

Substitute $\frac{5}{2}$ for x in Equation (2).

$$x+y=1$$
$$\frac{5}{2}+y=1$$
$$y=-\frac{3}{2}$$

The solution is $\left(\frac{5}{2},-\frac{3}{2}\right)$.

34. $2-3x<6$ and $2x+1>4$

$$-3x<4 \qquad 2x>3$$
$$x>-\frac{4}{3} \qquad x>\frac{3}{2}$$
$$\left\{x\middle|x>-\frac{4}{3}\right\}\cap\left\{x\middle|x>\frac{3}{2}\right\}=\left\{x\middle|x>\frac{3}{2}\right\}$$

35. $|2x+5|<3$

$$-3<2x+5<3$$
$$-3-5<2x<3-5$$
$$-8<2x<-2$$
$$\frac{1}{2}(-8)<\frac{1}{2}(2x)<\frac{1}{2}(-2)$$
$$-4<x<-1$$
$$\{x|-4<x<-1\}$$

36. $3x+2y>6$

$$2y>-3x+6$$
$$y>-\frac{3}{2}x+3$$

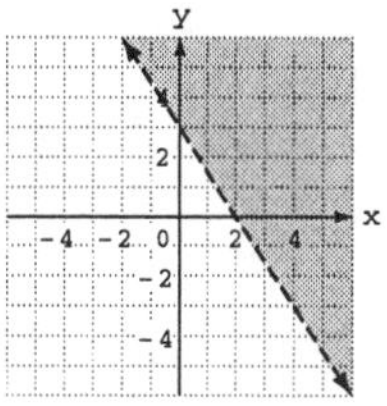

37.

$$f(x)=\log_2(x+1)$$
$$y=\log_2(x+1)$$
$$2^y=x+1$$
$$-1+2^y=x$$

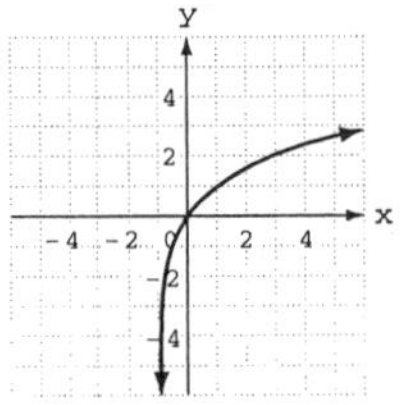

38. $2(\log_2 a-\log_2 b)=2\log_2\frac{a}{b}=\log_2\frac{a^2}{b^2}$

39. $\log_3 x-\log_3(x-3)=\log_3 2$

$$\log_3\left(\frac{x}{x-3}\right)=\log_3 2$$

Use the fact that if $\log_b u=\log_b v$, then $u=v$.

$$\frac{x}{x-3}=2$$
$$(x-3)\cdot\frac{x}{x-3}=2\cdot(x-3)$$
$$x=2x-6$$
$$-x=-6$$
$$x=6$$

The solution is 6.

40. $\sum_{i=1}^{5}2y^i=2y^1+2y^2+2y^3+2y^4+2y^5$

$$=2y+2y^2+2y^3+2y^4+2y^5$$

41. $0.5\overline{1}=0.5+0.01+0.001+0.0001+\ldots$

$$=\frac{5}{10}+\frac{1}{100}+\frac{1}{1000}+\frac{1}{10{,}000}+\ldots$$

$$S=\frac{a_1}{1-r}=\frac{\frac{1}{100}}{1-\frac{1}{10}}=\frac{\frac{1}{100}}{\frac{9}{10}}=\frac{1}{100}\cdot\frac{10}{9}=\frac{1}{90}$$

$$0.5\overline{1}=\frac{5}{10}+\frac{1}{90}=\frac{46}{90}=\frac{23}{45}$$

42. $n=9,\ a=x,\ b=-2y, r=3$

$$\binom{9}{3-1}x^{9-3+1}(-2y)^{3-1}=\binom{9}{2}x^7(-2y)^2$$
$$=36x^7\cdot 4y^2$$
$$=144x^7y^2$$

43. Strategy To find the range of scores on the fifth test, write and solve a compound inequality using x to represent the fifth test.

Solution

$$70\le \text{average of the 5 test scores}\le 79$$
$$70\le\frac{64+58+82+77+x}{5}\le 79$$
$$70\le\frac{281+x}{5}\le 79$$
$$350\le 281+x\le 395$$
$$69\le x\le 114$$

The range of scores is $69\le x\le 100$.

44. Strategy

- Average speed of jogger: x
  Average speed of cyclist: $2.5x$

	Rate	Time	Distance
Jogger	x	2	$2x$
Cyclist	$2.5x$	2	$2(2.5x)$

- The distance traveled by the cyclist is 24 more miles than the distance traveled by the jogger.

Solution

$$2x+24=2(2.5x)$$
$$2x+24=5x$$
$$24=3x$$
$$8=x$$
$$40=5x$$

The cyclist traveled 40 mi.

45. Strategy

- Amount invested at 8.5%: x
  Amount invested at 6.4%: $12000-x$

	Principal	Rate	Interest
8.5%	x	0.085	$0.085x$
6.4%	$12000-x$	0.064	$0.064(12000-x)$

- The sum of the interest earned by the two investments is $936.

Solution

$$0.085x+0.064(12000-x)=936$$
$$0.085x+768-0.064x=936$$
$$0.021x+768=936$$
$$0.021x=168$$
$$x=8000$$
$$12000-x=4000$$

The amount invested at 8.5% is $8000.
The amount invested at 6.4% is $4000.

46. Strategy

- The width of the rectangle: x
  The length of the rectangle: $3x - 1$
- Use the formula for the area of a rectangle ($A = lw$) if the area is 140 ft^2.

Solution

$$A = l \cdot w$$
$$140 = (3x-1)x$$
$$140 = 3x^2 - x$$
$$0 = 3x^2 - x - 140$$
$$0 = (3x+20)(x-7)$$
$$3x+20=0 \qquad x-7=0$$
$$x = -\frac{20}{3} \qquad x = 7$$

The solution $-\frac{20}{3}$ does not check because the width cannot be negative.
$3x - 1 = 3(7) - 1 = 20$
The width is 7 ft. The length is 20 ft.

47. Strategy

To find the number of additional shares, write and solve a proportion using x to represent the number of shares.

Solution

$$\frac{300}{486} = \frac{300+x}{810}$$
$$(810 \cdot 486) \cdot \frac{300}{486} = \frac{300+x}{810} \cdot (810 \cdot 486)$$
$$810(300) = (300+x)486$$
$$243{,}000 = 145{,}800 + 486x$$
$$-486x = -97200$$
$$x = 200$$

The number of additional shares to be purchased is 200.

48. Strategy

- Rate of car: x
  Rate of plane: $7x$

	Distance	Rate	Time
Car	45	x	$\frac{45}{x}$
Plane	1050	$7x$	$\frac{1050}{7x}$

- The total time traveled is $3\frac{1}{4}$ h.

Solution

$$\frac{45}{x} + \frac{1050}{7x} = 3\frac{1}{4}$$
$$\frac{45}{x} + \frac{150}{x} = \frac{13}{4}$$
$$4x\left(\frac{45}{x} + \frac{150}{x}\right) = 4x\left(\frac{13}{4}\right)$$
$$180 + 600 = 13x$$
$$780 = 13x$$
$$60 = x$$
$$420 = 7x$$

The rate of the plane is 420 mph.

49. Strategy

To find the distance the object has fallen, substitute 75 ft/s for v in the formula and solve for d.

Solution

$$v = \sqrt{64d}$$
$$75 = \sqrt{64d}$$
$$75^2 = \left(\sqrt{64d}\right)^2$$
$$5625 = 64d$$
$$87.89 = d$$

The distance traveled is 88 ft.

50. Strategy

- Rate traveled during the first 360 mi: x
  Rate traveled during the next 300 mi: $x+30$

	Distance	Rate	Time
First part of trip	360	x	$\frac{360}{x}$
Second part of trip	300	$x+30$	$\frac{300}{x+30}$

- Total time traveled during the trip was 5 h.

Solution

$$\frac{360}{x}+\frac{300}{x+30}=5$$
$$x(x+30)\left(\frac{360}{x}+\frac{300}{x+30}\right)=5(x(x+30))$$
$$360(x+30)+300x=5(x^2+30x)$$
$$360x+10800+300x=5x^2+150x$$
$$660x+10800=5x^2+150x$$
$$0=5x^2-510x-10800$$
$$0=5(x^2-102x-2160)$$
$$0=(x+18)(x-120)$$

$x+18=0 \qquad x-120=0$

$x=-18 \qquad x=120$

The solution -18 does not check because the rate cannot be negative.
The rate of the plane for the first 360 mi is 120 mph.

51. Strategy To find the intensity:

- Write the basic inverse variation equation, replace the variable by the given values, and solve for k.
- Write the inverse variation equation, replace k by its value. Substitute 4 for d and solve for L.

Solution

$$L=\frac{k}{d^2}$$
$$8=\frac{k}{(20)^2}$$
$$8\cdot 400=k$$
$$3200=k$$
$$L=\frac{3200}{d^2}$$
$$L=\frac{3200}{4^2}$$
$$L=\frac{3200}{16}=200$$

The intensity is 200 foot-candles.

52. Strategy • Rate of the boat in calm water: x
Rate of the current: y

	Rate	Time	Distance
With current	$x+y$	2	$2(x+y)$
Against current	$x-y$	3	$3(x-y)$

• The distance traveled with the current is 30 mi. The distance traveled against the current is 30 mi.

$2(x+y)=30$
$3(x-y)=30$

Solution

$$2(x+y)=30 \quad \frac{1}{2}\cdot 2(x+y)=\frac{1}{2}\cdot 30$$
$$3(x-y)=30 \quad \frac{1}{3}\cdot 3(x-y)=\frac{1}{3}\cdot 30$$

$$x+y=15$$
$$x-y=10$$

$$2x=25$$
$$x=12.5$$

$$x+y=15$$
$$12.5+y=15$$
$$y=2.5$$

The rate of the boat in calm water is 12.5 mph. The rate of the current is 2.5 mph.

53. Strategy To find the value of the investment after two years, solve the compound interest formula for P. Use $A=4000,\ n=24,$ $i=\frac{9\%}{12}=\frac{0.09}{12}=0.0075$.

Solution

$$P=A(1+i)^n$$
$$P=4000(1+0.0075)^{24}$$
$$P=4000(1.0075)^{24}$$
$$P=4785.65$$

The value of the investment is $4785.65.

54. Strategy To find the value of the house in 20 years, use the Formula for the nth Term of a Geometric Sequence.

Solution $n=20,\ a_1=1.06(80{,}000)=84{,}800,$ $r=1.06$

$$a_n=a_1(r)^{n-1}$$
$$a_{20}=84{,}800(1.06)^{20-1}$$
$$=84{,}800(1.06)^{19}$$
$$\approx 256{,}571$$

The value of the house will be $256,571.